Teacher's Manual

Integrated Mathematics

Third Edition

Course I

Authors | Isidore Dressler
Edward P. Keenan

Revisers: second edition | Ann Xavier Gantert
Marilyn Occhiogrosso

Revisers: third edition | Edward P. Keenan
Ann Xavier Gantert

When ordering this book, please specify: **R 638 T** *or*
TEACHER'S MANUAL/INTEGRATED MATHEMATICS: COURSE I, Third Edition

AMSCO

AMSCO SCHOOL PUBLICATIONS, INC.
315 HUDSON STREET, NEW YORK, N.Y. 10013

Authors of the Teacher's Manual *Third Edition*

Authors **Isidore Dressler**
Former Chairman, Department of Mathematics
Bayside High School, New York City

Edward P. Keenan
Former Curriculum Associate, Mathematics
East Williston Union Free School District
East Williston, New York

Revisers: **Ann Xavier Gantert**
second edition *Department of Mathematics*
Nazareth Academy
Rochester, New York

Marilyn Occhiogrosso
Former Assistant Principal, Mathematics
Erasmus Hall High School, New York City

Revisers: **Edward P. Keenan**
third edition **Ann Xavier Gantert**

Consultants: **Ann Armstrong**
Mathematics Teacher, Retired
Schalmont High School
Schenectady, New York

Mary C. Genier
Coordinator of Mathematics, Retired
Rotterdam High School
Schenectady, New York

Consultants: **Peter Duffy**
SAT Preparation *Chairman of Mathematics*
Exercises Gonzaga Preparatory School
Spokane, Washington

Dr. Alice B. Farkouh
Principal
Fort Hamilton High School
Brooklyn, New York

Deanna M. De' Liberto
D Squared Assessments, Inc.
Hazlet, New Jersey

ISBN 0-87720-222-2

Copyright © 1998 by Amsco School Publications, Inc.

Printed in the United States of America

1 2 3 4 5 6 7 8 9 10   01 00 99 98 97

About the Teacher's Manual

This manual parallels the organization of the text and provides:

✔ suggestions for assessment.

✔ aims for each chapter.

✔ commentary on each individual section of the text.

✔ leading questions to stimulate classroom discussion.

✔ a variety of approaches to promote flexibility in problem-solving.

✔ suggestions to maximize the effectiveness of specific examples and exercises.

✔ techniques for dealing with difficulties that students may encounter.

✔ reproducible Enrichment Activities and suggestions for more challenging aspects of topics in the text.

✔ applications showing use of graphing calculators.

✔ appropriate hands-on activities.

✔ suggestions for extended tasks and investigations to be undertaken by students.

✔ supplementary material that reflects current thinking in mathematics education.

✔ a set of SAT Preparation Exercises for each chapter.

✔ questions to form the basis for chapter tests.

✔ an answer key for the Enrichment Activities, the Suggested Test Items, the SAT Preparation Exercises, and the text.

Assessment

As a student studies the content of the text associated with this manual, it is important that the student, teacher, parents, and administrators have tangible evidence of the student's progress toward established goals. That evidence can be obtained in a variety of ways. Some of these tangibles, and the features of the student text and teacher's manual that can aid in assembling that evidence, are listed.

Homework Assignments

The need for consistent reflection on and practice with the content of each day's lesson has always been accepted as a necessary factor in promoting the student's understanding and skills. Each day's homework assignment should enable the student and the teacher to recognize progress as well as identify needs. The text provides both routine and challenging exercises at the end of each section for this purpose.

Journals

A journal can be a useful tool to promote a studied reflection upon day-by-day progress. A journal may be a record of feelings, understandings, fears, insights, and questions. Putting these into words can help students to clarify ideas and identify concepts that need further explanation and exploration. The content of the journal can be the choice of the student, a response to a teacher's question or prompt, or both.

Portfolio

A portfolio is a record of a student's progress. The selection of materials to be included in the portfolio presents opportunities for the student to reflect upon what he/she has done, improve upon faulty work, and take pride in work that is well done and insightful information that has been gained. Significant examples of homework assignments, tests, and independent research or readings, as well as completed Enrichment Activities, Hands-On Activities, Bonus Questions, or Extended Tasks from the student text or this manual, are excellent materials for inclusion.

Tests and Quizzes

Tests give the student opportunities to demonstrate that he/she understands concepts and has the ability to make use of that understanding. This manual provides Suggested Test Items for each chapter. These questions can be used by the teacher when constructing a test based on the instructional goals established for the class.

Independent and Group Projects

Mathematical understanding and enthusiasm is increased by opportunities to explore in-depth topics of special interest to the students. Some of these topics may be suggested by the students themselves. Others are given as Explorations in the Cumulative Reviews of the chapters of the text or as Enrichment Activities in this manual. Many of these Explorations and Activities lend themselves to either individual or group study.

Contents

Chapters

Answer Keys

Suggested Time Outlines

Since teaching from a new text can create time problems during the first year, the timetable below is offered to assist you in planning your work.

CHAPTER	TOPIC	SUGGESTED TIME (in days)
1	The Real Numbers	6 – 8
2	Operations and Properties	5 – 6
3	Problem Solving	8 – 10
4	Algebraic Expressions, Geometric Formulas, and Open Sentences	6 – 7
5	Signed Numbers	4 – 5
6	Introduction to Solving Equations	5 – 6
7	Introducing Logic	8 – 9
8	Using Logic	7 – 8
9	Operations with Algebraic Expressions	10 – 12
10	First-Degree Equations and Inequalities in One Variable	10 – 12
11	Angle Measure in Geometry	6 – 8
12	Congruence and Transformations	7 – 9
13	Ratio and Proportion	7 – 8
14	Probability	12 – 14
15	Statistics	8 – 10
16	Graphing Linear Functions and Equations	10 – 12
17	Systems of Linear Open Sentences in Two Variables	7 – 8
18	Special Products and Factors	8 – 9
19	Algebraic Fractions, and Equations and Inequalities Involving Fractions	5 – 6
20	Operations with Radicals	6 – 7
21	Quadratic Equations	5 – 6

Total days 150 – 180

Chapter *1*
The Real Numbers

Aims

- To develop an understanding of the real number system and its subsets, including definitions, order, and number sense.
- To set the stage for the use of calculators, stressing estimation skills and the use of rational approximations.
- To begin the integration of mathematics through the study of numbers and geometry, specifically in number lines, rulers, and graphs.

CHAPTER OVERVIEW

Students should realize that we live in a world of numbers. Wherever we turn, we are surrounded by numerical facts, data, and statistical information. The numbers mentioned here, from the 1990 U.S. census, merely serve as motivation for the work that lies ahead.

Students may consider doing a simple study of their own, such as comparing the average size household for students in their class with that found in the national 1990 census. A more detailed long-range statistical study may be undertaken to culminate with the study of Chapter 14, Statistics.

1-1 THE WHOLE NUMBERS

Although numbers are only a small part of mathematics, they serve as a foundation for many other branches of this discipline: algebra, geometric measurement, probability, and statistics, to name a few.

A real number line is presented at the start of this section, complete with repeating decimals, radicals, pi, and signed numbers. The meaning of these numbers will be explained in the first five sections of this chapter. As a start, counting numbers and then whole numbers are defined and shown as first steps in building a number line. These first steps may be simple, but they are necessary. And, as seen in the next few sections, the real number line will be built quickly.

Students should be familiar with the basic types of sets discussed here, as well as the four fundamental operations of arithmetic. Some review of terms, such as *sum, difference, product,* and *quotient,* may be necessary and is provided through exercises.

Calculator usage is introduced in Examples 3 and 4. The order in which numbers and operations are entered on a calculator is critical.

Consider Example 3: "Add 6 to the product of 3 and 9." The text shows a calculator entry that yields the correct solution, 33. After the solution is seen and understood, ask this question: "Will your calculator display 33 as an answer for the following entry?"

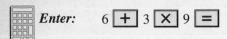

Enter: 6 ☐+ 3 ☐× 9 ☐=

Most *four-function* or *basic* calculators will display 81, which is not the correct answer to the question asked in Example 3. These calculators are *entry-order* calculators and perform operations in the order in which they are entered, not in the correct mathematical order. Thus, the sum of 6 and 3 is found first and that sum, 9, is multiplied by 3. To find the correct answer to the problem "Add 6 to the product of 3 and 9" on an entry order calculator, changing the order in which the number and operation keys are pressed.

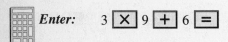

Enter: 3 ☐× 9 ☐+ 6 ☐=

Most scientific calculators, however, will display the correct answer, 33, because their circuitry follows the correct order of operations (a topic that will be studied in Chapter 2).

The calculator should be regarded as an everyday tool, as familiar to students in a mathematics class as paper, pencil, and a ruler. Calculators should be used with relatively simple exercises, such as the example shown above, and not reserved for more complicated arithmetic. Correct usage demands, however, that students understand the concepts involved in a problem and have good sense of estimation.

Throughout this textbook, we strongly recommended that students use, as a minimum, a **scientific calculator** in their study of secondary mathematics.

1-2   THE INTEGERS

The number line, introduced with the set of counting numbers and extended to include 0, is now extended to the set of integers.

Emphasis is placed on *ordering* these numbers, that is, determining which of two unequal integers is the greater. To this end, the symbols of inequality are introduced. Operations with integers are *not* discussed here; they will be studied in detail in Chapter 5, Signed Numbers.

Some students will experience difficulty in perceiving that -2 is greater than -10. To help them grasp this concept quickly, make mention of temperature and of a thermometer, which is represented by the standard vertical number line. The greater the temperature, the higher the number. A comparison can then be made to the standard horizontal number line, where the greater of two numbers always appears on the right.

The basic definition of subset is also given in this section, and various subsets of the integers are illustrated both in diagrams and through lists. Concepts already known by students, such as odd and even numbers, are extended here to include 0 and negative integers.

Ask the question, "Is 0 even, odd, or neither?" Zero can be shown to be even by skip counting by 2's. Start with positive even numbers and count backwards: 12, 10, 8, 6, 4, 2, 0, -2, -4, -6, -8, -10, and so on.

Each of these numbers, when divided by 2 or when multiplied by one half, is again an integer, indicating another approach to determining even integers. Odd integers, when divided by 2 or when multiplied by one half, will not produce other integers.

It is essential that students understand what an integer is before continuing on to rational numbers in the next section.

1-3   THE RATIONAL NUMBERS

Rational numbers are defined in various ways: first, as fractions of the form $\frac{a}{b}$, where a and b are integers and $b \neq 0$. Ask the question, "Why can't $b = 0$?" Have students attempt to divide a number by 0 using a calculator. No matter what type of calculator is used, an error message will appear.

Fractions can be changed to decimals. As students perform these conversions, they will see that a fraction will become either a terminating decimal (such as 0.25) or a repeating decimal (such as 0.33333333 . . .). Every terminating decimal, however, is actually a repeating decimal in which 0 keeps repeating (0.25 = 0.25000000 . . .).

This fact leads to definitions of rational numbers in terms of decimals. Rational numbers can be defined as the set of terminating decimals and repeating decimals. Finally, since every terminating decimal actually repeats, rational numbers are simply defined as numbers that can be expressed as repeating decimals.

Students will appreciate the use of calculators in converting fractions to decimals. One of the most important applications of this conversion is as an aid in *ordering* rational numbers, that is, in trying to determine which of two unequal fractions is the greater.

Converting a decimal to a fraction, on the other hand, is not a simple matter of pressing keys on a calculator; some paper and pencil work is required.

A terminating decimal can be quickly written as a fraction because its denominator is a power of 10. Here, students need to know how to read the place values of decimals.

A repeating decimal requires some manipulation, as shown in examples in the book. Typically, these examples are restricted decimals in which either one or two digits repeat. Generalizations can be made for such repeating decimals:

$$0.xxxxx \ldots = 0.\bar{x} = \frac{x}{9} \quad \text{and} \quad 0.xyxyxy \ldots = 0.\overline{xy}$$
$$= \frac{xy}{99}$$

The more capable student may be interested in examining other repeating decimals, to find similar but more complex generalizations.

Operations with rational numbers are *not* studied in this section. These operations will be discussed in Chapter 2 and used throughout the book. However, in determining the mean (or average) of two rational numbers to show the concept of density, some operations do occur. A calculator entry makes use of parentheses, which are found on scientific calculators but not on basic four-function devices:

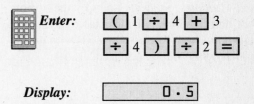

Enter: (1 ÷ 4 + 3 ÷ 4) ÷ 2 =

Display: 0 . 5

On an entry-order calculator that has no parentheses, it is necessary to make use of the memory of the calculator to obtain this result. Use STO to store the value of the first fraction, M+ or SUM to add the value of the second fraction to the first, and RCL to recall the sum to the screen. If there is no STO key, press MC to clear the memory and then use M+ or SUM to store the first value.

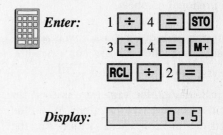

Enter: 1 ÷ 4 = STO
3 ÷ 4 = M+
RCL ÷ 2 =

Display: 0 . 5

Ask the question, "Will the following alternative entry yield the same display?"

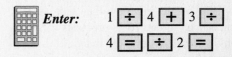

Enter: 1 ÷ 4 + 3 ÷
4 = ÷ 2 =

The answer is "yes" for a scientific calculator, where the order of operations is used, but "no" for a basic four-function calculator.

Be aware that more than one lesson may be required to cover the material in this section.

See *Enrichment Activity 1-3A: Repeating Decimals.* Students investigate patterns with fractions that are equivalent to repeating decimals.

See *Enrichment Activity 1-3B: Fraction-Decimal Multiples.* Students multiply the decimal forms of unit fractions to build a table of fraction-decimal equivalents. The activity ends with the discovery that 0.9999 . . . or $0.\bar{9}$ is equal to 1.

1-4 THE IRRATIONAL NUMBERS

In the same way that rational numbers can be thought of as infinite by repeating decimals, irrational numbers are infinitely nonrepeating decimals. Patterns are often used to show irrational numbers. For example:

0.12345678910111213 . . .   is irrational.
0.122333444455555 . . .   is irrational.

Students should realize, however, that numbers such as π, $\sqrt{2}$, and $\sqrt{3}$ are the more frequently encountered irrational numbers.

A side trip in this section serves as a reminder to students of squares and square roots. This is accompanied by an introduction to the corresponding calculator keys, $\boxed{x^2}$, and $\boxed{\sqrt{x}}$ (or $\boxed{\sqrt{}}$).

On some calculators, the same key is used for the square and the square root functions. When the key is pressed, the function whose symbol is on the key is performed. When $\boxed{\text{INV}}$ or $\boxed{\text{2nd}}$ is pressed before a function key, the function whose symbol is written above the key is performed.

When writing or reading a number such as $\sqrt{5}$, the function name, square root, precedes the radicand, 5. On some calculators, the radicand must be entered first, before the square root function key is pressed. On other calculators, the keys are pressed in the order in which they are read or written. Have students experiment with their calculators to find which of the following sequences will display $\sqrt{5}$.

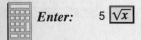 *Enter:*   5 $\boxed{\sqrt{x}}$

Enter: 5 $\boxed{\text{INV}}$ $\boxed{\sqrt{x}}$

Enter: 5 $\boxed{\text{2nd}}$ $\boxed{\sqrt{x}}$

Enter: $\boxed{\sqrt{x}}$ 5

Enter: $\boxed{\text{INV}}$ $\boxed{\sqrt{x}}$ 5

Enter: $\boxed{\text{2nd}}$ $\boxed{\sqrt{x}}$ 5

The irrational number $\sqrt{2}$ is presented in the text as the measure of a diagonal of a square whose side is 1. This can be shown by using the following diagram.

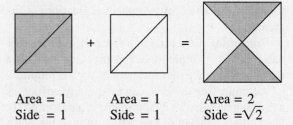

Area = 1   Area = 1   Area = 2
Side = 1   Side = 1   Side = $\sqrt{2}$

The diagonal $\sqrt{2}$ is compared to the side of 1 by placing both lengths on a common number line, showing that there are points on the number line that correspond to irrational numbers. The use of a calculator leads to another important concept, rational approximations.

Pi (π) is another irrational number introduced in this section. Its study leads to the use of a scientific calculator, the key for $\boxed{\pi}$, and a quick review of the rules for rounding decimals as an aid in writing rational approximations.

In Exercises 21–30 caution students to return to the original calculator display in Part **a** before attempting to answer Part **c**, successive roundings, such as moving from Part **a** to Part **b** to Part **c**, could result in errors.

Operations with irrational numbers are not studied here, although some use is made of the formula for the circumference of a circle to compare exact measurements involving π with rational approximations. Operations with radicals will be studied in Chapter 19.

Students are encouraged to investigate some basic ideas involving irrational numbers by using different strategies, including estimation skills and calculator usage, as shown in Example 1 in the book.

1-5 THE REAL NUMBERS

The set of real numbers consists of all rational numbers and all irrational numbers. In other words, the real numbers consist of all decimal numbers, both repeating and infinitely nonrepeating decimals. The real number line is now complete.

Students should now know two ways to *order* real numbers: by examining their placement on a number line, and by comparing decimal values, including those of rational approximations.

In Example 1, we return to the number line first seen in Section 1-1. Radicals, pi, repeating decimals, and signed numbers should be easily identified and categorized as various subsets of the real numbers.

1-6 NUMBER LINES AND RULERS

The number line, which serves as a basic tool of measurement in mathematics, has many applications. Here, the concept of a ruler is presented, and the metric and the English rulers are shown.

In this section, the correct placement of numbers on a number line, the need for good estimation skills in finding rational approximations, and continued use of the calculator should be stressed.

Students should realize that any ruler is determined by exactly two points, whose coordinates are 0 and 1. These points not only define the unit measure of the ruler, but also determine the placement of all other coordinates on the number line.

In the text, horizontal number lines are presented in standard form, where 0 is to the left of 1. To more capable students, you may wish to present exercises where 0 lies to the right of 1. For example:

Name the coordinates of each labeled point on this number line:

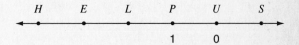

The solution, wherein numbers increase by moving to the left, can be demonstrated by holding any standard ruler upside down.

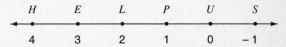

Special attention should be given to Exercise 21 to see whether students have a good sense of standard English and metric measures. If not, it may be helpful to present them with tables of linear measure in both systems.

1-7 NUMBER LINES AND GRAPHS

Another application of number lines can be found in familiar graphs that students should have seen in earlier studies. The popular saying "One picture is worth a thousand words" demonstrates the importance of graphs in presenting facts and information.

A single number line is used to present bar graphs and picture graphs. These graphs typically compare different items, such as the weights of several different objects.

Two number lines are used as the vertical and horizontal scales on a line graph. These graphs illustrate changes in a single item, such as one person's weight over a long period of time.

Have students find examples of these graphs in newspapers and magazines, and ask them to list observations that can be made from the numerical facts presented in the graphs.

Hands-On Activity

Instructions:

1. Have students find examples of any two of the following graphs from a newspaper or magazine: line graph; bar graph; picture graph.
2. Attach each graph to a piece of paper, identify its source, and then list five different observations that can be made from the numerical facts presented in the graph.

SAT PREPARATION EXERCISES

Students planning to enter college often have to prepare for the College Board's SAT I Reasoning Tests for admission purposes. The topics covered in the mathematics section of this examination are predominantly arithmetic, algebra, geometry, logic, and statistics. This manual for *Integrated Mathematics, Course I* covers the basic questions and gives students practice in increasing their success in standardized testing. In keeping with the philosophy that the classroom teacher is uniquely qualified to provide students with the testing skills to use their mathematical ability, this Manual provides a set of SAT Preparation Exercises for each of the 21 chapters of the Manual.

When completing these exercises students should be encouraged to reason as much as possible without using their pencils since the SAT is basically not an achievement test but a reasoning test as noted in its title. These exercises are divided into three groups: Multiple-Choice Questions, Quantitative Comparisons Questions, and Student-Produced Response Questions. Each set of problems reflects the basic concepts of the chapter, but many of these questions are quite challenging. Students should be encouraged to integrate their regular assignments with two or three SAT questions each night or to work in cooperative group settings in the classroom. No matter how these problems are assigned, students should not be discouraged if they find them difficult. Teachers should encourage the students and reinforce the concept that if students understand their faulty reasonings and can learn from their mistakes, future success can be attained. In time, students will begin to learn how to approach these questions and how to achieve increasing success.

It is to be noted that students are allowed to use almost any four-function scientific or graphing calculator. Specific limitations of the use of a calculator should be reviewed by the teacher prior to working on the SAT questions in this Manual.

Name _____ Class _____ Date _____

ENRICHMENT ACTIVITY 1-3A

Repeating Decimals

Change each fraction to a repeating decimal, and use an overbar to show the digits that repeat. For example:

$$\frac{1}{11} = 0.090909\ldots = 0.\overline{09}$$

$\frac{1}{9} =$	$\frac{1}{11} =$	$\frac{1}{7} =$	$\frac{1}{14} =$
$\frac{2}{9} =$	$\frac{2}{11} =$	$\frac{2}{7} =$	$\frac{2}{14} =$
$\frac{3}{9} =$	$\frac{3}{11} =$	$\frac{3}{7} =$	$\frac{3}{14} =$
$\frac{4}{9} =$	$\frac{4}{11} =$	$\frac{4}{7} =$	$\frac{4}{14} =$
$\frac{5}{9} =$	$\frac{5}{11} =$	$\frac{5}{7} =$	$\frac{5}{14} =$
$\frac{6}{9} =$	$\frac{6}{11} =$	$\frac{6}{7} =$	$\frac{6}{14} =$
$\frac{7}{9} =$	$\frac{7}{11} =$		$\frac{7}{14} =$
$\frac{8}{9} =$	$\frac{8}{11} =$		$\frac{8}{14} =$
	$\frac{9}{11} =$		$\frac{9}{14} =$
	$\frac{10}{11} =$		$\frac{10}{14} =$
			$\frac{11}{14} =$
			$\frac{12}{14} =$
			$\frac{13}{14} =$

What pattern is found in these decimals?	What pattern is found in these decimals?	What pattern is found in these decimals?	What pattern is found in these decimals?

Name _____ Class _____ Date _____

Challenge: In the space provided below, show all fraction-decimal equivalents for

$$\frac{1}{13}, \frac{2}{13}, \frac{3}{13}, \frac{4}{13}, \frac{5}{13}, \frac{6}{13}, \frac{7}{13}, \frac{8}{13}, \frac{9}{13}, \frac{10}{13}, \frac{11}{13}, \frac{12}{13}$$

Discuss the patterns found in these decimals.

Name _____ Class _____ Date _____

ENRICHMENT ACTIVITY 1-3B

Fraction-Decimal Multiples

When the decimal form of a unit fraction is known, multiplication can produce a table of fraction-decimal equivalents. For example:

$$\frac{1}{5} = 0.2$$

Multiply by 2: $\quad 2\left(\frac{1}{5}\right) = \frac{2}{5}$ and $\quad 2(0.2) = 0.4 \quad \longrightarrow \quad \frac{2}{5} = 0.4$

Multiply by 3: $\quad 3\left(\frac{1}{5}\right) = \frac{3}{5}$ and $\quad 3(0.2) = 0.6 \quad \longrightarrow \quad \frac{3}{5} = 0.6$

1. Complete this table using multiples of 0.125

$\frac{1}{8} = 0.125$	$\frac{3}{8} =$	$\frac{5}{8} =$	$\frac{7}{8} =$
$\frac{2}{8} =$	$\frac{4}{8} =$	$\frac{6}{8} =$	$\frac{8}{8} =$

2. Multiply the decimal form of the unit fraction to find decimal values for the given fractions.

$\frac{1}{20} = 0.05$	$\frac{1}{40} = 0.025$	$\frac{1}{16} = 0.0625$	$\frac{1}{3} = 0.33333\ldots = 0.\overline{3}$
$\frac{7}{20} =$	$\frac{17}{40} =$	$\frac{9}{16} =$	$\frac{2}{3} =$
$\frac{19}{20} =$	$\frac{29}{40} =$	$\frac{12}{16} =$	$\frac{3}{3} =$

3. You know $\frac{3}{3} = 1$. The answer to the question in Part b should be $\frac{3}{3} = 0.\overline{9}$.

   a. Is it true that $0.9999\ldots = 0.\overline{9} = 1$?

   To answer this question, complete the work at the right by using the process shown in Section 1-3 to find a value for $0.9999999\ldots$

   b. What conclusions can you draw?

Let the original number $\quad\quad = 0.99999\ldots$

Then 10 times this number $\quad =$

Subtract the original number.

Therefore, 9 times the number $=$

Divide by 9 to find the original number.

Name _____ Class _____ Date _____

4. a. Write each fraction in decimal form. **b.** Add the given fractions, add their decimal values, and write each sum as a fraction-decimal equivalent in simplest form.

$\dfrac{1}{40} = 0.025$	$\dfrac{1}{16} = 0.0625$	$\dfrac{1}{32} = 0.03125$	$\dfrac{1}{21} = 0.\overline{047619}$
$+\dfrac{7}{40} =$ _____	$+\dfrac{7}{16} =$ _____	$+\dfrac{7}{32} =$ _____	$+\dfrac{6}{21}$ _____

$\dfrac{1}{11} = 0.0909\ldots$	$\dfrac{1}{7} = 0.\overline{142857}$	$\dfrac{1}{30} = 0.03333\ldots$	$\dfrac{1}{12} = 0.083333\ldots$
$\dfrac{2}{11} =$	$\dfrac{2}{7} =$	$+\dfrac{2}{30} =$ _____	$+\dfrac{2}{12} =$ _____
$+\dfrac{3}{11} =$ _____	$+\dfrac{4}{7} =$ _____		

c. What conclusions can you draw?

SUGGESTED TEST ITEMS (CHAPTER 1)

1. Determine: **a.** the difference of 17 and 5   **b.** the product of 9 and 12
   c. the quotient of 76 and 4   **d.** the sum of 96 and 16

2. State whether each set is finite, infinite, or empty.

   a. whole numbers   **b.** digits   **c.** rational numbers   **d.** negative counting numbers

   In 3-8, state whether the sentence is true or false.

3. $5 > -8$

4. $-8 > -2$

5. Every irrational number is a real number.

6. $-9 \le -9$

7. $\sqrt{8} \ge 3$

8. Some integers are irrational numbers.

9. Write each rational number in the form $\dfrac{a}{b}$ where a and b are integers and $b \ne 0$.

   a. 0.3   **b.** $5\dfrac{1}{3}$ **c.** 0   **d.** 73   **e.** -0.21

10. Determine a rational number midway between 18.1 and 18.

11. Write the decimal equivalent for each rational number.

    a. $\dfrac{1}{20}$ **b.** $\dfrac{2}{3}$ **c.** $\dfrac{4}{9}$ **d.** $-3\dfrac{1}{6}$

12. Write $0.77777\ldots = 0.\overline{7}$ as a fraction in simplest form.

13. State whether each number is rational or irrational.

    a. 35   **b.** $\sqrt{35}$ **c.** 35π **d.** -35

14. Write a rational approximation, to the *nearest thousandth,* for each number.
    a. $\sqrt{14}$ **b.** $\sqrt{1.4}$ **c.** π **d.** $\pi - 3$

    In 15 and 16, use the following number line where D = 0, F = 1, and the letters shown are equally spaced.

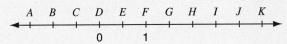

15. Write the coordinates of all points named by letters on the line shown above.

16. Between what two consecutive points on this number line is the graph of each of the following?

    a. -1.3 **b.** π **c.** $\dfrac{9}{4}$ **d.** $\sqrt{2}$ **e.** $0.\overline{13}$

17. Kayvan compared the cost of hiking boots in five different catalogs: Beams, $75; Sundog, $93; Homefront, $90; Trails Ahead, $127; and Daks, $109.
    a. Construct a bar graph to represent these data.
    b. State one conclusion based on the data.
    c. Can a line graph be used to the graph the data? Explain why or why not.

SAT PREPARATION EXERCISES (CHAPTER I)

I. Multiple-Choice Questions

In 1-10, select the letter of the correct answer.

1. If W is the set of whole numbers less than 10, what is the sum of the least even number in W and the greatest odd number in W?

(A) 11   (B) 10   (C) 9

(D) 8   (E) 7

2. The product of x and y is 40, and the average (arithmetic mean) of x and y is an odd number. How many possible values are there for x if x is a whole number?

(A) 1   (B) 2   (C) 3

(D) 4   (E) 5

3. Let $\boxed{n}$ denote the sum of the first n natural numbers divided by n. For example,

$$\boxed{7} = \frac{1 + 2 + 3 + 4 + 5 + 6 + 7}{7}$$

Evaluate the average of 1 and 4.

(A) $\boxed{2}$ (B) $\boxed{3}$ (C) $\boxed{4}$

(D) $\boxed{7}$ (E) $\boxed{6}$

4. Which set of numbers is listed in ascending order (from smallest to greatest)?

(A) $-\frac{1}{3}, -\frac{1}{2}, \frac{2}{3}, \frac{3}{4}$ (B) $-\frac{1}{2}, -\frac{1}{3}, \frac{2}{3}, \frac{3}{4}$

(C) $-\frac{1}{3}, -\frac{1}{2}, \frac{3}{4}, \frac{2}{3}$ (D) $-\frac{1}{2}, -\frac{1}{3}, \frac{3}{4}, \frac{2}{3}$

(E) $\frac{3}{4}, \frac{2}{3}, -\frac{1}{3}, -\frac{1}{2}$

5. If n is an odd number, what is the average of n and five times n?

(A) twice n (B) six times n (C) odd

(D) even   (E) positive

6.

Number of Donuts	Total Price
1	$ 0.40
Box of 6	$ 1.89
Box of 12	$ 3.59

Based on the table above, what would be the *least* amount of money needed to purchase exactly 21 donuts?

(A) $5.88   (B) $6.68   (C) $7.19

(D) $7.38   (E) $8.40

7. A list of numbers 2, 4, 8 . . . is formed by doubling each of the preceding numbers. What is the remainder when the 15th number is divided by 6?

(A) 0   (B) 2   (C) 4

(D) 6   (E) 8

8.

The cube above has a number on each of its six faces. If the sum of the numbers on each pair of opposite faces is 10, what is the sum of the numbers on the faces *not* shown?

(A) 8   (B) 10   (C) 12

(D) 14   (E) 16

9. Which day of the week could a month with 5 Wednesdays start on?

(A) Sunday   (B) Monday   (C) Thursday

(D) Friday   (E) Saturday

10. A small bus has 3 empty seats, 6 seated passengers, and 2 standing passengers. If 3 passengers get off, 4 get on, and everyone on the bus is seated, how many empty seats would there be?

(A) None   (B) One   (C) Two

(D) Three   (E) Four

II. Quantitative Comparison Questions

Questions 11-20 each consist of two quantities, one in Column A and one in Column B. You are to compare the two quantities and choose:

    A   if the quantity in Column A is greater;
    B   if the quantity in Column B is greater;
    C   if the two quantities are equal;
    D   if the relationship cannot be determined from the information given.

Notes

1. In certain questions, information concerning one or both of the quantities to be compared is centered above the two columns.
2. In a given question, a symbol that appears in both columns represents the same thing in Column A as it does in Column B.
3. Letters such as x, n, and k stand for real numbers.

Column A	*Column B*
11. $\dfrac{2}{\sqrt{9}}$	0.25

	Column A	Column B
12.	$\dfrac{1}{20}$	$\dfrac{5}{100}$

13. $x > 0$

    3 avg x   5 avg x

	Column A	Column B
14.	$\dfrac{3}{2}$ avg $\dfrac{1}{2}$	$\sqrt{1} + \sqrt{1}$

15. The lengths of three sides of a triangle are consecutive integers.

The average (arithmetic mean) of the the lengths of all sides of the triangle	The average (arithmetic mean) of the smallest and the largest sides of the triangle

	Column A	Column B
16.	$\dfrac{1}{4} + \dfrac{1}{9}$	$\sqrt{\dfrac{1}{4}} + \sqrt{\dfrac{1}{9}}$
17.	$\sqrt{5} + \sqrt{5}$	$\sqrt{16}$
18.	$\dfrac{1}{5}$	$\sqrt{\dfrac{1}{24}}$
19.	$\pi - 1$	$\sqrt{10}$
20.	$\sqrt{\dfrac{16}{25}}$	$\left(\dfrac{16}{25}\right)^2$

III. Student-Produced Response Questions

In questions 21-25, you are to solve the problem.

21. Irene has 15 bags of grain in her barn. If she can carry at most 2 bags of grain at a time, what is the least number of trips she must make in order for her to carry all of the bags to her truck?

22. If x equals the largest possible 3-digit number where no digit is repeated and y equals the smallest 3-digit number which can be made using the digits of x, what is the value of $x - y$?

23. Let $r \ ? \ t$ be defined as the sum of all even integers between r and t. For example $4 \ ? \ 9 = 6 + 8 = 14$. Determine the value of
$$(80 \ ? \ 110) - (81 \ ? \ 109).$$

24. What is the sum of the product $2^3 \cdot 3^2$ and the quotient $\dfrac{16}{2} \div \sqrt{4}$?

25.

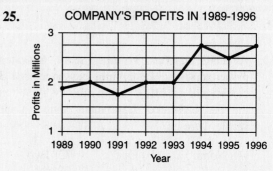

COMPANY'S PROFITS IN 1989-1996

The graph above displays the profit earned by a company for an eight-year period. For the two intervals during which the company showed the greatest increase in profit, what is the average increase?

Chapter 2
Operations and Properties

Aims

- To review the basic operations in arithmetic and to introduce new operations with familiar sets of numbers.
- To show that operations exist in geometry and in sets as well as in arithmetic.
- To establish basic properties of operations with rational numbers, and to state that these properties will hold true for the set of real numbers.

As the definition of binary operation is formalized and applied to arithmetic, geometry, and sets, the stage is set for integration of topics throughout the book.

2-1 OPERATIONS IN ARITHMETIC

The familiar operations of addition, subtraction, multiplication, and division are reexamined in the light of the formal definition of binary operation. This definition requires that we consider the important concepts of order and *uniqueness*.

The property of *closure* is introduced in this section because of its direct connection to the definition of binary operation. By examining the four basic operations with the set of whole numbers, students should see why this set is closed under addition and multiplication, but not under subtraction and division. Even though operations with signed numbers will not be studied until Chapter 5, students should

grasp why integers and rational numbers are or are not closed under these operations.

Beginning with the definition of binary operation, students see how letters (*a, b, c*, etc.) are used to designate variables in general statements. Some use of letters is made throughout this introductory work, preceding the definition of variable in Chapter 4, where the formal study of algebra begins.

We introduce additional arithmetic operations, such as the average of two numbers and the maximum of two numbers, to show that there are more binary operations than just addition, subtraction, multiplication and division. You may give problems such as $\frac{3}{8}$ avg $\frac{3}{4} = \left(\frac{9}{16}\right)$ and $\frac{7}{4}$ max 1.8 = 1.8 to reinforce computational skills with fractions, mixed numbers, and decimals. Note that the binary operation called *avg* is the average of *two* numbers and cannot be extended to define the average of a larger set of numbers, the way addition of two numbers can be extended to define the addition of three, four, or more numbers.

Hands-On Activity

Note to the Teacher:

Encourage some creativity by starting a classroom discussion or by giving a homework assignment where students invent their own binary operations for numbers in arithmetic. One obvious operation would be that of finding the minimum or smaller of two unequal numbers, written in symbols as $a * b = a$ min b. This operation parallels that of max and includes the notation $a * a = a$, which means that two quantities are equal.

Many other operations are also possible, such as:

$$a * b = 10a + b$$
$$a * b = a$$
$$a * b = a^2 + b^2$$

Students should be able to find truly creative operations. However, some examples provided by students will not fit the definition of binary operation. This should lead to further discussion and eventual clarification of the definition.

Instructions to Students:

1. Create a new operation, $*$.
2. **a.** Is the operation $*$ closed in the set of rational numbers?
   b. Is the operation $*$ closed in the set of integers?
   c. Is the operation $*$ closed in the set of whole numbers?
3. Is the operation $*$ a binary operation?

Exercises 103 and 104 require the use of division in which only the integral part of the quotient is used in the solution. If students are familiar with a computer language, ask them to compare the binary operation that could be defined to give the solution of Exercise 103 with DIV in Pascal, and INT (A/B) in BASIC and in LOGO. Note that it may be necessary to define the required binary operation in words. For example, the binary operation for Exercise 103 may be defined as $a * b =$ the smallest integer that is greater than or equal to $a \div b$. The binary operation for Exercise 104 may be defined as the greatest integer that is less than or equal to $a \div b$.

See ***Enrichment Activity 2-1: Operations With Fractions.*** Practice with the basic operations is provided in the form of a puzzle.

2-2 BASES, EXPONENTS, AND POWERS

Make sure that students are familiar with the terms *base, exponent,* and *power.* Once they realize that the exponent tells how many times the base is to be used as a factor, incorrect answers such as $2^3 = 6$ will no longer be commonplace.

Two calculator keys are used in this section: the key for squaring a number $\boxed{x^2}$, which was first seen in Chapter 1, and a key for raising a number to a power other than 2, $\boxed{y^x}$. This second key, called the *exponent key,* can also be used to square a number.

The exponent key typically is found on scientific calculators and other devices that are more sophisticated than the basic four-function calculator. Students may need some practice in knowing how to enter powers greater than 2 on such calculators. Be aware that this key may appear in different forms on various models of scientific calculators, including:

In some calculators, this key also appears as a second function, requiring that a different key, such as $\boxed{\text{INV}}$, first be pressed to obtain the exponent function.

Exponents here are restricted to natural numbers. In later work, students will investigate negative and positive fractional exponents. Additional reference to base, exponent, and power will be made when we consider the vocabulary used in algebraic terms and expressions, and when we develop monomial operations.

Exercises 1–32 are, for the most part, simple ones in which students are encouraged to use mental arithmetic.

Exercises, 33–50, however, are intended to give students practice with the calculator when evaluating powers. Note specifically, in Exercises 43–48, that students can find an exact fractional answer quickly but then must provide a rational approximation rounded to four decimal places. Exercises 49 and 50 show the power of compound interest, and you may wish to discuss the development of a formula for compound interest at this time.

2-3 ORDER OF OPERATIONS

In the definition of a binary operation, students are introduced to the concept of an ordered pair; 2^3 and 3^2 do not name the same number. Similarly, when numerical expressions contain two or more operations, a need for an agreed order of operations becomes apparent.

In this section, students are shown that not all calculators will produce the same answer. This may be a big surprise to many who think that "the calculator is always correct."

A *mathematical order calculator* follows the procedures that we know as the order of operations, while an *entry order calculator* performs operations in the order in which they are entered.

Scientific calculators are mathematically ordered and will not display an answer until the entry key is pressed. The advantage of working with a scientific calculator is obvious: it follows the order of operations. The disadvantage is that a student may tend to become lazy and rely on the device for answers; for this reason, encourage students to simplify expressions mentally and then use the calculator as a check.

Special attention should be given to the sign-change key, $\boxed{+/-}$, which is used to enter negative numbers into the calculator. There will be more work with this key in Chapter 5 on signed numbers.

Probably one of the most common errors that students make in entering numerical expressions on a calculator is forgetting to press the multiplication key, $\boxed{\times}$, when a constant other than 1 appears before the start of parentheses. Remind them of a simple rule: When no symbol is shown between two expressions, the operation being used is multiplication. For example:

Evaluate: $5(3 + 7)$

On most scientific calculators, omitting the $\boxed{\times}$ key between 5 and the parentheses yields a wrong answer.

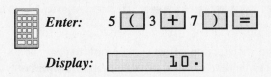

Enter: 5 ⎡(3 ⎡+ 7 ⎡) ⎡=

Display: ⎡ 10.

Use of the multiplication key always yields the correct value.

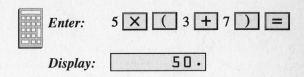

Enter: 5 ⎡× ⎡(3 ⎡+ 7 ⎡) ⎡=

Display: ⎡ 50.

Grouping symbols such as parentheses are used to change the order of operations. Once students feel comfortable with the procedures for order of operations, they should be introduced to sentences written in words. To translate these verbal sentences into numerical symbols, parentheses are needed to establish the correct order. For example, ask students to compare "the sum of 8 and 5, times the product of 2 and 3," written as $(8 + 5)(2 \times 3) = 78$, with "the sum of 8 and 5 times the product of 2 and 3," written as $8 + 5(2 \times 3) = 38$. Discuss ways of rewording these expressions to clarify their meanings.

2-4 PROPERTIES OF OPERATIONS

When numbers behave in a certain way for an operation, this behavior is described as a *property*. The most important of these properties involve addition and multiplication, since these operations are helpful in every branch of mathematics studied in this course.

Most students are already aware of the commutative property of addition and the commutative property of multiplication as described for the familiar operations they have performed on positive rational numbers. Let the class test the binary operations of maximum and average for commutativity. Students should conclude that the commutative property holds for many binary operations.

There are, however, binary operations for which the commutative property does not hold. For example, if $\oplus$ is defined as $2a + b$, then the operation $\oplus$ does not have the commutative property, since $5 \oplus 3 \neq 3 \oplus 5$.

To conclude that the commutative property does not hold for a given operation, it is sufficient to show one counterexample. At this level, if a counterexample for a given operation cannot be found, it would appear that the commutative property holds for that operation.

Addition and multiplication are associative as well as commutative operations. Subtraction and division are not commutative and not associative. Students may think that commutative operations are also associative, but the binary operation of averaging will show that this is not the case. Averaging is commutative but not associative.

Later, students will use the distributive property of multiplication over addition when performing algebraic operations such as adding like monomials and finding the product of two binomials. For now, they are introduced to the idea that this property can be used to change the form of an expression.

Keep in mind that students may mistake $2(x + 4)$ for $2x + 4$. Such incorrect applications of the distributive property are dealt with in the exercises provided.

The substitution principle is introduced to assist in computations.

After students recognize that 0 is the identity element for addition and 1 is the identity element for multiplication, ask them if there is an identity element for subtraction. Some will answer 0, since $5 - 0 = 5$ or $a - 0 = a$. Point out, however, that if 0 is the identity element for subtraction, then $a - 0 = 0 - a = a$, which is not true.

Establish that, in general, an identity element for a given operation allows every element in the set to remain unchanged under that operation.

Certain calculator keys lend themselves to properties being studied in this section.

Additive inverse (opposites): $\boxed{+/-}$

Multiplicative inverse (reciprocals): $\boxed{1/x}$

The text again discusses differences in calculators. Some calculators, such as most four-function types, perform operations only with the numbers shown in their displays. Other calculators, however, such as most scientific calculators, maintain a greater number of decimal places in their operating systems than those shown in their displays. Be certain that students understand this distinction, as shown in the example in which multiplication of a number and its reciprocal display sometimes yields 1 and sometimes does not.

See *Enrichment Activity 2-4: Clock Arithmetic.* Basic properties are tested using addition on a clock, similar to the problem presented in the introductory page of this chapter.

Also, see *Enrichment Activity 2-5: Digital Addition and Digital Multiplication* for a look at basic properties in a different format.

2-5 PROPERTIES OF A FIELD

It is *not* necessary for students to know the definition of a field. This section serves primarily as a compact listing of important properties used in the study of mathematics.

See *Enrichment Activity 2-5: Digital Addition and Digital Multiplication.* The 11 field properties are examined using simple arithmetic in a format that is probably unfamiliar to most students.

2-6 OPERATIONS IN GEOMETRY

It is important for students to realize that operations exist in geometry as well as in arithmetic. Certain binary operations in geometry that depend upon operations in arithmetic, such as finding the distance between two points on a number line, the midpoint of a line segment, and the measure of an angle, are introduced in this section.

By relating distance to subtraction, or midpoint of a line segment to averaging, students will see relatively simple examples of the integration of geometry and arithmetic.

The difference between segment AB ($\overline{AB}$) and the distance AB (AB) should be clarified at this point and will be reviewed in Chapter 11 (Geometry).

2-7 OPERATIONS WITH SETS

The intersection of sets, the union of sets, and the complement of a set are three more examples of binary operations. Point out again that operations are a common thread running through the various branches of mathematics.

Since this course does not require an in-depth study of set theory, it is recommended that you do not go beyond the scope of the material presented in this section. You may wish to use simple Venn diagrams to illustrate some concepts. For example:

Intersection
of Sets

Union
of Sets

The Complement
of a Set

Name _____ Class _____ Date _____

ENRICHMENT ACTIVITY 2-1

Operations With Fractions

(1) Answer the 20 questions at the bottom of this sheet. (*Hint:* Every answer is a whole number from 1 to 20.)

(2) Write each answer on the OUTSIDE of the circle, next to its corresponding letter. (For example, if the answer to *C* is 7, write 7 next to the *C* outside the circle.)

(3) Using a ruler, connect the points INSIDE the circle by drawing a line segment from the point where the answer is 1 to the point where the answer is 2. Draw another line connecting the points for 2 and 3. Draw again, connecting the points for 3 and 4. Continue in this way until you connect the points for 19 and 20. Finally connect the points for 20 and 1.

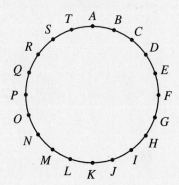

A. $3\frac{1}{2} \times \frac{2}{7} =$

B. $1\frac{2}{5} + 2\frac{3}{5} =$

C. $\frac{1}{2} \times 14 =$

D. $2\frac{1}{2} + 3\frac{1}{3} + 4\frac{1}{6} =$

E. $6\frac{1}{5} + 6\frac{3}{10} + \frac{1}{2} =$

F. $44 \div 2\frac{3}{4} =$

G. $2\frac{1}{8} \times 8\frac{16}{17} =$

H. $5\frac{1}{3} \div 2\frac{2}{3} =$

I. $2\frac{1}{7} \times 2\frac{1}{3} =$

J. $26 \div 3\frac{1}{4} =$

K. $19\frac{6}{7} - \frac{62}{7} =$

L. $18\frac{9}{12} - 4\frac{3}{4} =$

M. $30.\overline{3} - 13\frac{1}{3} =$

N. $34 \div 1\frac{7}{10} =$

O. $7\frac{17}{51} - 4\frac{1}{3} =$

P. $8\frac{1}{3} + 2\frac{1}{6} - 4\frac{1}{2} =$

Q. $8 \times 1\frac{1}{2} \times \frac{3}{4} =$

R. $37\frac{1}{2} \div 3\frac{1}{8} =$

S. $\left(\frac{1}{2}\right)^3 \times 120 =$

T. $10\frac{1}{5} + 8\frac{5}{6} - 1\frac{1}{30} =$

Name _____ Class _____ Date _____

ENRICHMENT ACTIVITY 2-4

Clock Arithmetic

On a clock, 3 hours after 7 is 10, so $7 + 3 \; = 10.$
On a clock, 4 hours after 9 is 1, so $9 + 4 \; = \; 1.$
On a clock, 12 hours after 3 is 3, so $3 + 12 = \; 3.$
On a clock, 8 hours after 9 is 5, so $9 + 8 \; = \; 5.$

These answers have been placed in the table below.

a. Complete the table using the numbers on the clock and clock addition.

+	1	2	3	4	5	6	7	8	9	10	11	12
1												
2												
3												3
4												
5												
6												
7		10										
8												
9			1					5				
10												
11												
12												

b. Answer the following questions using the set of clock numbers and clock addition:

1. Is the set closed under clock addition?   _____

2. Is clock addition commutative? (Test some cases.)   _____

3. Is clock addition associative? (Test some cases.)   _____

4. What is the additive identity for these clock numbers?   _____
   (*Hint:* It cannot be 0 because 0 is not in the set of clock numbers.)

5. Below each clock number, write its additive inverse.
   (Remember that the number and its inverse must add up to the identity.)

Number	1	2	3	4	5	6	7	8	9	10	11	12
Inverse												

Name _____ Class _____ Date _____

ENRICHMENT ACTIVITY 2-5

Digital Addition; Digital Multiplication

	Regular Arithmetic		*Digital Arithmetic*	

Answers contain as many digits as needed.   Answers contain only the digit in the ones place.

$4 + 8 = 12$ $4 \times 8 = 32$ $4 \oplus 8 = 2$ $4 \otimes 8 = 2$

$6 + 4 = 10$ $6 \times 4 = 24$ $6 \oplus 4 = 0$ $6 \otimes 4 = 4$

---

1. Complete the table using digital addition.

$\oplus$	0	2	4	6	8
0					
2					
4					
6					
8					

2. Write *Yes* if the property is true, and *No* if it is not true, for the set $\{0, 2, 4, 6, 8\}$ under the operations of digital addition $\oplus$.

a. Closure under $\oplus$ _____

b. Commutative under $\oplus$
(Test some cases.)   _____

c. Associative under $\oplus$
(Test some cases.)   _____

d. Name the identity element
from this set for $\oplus$.   _____

e. Next to each number, write its
inverse under $\oplus$ so that
"Number $\oplus$ Inverse = Identity"

$0 \oplus$ _____ = _____

$2 \oplus$ _____ = _____

$4 \oplus$ _____ = _____

$6 \oplus$ _____ = _____

$8 \oplus$ _____ = _____

Name _____ Class _____ Date _____

3. Complete the table using digital multiplication.

⊗	0	2	4	6	8
0					
2					
4					
6					
8					

4. Write *Yes* if the property is true, and *No* if it is not true, for the set {0, 2, 4, 6, 8} under the operations of digital multiplication ⊗.

a. Closure under ⊗ _____

b. Commutative under ⊗ (Test some cases.) _____

c. Associative under ⊗ (Test some cases.) _____

d. Name the identity element from this set for ⊗. _____

e. Zero has no multiplicative inverse. Next to each nonzero number, write its inverse under ⊗ so that "Number ⊗ Inverse = Identity"

2 ⊗ _____ = _____

4 ⊗ _____ = _____

6 ⊗ _____ = _____

8 ⊗ _____ = _____

5. Does ⊗ distribute over ⊕ for this set of numbers? (Test some cases.) _____

Conclusion: If all 11 properties of the set are true, then {0, 2, 4, 6, 8} is a field under the operations of ⊕ and ⊗. Is this a field? _____ If not, what failed? _____

SUGGESTED TEST ITEMS (CHAPTER 2)

1. Which of the following is *not* a binary operation for the set of rational numbers?

   (1) addition   (2) subtraction   (3) multiplication   (4) division

2. Which of the following is *not* a binary operation for the set of whole numbers?

   (1) addition   (2) subtraction   (3) multiplication   (4) max

3. If $a * b = 2(a + b)$, what is the value of $5 * 3$?

4. In each question, $a - d$, which number is *not* equivalent to the other three?

   a. 0.25 $\frac{1}{4}$ $\frac{1}{2}$ avg $\frac{1}{6}$ $\frac{25}{100}$ **b.** $\frac{1}{20}$ 0.5   0.05 $\frac{5}{100}$

   c. 0.2   0.20 $\frac{1}{5}$ 0.02   **d.** $\frac{1}{8}$ 0.125 $\frac{1}{8}$ max $\frac{1}{10}$ 1.25

5. Simplify each numerical expression.

   a. $3 + 7 - 2^2$ **b.** $\dfrac{12 + 2^2}{4}$ **c.** $8 \div (20 - 4) + \dfrac{1}{2}$ **d.** $0.3[2 - (1.4 - 0.6)]$

6. State whether each of the following sentences is true or false. If it is true, name the property illustrated.

   a. $6(4 + 2) = 6(4) + 6(2)$ **b.** $5(3 + 7) = 5(7 + 3)$ **c.** $10 + 0 = 10$

   d. $5 \times (2 \times 18) = (5 \times 2) \times 18$ **e.** $14 - (7 + 2) = (14 - 7) + 2$

7. Evaluate each expression and replace $\neq$ by $<$ or $>$ in order to make the resulting statement true.

   a. $3 \times 5 - 2 \neq 3(5 - 2)$ **b.** $3(4)^2 \neq (3 \times 4)^2$ **c.** $5.2 - (3 - 0.8) \neq (5.2 - 3) - 0.8$

8.
```
   A   B   C        D      E
  ←—+———+———+————————+——————+——→
    5   6            d      9
```

   Use the number line to answer the following questions.

   a. If B is the midpoint of $\overline{AC}$, what number should be assigned to B?

   b. If d is the number assigned to D, what is the value of d max 9?

   c. What is the length of CE?

9.

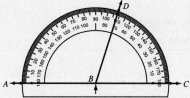

   In the figure, B is on $\overleftrightarrow{AC}$.

   a. Name three rays.

   b. Name a straight angle.

   c. Determine $m\angle ABD$.

10. $A = \{1, 2, 3, 4, 5, 6, 7, 8, 9, 10\}$ $B = \{3, 6, 9, 12\}$ $U = \{1, 2, 3, 4, \ldots, 20\}$

    Perform the given operations and list the element(s) of the resulting sets.

    a. $A \cup B$ **b.** $A \cap B$ **c.** $\overline{A}$ **d.** $\overline{A} \cup A$ **e.** $\overline{A} \cap A$

BONUS I: A salesperson is offered a job that pays $250 a week or a commission of $3.50 on each sale. Which is a better wage if the salesperson averages 75 sales per week?

BONUS II: Place parentheses to make the following statement true: $3 + 3 \div 3 - 3 \times 3 = 3$

SAT PREPARATION EXERCISES (CHAPTER 2)

I. Multiple-Choice Questions

In 1-10, select the letter of the correct answer.

1. If set H contains 3 elements and set G contains 2 elements, what is the least number of elements in H $\cup$ G?

(A) 0   (B) 1   (C) 2

(D) 3   (E) 5

2. The expression $27 - 27 \div 3[(5 + 7) - 3^2]$ equals

(A) 0   (B) 9   (C) 18

(D) 27   (E) 45

3. Which of the following is greater than 1?

(A) $5 - 2 \cdot 2 - 1$ (B) $(0.99)^2$

(C) 0.8 avg 1.2   (D) $3\frac{1}{4} \div 3\frac{1}{5}$

(E) $5 - 3 \cdot 2 - 5 \cdot 79 + 4$

4.

Three squares R, S, and T are shown above. The area of R is twice the area of S, and the area of S is twice the area of T. If the area of S is 1, what is the sum of the areas of all three squares?

(A) $2\frac{1}{2}$ (B) $3\frac{1}{2}$ (C) 4

(D) $5\frac{1}{4}$ (E) 6

5. In the equation $S = 4\pi r^2$, if the value r is tripled, then the value of S is multiplied by

(A) $\frac{1}{3}$ (B) 2   (C) 9

(D) 12   (E) 36

6. Which of the following is the best approximate value of $\dfrac{8.4213 \times 10.0432}{0.1000123}$?

(A) 0.08   (B) 0.80   (C) 8.00

(D) 80   (E) 800

7. Club A has 10 members and Club B has 15. If a total of 21 people belong to at least one club, how many people belong to both clubs?

(A) 4   (B) 5   (C) 6

(D) 7   (E) 8

8.

$$\begin{array}{r} 7X \\ + X1 \\ \hline 1Y7 \end{array}$$

The correct addition problem above shows the sum of 2-digit numbers. If X and Y represent different nonzero digits, then $Y =$

(A) 1   (B) 3   (C) 6

(D) 7   (E) 8

9.

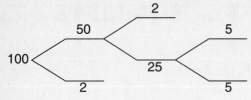

Figure I

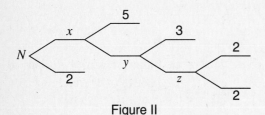

Figure II

Figure I is an example of a "factor diagram" of 100. What is the value of N if Figure II is a "factor diagram" of N?

(A) 30   (B) 60   (C) 90

(D) 120   (E) 150

10.

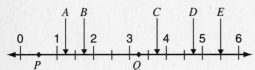

If P and Q are numbers on the number line above, which one of the points shown best represents $P \times Q$?

(A) A (B) B (C) C

(D) D (E) E

II. Quantitative Comparison Questions

Questions 11-20 each consist of two quantities, one in Column A and one in Column B. You are to compare the two quantities and choose:

A if the quantity in Column A is greater;
B if the quantity in Column B is greater;
C if the two quantities are equal;
D if the relationship cannot be determined from the information given.

Notes

1. In certain questions, information concerning one or both of the quantities to be compared is centered above the two columns.
2. In a given question, a symbol that appears in both columns represents that same thing in Column A as it does in Column B.
3. Letters such as x, n, and k stand for real numbers.

Column A	*Column B*
11. $\left(1\frac{1}{2}\right)^2$	$2\left(1\frac{1}{2}\right)$
12. $\left(\frac{1}{2}\right)^3$	$\left(\frac{1}{3}\right)^2$
13. The multiplicative identity for the real numbers	The additive identity for the real numbers

14. $x > 0$

     3 max x 5 max x

15. $\frac{9}{10}$ of $1\frac{1}{10}$ $\frac{9}{10}$ avg $1\frac{1}{10}$

16. $(2 \cdot 3^2)$ max $(2 \cdot 3)^2$ $3 + 6.4$ max $3.6 + 4$

17. If $a * b = 3 (a + b)$

$7 * 2$ $\qquad\qquad$ $2 * 7$

_____

18. The number of steps forward, if 2 & 1 means "take 2 steps forward and one step back."

(5 & 3) & 1 $\qquad\qquad$ 5 & (3 & 1)

_____

19. In the last step of an arithmetic problem, John added 15 to the value he had obtained so far, when he should have subtracted 30. He made no other mistakes.

The correct answer $\qquad$ John's answer to the
to the problem $\qquad\qquad$ problem

_____

20. $5(30124 + 500)$ $\qquad$ $5(500) + (30124)5$

III. Student-Produced Response Questions

In questions 21–25, you are to solve the problem.

21. The universal set U = {1, 2, 3, 4, 5, 6, 7, 8, 9, 10}, the set A = {1, 2, 3} and the set B = {3, 4, 5}. What is the number of elements in $\overline{A} \cap \overline{B}$?

22.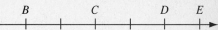

On the number line above, the marks are equally spaced and the coordinates of points C and D are 12 and 20 respectively. What is the difference of the sum of the measure of line segments $\overline{AB}$ and $\overline{AC}$ and the average of the coordinates of points A and E?

23. Twice the average of Jim's 5 test scores 80, 85, 75, 90 and X is 160.8. What is the value of Jim's last test score X?

24. If $(3^x)^x = 81$, what is the value of x?

25.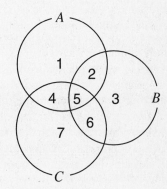

Given A = {1, 2, 4, 5}, B = {2, 3, 5, 6}, and C = {4, 5, 6, 7}. Then A/B = {1, 4} and B/C = {2, 3}. Write the elements in the set $(A \cup B)/(A \cap C)$.

Chapter 3
Problem Solving

Aims

- To review the general techniques for problem solving.
- To review some of the strategies that are useful in finding the solution to a nonroutine problem.

In the study of mathematics and in the application of mathematics to situations outside the classroom, it is useful to be able to perform routine calculations either mentally or by using some type of electronic or mechanical device. But before calculations can be performed, one must be able to determine which calculations are appropriate by understanding and relating the concepts involved. This ability to find relationships is the essence of problem solving.

Students vary greatly in their ability to solve problems, and this ability does not always accompany computational skill. However, problem solving is a skill that can be developed and that must be taught and encouraged in the mathematics classroom in a variety of ways.

Chapter 3 is intended to be a review and extension of problem-solving techniques that students should have encountered in previous mathematics courses. The inclusion of these strategies in a separate chapter at the beginning of the book is not intended to imply that they should be taught in isolation from the mathematical concepts and computational principles to which they are related. Rather, some strategies of problem solving are illustrated here in order that they may serve as

useful resources to students as they encounter problem solving throughout the text. The relationships that are developed in the solution of these problems will provide insights that will be helpful in writing equations when algebraic skills are acquired and an algebraic strategy is employed.

Teachers are encouraged to make use of the material in this chapter in any or all of the ways listed here, according to the needs and abilities of their students.

1. Spend 5 to 8 days reviewing the general problem-solving technique described and illustrated here. Continue to use the exercises given in this chapter throughout the course, returning to problems previously solved when the development of algebraic skills makes new methods of solution possible.
2. Set aside 1 day a week to discuss nonroutine problems in the classroom. Allow students to work in small groups, sharing insights and skills. Encourage students to find more than one method of solution.
3. As often as possible, begin the class with a problem. A relatively simple one may be solved by the class in a few minutes. A more difficult problem can be left unsolved for students to work on the next day. Some problems may require several days or weeks before a solution is found.
4. Use more difficult problems as a weekly challenge. Encourage a variety of methods of

solution. Allow students to explain their solutions to the rest of the class.

5. Put a nonroutine problem at the end of each test. A really challenging problem will present useful activity for students who complete the test before other students have finished. Offer extra credit or some other reward, such as a shorter homework assignment, for the solution. Base your reward on the quality of the effort as well as on the correctness of the solution.

The strategies illustrated in this chapter are intended to give students a way to begin thinking about a problem. Many students do nothing if they cannot immediately identify a sequence of computations that will provide the answer. In a classroom discussion, create an atmosphere in which any suggestion is welcome even if it does not lead to a solution. Show students how, by evaluating why a suggested strategy fails, a successful strategy may be developed.

Many of the problems that are solved in this chapter by working backward or by trial and error can be solved later in the course by using equations. As students develop algebraic skills, they will recognize that these skills enable them to solve problems more efficiently. The ability to use reasoning skills in the solution of routine and nonroutine problems is an ongoing goal of mathematics instruction. Do not, however, expect mastery at this level. The development and use of an algebraic strategy to solve a problem is a specific goal of this course and, as such, is emphasized throughout this book. On final examinations, students should be expected to demonstrate mastery of an algebraic technique.

3-1 THE GENERAL TECHNIQUE FOR PROBLEM SOLVING

The four steps listed in this section as a general technique for the solution of a problem will be particularly helpful for students who, when faced with a nonroutine problem, don't know where to start. On the other hand, students whose insights and experience enable them to go directly to the solution should not be asked to work through each step.

Not all suggested parts of the planning step are applicable to all problems. Estimating an answer is often not possible and should be used only when appropriate. Notice that, in many of the problems that are solved in this chapter, no estimate is given.

The strategies listed are ones commonly accepted as useful approaches. You may add other strategies to the ones given or may wish to combine two or more of these strategies. The problems solved as examples of these strategies presuppose a knowledge of the numbers, operations, and symbolism that were reviewed in Chapters 1 and 2.

3-2 GUESSING AND CHECKING

While even wild guesses are acceptable since they can be gradually refined to arrive at the answer, suggest that students try to start with an "educated guess," based on the largest and smallest possible values. Encourage students to make orderly lists of the numbers that they try in order that trials will not be repeated.

After Exercise 3 has been solved, ask the students to determine the largest and the smallest values for 24 nickels and dimes. Could the value of the 24 nickels and dimes have been $2.50. Could it have been $1.00? Could it have been $2.12? Ask similar questions about the number of legs in Exercise 4 and the number of flowers in Exercise 5. Encourage students to ask themselves, "Is a solution possible?"

In Exercise 6, be sure that students recognize the distinction in meaning between *digit* and *number,* by showing an example such as the digits 1 and 5 forming the numbers 15 and 51. After the problem has been solved, ask the students to write several pairs of numbers, with the numbers in each pair consisting of the same two digits. What is always true of the difference of the numbers in such a pair? (It is always a multiple of 9.) Could you find a pair of numbers that use the same two digits and have a difference of 21? (No, 21 is not a multiple of 9.)

3-3 USING A SIMPLER RELATED PROBLEM

Using a simpler related problem is less familiar to students than guessing and checking, and may require more practice. Thus, although the exercises in this section can be done using a variety of approaches, encourage students to reinforce their understanding.

Exercise 8 offers good motivation for using problem-solving strategies. Although students may at first think that there is not enough information to solve this problem, they will appreciate how perseverance in trying a succession of numbers can lead to a surprising result.

In this exercise, if m families each have 1 child, then these m families have m children. If n families each do not have 1 child, then each of $\frac{1}{2}n$ families has two children. Therefore, $\frac{1}{2}n$ families have $2\left(\frac{1}{2}\right)n$ or n children. Since the other $\frac{1}{2}n$ families have no children, the total number of children for the n families is n. Demonstrate this with specific numbers first. If there were 200 families and 80 had 1 child, then 120 would have 2 or 0. If half of the 120 families had 2 children each, then 60 families would have 2 and 60 would have 0. These 120 families would have $2(60) + 0(60)$, or 120 children. Thus, the total number of families is $80 + 120$, or 200. Try this using different numbers of families with 1 child until the pattern is clear. Then use a different total number of families.

3-4 WORKING BACKWARD

Many of these problems could be solved by writing and solving an algebraic equation. Students who are already familiar with simple algebraic equations may want to use an algebraic strategy. If students do suggest the use of an equation, point out that the solution of an equation is, in fact, an organized way of working backward. Additive and multiplicative inverses are used to simplify and solve equations; these inverses play an important role in working backward.

It may be helpful to discuss fractional relationships. In Exercise 3, if Shaquille scores twice as many points in the second quarter as in the first, ask what fractional part of the points scored in the first half were scored in the first quarter and what fractional part in the second quarter. In Exercise 7, if Kim saved two-thirds of what was left of her money, ask students what fractional part was left. Thus we know that, if one-third of some number is $40, then that number is 3 times $40. Some of these problems present an opportunity to review division by a fraction.

See *Enrichment Activity 3-4: Elimination by Pairs.* Students investigate a sorting technique involving comparison by pairs.

3-5 DISCOVERING PATTERNS

The problems discussed is this section require an investigation of some of the patterns that occur in the set of whole numbers. Students may consider the patterns used to solve Example 2 as one that they might never discover by themselves. Reassure them that such patterns are far from obvious and do require searching ingenuity. However, by studying a variety of examples, students will acquire a familiarity with number patterns.

Present the following sequences to the class:

1, 2, 3, 4, 5, 7, 9, 11, 13, 15, 18, 21, 24, . . .
1, 2, 3, 4, 5, 4, 3, 4, 5, 6, 7, 6, 5, 6, 7, . . .
1, 2, 3, 4, 5, 10, 11, 12, 13, 14, 28, 29, 30, . . .
1, 2, 3, 4, 5, 10, 12, 14, 16, 32, 35, 38, 41, . . .

Each of these sequences begins with 1, 2, 3, 4, 5, ... Infinitely many patterns are possible. However, if we were asked to write the next term of the sequence 1, 2, 3, 4, 5, . . ., we would use the pattern that has already been introduced, for which the next term is 6. For each of the other sequences that begin with 1, 2, 3, 4, 5, more terms are needed before it is possible to discover the pattern used.

In Exercises 5–7, the next term in the given sequence can be found in several ways. For example, in Exercise 5, each term can be obtained by adding two more than the number added to obtain the preceding term.

Position number: 1 2 3 4 5 6 7 8
Value of term: 1 3 7 13 21 31 43 ?
Number added: 2 4 6 8 10 12 14

It is also possible to think of each number in terms of its position number.

First number:	$0(1) + 1$
Second number:	$1(2) + 1$
Third number:	$2(3) + 1$
Fourth number:	$3(4) + 1$
$\vdots$	
nth number:	$(n - 1)(n) + 1$

Students may not be ready to think in terms of $(n - 1)(n) + 1$, but they can think in terms of finding the 7th term by using $6(7) + 1$ and finding the 8th term by using $7(8) + 1$. Ask students which of these methods they would use to find the 100th term of the sequence.

Exercises 8 and 9 are more challenging. Allow students time to investigate possibilities on their own. If they have difficulty, suggest that they find sums or products and compare these to the assigned value of the binary operation. For example, in Exercise 8, $4(3) = 12$, $8(2) = 16$, and $1(5) = 5$. Each product is half of the assigned value. Therefore, we might think of this operation as taking twice the product of the numbers ($a * b = 2ab$).

In Exercise 9, $2(3) = 6$, $3(5) = 15$, and $4(5) = 20$. Each product is a factor of the assigned value. In each case, if we divide the assigned value by the product, the quotient is the first number of the pair. Therefore, we might think of $2 * 3$ as $2(2)(3)$, $3 * 5$ as $3(3)(5)$, $4 * 5$ as $4(4)(5)$, and $a * b$ as $a(a)(b)$ or a^2b. Ask students to write similar exercises by thinking of a pattern using two numbers. Have students present these exercises to the class, giving the results of using their patterns in three or four cases, and have the class determine the unknown value.

Hands-On Activity

Instructions:

(1) Make up an algebraic expression using two variables. Call it $a * b$ where a represents one of the variables and b the other.

(2) Find the value of $a * b$ for three pairs of values.

(3) Tell a classmate the values of a, b, and $a * b$ for these three pairs of values and ask him/her to guess the rule.

3-6 DRAWING PICTURES AND DIAGRAMS

Encourage students to draw diagrams whenever possible, even when using other strategies. The solution of any problem that involves a geometric figure should include a diagram.

In Exercise 2, a diagram will help students to remember that there must be one fence post at the beginning of the fence plus one at the end of each 6 feet. Therefore $1 + \frac{30}{6}$ fenceposts are needed.

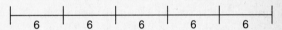

In Exercise 3, students should first find the smallest number of feet that can be fenced before it is possible to use one less post. When finding the required number of posts, they must not forget the beginning post.

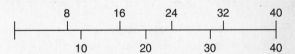

In Exercise 7, there may be 2 bottles or 4 bottles in each row or column. Although there are many possible arrangements, each arrangement must use three rows of 4 and one row of 2.

In Exercise 8, there may be 1, 3, or 5 bottles in each row. An arrangement may have either three rows of 3 or two rows of 1 or one row of 5, one row of 3, and three rows of 1. Ask students whether this problem could be done using a crate with four rows of 5. (No, because there would be an even number of rows, each containing an odd number of bottles. This would require an even number of bottles. At the same time, however, there would also have to be an odd number of columns, each with an odd number of bottles. This would require an odd number of bottles. Therefore, it is impossible to put an odd number of bottles in each row and column of a crate with four rows of 5.)

See *Enrichment Activity 3-6: Guessing a Number by Bisection.* This activity, which can be used as a game by the students, demonstrates a common computer method of locating names or numbers in ordered lists such as telephone numbers or customer files.

3-7 MAKING LISTS AND CHARTS

The use of a chart or an organized list is a very useful strategy in problem solving. Often such a list or chart is used in combination with other strategies, including an algebraic strategy, in order to organize data.

In Example 2, a Venn diagram is used. The diagram below shows an alternative approach.

Cartoon *B*

	Like	Don't like	Total
Like	172		275
Don't like		37	
Total			500

(left axis label: Cartoon *A*)

Exercises 9 and 10 are similar problems.

Problems such as Exercises 3–6 require that the number of bills or flowers, as well as the value of those bills or flowers, be considered. Several solutions are possible.

See *Enrichment Activity 3-7: Arrangements.* Students investigate cyclic arrangements.

3-8 CHOOSING AND COMBINING STRATEGIES

The examples in this section illustrate two important ideas to keep in mind when solving problems.

1. There is often more than one strategy that can be used to solve a problem.
2. A problem is not always solved by the first strategy that is tried.

Example 1 shows the same problem solved by two different strategies. Example 2 shows the use of a strategy that does not give the answer but does provide useful insights that make solution by a different strategy possible.

The varied set of exercises includes some relatively easy and some very challenging problems. Give the students sufficient time to find their own solutions. Ask questions that may lead students to a strategy if they are having difficulty. Encourage students to formulate their own questions when they are unsure of what strategy to use. Listed below are some questions for these exercises that may serve as suggestions.

Exercise 1: Can you draw a picture?

Exercise 2: If you combine the weights of the kitten in the bucket and the rabbit in the bucket, what does this result represent?

Exercise 3: If you knew the number of benches, would you also know the number of people? Try some numbers.

Exercise 4: What number could you try near the middle of the range of possible numbers of tickets?

Exercise 5: How much money and what part of the car has Greg earned?

Exercise 6: What fractional part of the number of customers ordered salad?

Exercise 7: What is the smallest number of points in which the two squares can intersect if part of one square is inside, and part outside, the other? What is the greatest number of points of intersection if one square is inside the other?

The problem does not require that the squares be the same size. Ask students to consider the problem again with this condition. Does it make a difference? (It is possible to find a solution for every required number of intersections for squares of the same size and of different sizes. However, some solutions must be different if the squares must be the same size. For example, if two or four intersections are required, solutions with one square inside the other are possible with squares of different sizes, but not with squares of the same size.)

Exercise 8: Does the number of days in a month determine how many days Rosa works in a month? Does the day of the week on which the month starts determine this?

Exercise 9: Could Glenn buy all gumdrops? Could he buy all chocolate drops? How many pieces of candy could he buy for 5 cents?

Exercise 10: Can you count the number of triangles having any one side of the pentagon as a side? Are there triangles that do not use a side of the pentagon as a side of the triangle?

Exercise 11: How much of the chore is completed in 1 minute: **a.** by Mary? **b.** by Eddy? **c.** together?

Exercises 12, 13, and 14, which all relate to exercise 11, should be attempted by students without benefit of specific hints.

Review Exercises

The following suggestions and/or questions may be helpful in solving the review exercises.

Exercise 1: Some answers must be whole numbers and others can be rational numbers. When the answer must be a whole number, sometimes the computational result must be rounded up to obtain the answer and sometimes it must be rounded down. Ask students to suggest other problems in which the computational result must be rounded up to a whole number, must be rounded down to a whole number, or can be a rational number.

Exercise 2: What is the maximum amount that would be collected if all the tickets were adult tickets?

Exercise 3: Whose places in line are given in the problem?

Exercise 4: How much older than Chris was Carl 5 years ago?

Exercise 5: If the student sets aside 25 cents for each charity, what multiple of 5 cents will she have left if she takes 5 cents from each and gives only 20 cents?

Exercise 6: If Lucy is 1, how old is Ernestine, and how long will it take before Ernestine is twice as old as Lucy? What if Lucy is 2?

Exercise 7: How many voters were in favor of at least one of the issues? If you combine the number of persons in favor of the first issue with the number of persons in favor of the second, how many persons were counted twice?

Exercise 8: What is the product of each pair? What is the sum of each pair?

Exercise 9: Can the boxes fit without wasted space? Can more boxes fit if they are not all aligned in the same way?

Exercise 10: Can you make a chart listing Canadians and Americans in categories of boys, girls, men, and women?

Exercise 11: What day of the year is July 4? Does it matter if it is leap year? Are two answers possible?

Exercise 12: Compare the costs of transporting the metal using only the larger trucks, only the smaller trucks, and a combination of larger and smaller trucks. Note that, if all larger trucks are used, at least one will not have a full load.

Exercise 13: First find the cost of a share of Gardener on Monday. When the price of a share of Kent increased, what must have happened to the cost of a share of Gardener? Since Nicole purchased twice as many shares of Gardener as of Kent, how does a change in Kent stock compare to the change in a share of Gardener stock if there is no change in the total value of the stock?

Name _____ Class _____ Date _____

ENRICHMENT ACTIVITY 3-4

Elimination by Pairs

A basketball league arranges playoffs at the end of the season to determine the champion team in the following manner. In the first round of the playoffs, the eligible teams are paired to play against one another and the losing teams are eliminated from the competition. In the second and in each subsequent round, the winners of the preceding round are paired. If the number of teams in any round is odd, one team does not play in that round but advances to the next round. The process continues until there is one winning team.

a. How many games are needed in the playoffs if there are four eligible teams in the first round?

b. How many games are needed for each larger given number of eligible teams in the first round?

Number of Eligible Teams	Number of Games Needed
4	_____
5	_____
6	_____
7	_____
8	_____
9	_____
n	_____

c. Explain how this playoff procedure can be used to find the largest number in an unordered list of numbers.

d. Can you suggest an alternative approach? Does your alternative approach require fewer steps, the same number of steps, or more steps?

Name _____ Class _____ Date _____

ENRICHMENT ACTIVITY 3-6

Guessing a Number by Bisection

The group decides on a whole number that is unknown to the person who is "it." That person, knowing only the maximum number possible, guesses a number and the group responds that the guess is too large, too small, or correct.

Example:

The group selects 584 and tells the person who is "it" that the number is less than 1,000.

Guess	Group Response	Finding the Next Guess
		The number is between 0 and 1,000, or $0 < n < 1,000$. Guess the average of 0 and 1,000.
500	Too small	Therefore, $500 < n < 1,000$. Find the average of 500 and 1,000.
750	Too large	Therefore, $500 < n < 750$. Find the average of 500 and 750.
625	Too large	Therefore, $500 < n < 625$. Find the average of 500 and 625, rounded.
563	Too small	Therefore, $563 < n < 625$. Find the average of 563 and 625.
594	Too large	Therefore, $563 < n < 594$. Find the average of 563 and 594, rounded.
579	Too small	Therefore, $579 < n < 594$. Find the average of 579 and 594, rounded.
587	Too large	Therefore, $578 < n < 587$. Find the average of 578 and 587, rounded.
583	Too small	Therefore, $583 < n < 587$. Find the average of 583 and 587.
585	Too large	Therefore, $583 < n < 585$. Find the average of 583 and 585.
584	CORRECT!	

Name _____ Class _____ Date _____

a. How many guesses were needed?

b. If the number had been 583, how many guesses would have been needed?

c. If the number had been any number less than 2000, what do you think would have been the maximum number of guesses?

Play the game with numbers less than 1,000, numbers less than 500, numbers less than 250, numbers less than 125. Do you think that the maximum number of guesses is dependent on the given maximum value of the hidden number? If so, how?

How do you think that this procedure could be applied to searching for a word in a dictionary or a name on a list of thousands of names that are in alphabetical order?

Name _____ Class _____ Date _____

ENRICHMENT ACTIVITY 3-7

Arrangements

Audrey, Bonita, Carlos, Dov, and Ezra are play-ing cards, seated around a circular table as shown at the right.

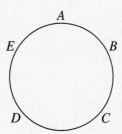

a. After the first game, they change places so that no person is seated next to the same persons as before. Draw a diagram showing the new seating arrangement.

Is more than one arrangement possible? (For the arrangement to be considered different, at least one person must be seated next to a different person.)

b. After the first two games, Fran joined the group, which again changed places so that they were seated as shown at the right. In this third game each person played as the partner of the person opposite. After the game, the group wanted to change places again so that no one was seated next to the same person and no one had the same partner as in the third game.

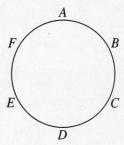

Is such an arrangement possible? Is more than one arrangement possible?

c. What if there are 8, 10, or 12 persons in the group? As the number increases, is it harder or easier to find a change in seating that provides for both new neighbors and new partners?

p281

ADDITIONAL PROBLEMS (CHAPTER 3)

Here are some problems that may be used to continue problem solving in the classroom, as bonus questions at the end of a test, or as work for extra credit. It is recommended that they *not* be used as a classroom test.

1. Sylvia has $6 more than Sara. Together the two girls have $24. How much money does each girl have?

2. Chocolate kisses cost 2 cents each, and peppermints cost 5 cents each. Robin bought some kisses and some peppermints and spent 20 cents. How many kisses and peppermints did she buy?

3. Judy has 100 math problems to solve. She decided to work some on Monday, and on each day after that, to work twice as many as she did the day before. Judy kept to this plan and, after working problems on Friday, still had seven problems left to complete. How many problems did she work each day?

4. Ann, Beth, and Chris are the daughters of Mrs. Adams, Mrs. Burke, and Mrs. Carroll. Each girl works for the mother of one of the other girls. From the following clues, determine the mother and the employer of each girl.
   (1) Ann is not Mrs. Burke's daughter and does not work for Beth's mother.
   (2) Chris is Mrs. Adams' daughter.

5. There are fewer than 50 students in a class. The teacher wants to divide the class into discussion groups of equal size. There is one extra student when she tries to make four groups, and there is one student too few when she tries to make five or six groups. How many students are in the class?

6. Of 400 students surveyed, 325 like pizza, 290 like cheeseburgers, and 12 liked neither pizza nor cheeseburgers. How many of the students surveyed liked both pizza and cheeseburgers?

7. Mr. Winters bought four packages of ground beef. The second package weighed 3 times as much as the first, and the third package weighed half as much as the second. The fourth package weighed 15 ounces, which was 3 ounces more than the third. How many ounces of ground beef did Mr. Winters buy?

8. What is the greatest number of 3-centimeter by 4-centimeter rectangles that can be cut from a 12-centimeter by 10-centimeter piece of cardboard?

9. At a movie theatre, admission for adults was $4.00 and admission for children was $2.00. At the end of the day, the cashier's records showed $825 had been collected for 250 tickets. Determine whether the cashier's records were correct.

Be sure to show or explain the method used to obtain your answer.

SAT PREPARATION EXERCISES (CHAPTER 3)

I. Mutiple-Choice Questions

In 1-10, select the letter of the correct answer.

1. What is the product of the numerators $\frac{4}{8}$ and $\frac{8}{10}$ when these fractions are written in lowest terms?

   (A) 2   (B) 4   (C) 8

   (D) 16   (E) 32

2. What is the least number of trips an elevator with a capacity of 20 people must make to carry 88 people down from the top floor of a building to the lobby?

   (A) 1   (B) 4   (C) 4.4

   (D) 5   (E) 20

3. What is the difference between $\frac{3}{4}$ of 500 and $\frac{1}{2}$ of 300?

   (A) 50   (B) 75   (C) 125

   (D) 225   (E) 250

4. Several people are standing in a straight line to buy concert tickets. Starting at one end of the line, Bill is counted as the 15th person, and starting at the other end, he is counted as the 37th person. How many people are in the line?

   (A) 22   (B) 23   (C) 50

   (D) 51   (E) 52

5. $$A = \{3, 6, 9\}$$
   $$B = \{5, 7, 9\}$$
   $$C = \{7, 8, 9\}$$

   If six *different* numbers are selected, two from each of the sets shown above, what is the greatest sum that these six numbers could have?

   (A) 36   (B) 38   (C) 42

   (D) 45   (E) 48

6. Colored banners are strung on a cord to advertise a carnival. If the colors form a repeating pattern starting with white, red, yellow, blue, green, purple; white, red, yellow, blue, green, purple, and so on, what is the color of the 76th banner?

   (A) Red   (B) Yellow   (C) Blue

   (D) Green   (E) Purple

7. If 25 squares, each painted one of the solid colors red, green, yellow, or blue, are lined up side by side in a single row so that no two adjacent squares are the same color and there is at least one square of each color, what is the maximum possible number of blue squares?

   (A) 7   (B) 10   (C) 11

   (D) 12   (E) 13

8. John had exactly $7 before Bill paid him a $26 debt. After the debt was paid, Bill had $\frac{1}{3}$ the amount that John then had. How much did Bill have before the debt was paid?

   (A) $33   (B) $35   (C) $36

   (D) $37   (E) $47

9. Joe had a balance of $60 in his checking account immediately before he deposited his weekly salary. He wrote a check to the electric company for $30, a check to the telephone company for $90, and one to the gas company for $40. He withdrew the remaining $350 to spend on food and clothes. His friend Dan then paid him a $75 debt. What is Joe's weekly salary?

(A) $375   (B) $450   (C) $510

(D) $525   (E) $585

10. Pencils cost 25 cents each and pens cost 30 cents each. If Robin spent $2.50 on pens and pencils, how many pens did she buy?

(A) 3   (B) 4   (C) 5

(D) 6   (E) Cannot be determined

II. Quantitative Comparison Questions

Questions 11–20 each consist of two quantities, one in Column A and one in Column B. You are to compare the two quantities and choose:

A if the quantity in Column A is greater;
B if the quantity in Column B is greater;
C if the two quantities are equal;
D if the relationship cannot be determined from the information given.

Notes

1. In certain questions, information concerning one or both of the quantities to be compared is centered above the two columns.
2. In a given question, a symbol that appears in both columns represents the same thing in Column A as it does in Column B.
3. Letters such as x, n, and k stand for real numbers.

Column A	*Column B*

11. For a science project, Erica attempted to balance a beam with some feathers on one side and some coins on the other side. She found the feathers were so light that many more were needed to equal the weight of the coins.

Weight of one pound of feathers	Weight of one pound of silver

12. Eggs cost y cents per dozen where $y > 0$.

The cost in cents of 60 eggs	$6y$ cents

13. The numerator x of a fraction is doubled and its denominator y is tripled.
$$\frac{x}{y} > 0$$

The original fraction	The new fraction

14.
The number of 10¢ items that can be purchased for ten dollars	The number of cents in ten dimes

15.

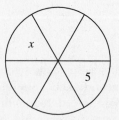

Each of the six regions in the circle above is assigned a number such that the sum of the numbers in any two sectors adjacent to each other is 9.

x	5

16.

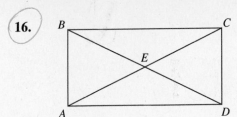

The greatest number of tri-   6
angles that can be named
in quadrilateral *ABCD*

---

17. In a certain game, there are only four types of
moves. These moves advance a playing piece
2, 3, 7, or 9 spaces, in any order.

The minimum number   5
of moves required to
advance a piece exactly
26 spaces

---

18. There is a group of 21 coins consisting only of
nickels and dimes. There are six times as
many dimes as there are nickels.

| Value of all | Value of |
| the coins | 30 nickels |

---

19. José and Sue go fishing. If José gives
Sue a fish, they will have the same number of fish. If Sue gives José a fish, José
will have twice as many fish as Sue.

| The number of | The number of |
| fish José caught | fish Sue caught |

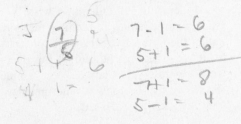

20.   *yes*   There are 26 chairs arranged in rows so
that the first has 5 chairs and each successive row has one more chair than the row
immediately preceding it.

The number of   4
rows used to arrange
the chairs

III. Student-Produced Response Questions

In questions 21–25, you are to solve the problem.

21. In Sunset Hill High School, there are 30 students in an official class. Fifteen of them take
physics, eighteen take chemistry and eight
take both physics and chemistry. How many
take physics but not chemistry?

22. How many of the first one hundred positive
integers contains the digit 9.

23. How many prime numbers are there between
45 and 72?

24. A recipe for a glass of banana shake calls for
$\frac{1}{2}$ cup of milk, 2 teaspoons of sugar and 3
bananas. How many glasses of banana shake
can Ann make with 3 cups of milk, 20 teaspoons of sugar and 24 bananas?

25. Kevin bought 3 red marbles, 2 blue marbles
and 5 green marbles. He lost 2 red and 1
green to Tom in a game that afternoon. He
then exchanged some with Julie. At the end
of the day, he realized that he had 2 red, 2
blue, 2 green and 1 yellow. How many green
marbles did Kevin give away in the exchange?

Chapter *4*
Algebraic Expressions, Geometric Formulas, and Open Sentences

Aims

- To translate verbal phrases and sentences into algebraic language.

- To evaluate algebraic expressions and formulas, including those related to geometric figures.

- To review formulas for perimeter, area, and volume.

- To determine the solution set of an open sentence by replacing the variable with elements from the domain.

- To lay the foundation for the understanding of an algebraic approach to problem solving.

This chapter uses students' knowledge of arithmetic to introduce the use of variables to represent related numerical values. Examples are drawn from the common life experiences of students as well as from their knowledge of perimeter, areas and volume. In this way, these geometric formulas are reviewed and new ways of looking at them are explored. Also, preparation is made for the algebraic solution of problems.

4-1 TRANSLATING VERBAL PHRASES INTO ALGEBRAIC LANGUAGE

As verbal phrases are translated into algebraic expressions, compare the process with translation from one language to another. Sometimes a word-by-word change into symbol is possible, but it is often necessary to use a different order, just as different languages use different word orders. For example, the English "white house" is in Spanish, the "casa blanca," with the adjective after the noun. In algebra, "5 more than x" can be written in the same order, as $5 + x$; but "5 less than x" must be written in a different order, as $x - 5$.

It can prove helpful to students to treat "more than" and "less than" in the same manner. In other words, encourage students to write $x + 5$ for "5 more than x," thus cultivating the correct $x - 5$ rather than the incorrect $5 - x$ for "5 less than x."

It is sometimes helpful to insert commas into verbal phrases for clarity. For example, "twice x decreased by 10" could be interpreted as $2(x - 10)$, but "twice x, decreased by 10" clearly means $2x - 10$.

Once students have changed verbal phrases into algebraic expressions, ask them to change the algebraic expressions into verbal phrases that are different from the original ones.

See *Enrichment Activity 4-1: Number Play.* A number is changed by use of addition, multiplication, subtraction, and division. After following the pattern a few times with whole numbers, students are asked to perform these operations on a variable *n*.

4-2 USING LETTERS TO REPRESENT VARIABLES

In this section, students are encouraged to apply the strategy of using a simpler related problem. They are asked to focus first on a numerical expression to help them see how to write a corresponding algebraic expression.

As occurs throughout the text, integration of topics is achieved in the exercises at the end of this section. Metric units, geometry, basic operations, and everyday relationships are included in the study of algebraic expressions.

In Exercises 26 and 27, after translating words into symbols, students are asked whether the expressions just written represent whole numbers. For example, in Exercise 26, 1 pound of grapes costs *b* dollars. Then, with *d* dollars, you can buy $\frac{d}{b}$ pounds.

If *d* is a multiple of *b*, the answer will be a whole number. But if *d* is not a multiple of *b*, the answer must include a fraction. Assume *d* = $11, and the cost of 1 pound of grapes is *b* = $3. Then,

$$\frac{d}{b} = \frac{11}{3} = 3\frac{2}{3}.$$

You can, of course, buy a fractional part of a pound of grapes. However, if the item had been baseballs, you would not have been able to purchase a fractional part of a baseball. The greatest number of baseballs that could be purchased here is 3. This can lead to a discussion of the **greatest integer function,** written as INT (*x*) or [*x*].

INT (*x*) or [*x*] is defined as the greatest integer that is equal to or less than *x*.

INT (3) = 3   INT (3.2) = 3   INT (3.99999) = 3

If Exercise 26 had named any object that must be purchased in whole-number quantities, the correct answer would be INT $\left(\frac{d}{b}\right)$ or $\left[\frac{d}{b}\right]$.

In Exercise 27, if the cost of a single apple is not a whole number, the store would most probably round the cost *upward* to the next nearest cent.

4-3 ALGEBRAIC TERMS AND VOCABULARY

Just as you, the teacher, use the correct terminology in discussing algebraic expressions, students should also begin to use proper terminology, as presented in this section. The terms *base, exponent,* and *power,* previously studied in Section 2-2, are now applied to algebraic expressions.

Point out that the numerical coefficient need not be restricted to whole numbers. A coefficient may be negative, such as the integer -1. A coefficient may also be a rational number that is not an integer, such as $\frac{1}{2}$, or an irrational number, such as π or $\sqrt{2}$.

4-4 EVALUATING ALGEBRAIC EXPRESSIONS

The order of operations studied in earlier chapters is now applied to evaluating algebraic expressions. Be aware that all replacements for variables in this chapter are restricted to positive rational numbers and zero. In Chapter 5 (Signed Numbers), students will evaluate expressions using negative quantities.

Since a chief aim of this section is to provide students with additional practice in using the order of operations, it is recommended that Exercises 1–75 be tried *first* without the use of a calculator. As a *second* step, these exercises should be checked using the device.

Note that Exercises 76–92 call for use of a calculator, specifically because of the nature of the numbers being used to replace the variables.

Students will continue to make errors with calculators until they get sufficient practice. One of the common errors that may occur here is forgetting to use the multiplication key when a number is written before parentheses.

4-5 TRANSLATING VERBAL SENTENCES INTO FORMULAS

While learning how to translate verbal sentences into formulas, students also review the formulas for area, perimeter, volume, rate of speed, and Fahrenheit/Celsius conversion, in a broad integration of topics. As students write and evaluate formulas in this and the next few sections, they should become familiar with most of the formulas and relationships presented.

4-6 FORMULAS FOR PERIMETER AND AREA OF POLYGONS

In this section, formulas for the perimeters and areas of familiar geometric figures are considered. You may wish to review some of the properties of the quadrilaterals presented in this section before evaluating the formulas algebraically. Be aware, however, that these polygons will be studied in greater detail in Chapters 11 and 12 on geometry.

Unit measures play an important role in the examples and exercises included here. For example, to find the area of a polygon, all lengths *must* be expressed in the same unit of measure so that, in turn, the area is expressed in square units of that measure.

Ask students to draw a length of 14 centimeters:

Then ask them to draw a row containing 10 square centimeters:

Now ask them to compare these two drawings to the diagram of a rectangle shown in the text when

area is introduced. The dimensions of the rectangle are given as 5 by 2. If these measures are 5 cm and 2 cm, then the length of 14 cm shows the perimeter of the rectangle, while the row of squares that measures 10 cm^2 represents the area of the rectangle.

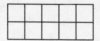

In the text, the diagrams used to demonstrate the areas of parallelogram, trapezoid, and triangle relate back to the initial diagram illustrating the area of a rectangle. Simple transformations show how portions of these figures can be moved to reconstruct the original rectangle.

When applying the formula for the area of a triangle, some students mistakenly take half of the measure of the base *and* half of the measure of the altitude.

$$\frac{1}{2}(6)(4) \neq (3)(2)$$

If this happens, ask students to interpret the formula verbally and to make the arithmetic correspond to the words.

One half of the product of base and altitude

$$\frac{1}{2} \qquad \times \qquad (6)(4)$$

$$= \frac{1}{2} \qquad \times \qquad (24)$$

$$= 12$$

If students wish to cancel when applying this formula, encourage them to use a cancellation symbol on the numbers that have been used so that they will not be tempted to use them again.

$$\frac{1}{2}(\overset{3}{\cancel{6}})(4) = 3(4) = 12$$

The exercises in this section are relatively straightforward. Greater thinking skills and reasoning will be required in Section 4-8 after studying the circumference and area of a circle.

4-7 FORMULAS FOR CIRCUMFERENCE AND AREA OF A CIRCLE

In this section, students are shown the relationships that exist among the radii, diameters, and chords of a circle. Ask why a radius is not a chord. Does the fact that a diameter is the longest chord of a circle relate to a popular expression that "viewpoints are *diametrically* opposed"?

The irrational number π plays an important role in the circumference and area of a circle. As seen in Example 3, the *exact* area of a circle with a radius of 14 feet is 196π square feet. In the other parts of the same example, the use of different approximations for π results in different approximations of the area. Notice that no two approximations are the same. All answers, however, are close in value and perhaps more understandable at this time to students.

If any students are working with scientific calculators where π is entered as the second function of a key, they may need help in learning how to enter this number.

See *Enrichment Activity 4-7: Surface Area.* Students are asked to find the surface area of a rectangular solid and a cylinder, and to develop general formulas for these figures.

4-8 REASONING WITH PERIMETER, AREA, AND SHADED REGIONS

Now that the areas and perimeters of polygons and circles have been studied, this section aims to develop reasoning and thinking skills with these concepts.

In Example 1, a solution is reached by applying two formulas. There are, of course, many other problem-solving strategies that can be helpful here, including the use of diagrams, simple arithmetic, and the guess-and-check approach.

In Example 2, the area of a shaded region is found by subtracting a smaller area from a larger one. In other problems, areas may be found by the addition of a series of smaller areas.

The exercises start simply, and students are asked to find perimeters and areas without being given formulas. In Exercises 17-29, algebraic expressions must be evaluated before areas are found. By Exercise 31, true problem-solving skills are required. Some comments are given below regarding a few of the exercises.

Exercise 31: Drawing a diagram will help to solve the problem.

(1) Plant 16 seedlings 2 feet apart along each of the 30-ft lengths, thus accounting for 32 seedlings.
(2) Divide the remaining 16 seedlings between the two widths, and plant them at 2-ft intervals between the end seedlings.
(3) Note that the diagram shows the number of 2-ft intervals established along the widths, thus leading to the required measure of the width.

Exercises 32, 33, and 37–41: Areas of basic polygons and circles may be added or subtracted, depending upon the diagram, to find the area of the shaded region.

Exercise 36: Some students may choose to find the area of the region to be carpeted by separating the given figure into rectangular regions.

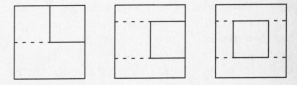

Others may wish to subtract the area of the smaller noncarpeted region from the area of the room.

Exercise 42: This problem calls for the use of diagrams and working backward to find the dimensions of the animal pen. From the 26 ft of fence, subtract the number of feet needed for the length parallel to the garage. Then divide the remaining piece into two parts for the two sides of the pen. Trial and error will lead to the maximum area in part **c**. Note that the products 6×14 and 7×12 both give a seemingly maximum area of 84 sq. ft. The actual maximum area of $84 \frac{1}{2}$ sq. ft. is obtained when the length parallel to the garage is 13 ft.

Although a strategy has been suggested here for each of several problems, there is no one correct strategy. Allow students sufficient time to develop a familiarity with the applications of the various strategies and to build confidence in their own ability to solve problems.

See *Enrichment Activity 4-8: Shaded Areas.* Students are to find areas, each of which is described somehow in terms of π. Which area is the largest?

4-9 FORMULAS FOR VOLUME OF A SOLID

The volume of a right prism or a right circular cylinder is simply equal to the area B of the base times the height h of the solid:

$$V = Bh$$

Volume is measured in cubic units, illustrated in the text as blocks to be counted.

The concept of volume is easy, but terminology seems to get in the way. For example:

The base of a triangular right prism or a trapezoidal right prism includes sides that are also called *bases*. When we work only with plane figures, students can identify the base of a triangle and the base of a trapezoid. Here, however, there is confusion with the other form of the word *base*. To help ease this situation, emphasize that the capital letter B refers to the area of the two-dimensional base on which the solid rests.

Similar problems occur with the word *height*. Write the letter h *only* when referring to the height h of the solid.

Many interesting relationships exist in volume when certain measures are equal, including those given throughout the exercise set at appropriate points:

$$\text{Volume of pyramid} = \frac{1}{3}\text{ Volume of right prism}$$

$$\text{Volume of cone} = \frac{1}{3}\text{ Volume of right cylinder}$$

Plastic models of these figures may be filled with colored water to demonstrate these relationships.

Exercise 39 describes one such set of plastic models. In this set, the radii of all three figures (cone, sphere, and cylinder) are equal, and the height of the cone and the cylinder is equal to the diameter of the sphere.

Noting that the volume of the cone equals one-third the volume of the cylinder, and that the volume of the sphere is equal to twice the volume of the cone, we can deduce:

$$\text{Volume of sphere} = \frac{2}{3}\text{ volume of cylinder}$$

By substituting, we can now say:

$$\text{Volume of sphere} = \frac{2}{3}(\pi r^2 h)$$

$$= \frac{2}{3}(\pi r^2 \cdot 2r)$$

$$= \frac{4}{3}\pi r^3$$

The formula given in the text now has a foundation from which it has been derived.

4-10 OPEN SENTENCES AND SOLUTION SETS

Just as we started this chapter by replacing variables with numbers to evaluate algebraic expressions, we now end the chapter by replacing variables with numbers to find a solution set. What has changed is that we have moved from algebraic expressions to equations and inequalities.

Since the equations being studied here are linear, there will be either one element in the solution set, or none. On the other hand, inequalities have solutions that range from the empty set to an infinite set of numbers.

In the text, Example 2 presents an open sentence, $3y = 12$, that is to be studied using two different domains. In one case, the solution set is empty and, in the other, the solution set is $\{4\}$. This example points to the importance of the domain and its role in determining the solution set. Imagine having a pocket filled with coins but no quarters, and trying to get a soda from a machine that accepts only quarters. The result: no soda, the empty set. Someone else, with enough quarters, gets a different result: the soda.

In subsequent chapters, we will study the standard procedures to simplify equations and find their solutions. Here, we are simply using replacement as a means of finding a solution.

Name _____ Class _____ Date _____

ENRICHMENT ACTIVITY 4-1

Number Play

First fill in all the numbers in Column 1 by following the directions given on the left-hand side of the page.

Second, write any number to start Column 2. Fill in that column by following the same set of directions on the left-hand side of the page.

Third, write any number on the first line in Column 3 and follow the directions again.

Finally, try to complete Column 4, starting with the variable n and following the directions.

	Col. 1	Col. 2	Col. 3	Col. 4
1. Start with this value.	15			n
2. Double the number on line 1.				
3. Add 8 to the number on line 2.				
4. Multiply the number on line 3 by 100.				
5. Subtract 200 from the number on line 4.				
6. Divide the number on line 5 by 10.				
7. Add 40 to the number on line 6.				
8. Divide the number on line 7 by 20.				
9. Subtract 5 from the number on line 8.				

Hint for Column 4:

$$a\,(b + c) = a \cdot b + a \cdot c$$
$$(b + c) \div a = (b + c) \cdot \frac{1}{a} = \frac{b}{a} + \frac{c}{a}$$

Write a conclusion:

Name _____ Class _____ Date _____

ENRICHMENT ACTIVITY 4-7

Surface Area

A cardboard box, in the shape of a *cube,* has an edge e = 5 cm. The box is taken apart and flattened out, as shown at the right. This surface has an area made up of six squares, each with a side of 5 cm.

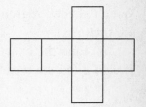

The surface area SA of this cube = $6 (5^2)$ = $6 (25)$ = 150 cm^2.
The general formula for the surface area of a cube is $SA = 6e^2$.

---

1. A cereal box is a rectangular solid, with length ℓ = 19.4 cm, width w = 6.5 cm, and height h = 27.5 cm.

   a. Find its surface area.

   b. Write a general formula for the surface area of a rectangular solid.

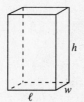

2. A cereal box is a right circular cylinder, with radius r = 5 cm, and height h = 16.8 cm.

   a. Find its surface area.

   b. Write a general formula for the surface area of a right circular cylinder.

3. Manufacturers can package cereal in more compact boxes, such as the cube shown at the top of the page. They would save paper and cut down on their costs. Why don't they do this?

Name _____ Class _____ Date _____

ENRICHMENT ACTIVITY 4-8

Shaded Areas

Which shaded region shown here has the greatest area? Can you tell by simply looking at the pictures?

    a. Find the exact area of each shaded region, expressed in terms of π.

    b. Find the area to the *nearest hundredth* of a square unit.

$\overline{AB}$, $\overline{BC}$, and $\overline{ED}$ are diameters of circles. *ACDE* is a rectangle where $AE = 2ED$, and $AB = BC = 4$.

In circle *O* and circle *B*, $\overline{AB}$ and $\overline{AC}$ are diameters, $AB = BC$, and $OA = 3$.

If drawn, *ABCD* would be a square with a perimeter of 24, and each side of *ABCD* would be a diameter.

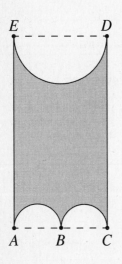

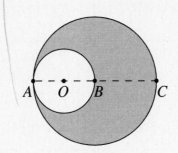

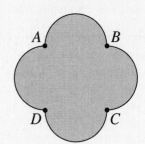

Figure 1

a.

b.

Figure 2

a.

b.

Figure 3

a.

b.

SUGGESTED TEST ITEMS (CHAPTER 4)

1. Using the letter n to represent a number, write each verbal phrase as an algebraic expression.
    a. a number increased by 12   **b.** 7 less than a number   **c.** 4 added to twice a number
    d. one-half of a number, decreased by 6   **e.** the sum of 4 and a number, divided by 3

2. Use the given variable(s) to represent each answer in algebraic language.
    a. Jan spent x dollars. Jim spent 5 dollars more than Jan. Represent the number of dollars Jim spent.
    b. Bus fare is c cents. If Ian rode the bus 10 times this week, represent the total he spent on bus fare.
    c. Represent the number of minutes in h hours and m minutes.
    d. Represent in cents the total value of q quarters and d dimes.
    e. A car rental agency charges \$35 a day to rent a car. This charge includes the cost of the first 100 miles or less. The agency charges \$0.15 per mile for mileage over 100. Represent the cost, in dollars, of renting a car for a day when the car is driven m miles, if m is greater than 100.

3. List the factors of $17ab$.   **4.** Identify the base and the exponent of the power of x^7.

5. Write each expression using exponents.
    a. $3 \cdot a \cdot a$ **b.** $5 \cdot x \cdot x \cdot x \cdot y \cdot y \cdot y \cdot y \cdot y$ **c.** $(5a)(5a)(5a)$

6. For each given term, identify the coefficient, base, and exponent.
    a. $6h^2$ **b.** w^5 **c.** πr^3 **d.** $-m$

7. What is the value of each expression when $a = 3$, $b = 5$, and $c = \frac{1}{3}$?
    a. ac **b.** $2a - b$ **c.** $(a + b)^2$ **d.** $\frac{a + b}{2}$
    e. $27c^2$ **f.** $4a + b^2$ **g.** $b^2 - a^2$ **h.** $a - (b - 2)$

8. When $g = 0.26$ and $t = 17.5$, what is the value of the expression $(gt)^2 + gt^2$?

9. The radius of a circle is 12 centimeters. Express its area:
    a. in terms of π **b.** to the *nearest thousandth*

10. The radius of a circle is 26.5 feet. Express its circumference:
    a. in terms of π **b.** to the *nearest thousandth*

11. Write a formula for computing the cost c of ordering by mail when postage p in cents is added to the price of 4 articles that cost n cents each.

12. The formula for the area of a trapezoid is $A = \frac{1}{2}h (b + c)$. What is the area A when $h = 7$ cm, $b = 12$ cm, and $c = 10$ cm?

13. What is the perimeter of a square whose area is 196 square millimeters?

14. Use the domain $\{1, 2, 3, 4, 5\}$ to find the solution set of $2x - 1 > 5$.

BONUS: A bicycle wheel with a 26-inch diameter revolves 10 times. How many times must a bicycle wheel with a diameter of 20 inches turn to cover the same distance?

SAT PREPARATION EXERCISES (CHAPTER 4)

I. Multiple-Choice Questions

In 1-8, select the letter of the correct answer.

1. If $3(7) = 7y$ and $y + 3 = z - 3$, then z equals

(A) 0   (B) 3   (C) 6   (D) 9   (E) 12

2. If $w = 1$, $x = 2$, $y = 3$, and $z = 4$, which expression has a value different from the others?

(A) $ywx + w$ (B) $w + yx$

(C) $yz - wx$ (D) $w + x + y + z$

(E) $xz + y - w$

3.

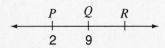

Q is the midpoint of segment PR. If $2x$ is the number assigned to R, then x equals

(A) $3\frac{1}{2}$ (B) 8   (C) 12   (D) 16   (E) 24

4.

The perimeter of rectangle $PQRS$ is 24. If $PQ = x$ and $PQ < QR$, then which of the following must be true for the value of x?

(A) $0 < x < 4$ (B) $0 < x < 6$

(C) $0 < x < 8$ (D) $0 < x < 10$

(E) $0 < x < 12$

5. If the perimeter of a rectangle is 42, which of the following could represent the dimensions of the rectangle?

(A) 4 and 13   (B) 5 and 16

(C) 6 and 7   (D) 19 and 23

(E) 7 and 15

6. The perimeter of a rectangle is more than 20, but less than 28. If the width is 3, then the length could not be a number that is

(A) even   (B) odd

(C) prime   (D) composite

(E) rational

7. $\qquad \dfrac{2}{x} \qquad \dfrac{3}{x + 1} \qquad \dfrac{4}{x + 2}$

If each of the fractions above is in simplest form, which of the following could be the value of x?

(A) 4   (B) 5   (C) 6   (D) 8   (E) 9

8.

What is the area of the shaded region in the figure above, if the radius of the circle is $\frac{1}{2}s$?

(A) $s^2 - \frac{1}{2}s^2\pi$ (B) $\dfrac{4s^2 - s^2\pi}{4}$

(C) $s^2 - \dfrac{\pi s^2}{2}$ (D) $\dfrac{s^2 - 4s^2}{4}$

(E) $\dfrac{2s^2 - \pi s^2}{2}$

II. Quantitative Comparison Questions

Questions 9-16 each consist of two quantities, one in Column A and one in Column B. You are to compare the two quantities and choose:

    A if the quantity in Column A is greater;
    B if the quantity in Column B is greater;
    C if the two quantities are equal;
    D if the relationship cannot be determined from the information given.

Notes

1. In certain questions, information concerning one or both of the quantities to be compared is centered above the two columns.
2. In a given question, a symbol that appears in both columns represents the same thing in Column A as it does in Column B.
3. Letters such as x, n, and k stand for real numbers.

	Column A	*Column B*

9.
$$x = \frac{3}{4}$$
$$y = 0.75$$

x^3	$y \cdot y \cdot y$

10.
$$0 < x < 1$$

x^2	x^3

11.
$$x > 0$$

$2x^2$	$3x^3$

12. $A = (12x - 1)(6x - 2)$

The value of A when $x = \frac{1}{2}$	The value of A when $x = \frac{2}{3}$

13.

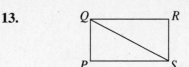

The perimeter of triangle QRS	The semi-perimeter of rectangle $PQRS$

14.
$$x = \frac{1}{2}$$

$x(x + \frac{1}{2})$	$x^2 + \frac{1}{2}x$

15.
$$x = 10$$

$10 + 10$	$\dfrac{10x + 10}{10}$

16.

The area of a triangle whose base and height each equal $1\frac{2}{3}$	The area of a square with each side equal to $1\frac{1}{3}$

III. Student-Produced Response Questions

In questions 17-20, you are to solve the problem.

17. Evaluate, to the *nearest tenth*, the circumference of a circle whose area is 20.

18. If $3x + 1 = 5$, then what is the value of $1 \cdot 2 \cdot 3 \cdot x$?

19. Luke ate a boiled egg in 36 seconds. At the same rate, how many can he eat in 3.5 minutes?

20. If $1 \cdot 2 \cdot 3 \cdot x = 1 + 2 + 3 + x$, then what is the value of $(1 + 2 + 3 + 4)x$?

Chapter *5*
Signed Numbers

Aims

- To define the opposite and the absolute value of a number.
- To formulate the rules for addition, subtraction, multiplication, and division of signed numbers.
- To use positive and negative numbers when evaluating algebraic expressions.
- To graph ordered pairs of signed numbers on the coordinate plane.

The emphasis in this chapter is on developing rules for operations with signed numbers. Graphs, familiar applications, the properties of real numbers, and the calculator all serve to show the results in particular cases. From these particular cases, patterns are observed and rules developed. The coordinate plane is introduced to encourage students to make use of the integration of arithmetic and geometry, to investigate geometric figures, and to observe patterns.

5-1 THE OPPOSITE OF A DIRECTED NUMBER

Students are often confused about the use of the symbol − to mean both a negative number and the oppposite of a number. First, discuss the use of the symbol with whole numbers. For example, −3 means the opposite of 3 or the number negative 3, and, −12 means the opposite of 12 or the number negative 12. Similarly, −(−3) means the opposite of −3 or + 3, and −(−12) means the opposite of 12 or +12. Then ask whether −a represents a positive or a negative number. Encourage students to read −a as the opposite of a, which is negative when a is positive and positive when a is negative.

Call attention to the way in which the opposite of a number is entered on the calculator. On a scientific calculator with a $\boxed{+/-}$ key, −3 should be entered as 3 $\boxed{+/-}$. However, since 0 is already in the display and subtracting 3 is the same as adding −3, entering $\boxed{-}$ 3 will return −3. On the other hand, −(−3) cannot be entered as $\boxed{-}$ $\boxed{-}$ 3. It should be entered as 3 $\boxed{+/-}$ $\boxed{+/-}$, although $\boxed{-}$ 3 $\boxed{+/-}$ is also permissible.

On a graphing calculator that has a $\boxed{(-)}$ key, −3 must be entered as $\boxed{(-)}$ 3. If $\boxed{-}$ 3 is entered, an error message will result.

The graphs of opposites allow for an informal introduction of the concept of reflection. If the number line is folded at 0, each number will coincide with its opposite. Also, each number is the image of its opposite in a mirror placed perpendicular to the number line at 0.

5-2 THE ABSOLUTE VALUE OF A NUMBER

In this section, students are presented with several different ways of thinking about the absolute value of a number. Emphasize that the absolute value of a number is always a positive number.

You may wish to present the formal definition of absolute value:

$$|a| = \begin{cases} a & \text{if } a \geq 0 \\ -a & \text{if } a < 0 \end{cases}$$

Students have no problem with the first part of the definition but are often confused by the second part since they may think of $-a$ as negative. Emphasize that $-a$ means the opposite of a and that the opposite of a negative number is a positive number.

Most scientific calculators have no key for absolute value. Most graphing calculators have a key or the second function of a key labeled $\boxed{\text{ABS}}$, or they list absolute value as part of the menu under some other key.

The absolute value symbol is a grouping symbol and acts like parentheses. The computation within the absolute value bars must be performed first, before other computations.

$$|12 - 2| = |10| = 10$$
$$|12| + |-2| = 12 + 2 = 14$$

5-3 ADDITION OF SIGNED NUMBERS

In this section, the rules for adding signed numbers are developed by observing the results obtained by adding on the number line or on a calculator. If students are unfamiliar with these rules, you may wish to use **Enrichment Activity 5-3: Adding Signed Numbers** to have them investigate the sum of two signed numbers by using the number line and to formulate their own rules before beginning this section.

The examples that lead to the formulation for the rules of addition of signed numbers make use of the

properties of addition of real numbers studied in Chapter 2.

Exercises 49 through 54 represent the most common way of indicating the sum of two or more numbers. Encourage students to think of the sign between two numbers as the sign of the number that follows it, rather than as the sign of the operation. Thus, $+18 - 15 + 9$ should be thought of as the sum of $+18$, -15, and $+9$.

Hands-On Activity

Instructions:

Use small plastic disks of two different colors to represent positive and negative numbers. (For example, let each red disk represent $+1$ and each green disk represent -1.) Use the disks to model the addition of signed numbers.

1. To add two or more signed numbers, select the number of disks of the appropriate color for each number to be added.
2. Combine all of the disks into a single set.
3. Remove from the set pairs that consist of one red and one green disk. Each pair represents zero. When all zero pairs have been removed, the remaining disks will all be of the same color.
4. Count the number of remaining disks and assign the appropriate sign.

Use steps 1-4 to model each addition in Exercises 1-18 on page 145.

5-4 SUBTRACTION OF SIGNED NUMBERS

Students often ask, "How do we know whether a minus sign between two numbers means that the second number is negative or that the numbers are to be subtracted?" For example, does $8 - 9$ mean the sum of $+8$ and -9 or the difference between $+8$ and $+9$? Since $(+8) - (+9) = (+8) + (-9)$, we can think of it either way. On the number line, $8 - 9$ represents a *directed* distance from 9 to 8. Since to go from 9 to 8 we move 1 unit in the negative direction, the difference is -1. The absolute value of the answer gives the distance between the two numbers, and the sign of the answer gives the direction from 9 to 8.

Hands-On Activity

Instructions:

See instructions in **Hands-On Activity** Section 5-3, and use steps 1-4 to model each subtraction in Exercises 1-28 on page 150.

5-5 MULTIPLICATION OF SIGNED NUMBERS

Students usually find it difficult to accept that the product of two negative numbers is positive. Number patterns can be useful in establishing this rule.

$$+2[(+3) + (-3)] = +2(+3) + 2(-3)$$
Distributive property

$$+2 \quad [\ 0\ ] = +2(+3) + 2(-3)$$
Addition property of opposites

$$0 = +2(+3) + 2(-3)$$
Multiplication property of 0.

Thus, $+2(+3)$ and $+2(-3)$ must be opposites since their sum is 0. Since $+2(+3) = +6$, $+2(-3)$ must equal -6. If $+2(-3) = -6$, then, since multiplication is commutative, $(-3)(+2) = -6$.

$$-3[(+2) + (-2)] = -3(+2) + (-3)(-2)$$
Distributive property

$$-3 \quad [\ 0\ ] = -3(+2) + (-3)(-2)$$
Addition property of opposites

$$0 = -3(+2) + (-3)(-2)$$
Multiplication property of 0.

Thus, $-3(+2)$ and $-3(-2)$ must be opposites since their sum is 0. Since $-3(+2) = -6$, $-3(-2)$ must equal $+6$.

Patterns also help us to see that the product of two negative numbers is positive.

$-2(+4) = -8$ Note that, as the num-
$-2(+3) = -6$ bers being multiplied by

$-2(+2) = -4$ -2 decrease, the pro-
$-2(+1) = -2$ ducts increase. As the
$-2(\ 0) = \ 0$ second factors change
$-2(-1) = +2$ by -1, the products
$-2(-2) = +4$ change by $+2$. Note
$-2(-3) = +6$ that as the numbers
$-2(-4) = +8$ being multiplied by -2
continue to decrease, the products continue to increase. As the second factor changes by -1, the product changes by $+2$.

Two common errors result from incorrectly stating the rule for the product of two negative numbers. "The product of like signs is positive" is an incorrect statement and results in errors such as $(-2)(-2)(-2) = +8$. "Like signs give plus" is also incorrect and results in errors such as $(-2) + (-3) = +5$.

"The product of two numbers with the same sign is a positive number" is a correct statement.

5-6 DIVISION OF SIGNED NUMBERS

Once students have learned the rules for the multiplication of signed numbers, they usually have little difficulty in finding the quotient of signed numbers.

Students learned to divide by a number by multiplying by its reciprocal when they were taught to divide by a fraction. In section 5-6, this principle is applied to division by a signed number and will be useful when solving an equation in which the coefficient of the variable is a fraction.

Use the definition of division in terms of multiplication to demonstrate why the denominator of a fraction cannot be 0.

$$\frac{a}{b} = c \quad \text{means that} \quad b \cdot c = a$$

Therefore, $\dfrac{a}{0} = c$ means that $0 \cdot c = a$, and

for all c, $0 \cdot c = 0$.

5-7 EVALUATING ALGEBRAIC EXPRESSIONS USING SIGNED NUMBERS

This section offers students an opportunity to practice using signed numbers with all of the operations. Encourage students to place parentheses around the variable and to replace that variable by its given value. Then perform the operations in the correct mathematical order.

Students should evaluate the expressions in the exercises with a calculator as well as with paper and pencil. Students do not always enter computations into the calculator correctly, and it is important that they learn to place parentheses where needed, to use $+/-$ and $-$ keys correctly, and to use the $\times$ key for multiplication when needed even when that sign is not written in the algebraic expression. Emphasize that, when we write an algebraic expression, multiplication is indicated by using no sign between two variables, between a number and a variable, or between a number and parentheses; but on most scientific calculators, the multiplication key must be used when entering these computations. Graphing calculators, however, will accept symbolism similar to that used in writing algebraic expressions.

Example: Evaluate: $(-3)^2 - 2(-3)$.

On a scientific calculator:

Enter: 3 $+/-$ x^2 $-$
2 $\times$ 3 $+/-$ $=$

On a graphing calculator:

Enter: $($ $(-)$ 3 $)$ x^2
$-$ 2 $($ $(-)$ 3 $)$ $=$

On a graphing calculator, an algebraic expression can be evaluated for any value of the variables by storing the values of the variables and entering the algebraic expression to be evaluated.

Example: Evaluate: $x^2 - 2x$ at $x = -3$.

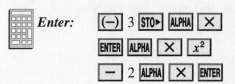

Enter: $(-)$ 3 STO▶ ALPHA $\times$
ENTER ALPHA $\times$ x^2
$-$ 2 ALPHA $\times$ ENTER

The keystrokes listed in this example are for the TI-82 calculator. A similar sequence of steps can be used on other graphing calculators.

5-8 NUMBER LINES AND GRAPHS USING SIGNED NUMBERS

If students are unfamiliar with the coordinate plane, you may want to begin this lesson with *Enrichment Activity 5-8: Graphing Ordered Pairs of Numbers.* Students should recognize that points on the plane are located in relation to two reference lines, one horizontal and the other vertical. These reference lines are simply two number lines, similar to those used in Chapter 1, placed perpendicular to each other and intersecting at 0. The same convention for positive and negative is used: on the horizontal number line, a number to the right of 0 is positive and a number to the left of 0 is negative; on the vertical number line, a number above 0 is positive and a number below 0 is negative.

Drawing polygons by graphing their vertices provides practice in locating points and a review of area and perimeter formulas. Encourage students to observe properties of polygons such as symmetry, parallel and perpendicular lines, and sides of equal length. These properties will be studied in detail in Chapters 11 and 12.

Name _____ Class _____ Date _____

ENRICHMENT ACTIVITY 5-3

Adding Signed Numbers

When numbers are added on the number line, a positive number is represented by an arrow that points to the right and is equal in length to the absolute value of the number; a negative number is represented by an arrow that points to the left and is equal in length to the absolute value of the number.

a. Starting at 0, draw an arrow representing the first number to be added. Then, starting at the tip of that arrow, draw a second arrow representing the second number. The number at the tip of the second arrow is the sum of the numbers.

For example:

$(+4) + (+1)$ 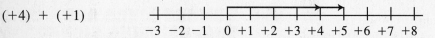 Answer: __+5__

Use the number lines below to find the sums.

$(+2) + (+3)$

```
+--+--+--+--+--+--+--+--+--+--+--+
-3 -2 -1  0 +1 +2 +3 +4 +5 +6 +7 +8
```

Answer: _____

$(-4) + (-1)$

```
+--+--+--+--+--+--+--+--+--+--+--+
-6 -5 -4 -3 -2 -1  0 +1 +2 +3 +4 +5
```

Answer: _____

$(-3) + (-5)$

```
+--+--+--+--+--+--+--+--+--+--+--+
-9 -8 -7 -6 -5 -4 -3 -2 -1  0 +1 +2
```

Answer: _____

$(-2) + (-3)$

```
+--+--+--+--+--+--+--+--+--+--+--+
-5 -4 -3 -2 -1  0 +1 +2 +3 +4 +5 +6
```

Answer: _____

$(-4) + (-2)$

```
+--+--+--+--+--+--+--+--+--+--+--+
-7 -6 -5 -4 -3 -2 -1  0 +1 +2 +3 +4
```

Answer: _____

$(-2) + (-1)$

```
+--+--+--+--+--+--+--+--+--+--+--+
-5 -4 -3 -2 -1  0 +1 +2 +3 +4 +5 +6
```

Answer: _____

$(-5) + (+2)$

```
+--+--+--+--+--+--+--+--+--+--+--+
-5 -4 -3 -2 -1  0 +1 +2 +3 +4 +5 +6
```

Answer: _____

Name _____ Class _____ Date _____

(+1) + (−3)

-5 -4 -3 -2 -1 0 +1 +2 +3 +4 +5 +6

Answer: _____

(+4) + (−3)

-5 -4 -3 -2 -1 0 +1 +2 +3 +4 +5 +6

Answer: _____

(−4) + (+3)

-5 -4 -3 -2 -1 0 +1 +2 +3 +4 +5 +6

Answer: _____

(−1) + (+4)

-5 -4 -3 -2 -1 0 +1 +2 +3 +4 +5 +6

Answer: _____

(−5) + (+6)

-5 -4 -3 -2 -1 0 +1 +2 +3 +4 +5 +6

Answer: _____

(+5) + (−8)

-5 -4 -3 -2 -1 0 +1 +2 +3 +4 +5 +6

Answer: _____

b. Study the answers that you found when the two numbers had the same sign. Can you write a rule for finding the sum of two numbers with like signs?

(*1*) How can the absolute value of the sum of two positive numbers or two negative numbers be found using the absolute value of the numbers?

(*2*) What is the sign of the sum of two positive numbers?

(*3*) What is the sign of the sum of two negative numbers?

c. Study the answers that you found when the two numbers had different signs. Can you write a rule for finding the sum of two numbers with unlike signs?

(*1*) How can the absolute value of the sum of a positive and a negative number be found using the absolute values of the numbers?

(*2*) What is the sign of the sum of a positive number and a negative number?

Name _____ Class _____ Date _____

ENRICHMENT ACTIVITY 5-8

Graphing Ordered Pairs of Numbers

Below is the map of a small town. The center of town is at O, the intersection of Main Street and State Street. All buildings can be located by giving their distances east (to the right) of west (to the left), and north (up) or south (down) from O.

a. On the map, locate each of the buildings listed by writing, at the correct point, the capital letter (*S, L,* etc.) that designates that building.

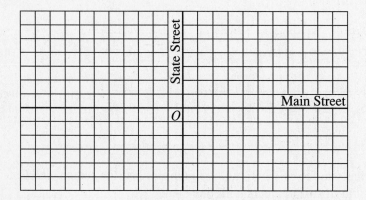

School (*S*)	4 blocks east and 3 blocks north	(4, 3)
Library (*L*)	2 blocks west and 1 block north	(−2, 1)
Firehouse (*F*)	3 blocks east and 2 blocks south	(3, −2)
Hardware store (*H*)	1 block west and 3 blocks north	(−1, 3)
Grocery store (*G*)	5 blocks west and 1 block south	(−5, −1)
Pharmacy (*P*)	2 blocks east and 2 blocks south	(2, −2)
Auto repair shop (*A*)	3 blocks west and 1 block north	(−3, 1)
Dry cleaner (*D*)	4 blocks west and 3 blocks south	(−4, −3)
Video Store (*V*)	on State Street, 2 blocks south	(0, −2)
City Hall (*C*)	1 block west, on Main Street	(1, 0)

b. From school, Murial walks 6 blocks west and 4 blocks south to her home. Locate Murial's home (*M*) on the map. Describe the position of *M* from the center of town (*O*).

c. Explain the meaning of the pair of numbers given in part **a** after each description of the locations of the listed buildings.

SUGGESTED TEST ITEMS (CHAPTER 5)

In 1–4, determine the value of each expression.

1. $|-4|$
2. $|7|$
3. $|3 - 9|$
4. $|3| - |9|$

In 5–12, evaluate each sum.

5. $\begin{array}{r} +7 \\ -3 \\ \hline \end{array}$
6. $\begin{array}{r} +12 \\ +18 \\ \hline \end{array}$
7. $\begin{array}{r} -\ 6 \\ -16 \\ \hline \end{array}$
8. $\begin{array}{r} -17 \\ +\ 4 \\ \hline \end{array}$
9. $\begin{array}{r} -5 \\ +5 \\ \hline \end{array}$
10. $\begin{array}{r} -7.4 \\ -\ 6.7 \\ \hline \end{array}$

11. $-6 + 6 - 4$
12. $-4 + 0 + 8 - 4$

In 13–20, evaluate each difference.

13. $\begin{array}{r} +7 \\ +10 \\ \hline \end{array}$
14. $\begin{array}{r} +7 \\ -10 \\ \hline \end{array}$
15. $\begin{array}{r} +3 \\ -1 \\ \hline \end{array}$
16. $\begin{array}{r} 0 \\ -3 \\ \hline \end{array}$
17. $\begin{array}{r} +6 \\ 0 \\ \hline \end{array}$
18. $\begin{array}{r} +6 \\ -6 \\ \hline \end{array}$

19. $-6 - \left(+9\frac{1}{4}\right)$
20. $-14.2 - (-8.5)$

In 21–26, evaluate each product.

21. $\begin{array}{r} +3 \\ +5 \\ \hline \end{array}$
22. $\begin{array}{r} -7 \\ -8 \\ \hline \end{array}$
23. $\begin{array}{r} +7 \\ -7 \\ \hline \end{array}$
24. $\begin{array}{r} -14 \\ +3 \\ \hline \end{array}$
25. $\begin{array}{r} -3.8 \\ 0 \\ \hline \end{array}$
26. $\begin{array}{r} -8 \\ +0.2 \\ \hline \end{array}$

In 27–32, evaluate each quotient.

27. $\dfrac{+30}{-6}$
28. $\dfrac{+72}{+8}$
29. $\dfrac{-28}{-7}$
30. $\dfrac{-51}{+3}$
31. $\dfrac{-12}{-0.2}$
32. $\dfrac{0}{-5}$

33. From the sum of -7 and $+14$, subtract -5.

In 34–37, what is the value of the expression when $a = -6$, $b = +8$, $c = -0.05$?

34. $-7a$
35. a^2c
36. $b - a$
37. $(a + b)^2$

38. Write the coordinates of each of points $A, B, C, D, E,$ and $F,$ shown on the graph at the right.

39. Draw a pair of coordinate axes and graph each point whose ordered pair is given.

    a. $(5, -1)$ **b.** $(-6, 2)$ **c.** $(2, 5)$

    d. $(0, -2)$ **e.** $(-3, -4)$ **f.** $(3, 0)$

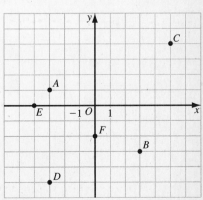

40. a. On a pair of coordinate axes, draw $\triangle ABC$, whose vertices are points $A(-2, 1)$, $B(3, 1)$, $C(1, 5)$.

b. What is the area of $\triangle ABC$?

BONUS: In the country of Tollifer, the unit of money is a *toll*. Coins have values of 3, 7, and 11 tolls. A purchase that costs any whole number of tolls can be made, but often only by giving in payment a larger sum and receiving change. For each whole number from 1 to 30, show how a purchase that costs that number of tolls can be paid. (*Hint:* One way to pay for a purchase worth 1 toll would be to pay a 7-toll coin and receive two coins each worth 3 tolls in change. If change is considered to be a negative value, you can write $7 + 2(-3) = 1$. Other combinations of coins are also possible.)

SAT PREPARATION EXERCISES (CHAPTER 5)

I. Multiple-Choice Questions

In 1-9, select the letter of the correct answer.

1. If x is between -1 and 2, and y is between 3 and 4, then x^2y is between what values?

    (A) 0 and 8   (B) 0 and 16   (C) 3 and 8

    (D) 3 and 16   (E) 8 and 16

2. Which expression is equivalent to
$$\frac{(c \max e)(a \text{ avg } e)a}{|c-|b-d||}?$$

    (A) $\dfrac{(c \max e)(a \text{ avg } e)a}{c-(b-d)}$

    (B) $\dfrac{(c \max e)^a(a \text{ avg } e)}{|c-|b-d||}$

    (C) $\dfrac{(c \max e)(a \text{ avg } e)a}{c-b-d}$

    (D) $\dfrac{(c \text{ avg } e)(a \max e)a}{|c-|b-d||}$

    (E) $\left[\dfrac{1}{|c-|b-d||}\right]\left[\left(\dfrac{a+e}{2}\right)^a (e \max c)\right]$

3. The product of a negative odd number and a positive even number is

    (A) negative and odd
    (B) negative and even
    (C) positive and even
    (D) positive and odd
    (E) cannot be determined

4. If $x = -2$, which of the following gives the largest value?

    (A) $2x^3$ (B) $(2x)^3$ (C) $(-2x)^3$
    (D) $-2x^3$ (E) 2^3x

5. If $x = -3 + 5 + (-1)$ and $y = -8 + (-9) + 4$, what is the average (arithmetic mean) of x and y?

    (A) -7 (B) -6 (C) -2
    (D) 2   (E) 6

6. If $3 = x + (-3)$, and $4 = y + (-2)$, what is the product of x and y?

    (A) 6   (B) 12   (C) 24
    (D) 36   (E) 42

7. If $x + 7 = 3$, what is the value of $3x + 21$?

    (A) 9   (B) 11   (C) 33
    (D) -33 (E) 51

8. The product of a negative even number raised to an odd power and a positive odd number raised to an odd power is always

    (A) negative and odd
    (B) negative and even
    (C) positive and odd
    (D) positive and even
    (E) cannot be determined

9. If $\boxed{x} = \dfrac{x}{|x-1|}$, then which of the following values is closest to zero?

    (A) $\boxed{-1}$ (B) $\boxed{-2}$ (C) $\boxed{2}$

    (D) $\boxed{\boxed{-3}}$ (E) $\boxed{3}$

II. Quantitative Comparison Questions

Questions 10-19 each consist of two quantities, one in Column A and one in Column B. You are to compare the two quantities and choose:

   A if the quantity in Column A is greater;
   B if the quantity in Column B is greater;
   C if the two quantities are equal;
   D if the relationship cannot be determined from the information given.

Notes

1. In certain questions, information concerning one or both of the quantities to be compared is centered above the two columns.
2. In a given question, a symbol that appears in both columns represents the same thing in Column A as it does in Column B.
3. Letters such as x, n, and k stand for real numbers.

Column A	*Column B*
10. $-1-2-3$	$(-1)(-2)(-3)$
11. $-1-3-5$	$(-1)(-3)(-5)$
12. $x > 0, y > 0$	
$x + y$	$\lvert x \rvert + \lvert y \rvert$
13. $a < 0, b > 0$	
ab	$\lvert a \rvert \cdot \lvert b \rvert$
14. $h < 0$	
h	h^3
15. $x = -3$	
$\dfrac{x-2}{\lvert x-2 \rvert}$	$\dfrac{x-2}{\lvert x \rvert -2}$

16.
$$-x + 7 = 14$$
$$y - (-7) = 7$$

The value of x	The value of y

17.   Using $2(x + 5) + 2(-\dfrac{1}{2}x + 3)$

to evaluate the perimeter P of a rectangle

The value of P when $x = -2$	The value of P when $x = 4$

18.
$$y < -3$$

$4 - 3y$	13

19. $x > 0;\ y < 0$

$\dfrac{x}{y}$	$\dfrac{y}{x}$

III. Student-Produced Response Questions

In questions 20-26, you are to solve the problem.

20. How much is twice a number increased by 5, if half of the same number decreased by 5 is one?

21.

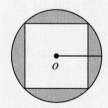

Determine the area of the shaded region in the figure above, if the diameter of the circle O is 14, and the measure of the radius is one more than half the width of the square.

22.

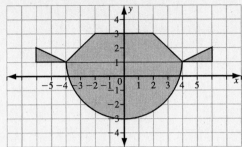

In the diagram above, the curved portion is a semi-circle. Find the area of the enclosed region to the nearest thousandth of a unit.

23. Evaluate the following expression for x if

$$x - 18 = [3 + \frac{10}{2} - (7 - 4)^2].$$

24. On Monday morning John noticed the thermometer read 37 degrees Celsius. By noon, it had risen by 4°, but by mid afternoon he noticed the temperature had fallen by 6°. On the morning of the next day, he observed a new reading 27° on the thermometer. List the absolute value of the changes in temperature in order from the least to the greatest.

25.

If QR is 50% of PQ, how far is $(3 + x)(3 - x)$ from P?

26. The perimeter of rectangle MATH is twice its area. If the perimeter of the rectangle is 24 and AT is greater than MA, what is one possible value for the length of rectangle MATH?

Chapter *6*

Introduction to Solving Equations

Aims

- To use correctly the vocabulary of equations and their solutions.
- To demonstrate that a given number is a solution of an equation.
- To use the addition and multiplication properties of equality to solve equations.
- To use equations to solve problems.

This chapter presents the terminology and techniques necessary to solve first-degree equations in one variable. Most students have used these terms and procedures in their previous study of mathematics. However, it is useful to have students discuss and work with the concepts presented here since they are fundamental to all future work with equations and problem solving.

Many of the equations in this chapter can be solved by inspection. Encourage students to identify the steps that lead to a solution since these same steps will be used to solve more complex equations.

6-1   PREPARING TO SOLVE AN EQUATION

Finding the solution to an equation is like finding the correct key for a lock. If you have a ring with many keys on it, this set of keys is the replacement set. The key or keys that fit the lock are the solution set of the lock.

One way of finding the correct key is to try each key in the lock. In this section, the solution of an equation is found by trying each element of the replacement set in the equation. Often, when trying to unlock a door by placing each key from the ring in the lock until we find the one that works, we skip over some because they are obviously too big or too small. Encourage students to use estimation skills to determine which elements of the domain are the most likely solutions.

Graphing calculators have the capability of determining whether a given number is a solution of an equation. ***Enrichment Activity 6-1: Finding Solution Sets*** uses a graphing calculator to find which elements of a domain are solutions.

6-2   SOLVING EQUATIONS USING ADDITION

Some students may suggest that an equation such as $x + 3 = 5$ can be solved by subtracting 3 from both sides of the equation. Ask students whether these two methods are different: subtracting 3 from both sides, and adding -3 to both sides. Students should recognize that these methods and results are the same.

66

Example 3 shows the solution of an equation in which the left member is a constant and the right member contains the variable. Remind students that the member that contains the variable determines the procedure used. Students may wish to use the symmetric property of equality to rewrite $3 = x + 12$ as $x + 12 = 3$. Ask students to explain why a negative solution is expected.

Students often ask whether a calculator can be used to solve an equation. A scientific calculator cannot solve an equation, although it can be used to perform the necessary computations after the sequence of calculations needed to obtain the solution is determined. Although graphing calculators sometimes have the ability to solve equations, they usually require that the equation be entered in a special form.

6-3 SOLVING EQUATIONS USING MULTIPLICATION

In Example 1 in the text, the equation $5x = 35$ is solved by two methods: multiplying both sides of the equation by $\frac{1}{5}$ and dividing both sides of the equation by 5. Be sure that the students understand that these two operations are equivalent. Ask students if the equation $-\frac{2}{3}y = 18$, which is solved in Example 3 by multiplying both sides of the equation by $-\frac{3}{2}$, could be solved by dividing both sides by $-\frac{2}{3}$.

Students should recall the rule that they used when they first learned to divide fractions: to divide by a fraction, multiply by the reciprocal of the fraction. Encourage students to choose the method that is easier for the particular equation. When the coefficient of the variable is an integer of a decimal number, it is usually easier to divide both sides of the equation by that number. When the coefficient of the variable is a fraction, however, is is usually easier to multiply by the reciprocal of that fraction.

Call attention to the need for parentheses when finding the approximate value of the variable in Example 4 by dividing by 2π. In the written form

$\frac{12}{2\pi}$, the line of the fraction acts both as an indication of division and as a symbol of inclusion. When the line of the fraction is replaced by the division sign as on page 179, the parentheses must be included as the symbol of inclusion.

6-4 SOLVING EQUATIONS USING MORE THAN ONE OPERATION

Section 6-4 combines the procedures of Sections 6-2 and 6-3. Students may ask whether it is possible to solve an equation such as $7x + 15 = 71$ by dividing first. The equation can be solved as shown below.

$$7x + 15 = 71$$

$$\frac{7x}{7} + \frac{15}{7} = \frac{71}{7}$$

$$x + 2\frac{1}{7} = 10\frac{1}{7}$$

$$-2\frac{1}{7} = -2\frac{1}{7}$$

$$x = 8$$

Students usually prefer not to work with the fractions and opt to use the usual order of additions before divisions.

In Method 2 of Example 3 the variable x is added to each side of the equation. Remind students that x represents a number and that the sum of a number and its inverse, that is, the sum of x and $-x$, is always 0.

6-5 WRITING VERBAL SENTENCES AS EQUATIONS

An equation is a powerful problem-solving tool, and the ability to write an equation that incorporates the conditions of a problem is an important skill.

This section concentrates on simple number problems intended to help students translate words into the symbols of algebra.

Many students speak more than one language and are familiar with translating from one language to another. Writing an equation involves translating from words to symbols. Often, in translating from one language to another, the order of the words must be changed to write a sentence correctly. Similarly, in translating from words to symbols, sometimes the order in which the symbols are written in the equation is different from the order of the words in the English sentence.

6-6 USING EQUATIONS TO SOLVE PROBLEMS

Since this section lays the groundwork for solving verbal problems algebraically, sufficient time should be devoted to understanding the procedures outlined here. Students should identify the variable and what it represents before writing the equation. Often they skip this step, write and solve an equation, and are then unable to relate the solution of the equation to the answer.

The check is equally important. The answer should be checked using the words of the problem, as shown in Example 1. Checking the solution by substituting in the equation verifies that the equation has been solved correctly, but not that the equation correctly represents the problem.

Compare the solution of an equation with the problem-solving strategy of working backward.

Example: A group of friends ordered four colas and a pizza. If the pizza cost $8.75 and the total cost without tax was $11.55, what was the cost of one cola?

Some students may suggest that we work backward. If we subtract the cost of the pizza from the total cost, the resulting $2.80 must be the cost of the four colas. If we then divide $2.80 by 4, the result, $0.70 is the cost of a cola.

These are exactly the steps necessary to solve the equation, $4x + 8.75 = 11.55$, that might be written when using an algebraic solution.

Encourage students to use equations to solve problems in these simple cases even though other methods of finding the solution may seem shorter. Using equations will help students to develop both their algebraic and their critical thinking skills, thus preparing them for solving more complex problems for which algebraic solutions are most efficient.

6-7 SOLVING PERCENT PROBLEMS

For some students, a review of the techniques for changing percents to decimals or common fractions may be necessary. Emphasize that, while the percent sign is used to discuss percents, the decimal or common fraction must be used in computation. Problems that require students to find selling prices, dealer costs, discounts, and taxes present realistic applications suitable to this level.

6-8 MORE PRACTICE IN SOLVING EQUATIONS

This section presents no new concept, it simply provides additional practice in solving equations. Some equations have negative solutions, and possible problems that might be represented by equations of this type should be suggested.

Example: In the morning the temperature was 19 degrees. It changed at a constant rate of y degrees per hour for 5 hours until it was 4 degrees. Find the hourly rate of change of the temperature.

This problem can be solved by using the equation $19 + 5y = 4$. The solution is $y = -3$. Therefore the temperature decreased by 3 degrees each hour.

Name _____ Class _____ Date _____

ENRICHMENT ACTIVITY 6-1

Finding Solution Sets
Storing Values of the Domain

On the TI-81 and TI-82 graphing calculators, $\boxed{\text{TEST}}$ presents a menu of equality and inequality signs that can be used to determine whether a particular equality or inequality is true or false. If the statement is true, the calculator returns 1; if the statement is false, the calculator returns 0.

The keys used in the following example are for the TI-82. On the TI-81: use $\boxed{\text{X T}}$ in place of $\boxed{\text{X,T,}\theta}$ in step (1) below; do not press $\boxed{\text{ALPHA}}$ when storing a number in step (2); and delete one $\boxed{\text{ENTER}}$ in step (3).

■ EXAMPLE

Find the solution set of $8 - 2x = 10$ if the domain is $\{-3, -2, -1, 0, 1, 2, 3\}$.

Solution:

(1) Enter the equation to be tested as y_1.

Enter: $\boxed{\text{Y=}}$ 8 $\boxed{-}$ 2 $\boxed{\text{X,T,}\theta}$ $\boxed{\text{2nd}}$ $\boxed{\text{TEST}}$ $\boxed{\text{ENTER}}$ 10 $\boxed{\text{ENTER}}$

(2) Store -3 as x.

Enter: $\boxed{(-)}$ 3 $\boxed{\text{STO►}}$ $\boxed{\text{ALPHA}}$ $\boxed{\text{X,T,}\theta}$ $\boxed{\text{ENTER}}$

(3) Test y_1.

Enter: $\boxed{\text{2nd}}$ $\boxed{\text{Y-VARS}}$ $\boxed{\text{ENTER}}$ $\boxed{\text{ENTER}}$ $\boxed{\text{ENTER}}$

Display: $\boxed{\qquad 0 \qquad}$

Since the calculator returns 0, the equation is false when x is –3, and –3 is not a root.

(4) Repeat step (2), storing -2 as x.

(5) Repeat step (3).

(6) Continue repeating steps (2) and (3) until all elements of the domain have been tested.

Answer: $\{-1\}$

Name _____ Class _____ Date _____

EXERCISES

Find the solution set for each equation if the domain is $\{-5, -4, -3, -2, -1, 0, 1, 2, 3, 4, 5\}$.

1. $3x - 5 = 1$

2. $\dfrac{x}{2} + 12 = 10$

3. $9 - 4x = 21$

4. $|x| - 3 = 0$

5. $x^2 + 1 = 5$

6. $\dfrac{2}{3}x = 0$

Using Tables

On the TI-82 calculator, tables make it possible to evaluate an expression for a range of values. The user enters the first value and the increment (or amount to add to each value) to obtain the next. If the expression being evaluated is entered as an equation, the calculator returns a value of 1 when the equation is true and a value of 0 when the equation is false.

EXAMPLE

Find the solution set of $8 - 2x = 10$ if the domain is $\{-3, -2, -1, 0, 1, 2, 3\}$

Solution:

(1) Enter the equation to be tested as y_1.

Enter: [Y=] 8 [−] 2 [X,T,θ] [2nd] [TEST] [ENTER] 10 [ENTER]

(2) Enter the elements of the domain into a table. Since the smallest value in the domain is –3, enter this value as TblMin, the table minimum. Since values of the elements of the domain differ by 1, enter 1 as ΔTbl, the table increment.

Enter: [2nd] [TblSet] [(−)] 3 [▼] 1 [▼] [ENTER] [▼] [ENTER]

(3) Read the results from the table. The values of the variable are given in the first column, and 1 for true or 0 for false in the second.

Enter: [2nd] [TABLE]

(4) The result is 1 (true) for $x = -1$. The result is 0 (false) for all other values.

Answer: $\{-1\}$

Name _____ Class _____ Date _____

EXERCISES

Find the solution set for each equation if the domain is $\{-5, -4, -3, -2, -1, 0, 1, 2, 3, 4, 5\}$. Use ▲ and ▼ to scroll to larger and smaller values of the variable if necessary.

1. $5x - 2 = 13$

2. $\dfrac{x}{3} + 11 = 2$

3. $\dfrac{2}{5}x + 3 = 1$

4. $x^2 = 4$

5. $9 - x^2 = 0$

6. $x^2 + 9 = 0$

7. $3x + 7 = -2$

8. $\dfrac{4x}{5} - 5 = -1$

9. $2x^2 - 16 = x^2$

SUGGESTED TEST ITEMS (CHAPTER 6)

1. Using the domain $\{-4, -3, -2, -1, 0, 1, 2, 3, 4\}$, determine whether each equation is a conditional equation or an identity. If it is a conditional equation, write its solution set.

   a. $2x - 1 = 5$ **b.** $4x + 1 = 1 + 4x$ **c.** $\frac{1}{2}x + 6 = 4$ **d.** $|2x + 1| = 5$

2. Solve and check each equation.

   a. $a + 7 = 12$ **b.** $3b = -18$ **c.** $y - 1.4 = 3.6$ **d.** $\frac{x}{7} = 2$

   e. $2n - \frac{1}{3} = 7\frac{2}{3}$ **f.** $\frac{1}{4}x + 10 = 1$ **g.** $0.7a - 3.2 = 1.7$ **h.** $8 - 5c = 13$

   i. $\frac{2}{3}y - 7 = 9$ **j.** $\frac{x}{5} + \frac{1}{2} = \frac{3}{2}$ **k.** $3y - 2 = 0$ **l.** $1 - \frac{5}{9}x = 16$

3. If $4x - 3 = 21$, what is the value of $\frac{2}{3}x$?

   In 4–7, solve each problem algebraically.

4. The length of a rectangle is 3 centimeters greater than twice the width. Find the width of the rectangle if the length is 33 centimeters.

5. The difference between the elevation of Mount Rainier and the elevation of the lowest point of Death Valley is 14,690 feet. If the elevation of Mount Rainier is 14,410 feet, what is the elevation of the lowest point of Death Valley?

6. The cost of a 2-pound box of chocolates plus $0.83 tax is $11.23. At the same rate, what is the cost of a one-pound box of chocolates?

7. A dress shop sells dresses for 135% of the cost. What was the cost of a dress that sells for $99.90?

Use any strategy to solve the following problems.

BONUS I: Eleanor needs the exact change to pay the bus fare of $0.80. If she has only quarters and dimes, how many of each type of coin can she use to pay the fare?

BONUS II: A carpenter wants to cut a board that is 400 centimeters long into pieces that are each 17 centimeters long. **a.** What is the greatest number of pieces 17 centimeters long he can cut? **b.** How long is the piece that is left over?

SAT PREPARATION EXERCISES (CHAPTER 6)

I. Multiple-Choice Questions

In 1-11, select the letter of the correct answer.

1. If $\frac{2}{3}$ of x is 10, how much is $\frac{1}{10}$ of x?

(A) $\frac{1}{15}$ (B) $\frac{3}{2}$ (C) $\frac{20}{3}$

(D) 10   (E) 15

2. If $\frac{x}{y} = 1$ and $x + y = 10$, evaluate xy.

(A) 1   (B) 5   (C) 10

(D) 25   (E) 55

3. If $3x + 5 = 7$ and $3x + 10 = 2 + y$, then y is

(A) 5   (B) 7   (C) 9

(D) 10   (E) 12

4. If $0.1x = 2$ and $2y = 0.1$, evaluate xy.

(A) 1   (B) 2   (C) 10

(D) 20   (E) 100

5. If x is $\frac{1}{3}$ of y and y is $\frac{3}{5}$ of z and $5x + 3 = 4$, what is the value of $z + 5$?

(A) 1   (B) 2   (C) 3

(D) 5   (E) 6

6. If $x + 5 = 4$ and $y - 3 = 6$, what is the average (arithmetic mean) of x and y?

(A) 4   (B) 5   (C) 6

(D) 9   (E) 12

7. The product of 4 and a number is 4 more than 12. What is half of the number?

(A) 2   (B) 3   (C) 6

(D) 7   (E) 8

8. If one number is half of another and their average is 15, what is the value of the smaller number increased by 2?

(A) 8   (B) 10   (C) 12

(D) 20   (E) 30

9. If $\frac{2}{3}x = 5$ and $3y = 7$, what is the value of xy?

(A) 70   (B) 35   (C) $17\frac{1}{2}$

(D) $10\frac{2}{3}$ (E) $10\frac{5}{6}$

10. If $\frac{(2)(3)(4)}{(5)(6)(7)} = \frac{x}{y}$ and $\frac{(3)(4)(5)}{(6)(7)(8)} = \frac{ax}{by}$, what is the value of $\frac{a}{b}$?

(A) $\frac{25}{16}$ (B) $\frac{25}{29}$ (C) 4

(D) $\frac{49}{16}$ (E) $\frac{1}{49}$

11. Which of the following expressions represents the phrase: five less than twice a number n?

(A) $3n$ (B) $4n$ (C) $5 - 2n$

(D) $2n - 5$ (E) $2n - 10$

II. Quantitative Comparison Questions

Questions 12-19 each consist of two quantities, one in Column A and one in Column B. You are to compare the two quantities and choose:

A if the quantity in Column A is greater;
B if the quantity in Column B is greater;
C if the two quantities are equal;
D if the relationship cannot be determined from the information given.

Notes

1. In certain questions, information concerning one or both of the quantities to be compared is centered above the two columns.
2. In a given question, a symbol that appears in both columns represents the same thing in Column A as it does in Column B.
3. Letters such as *x, n,* and *k* stand for real numbers.

Column A	*Column B*
12. $10^6 - 10$	$10^5 + 10$

13.   *x* is an integer, and $x < 1$.

$(x)(x + 2)$	$2(x + 1)$

14. $$\frac{x}{y} = 1$$

$\dfrac{x + y}{x}$	$\dfrac{x + y}{y}$

15. $x + y = 2$

$\dfrac{1}{x + y}$	$\dfrac{x}{x + y} + \dfrac{y}{x + y}$

16. $x < 0$

$\dfrac{x - \lvert -3 \rvert}{5}$	$\dfrac{x - 3}{x}$

17. $2x + y = -3$

$\lvert x \rvert$ when $y = 3$	$\lvert y \rvert$ when $x = 0$

18. $$F = \frac{9}{5}C + 32$$

25	The value of C when $F = 75$

19. $y < 6$

$6y - (y - 6)$	$6y - (6 - y)$

III. Student-Produced Response Questions

In questions 20-24, you are to solve the problem.

20. Mario has twice as much money as Manny. Together they have $27. How much is $5 more than one-third Manny's share?

21. If the sum of *x* and 4 is divided by 9, the quotient is 3. What is the remainder if 3,000*x* is divided by 9?

22. The average (arithmetic mean) of three numbers is 65. The largest number is 70, and the middle number is seven more than the smallest. What is the middle number?

23.

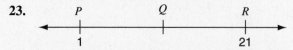

Point *Q* is the midpoint of segment $\overline{PR}$ shown above. If the coordinate assigned to *Q* is $3x - 10$, then what is the value of 3 less than *x*?

24. The original price of a coat was discounted 20% and put on sale at $100. The coat was later marked up 50% from this sale price. What was the difference between the original price and the final price?

Chapter 7
Introducing Logic

Aims

- To introduce the vocabulary and notation of mathematical logic.
- To introduce the basic connectives of logic and their truth tables.
- To examine the truth values of sentences using the basic connectives.

Since reasoning is based on the ways we put sentences together, this topic may initially resemble lessons in English grammar. However, its application to mathematics is soon apparent.

Only sentences that can be judged to be true or false (statements) are discussed in each section. The negation of a statement and the truth values of the conjunction, disjunction, and conditional are dealt with extensively. Truth tables are inserted where applicable, both to verify truth values and to strengthen powers of reasoning.

7-1 SENTENCES, STATEMENTS, AND TRUTH VALUES

Some students may believe that sentences and statements in the English language have no place in a mathematics classroom. It is not uncommon to hear students say, "This isn't math." The examples and exercises in this chapter and the next will show that mathematical logic is not restricted to mathematical settings.

Recall the work done with open sentences and solution sets in Section 4-10. These concepts are now expanded to include open sentences in logic, that is, sentences with truth values that depend upon the replacement of a pronoun. The solution set for the open sentence "$x - 3 = 5$" is $\{8\}$. The solution set for the open sentence "He was the first black major league baseball player" is {Jackie Robinson}. The addition of pronouns to the list of acceptable variables allows us to extend the concept of an open sentence beyond an equation or an inequality. From this point on, any sentence that can be judged to be true or false is called a *statement*.

Some graphing calculators can test the truth value of a numerical statement. For example, the TI-81 and TI-82 calculators return 1 when a true statement is entered and 0 when a false statement is entered. The TEST menu is used to enter the statement.

Example 1: Is the statement $84 - 17 = 67$ true or false?

Enter: 84 [−] 17 [2nd]
[TEST] 1 67 [ENTER]

Display: [1.]

Answer: True

Example 2: Is the statement $-7 > 5$ true or false?

Enter: $(-)$ 7 $\boxed{\text{2nd}}$ $\boxed{\text{TEST}}$ 3 5 $\boxed{\text{ENTER}}$

Display: $\boxed{0}$

Answer: False

7-2 NEGATIONS AND SYMBOLS

Students should readily see that a statement and its negation have opposite truth values. At times, some students will refer to the symbolic statement $\sim p$ as a false statement, since it carries the negation symbol. Dispel this erroneous thought by illustrations: if p represents "$2 + 2 = 5$," then $\sim p$ represents "$2 + 2 \neq 5$," a true statement.

A statement may contain more than one negation symbol. The truth value of $\sim(\sim(\sim p))$ can be determined by a truth table. The similarities that exist between $\sim(\sim(\sim p))$ and $-(-(-3))$ may help to promote understanding.

7-3 CONJUNCTIONS

Once you define the compound sentence called *conjunction,* students are confronted with the problem of considering a truth table that takes into account every possible combination of true and false statements.

A tree diagram is provided in this section as a means of explaining the four possible cases. The idea of a tree diagram reappears in Section 14-7 (The Counting Principle and Sample Spaces) of the probability chapter.

Make a statement: "Jeff is going to the store *and* he is going to the movies." Then, ask students to tell the conditions they think are required for this conjunction to be true. Students will probably give the correct response, "When Jeff does both." If Jeff did not go to the store or to the movies, or go to either, the claim is false. Stress the fact that a conjunction is true only when both conjuncts are true.

Since logic is the formal study of reasoning, it is desirable to have students draw conclusions

from the truth table. For example: If $p \wedge q$ is a false statement and it is known that p is true, it can be determined from the truth table that q must be false. If this method is employed throughout the study of logic in Course I, the transition from an informal treatment of logic in Course I to the formal treatment in Course II will be a smooth one.

The number of rows in a truth table is determined by the formula 2^n, where n is the number of variables in the logical sentence.

For example, when only one variable p is used, as in a negation, the truth table contains 2^1 or 2 rows.

Since $p \wedge q$ contains two variables, a truth table for $p \wedge q$ must contain 2^2 or 4 rows. If a third variable, r, is introduced, 2^3 or 8 rows are needed to display the truth table.

The eight possible arrangements of truth values for a statement containing three variables are shown below in a tree diagram and in the *standard* truth table configuration. Notice that each row in the truth table corresponds to the ending branch in the tree diagram.

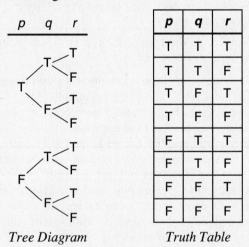

p	q	r
T	T	T
T	T	F
T	F	T
T	F	F
F	T	T
F	T	F
F	F	T
F	F	F

Tree Diagram   *Truth Table*

See *Enrichment Activity 7-3: Conjunction with Three Variables.* Practice is given with a truth table consisting of three variables.

7-4 DISJUNCTIONS

Use the compound sentence "Jeff is going to the store *or* he is going to the movies," and ask the students to determine the conditions under which this disjunction will be false. Students will probably give the correct response, "When Jeff does not do either one."

The difference between the *inclusive or* and the *exclusive or* should be discussed at this point. In our study of logic, we define *or* to be the *inclusive or.* Therefore, the disjunction is false only in the case when both disjuncts are false.

Mention is made in this section of the similarities that exist between negation, conjunction, and disjunction in logic and the complement, intersection, and union in set theory. This transfer of thought, or integration of topics, should serve as a review of the set operations in Section 2-7.

See *Enrichment Activity 7-4A: Breakfast at the Diner: Not, And, Or.* By analyzing a series or sentences containing the words *not, and,* and *or,* students are asked to determine the breakfast orders placed by five women at a diner.

See *Enrichment Activity 7-4B: Conjunction, Disjunction, and the Distributive Property.* Truth tables are used to prove that disjunction is distributive over conjunction, and that conjunction is distributive over disjunction:

$$p \lor (q \land r) \leftrightarrow (p \lor q) \land (p \lor r)$$
$$p \land (q \lor r) \leftrightarrow (p \land q) \lor (p \land r)$$

7-5 CONDITIONALS

The truth table for the conditional is not as obvious to students as are the truth tables for other kinds of statements. You may present a conditional statement to the class, such as "If it is raining, then I'll carry an umbrella." If it rains and I carry an umbrella, or $T \to T$, the statement is true. If it rains and I do not carry an umbrella, or $T \to F$, then this claim is false. In other words, I have told a lie.

Students will see the truth values of these first rows easily. The next two rows, however, will pose problems. If it does not rain, whether I carry an umbrella or not, the original statement cannot be judged to be a lie. Since the statement or claim is not a lie, the conditional statement is deemed to be true in these cases. In other words, the *only* time

that a conditional statement is false is when a deliberate lie has been told, namely, when $T \to F$.

It may be necessary to give many more examples at this stage. In addition to the conditional statements given in the text, provide the class with some examples of your own: "If you do the extra report, then you'll get an *A* on the next report card"; "If you talk one more time, then I'll call your parents." Encourage students to think of similar examples.

You may wish to present a hidden conditional without first explaining the concept: "Boat rides make me sick." The students may say this is not a conditional statement. Simply reply that this is a hidden conditional, and ask them to restate the sentence in the *if . . . then* form: If I go on a boat ride, then I'll get sick. Elicit from students other examples of hidden conditionals based, perhaps, on newspaper advertisements or TV commercials.

Order is important when symbolizing the conditional statement. For example, $p \to q$ and $q \to p$ do not necessarily have the same truth values, as do $p \land q$ and $q \land p$.

It is important to spend some time in having the students identify the antecedent and the conclusion. For example:

Let *b* represent "I will go to the beach."
Let *c* represent "It is cloudy."

The sentence "I will go to the beach if it is not cloudy" is *not* symbolized by $b \to \sim c$. Since "it is not cloudy" follows the word *if,* $\sim c$ is the antecedent. This sentence can be rewritten or thought of as "If it is not cloudy, then I will go to the beach," which is symbolized as $\sim c \to b$.

Some calculators have logic functions that return the truth values of numerical statements formed from other statements by using logical connectives. To access the LOGIC menu on the TI-82, press 2nd TEST ▶ . The LOGIC menu uses:

and	conjunction
or	disjunction (inclusive or)
xor	exclusive or
not	negation

Example 1: Is the statement $(5 > 2)$ and $(2 < 0)$ true or false?

Enter: 5 [2nd] [TEST] 3 2 [2nd] [TEST]
[▶] 1 2 [2nd] [TEST] 5 0 [ENTER]

Display: [0]

Answer: False

Example 2: Is the statement $(5 > 2)$ or $(2 < 0)$ true or false?

Enter: 5 [2nd] [TEST] 3 2 [2nd] [TEST]
[▶] 2 2 [2nd] [TEST] 5 0 [ENTER]

Display: [1.]

Answer: True

Example 3: Is the statement $\sim(5 > 2)$, that is, $(5 \not> 2)$, true or false?

Enter: [2nd] [TEST] [▶] 4 [(] 5
[2nd] [TEST] 3 2 [)] [ENTER]

Display: [0]

Answer: False

The calculator has no key for the conditional, $p \rightarrow q$. However, since it can be shown by using a truth table that $p \rightarrow q$ and $\sim p \lor q$ always have the same truth value, the disjunction can be substituted for the conditional.

Example 1: Is the statement $(5 > 2) \rightarrow (5 > 12)$ true or false?

Enter the statement $\sim(5 > 2) \lor (5 > 12)$.

Enter: [2nd] [TEST] [▶] 4 [(] 5
[2nd] [TEST] 3 2 [)] [2nd]
[TEST] [▶] 2 [(] 5 [2nd]
[TEST] 3 12 [)] [ENTER]

Display: [0]

Answer: False

Example 2: Is the statement $(5 > 12) \rightarrow (5 > 2)$ true or false?

Enter the statement $\sim(5 > 12) \lor (5 > 2)$.

Enter: [2nd] [TEST] [▶] 4 [(] 5
[2nd] [TEST] 3 12 [)] [2nd]
[TEST] [▶] 2 [(] 5 [2nd]
[TEST] 3 2 [)] [ENTER]

Display: [1.]

Answer: True

Name _____ Class _____ Date _____

ENRICHMENT ACTIVITY 7-3

Conjunction with Three Variables

Each of the three statements p, q, and r can be true or false.

Let p represent "I work."
Let q represent "I save money."
Let r represent " I buy roller blades."

When three such sentences or variables are combined, there are eight possible arrangements of truth values, as shown in the tree diagram at the right.

These eight arrangements are also displayed, line by line, in the truth table (below). Notice that the branches of the tree diagram and the rows in the truth table match: the first branch and row 1 both show T-T-T, the second branch and row 2 are both T-T-F, and so on.

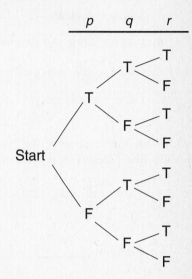

1. Use conjunction to complete the truth table shown here.

row	p	q	r	$p \wedge q$	$p \wedge r$	$q \wedge r$	$(p \wedge q) \wedge r$	$(p \wedge r) \wedge q$	$(q \wedge r) \wedge p$
1	T	T	T						
2	T	T	F						
3	T	F	T						
4	T	F	F						
5	F	T	T						
6	F	T	F						
7	F	F	T						
8	F	F	F						

2. Name the row (or rows) that represent the following statements.
   Example: I work and I do not buy roller blades.   Answer: rows 2, 4

   a. I work and I do not save money and I do not buy roller blades. _____

   b. I work and save money and I buy roller blades. _____

Name _____ Class _____ Date _____

    c. I do not work and yet I save money and buy roller blades.   _____

    d. I do not work and I do not save money.   _____

    e. I work and I do not save money.   _____

    f. I save money and yet I do not buy roller blades.   _____

3. Write the headings of the three columns that match, that is, have exactly the same truth values line by line. Then write a conclusion or observation.

       _____   _____   _____

Conclusion: _____

             _____

Name _____ Class _____ Date _____

ENRICHMENT ACTIVITY 7-4A

Breakfast at the Diner: Not, And, Or

Five women went for breakfast at a diner. The waiter brought these items to the table: 3 orders of eggs, 3 orders of bacon, 3 orders of pancakes; 3 glasses of juice; 3 cups of coffee.

On the basis of the following information, tell what each woman ordered.

1. Each woman ordered three items, and no two breakfasts were the same.

2. Donnelle observed that everyone ordered at least one beverage.

3. Caron ordered bacon *and* eggs.

4. Aleyda did *not* order coffee.

5. Aleyda ordered eggs *or* pancakes, *not* both.

6. Eudora *and* Belva both ordered juice.

7. Either Caron *or* Belva ordered bacon and pancakes.

8. Eudora did *not* order eggs.

Use the table as an aid to find the solution. Place a check in the boxes under the items you know were ordered by certain people. Cross out or blacken the boxes under the items you know were not ordered.

	Bacon	Eggs	Pancakes	Juice	Coffee
Aleyda					
Belva					
Caron					
Donnelle					
Eudora					

Name _____ Class _____ Date _____

ENRICHMENT ACTIVITY 7-4B

Conjunction, Disjunction, and the Distributive Principle

> It is true that multiplication is distributive over addition, as shown by:
> $$a \cdot (b + c) = a \cdot b + a \cdot c$$

1. If disjunction is distributive over conjunction, then

$p \vee (q \wedge r)$ has the same truth value as $(p \vee q) \wedge (p \vee r)$.

Complete the truth table below. Then compare the truth values in columns 5 and 8 to see whether they are exactly the same line by line, and write a conclusion.

Col. 1	Col. 2	Col. 3	Col. 4	Col. 5	Col. 6	Col. 7	Col. 8
p	q	r	$q \wedge r$	$p \vee (q \wedge r)$	$p \vee q$	$p \vee r$	$(p \vee q) \wedge (p \vee r)$
T	T	T					
T	T	F					
T	F	T					
T	F	F					
F	T	T					
F	T	F					
F	F	T					
F	F	F					

Conclusion: _____

_____

Name _____ Class _____ Date _____

2. Complete the truth table below. Compare the truth values in columns 5 and 8, and then write a conclusion.

Col. 1	Col. 2	Col. 3	Col. 4	Col. 5	Col. 6	Col. 7	Col. 8
p	q	r	$q \vee r$	$p \wedge (q \vee r)$	$p \wedge q$	$p \wedge r$	$(p \wedge q) \vee (p \wedge r)$

Conclusion: _____

_____

SUGGESTED TEST ITEMS (CHAPTER 7)

1. Determine whether each of the following is or is not a mathematical sentence.
   a. Chicago is a city in France.   b. How old are you?   c. Stop.
   d. Water freezes at 0° Celsius.   e. If I go.   f. x

2. Identify each of the following as true, false, or open.
   a. There are 7 days in a week.   b. $3^2 = 3 \cdot 2$ c. $2^4 = 4^2$
   d. He is 16 years old.   e. A triangle has three angles   f. $x + 7 = 10$

In 3–7: Let p represent "Peter is a rabbit."   (True)
        Let q represent "Peter is an animal."   (True)
        Let r represent "Peter lives in a pond." (False)
   a. Write each of the following sentences in symbolic form.
   b. Determine the truth value of each sentence.
3. Peter does not live in a pond.
4. Peter is not a rabbit and Peter is an animal.
5. Peter is not an animal or Peter lives in a pond.
6. If Peter is not a rabbit, then Peter is not an animal.
7. Peter is not a rabbit if Peter is an animal.

In 8–11: Let f represent "I study French."   (False)
        Let b represent "I study biology."   (True)
        Let s represent "Biology is a science." (True)
   a. Write a complete sentence in words to show what the symbols represent.
   b. Determine the truth value of each sentence.
8. $\sim f$ 9. $f \wedge \sim b$ 10. $s \rightarrow \sim b$ 11. $b \vee \sim s$

12. Use the domain $\{1, 2, 3, 4, \ldots, 10\}$ to determine the truth set of each of the following.
    a. $x < 5$ b. $x \not< 5$ c. $x \geq 7$
    d. $(x < 5) \wedge (x \not< 5)$ e. $(x \geq 7) \vee (x + 5 = 12)$

In 13 and 14:   a. Identify the hypothesis.   b. Identify the conclusion.
13. If today is Monday, then tomorrow is not Wednesday.

14. I will walk home if it does not rain.

In 15–20, complete the statement by writing "is true," "is false," or "may be true or false."

15. If p is false, then $\sim(\sim p)$ _____   16.   If p is true, then $p \vee q$ _____
17. If p is false, then $p \rightarrow q$ _____   18.   If $p \wedge q$ is true, then p _____
19. If $p \vee q$ is false, then p _____   20.   If p is false, then $p \vee q$ _____

BONUS: Andy, Ben, Carlos, Donna, and Elsie went to the movies and sat together in one row. Ben sat at the far left. There were two people between Elsie and Andy. Carlos did not sit next to Andy. Donna sat in the middle. In what order were these five friends sitting?

SAT PREPARATION EXERCISES (CHAPTER 7)

I. Multiple-Choice Questions

In 1-13, select the letter of the correct answer.

1. *p:* x is even.
   q: x is a multiple of 3.

Based on the statements p and q above, how many whole numbers less than 20 make $\sim p \wedge q$ true?

(A) 3   (B) 4   (C) 6   (D) 10   (E) 12

2. *p:* x is divisible by 3.
   q: x is divisible by 6.

Based on the statements p and q above, which of the following is true for $x = 27$?

(A) $p \wedge q$ (B) $\sim p \wedge q$ (C) $p \wedge \sim q$
(D) $\sim p \wedge \sim q$ (E) $q \wedge p$

3. *p:* $x < 2$
   q: $x^2 < 2x$

Using the statements p and q above, if the statement $p \to q$ is false, what is the value of x?

(A) 4   (B) 3   (C) 2   (D) 1   (E) 0

4. *p:* $x < (1 + 2)(3) + 4$
   q: $x < 1 + (2)(3 + 4)$

Based on the statements p and q above, which of the following is true for all values of x?

(A) $p \wedge q$ (B) $\sim p \wedge q$ (C) $p \to q$
(D) $\sim p \wedge \sim q$ (E) $q \to p$

5. If x is a number between -1 and 2, and y is a number between 4 and 10, then the expression $\dfrac{xy}{2}$ represents a number between

(A) -4 and 20   (B) -4 and 8
(C) -5 and 10   (D) -2 and 10
(E) -1 and 10

6. *p:* The area is 4π.
   q: The circumference is 4π.

Based on the statements p and q above, which is *not* true for a circle with a diameter of 4?

(A) $p \wedge q$ (B) $p \vee q$ (C) $\sim p \wedge q$
(D) $\sim p \vee q$ (E) $\sim p \to \sim q$

7. Let x represent a number.
   p: Twice x is greater than 10.
   q: x increased by 5 is greater than 12.

Based on the statements p and q above, how many counting numbers less than 10 make $p \to q$ true?

(A) 2   (B) 4   (C) 5
(D) 6   (E) 7

8. *p:* N divided by 3 gives a remainder 1.
   q: N divided by 5 gives a remainder 1.

Based on the statements p and q above, what is the greatest whole number less than 20 for which $p \to q$ is true?

(A) 19   (B) 18   (C) 15
(D) 13   (E) 11

9. p: $x + y = 10$
   q: $xy > 25$

Based on the statements p and q above, if x and y are whole numbers, which of the following *cannot* be true for any (x, y)?

(A) $p \wedge q$ (B) $p \vee q$ (C) $p \rightarrow q$
(D) $q \rightarrow p$ (E) $p \rightarrow {\sim}q$

10. p: 5 is the average (arithmetic mean) of x and y.
    q: 10 is the sum of x and y.

Based on the statements p and q above, which of the following is true for $x = 3$ and $y = 8$?

(A) $p \vee q$ (B) $p \wedge q$ (C) ${\sim}p \rightarrow q$
(D) $q \rightarrow {\sim}p$ (E) $p \wedge {\sim}q$

11. p: x and y are whole numbers.
    q: The product of x and y is 47.

Based on the statements p and q above, if the conjunction of $p \wedge q$ is true, then the *negation* of which the following is true?

(A) x avg $y = 24$ (B) x max $y = 47$
(C) x could not be 1.   (D) $x + y$ is even
(E) $|x - y| = 46$

12. p: x, the square of a counting number, is less than 20.
    q: x, a counting number, is a divisor of 36.

Based on the statements p and q above, the number of values that makes $p \wedge q$ true is

what percent of the number of values that makes $p \vee q$ true?

(A) 10   (B) 20   (C) 30   (D) $33\frac{1}{2}$ (E) 40

13. Let $\triangle\!\!\!x = x + 1$ for all real values of x. The statement "If $\triangle\!\!\!x + 2 = 5$, then $\triangle\!\!\!x + \triangle\!\!\!x = 6$" is true when x is

(A) 1 only   (B) 2 only   (C) 3 only
(D) 4 only   (E) any real number

II. Student-Produced Response Questions

In questions 14 and 15, you are to solve the problem.

14. Let p represent $x - 2 = 3$, and q represent $x + y = 19$. What is the value of $2x^2y$ when $(p \wedge q)$ is true?

15. Mary has a total of 12 marbles, and she has developed a game where a person must solve a riddle to determine the number of marbles she has of each color.

Clue 1: The marbles must be either blue, green, or yellow.

Clue 2: There are more green marbles than blue marbles.

Clue 3: The number of blue and yellow marbles is the same.

Based on the clues above, what is one possible answer for the number of green marbles Mary has?

Chapter 8
Using Logic

Aims

- To introduce related conditionals.
- To show the relationship of the converse, inverse, and contrapositive to a given conditional.
- To define the biconditional as the conjunction of a conditional and its converse.
- To define a tautology as a compound sentence that is always true.
- To define logical equivalence.
- To use logic to draw conclusions.

By considering logical equivalence, students further strengthen their reasoning powers. Problems presented in the sections are drawn from real-life situations as well as from the realm of mathematics. Applications of the biconditional statement are seen in the areas of geometry and algebra.

This first exposure to the use of formal logic ends with a preview of how logic is applied to draw conclusions. In Course II, we build upon this foundation to develop the laws of inference, and the nature of proof begins to play a major role in the study of mathematics.

8-1 COMPOUND STATEMENTS AND TRUTH VALUES

To find the truth value of any compound sentence, we must follow a specific order of operations. Once the truth values within the parentheses are simplified (working with the innermost group first), the negations must be simplified. The other connectives may then be simplified by working from left to right.

Example: Find the truth value of the compound sentence $(p \wedge q) \vee \sim r$ when p, q, and r are all true.

$$(p \wedge q) \vee \sim r$$
$$(T \wedge T) \vee \sim T$$
$$T \vee \sim T$$
$$T \vee F$$
$$T$$

Make sure that the truth values of conjunction, disjunction, and the conditional are understood by students before going on to further study of truth tables and tautologies. Encourage students to remember the special cases by asking:

"When is a conjunction true?"
"When is a disjunction false?"
"When is a conditional false?"

Once the unique case is identified, the remainder of the table is easy to reconstruct.

See *Enrichment Activity 8-1: Number Puzzles.* Students are to fill in numbers in a 5 by 5 grid, using only the digits 1 to 5, so that no number appears more than once in any row or any column. These puzzles are based on logical thinking, and students need to handle two or more clues at the same time.

For example, if $C_1 + C_2 = 8$, *and* if $C_2 + D_2 = 6$, so that these variables are digits from 1 to 5 where no digit is repeated in a column or row, there is only one possible answer for the values of C_1, C_2, and D_2.

	1	2
C		
D		

	1	2
C	7	1
D		5

	1	2
C	6	2
D		4

	1	2
C	5	3
D		3

	1	2
C	4	4
D		2

(7 and 6 are not allowed)   (3 and 4 cannot repeat)

The only correct solution is one in which $C_2 = 5$, resulting in the solution shown at the right. The puzzles are more complicated than the first steps illustrated here.

	1	2
C	3	5
D		1

8-2 COMPOUND SENTENCES AND TRUTH TABLES

Initially, it is best to supply students with the headings necessary for the completion of truth tables of given compound sentences. Once students become familiar with this structure, have them fill in their own headings before constructing the tables. Compound sentences that are always true are considered formally in Section 8-4 (Tautologies).

8-3 BICONDITIONALS

The truth table for $p \leftrightarrow q$ is best understood by considering the conjunction of $p \rightarrow q$ and $q \rightarrow p$. It is important that students realize the applications of the biconditional. Precise definitions include the words "if and only if," as seen in Chapters 11 and 12 (Geometry) and, to a larger degree, in Course II when geometry is formalized. Biconditional statements are an integral part of equations: "$2x = 10$ if and only if $x = 5$." If two statements always have the same truth value, these statements are logically equivalent, and one may be substituted for the other in any expression.

In section 8-5, students will learn that $p \rightarrow q$ and its contrapositive $\sim q \rightarrow \sim p$ are logically equivalent statements. The biconditional statement $(p \rightarrow q) \leftrightarrow (\sim q \rightarrow \sim p)$ represents the equivalence. Students will learn other equivalences in Course II when they develop concepts in proof.

8-4 TAUTOLOGIES

Tautologies are used to strengthen powers of reasoning. At first, students may approach this topic mechanically: place T-F values in the columns of the truth table, and claim a tautology exists only when every value in the last column is true. You should require that more be done. Specifically, in cases where two statements are related in a biconditional form and a tautology exists, the statements are logically equivalent; that is, each can be used as a replacement for the other. Use verbal sentences to illustrate.

For example, $\sim(p \rightarrow q) \leftrightarrow (p \land \sim q)$ is a tautology. Using simple verbal statements for p and q, present one compound statement in words and have students find a logically equivalent verbal statement. For example:

Given: $\sim(p \rightarrow q)$:   It is not the case that if it snows, I will swim.

Response: $p \land \sim q$:   It snows and I do not swim.

Understanding can also be enhanced by asking students to take alternate sides of a biconditional. For example, for the tautology $(\sim p \rightarrow q) \leftrightarrow (p \lor q)$, first give the conditional and ask for the disjunction.

Given: $(\sim p \rightarrow q)$:   If I don't eat, I get hungry.

Response: $(p \lor q)$:   I eat or I get hungry.

Then give the disjunction and ask for the conditional.

Given: $(p \lor q)$:   Ed will eat an orange or an apple.

Response: $(\sim p \rightarrow q)$:   If Ed doesn't eat an orange, he'll eat an apple.

8-5 INVERSES, CONVERSES, AND CONTRAPOSITIVES

After you introduce the three related conditionals, ask students which conditional "sounds" logically equivalent to the original. If the students are not sure, construct a truth table consisting of the original conditional, its inverse, and its contrapositive. Students will see that the contrapositive is logically equivalent to the original, since in each row these two statements have the same truth value. Note also that the converse and inverse, although not logically equivalent to the original, are logically equivalent to each other.

Use the illustrations to summarize that, although the converse and inverse are not logically equivalent to the given conditional, each may have the same truth value as the given conditional or each may have the opposite truth value of the given conditional. The given conditional itself can be either true or false.

Ask students to supply further examples, with or without mathematical settings, of the following:

1. A true conditional that has a true converse and inverse (if a polygon has three sides, then it is a triangle)
2. A true conditional that has a false converse and inverse (if the figure is a triangle, then it is a polygon)
3. A false conditional that has a false converse and inverse (if the figure is a polygon, then it is a triangle)
4. A false conditional that has a false converse and inverse (if a polygon is a triangle, then it is a quadrilateral)

Return to the different examples to stress that, no matter what the particular case is, a conditional and its contrapositive always have the same truth value.

From the various contexts, students can gain a sense that the forms of a conditional are not limited to mathematical circumstances. Some of the illustrations show how certain advertising tries to set logical traps. Later, students in this program can draw on their experiences with conditionals to avoid some logical traps traditionally encountered in the study of geometry.

See ***Enrichment Activity 8-5: Logical Equivalents with Three Variables.*** Students will examine a series of four sentences, each based on the variables *p, q,* and *r,* to find two sentences that are logically equivalent.

8-6 DRAWING CONCLUSIONS

In Course II, the rules of inference are developed formally to enable students to recognize patterns in drawing conclusions. This section is intended to prepare students for these formal rules. By referring to a truth table each time in order to decide whether a related sentence can be identified as true or false, the students will develop a familiarity with the combinations of sentences from which a conclusion can be drawn. At this time, the rules of inference should be used in drawing conclusions only if these rules are the result of students' observations.

To encourage student observations, it may be useful to "diagram sentences" in a manner similar to that used when translating verbal phrases to algebraic symbols. For instance, in Example 1 on page 258.

Today is Monday or I have gym.

$$F \lor ? = T$$
(given)   (given)

Students will see that, since at least one disjunction must be true to produce a true disjunction, the ? must be replaced by *T.*

Persons often disagree about the truth of a logical conclusion, not because the logic is incorrect but because they dispute the truth value of one or more of the premises to which the logic is applied. Present logical arguments such as the following to your students:

1. *Premises:*

If studying is more important than watching TV, then I should study even though my favorite program is on.

Studying is more important than watching TV.

Conclusion: I should study even though my favorite program is on.

2. *Premises:*

If my favorite group is to perform, it is worth standing in line all day to buy a ticket.

My favorite group is to perform next week.

Conclusion: It is worth standing in line all day to buy a ticket.

Each conclusion is true when the premises are true. Some students will not accept the conclusions as true because they do not accept the premises as true.

Name _____ Class _____ Date _____

ENRICHMENT ACTIVITY 8-1

Number Puzzles

Introduction

	1	2	3	4	5
A	1	3	2	5	4
B	4	2	5	1	3
C	3	5	4	2	1
D	2	1	3	4	5
E	5	4	1	3	2

In the table at the right, the digits 1 to 5 appear exactly *once* in each row and *once* in each column.

Each cell is identified by reading its heading in the row and then its column heading. For example, $C_1 = 3$, $C_2 = 5$, $D_2 = 1$, and so on.

A code shows the *sum* of the numbers in two or more cells. Using the table above:

Since $C_1 = 3$ and $C_2 = 5$, the sum of these two cells is written as $C_{12} = 8$.

Since $C_2 = 5$ and $D_2 = 1$, the sum of these two cells is written as $CD_2 = 6$.

Find the following sums by using the table given above.

1. $B_{34} = $ _____ **2.** $E_{345} = $ _____ **3.** $DE_1 = $ _____ **4.** $AB_1 = $ _____

5. $A_{45} = $ _____ **6.** $BCD_3 = $ _____ **7.** $C_{123} = $ _____ **8.** $ABCD_5 = $ _____

Puzzle 1: Use the codes and sums given below, in any order, to place the digits 1 to 5 in the cells of the table so that each digit appears *once* in each row and *once* in each column.

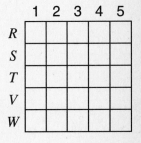

$$V_{45} = 5 \qquad S_{45} = 4$$

$$VW_2 = 4 \qquad TV_1 = 3$$

$$R_{12} = 8 \qquad RS_2 = 7$$

$$RST_4 = 6$$

Name _____ Class _____ Date _____

Puzzle 2: Use the codes and sums given below, in any order, to place the digits 1 to 5 in the cells of the table so that each digit appears *once* in each row and *once* in each column.

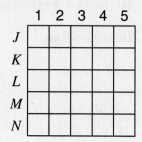

$$J_{34} = 3 \qquad\qquad N_{123} = 6$$

$$JK_4 = 4 \qquad\qquad MN_3 = 8$$

$$JK_2 = 8 \qquad\qquad L_{45} = 5$$

$$L_{12} = 9 \qquad\qquad KL_5 = 4$$

What observation, if any, can you make about the sum of the numbers in any row and in any column?

_____

_____

Try to construct your own puzzle using codes like those shown here.

Name _____ Class _____ Date _____

ENRICHMENT ACTIVITY 8-5

Logical Equivalents with Three Variables

A heat wave hit town in the middle of the summer. The movie theater is usually air-conditioned, and there is a great movie showing.

Let h represent: The weather is hot.
Let a represent: The theater is air-conditioned.
Let s represent: The movie is sold out.

a. Translate the following four sentences into symbolic form using a, h, and s.

(1) If the weather is hot and the theater is air-conditioned, then the movie is sold out. _____

(2) If the weather is hot and the movie is sold out, then the theater is air-conditioned. _____

(3) If the weather is hot and the theater is not air-conditioned, then the movie is not sold out. _____

(4) If the theater is air-conditioned and the movie is sold out, then the weather is hot. _____

b. Complete the following truth tables to determine the truth values of the four sentences.

h	a	s	$h \wedge a$	$h \wedge s$	$(h \wedge a) \rightarrow s$	$(h \wedge s) \rightarrow a$
T	T	T				
T	T	F				
T	F	T				
T	F	F				
F	T	T				
F	T	F				
F	F	T				
F	F	F				

h	a	s	~a	~s	$h \wedge \text{~}a$	$a \wedge s$	$(h \wedge \text{~}a) \rightarrow \text{~}s$	$(a \wedge s) \rightarrow h$
T	T	T						
T	T	F						
T	F	T						
T	F	F						
F	T	T						
F	T	F						
F	F	T						
F	F	F						

c. Which of the four sentences, if any, are logical equivalents? _____ Explain why.

SUGGESTED TEST ITEMS (CHAPTER 8)

In 1–4,　*p*:　A square is a rectangle　(True)
　　　　　q:　A square is a polygon.　(True)
　　　　　r:　A circle is a polygon.　(False)
　　a. Write each of the following in a symbolic form using *p*, *q*, and *r*.
　　b. Determine the truth value of each sentence.

1. If a square is not a rectangle, then a square is not a polygon.

2. If it is not true that a square is a rectangle and a polygon, then a circle is a polygon.

3. If a circle is a polygon or a circle is not a polygon, then a square is a rectangle.

4. A square is a polygon if and only if a circle is a polygon.

In 5–6 write, in each case: **a.** the inverse　**b.** the converse　**c.** the contrapositive

5. If today is Wednesday, then tomorrow is Thursday.

6. If a carrot is a vegetable, then vegetables do not grow on trees.

7. **a.** Construct a complete truth table for each of the following.

   (1) $p \rightarrow \sim q$　　*(2)* $\sim p \vee \sim q$　　*(3)* $p \wedge \sim q$

   b. What two sentences are equivalent?

8. **a.** Complete the following truth table for the sentence $\sim(p \wedge q) \leftrightarrow (\sim p \vee \sim q)$.

p	q	$\sim p$	$\sim q$	$p \wedge q$	$\sim(p \wedge q)$	$\sim p \vee \sim q$	$\sim(p \wedge q) \leftrightarrow (\sim p \vee \sim q)$

   b. Is $(p \wedge q) \leftrightarrow (\sim p \vee \sim q)$ a tautology?

   c. Justify your answer to part **b.**

In 9–12, assume that the first two sentences are true. State whether the truth value of the third sentence is true, is false, or cannot be determined.

9. Today is Thursday or Friday.
   Today is not Friday.
   Today is Thursday.

10. If I studied, I passed the test.
    I did not pass the test.
    I studied.

11. I speak Spanish or I speak English.
    I speak English.
    I speak Spanish.

12. If Peter asks Meg to the dance, then Inez
    will go to the dance with Greg.
    Peter asks Meg to the dance.
    Inez will go to the dance with Greg.

BONUS:　In the country of Tollifer, the unit of money is a toll. Coins have values of 3, 7, and 11 tolls.

　　　a. What is the least number of coins needed to have exactly 23 tolls?

　　　b. Is there more than one possible set of coins with a value equal to 23 tolls?

SAT PREPARATION EXERCISES (CHAPTER 8)

Multiple-Choice Questions

In 1-15, select the letter of the correct answer.

1. p: x is 10.
q: x is 3 units from 7 on the number line.

Based on the statements p and q above, which of the following is true for all values of x?

(A) $p \rightarrow q$ (B) $q \rightarrow p$ (C) $p \rightarrow \sim q$

(D) $p \leftrightarrow q$ (E) $q \rightarrow \sim p$

2. p: $x \div x = 1$
q: $(1)x = x$

Based on the statements p and q above, which of the following is true for all x?

(A) p (B) q (C) $p \wedge q$

(D) $p \leftrightarrow q$ (E) $q \rightarrow p$

3. p: The area is a multiple of 9.
q: One side is a multiple of 3.

Based on the statements p and q above, which of the following is true for all possible squares.

(A) $p \wedge \sim q$ (B) $p \rightarrow \sim q$ (C) $q \rightarrow p$

(D) $\sim p \wedge q$ (E) $q \rightarrow \sim p$

4. p: $\triangle JKL$ has exactly 2 equal sides.
q: $\triangle JKL$ has exactly 3 equal sides

Based on the statements p and q above, which of the following is true for all triangles?

(A) $p \wedge q$ (B) $p \vee q$ (C) $p \rightarrow q$

(D) $\sim p \vee \sim q$ (E) $p \leftrightarrow \sim q$

5. Given the statement: If $x = 0$, then $x + y = y$.

Which of the following is true?

   I. The converse
  II. The inverse
 III. The contrapositive

(A) I only   (B) II only

(C) III only   (D) I and II only

(E) I, II, and III

6. Given the statement: If $x = 1$, then $xy = y$.

Which of the following is true?

   I. The converse
  II. The inverse
 III. The contrapositive

(A) I only   (B) II only

(C) III only   (D) I and II only

(E) I, II, and III

7. Given the statement: If $x = 0$, then $xy = 0$.

Which of the following is true?

   I. The converse
  II. The inverse
 III. The contrapositive

(A) I only   (B) II only

(C) III only   (D) I and II only

(E) I, II, and III

8. Given the statement:
If $x = 2$, and $y = 3$, then $\dfrac{x}{y} = \dfrac{2}{3}$
Which of the following is true?

    I. The converse
    II. The inverse
    III. The contrapositive

(A) I only   (B) II only

(C) III only   (D) I and II only

(E) I, II, and III

9. Given the statement: If $PQ = QR$, then Q is the midpoint of $\overline{PR}$.

Which of the following is true?

    I. The converse
    II. The inverse
    III. The contrapositive

(A) I only   (B) II only

(C) III only   (D) I and II only

(E) I, II, and III

10.

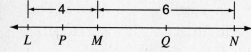

    L P M Q N

p: P is the midpoint of $\overline{LM}$.
q: Q is the midpoint of $\overline{MN}$.

Based on the statements p and q above, which of the following statements is true for the points shown above when $PQ = 5$?

(A) $p \wedge q$ (B) $p \vee q$ (C) $p \leftrightarrow q$
(D) $\sim p \vee \sim q$ (E) $\sim p \wedge \sim q$

11. p: $x > 0$
    q: $x^2 = 4$

Based on the statements p and q above, which of the following is true when $x = -2$

(A) $p \wedge q$ (B) $p \vee \sim q$ (C) $\sim p \wedge q$
(D) $\sim p \vee \sim q$ (E) $q \rightarrow p$

12.

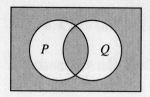

p: X is in set P.
q: X is in set Q.

Based on the statements p and q above, which of the following statements is true for all points X in the shaded areas above?

(A) $p \wedge q$ (B) $p \vee q$ (C) $p \wedge \sim q$
(D) $p \leftrightarrow q$ (E) $\sim p \vee \sim q$

13. Let $U = \{1, 2, 3 \ldots, 10\}$.
    p: x is in set P $\{1, 2\}$
    q: x is in set Q $\{2, 3\}$

The truth set for $p \rightarrow q$ is equivalent to which of the following?

(A) $\overline{P} \cap Q$ (B) $\overline{P} \cup Q$ (C) $P \cap \overline{Q}$
(D) $P \cup \overline{Q}$ (E) None

14. For the statement "If $x^2 > x$, then $x > 1$", which of the following is always true?

    I. The converse
    II. The inverse
    III. The contrapositive

(A) I only   (B) II only

(C) III only   (D) I and II only

(E) I, II, and III

15. p: The average of x, y, and 8 is 5.
    q: The sum of x and y is 8

Based on the statements p and q above, which of the following is true for all values of x and y?

(A) $p \rightarrow q$ (B) $p \rightarrow \sim q$ (C) $\sim p \rightarrow q$
(D) $\sim p \rightarrow \sim q$ (E) $q \rightarrow p$

Chapter 9
Operations With Algebraic Expressions

Aims

- To present the rules for the addition, subtraction, multiplication, and division of both monomials and polynomials.
- To develop the concepts of negative and zero exponents.
- To introduce the use of scientific notation.

Student mastery of both the principles and the skills covered in this chapter is essential for success in algebra.

Once students have learned to add, subtract, multiply, and divide monomials, the same skills can be applied to polynomials. In performing these operations, students should recognize that they are using the commutative, associative, and distributive properties. Division of a polynomial by a polynomial may be considered an optional topic.

Geometric applications and examples from common experience are included to prepare students to use algebraic strategies in solving more complex problems.

9-1 ADDING ALGEBRAIC EXPRESSIONS

Students should understand the use of the distributive property as the basic principle that enables us to add like terms. They are accustomed to seeing the form $a(b + c) = ab + ac$, and may need help in recognizing the altered form used here: $ba + ca = (b + c)a$. Show them how the text examples, such as $9x + 2x = (9 + 2)x$, follow this pattern.

Emphasize that other additions also use this principle. For example, to add fractions, we need common denominators:

$$\frac{3}{7} + \frac{2}{7} = 3 \cdot \frac{1}{7} + 2 \cdot \frac{1}{7} = (3 + 2)\frac{1}{7} = 5 \cdot \frac{1}{7} = \frac{5}{7}$$

$$3x + 2x = (3 + 2)x = 5x$$

Once students understand how to add like terms, they must identify terms as like or unlike when adding polynomials. Both vertical and horizontal formats are used in the text. To begin, the vertical format is convenient to reinforce the combination of like terms, and to highlight any missing terms. However, the horizontal format is more commonly used by mathematicians, and students should be comfortable with it. An important application of the horizontal format arises later when like terms are combined in the solution of an equation.

Hands-On Activity

Instructions:

Use algebra chips to model the addition of polynomials. Chips can be purchased commercially or cut from light plastic or cardboard. Chips that represent the number 1 can be 1 centimeter by 1 centimeter. Chips that represent n can be 1 inch by 1 centimeter, and those that represent n^2 can be 1 inch by 1 inch. Chips should be of two colors; one color to represent a positive number, and the other to represent a negative number. A pair of identical chips of different colors have a sum of 0 and can be added to or removed from a computation without changing the result.

Example: Model the sum of $(n^2 + 3n - 4)$ and $(2n^2 - 4n + 6)$.

1. Lay out one positive n^2 chip, three positive n chips, and four negative 1 chips.

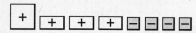

2. Now add another set: two positive n^2 chips, four negative n chips, and six positive 1 chips.

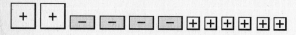

3. Combine the two sets of chips, and remove any pairs that sum to 0.

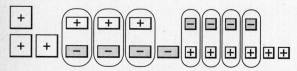

4. Count the remaining chips: $3n^2 - 1n + 2$.
5. Now use algebra chips to perform the following additions:
    a. $(3n^2 - 2n + 3) + (n^2 - 4n + 1)$
    b. $(-n^2 - 5n - 1) + (2n^2 + 2n + 1)$
    c. $(n^2 + 3n - 2) + (n^2 - 3n + 1)$
    d. $(2n^2 - 4n + 3) + (-n^2 + 4n - 3)$
    e. $(-n^2 - n + 2) + (n^2 + n + 1)$

Enrichment Activity 9-1: Sums and Squares gives students practice in recognizing patterns that use addition.

9-2 SUBTRACTING ALGEBRAIC EXPRESSIONS

Hands-On Activity

Instructions:

Use algebra chips to model subtraction of polynomials. From the chips that represent the poly-

nomial that is the minuend, the chips that represent the subtrahend are removed. If there are not enough chips in the minuend to correspond to the chips to be removed, a sufficient number of pairs of chips that have a sum of 0 can be added to the minuend without changing its value.

Example: Model the difference $(2n^2 + 3n - 4) - (n^2 - 2n + 2)$.

1. Lay out two positive n^2 chips, three positive n chips, and four negative 1 chips.

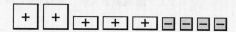

2. One positive n^2 chip, two negative n chips, and two positive 1 chips must be removed. Since there are no negative n chips and no positive 1 chips to remove, add two pairs of n chips and two pairs of 1 chips. In each pair of added chips, one chip must be positive and the other negative.

Added pairs
Original set

3. Remove one positive n^2 chip, two negative n chips, and two positive 1 chips.

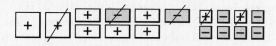

4. Count the remaining chips: $n^2 + 5n - 6$.
5. Now use algebra chips to perform the following subtractions:

    a. $(3n^2 - 4n + 3) - (n^2 - 2n + 1)$
    b. $(n^2 - 5n - 1) - (2n^2 + 2n - 1)$
    c. $(n^2 + 3n - 2) - (n^2 + 3n + 1)$
    d. $(2n^2 - 4n + 3) - (-n^1 - n - 3)$
    e. $(-n^2 - n + 2) - (n^2 + n + 1)$

Subtraction of monomials and polynomials applies the same principle as the subtraction of signed numbers: to the minuend, add the opposite of the subtrahend. Emphasize that, when the subtrahend is a polynomial, the sign of each term must be changed to form the opposite, as shown in the following example.

$$(2x^2 - 3x + 4) - (\ x^2 + 2x - 6)$$
$$= (2x^2 - 3x + 4) + (-x^2 - 2x + 6)$$
$$= 2x^2 - 3x + 4 - \ x^2 - 2x + 6$$
$$= x^2 \quad - 5x + 10$$

When the same example is done using a vertical format, it is helpful to circle the original signs of the terms being subtracted and then to write their opposite signs before using addition.

$$2x^2 - 3x + 4$$
$$\underline{\oplus x^2 \ \overline{\oplus} \ 2x \ \overset{+}{\ominus} \ 6}$$
$$x^2 - 5x + 10$$

Emphasize that the sum of an algebraic expression and its opposite is always 0 and that the difference between two equal algebraic expressions is always 0.

9-3 MULTIPLYING POWERS THAT HAVE THE SAME BASE

Students may readily accept that $x^2 \cdot x^3 = x^5$ but still have difficulty with $2^2 \cdot 2^3 = 2^5$. Students should understand that, when multiplying powers with like bases, they are just counting up how many times the base is used as a factor, not actually performing the computation. Emphasize that, when we write $2^2 \cdot 2^3 = 2^5$, we are multiplying $4 \cdot 8$, not $2 \cdot 2$, and the product, 32, written in exponential form is 2^5. In contrast, when $2^2 \cdot 2^3$ is entered into a calculator, the display will give 32, the value of 2^5.

Remind students that *every* base has an exponent. Thus, when working with the laws of exponents, they must remember that x means x^1 and that the exponent of 1 must be taken into account when doing multiplication. For example,

$$x \cdot x^2 = x^1 \cdot x^2 = x^{1+2} = x^3.$$

Section 9-3 indicates that the product of powers with different bases, such as $c^2 d^3$, cannot be simplified. On the other hand, you may wish to point out that different bases with the same exponent can be combined so that the exponent is written only once, as in $c^2 d^2 = (cd)^2$.

9-4 MULTIPLYING BY A MONOMIAL

Compare again operations with fractions and operations with monomials. The sum or difference of two fractions can be written as a single fraction only if the fractions to be combined have a common denominator, just as the sum or difference of two monomials can be written as a monomial only if the monomials have the same literal factor. However, the product of two fractions can be written as a single fraction even if the fractions have different denominators, and the product of two monomials can be written as a monomial even if the monomials have different literal factors.

For example:

$$(3x)(5y^2) = (3 \cdot 5) \ (x \cdot y^2) = 15xy^2$$

Note that the commutative and associative properties are applied to the multiplication of monomials. In time, students need not show the middle step.

After students have multiplied monomials, they should use the distributive property to multiply a polynomial by a monomial.

Continue to emphasize that solutions to problems should specify units of measure wherever appropriate, as in Exercises 75 and 76. Again, cancellation is a helpful visual device. In Exercise 76:

$$10z \ \frac{\text{miles}}{\cancel{\text{hour}}} \cdot 4 \ \cancel{\text{hours}} = 40z \ \text{miles}$$

9-5 MULTIPLYING POLYNOMIALS

When a polynomial is multiplied by a polynomial, each term of the first factor is multiplied by each term of the second factor. Thus, when multiplying a binomial by a binomial, there are 2×2 or 4 multiplications.

The product, in simplest form, has four terms when no two terms of the product are like terms:

$$(3a - 1)(2b + 1) = 6ab + 3a - 2b - 1$$

The product, in simplest form, has three terms when two terms of the product are like terms.

$$(3a - 1)(2a + 1) = 6a^2 + 3a - 2a - 1 = 6a^2 + a - 1$$

The product, in simplest form, has two terms when two terms of the product are opposites.

$$(3a - 1)(3a + 1) = 9a^2 + 3a - 3a - 1 = 9a^2 - 1$$

Encourage students to rewrite the square of a binomial as the product of two equal binomials. For example, when $(x + 3)^2$ is written as $(x + 3)(x + 3)$, students usually get the correct result, $x^2 + 6x + 9$, and are not likely to make the common error of writing $x^2 + 9$.

Included in the exercises are a few that require multiplication of three factors. Suggest that students simplify the product of the first two factors before multiplying by the third factor. For example:

$$\begin{aligned}(x + 3)^3 &= (x + 3)(x - 3)(x + 3) \\ &= (x^2 + 6x + 9)(x + 3) \\ &= x^3 + 6x^2 + 9x + 3x^2 + 18x + 27 \\ &= x^3 + 9x^2 + 27x + 27\end{aligned}$$

Note that, in the second line, to multiply a trinomial times a binomial, 3×2 or six multiplications are needed.

Enrichment Activity 9-5: Products, Sums, and Cubes investigates the relationship between sums and cubes.

9-6 DIVIDING POWERS THAT HAVE THE SAME BASE

Since division and multiplication are inverse operations, students should check their division by multiplying. For example, if $\frac{x^5}{x^2} = x^3$, then $x^2 \cdot x^3 = x^5$. To help students avoid making common errors such as $5^5 \div 5^2 = 1^3$, emphasize that there is only one procedure for dividing powers of the same base, whether the base is literal or numerical.

Common errors such as $\frac{5^5}{5^2} = 1^3$ can be avoided by reminding students that $1^3 = 1$ can be the quotient only when a number is divided by itself. Call attention to the similar case in multiplication. In the example above, we are not dividing 5 by 5 but rather canceling two of the factors of 5 in the numerator and the two factors of 5 in the denominator, leaving three factors of 5 in the quotient: $\frac{5^5}{5^2} = \frac{\cancel{5} \cdot \cancel{5} \cdot 5 \cdot 5 \cdot 5}{\cancel{5} \cdot \cancel{5}} = 5^3$.

9-7 POWERS WITH ZERO AND NEGATIVE EXPONENTS

After you establish that $x^0 = 1$, discuss why $x \neq 0$ in the definition. Point out that the definition $x^0 = 1$ is related to the fact that $\frac{xa}{xa} = 1$, a quotient that is not valid if $x = 0$. Emphasize the difference between $2y^0$, which is equal to 2, and $(2y)^0$, which is equal to 1.

Once the definition $x^{-n} = \frac{1}{x^n}$ $(x \neq 0)$ is formalized, you may show how all the laws of exponents remain valid. For example:

$$5^3 \cdot 5^{-1} = \frac{5^3}{1} \cdot \frac{1}{5^1} = \frac{5^3}{5^1} = 5^2$$

or

$$5^3 \cdot 5^{-1} = 5^{3 + (-1)} = 5^2$$

Stress the point that raising a number to a negative exponent does not imply that the answer is negative. Ask for two examples involving negative exponents, one where the answer is positive and one where the answer is negative. For example:

$$(-2)^{-2} = \frac{1}{(-2)^2} = \frac{1}{4}$$

and

$$(-2)^{-3} = \frac{1}{(-2)^3} = \frac{1}{-8} = \frac{1}{-8}$$

Conclude that, if the base is negative, the value of the power can be positive or negative depending on whether the exponent is even or odd. If the base is positive, the value of the power is always positive.

In the problem $4^{-3} \div 4^{-6}$, a common response is 4^{-9} rather than the correct solution, $4^{-3-(-6)} = 4^3$. If this error occurs, demonstrate another method of solution. For example:

$$4^{-3} \div 4^{-6}$$

$$= \frac{1}{4^3} \div \frac{1}{4^6} = \frac{1}{4^3} \cdot \frac{4^6}{1}$$

$$= \frac{4^6}{4^3} = 4^{6-3} = 4^3$$

From the viewpoint of manipulation, the definition

$$x^{-n} = \frac{1}{x^n} \qquad (x \neq 0)$$

has the effect that a negative exponent originally found in a numerator is changed to a positive exponent that then appears in a denominator.

$$x^{-3} = \frac{1}{x^3}$$

A corollary of the definition can be established from Example 1C on page 291.

$$\frac{1}{x^{-n}} = x^n \qquad (x \neq 0)$$

This corollary has the effect that a negative exponent originally found in a denominator is changed to a positive exponent that then appears in a numerator.

$$\frac{1}{x^{-3}} = x^3$$

When switching positions of the power with respect to numerator or denominator, students must be especially careful to move only the base that belongs with the negative exponent.

$$\frac{2}{x^{-3}} = 2x^3 \qquad \frac{1}{2x^{-3}} = \frac{x^3}{2} \qquad 2y^{-4} = \frac{2}{y^4}$$

Note that the coefficient 2, independent of the exponent, remains in its original position in every case shown above. On the other hand, in the case shown below, the coefficient 3, which is affected by the exponent, moves as part of the base.

$$(3x)^{-2} = \frac{1}{(3x)^2} \qquad \frac{1}{(3x)^{-2}} = (3x)^2$$

9-8 USING SCIENTIFIC NOTATION

Before you explain scientific notation, it is important that students see the need for a notation that will neatly handle very large numbers. A discussion about very large and very small measurements will establish that need. Concepts normally taught in science class, such as the distances of planets from the sun, can be reviewed as you prepare to put these numbers into scientific notation.

To understand scientific notation, students must first understand the place values in the decimal number system. Each time a number is multiplied by 10, each digit in the number is moved one place to the left; and each time a number is divided by 10, each digit in the number is moved one place to the right.

Students should be aware of the results of multiplying and dividing powers of 10. Ask the following questions: When some number x is multiplied by 10, is the result larger or smaller than x? When some number x is multiplied by 0.1, is the result larger or smaller than x? When some number x is divided by 10, is the result larger or smaller than x? When some number x is divided by 0.1, is the result larger or smaller than x?

The limitations of the display on a scientific calculator mandate the use of scientific notation. Students must be able to write a number in scientific notation in order to enter numbers with very large and very small absolute values and must be able to interpret scientific notation when the result of a calculator computation is too large or too small to be displayed in ordinary decimal notation. Students should experiment to determine when their calculators shift to scientific notation.

9-9 DIVIDING BY A MONOMIAL

The quotient of two monomials is a monomial if and only if all the liberal factors of the divisor are factors of the dividend; that is, no variable remains in the divisor. All of the divisions in this section are of this kind. In Chapter 18, fractions that are the quotients of two monomials will be considered. The simplified fraction that has a variable in the denominator is the quotient of two monomials but is not itself a monomial.

Students begin by dividing a monomial by a monomial and then use the distributive property to extend this concept to the division of polynomial by a monomial.

Students should be encouraged to check division by multiplication, thus forming a good habit as well as continuing to practice multiplication. The check, which may be written or performed mentally, is particularly important to avoid such common errors as $\frac{12x^2-3x}{3x} = 12x^2$ and $\frac{12x^2-3x}{3x} = 4x$.
Students should understand that, when a polynomial is divided by a monomial, the quotient will have the same number of terms as the polynomial.

9-10 DIVIDING BY A POLYNOMIAL

As illustrated in this section, the division of a polynomial by another polynomial follows a procedure similar to the division of two arithmetic numbers. The division process naturally comes to an end when the remainder is 0 or when the degree of the remainder is less than the degree of the divisor.

It is advisable to arrange the terms of both the divisor and the dividend in descending powers of the variable.

Start out with several division problems whose remainders are 0 until students feel at ease with the method. When there is a remainder of 0, the prob-

lem can be checked by multiplying the quotient and the divisor; the product should be the same as the original dividend. If there is a remainder other than 0, this remainder is added to the product of the quotient and divisor, resulting in the original dividend.

You may wish to challenge your students with a division problem such as:

$$x + 1 \overline{)x^4 - x^3 - 3x - 3}$$

When the division is performed without adding the term $0x^2$, the students will often write the steps for the first two terms of the divisor as follows:

$$
\begin{array}{r}
x^3 - 2x^2 \\
x + 1 \overline{)x^4 - x^3 - 3x - 3} \\
\underline{\oplus x^4 \oplus x^3} \\
-2x^3 - 3x \\
-2x^3 - 2x^2
\end{array}
$$

Students may then be unable to continue or they may continue in an incorrect manner. When the term in x^2 is added, the next step of the division is more easily accomplished.

$$
\begin{array}{r}
x^3 + 2x^2 - 2x - 4 \\
x + 1 \overline{)x^4 - x^3 + 0x^2 - 3x - 3} \\
\underline{\oplus x^4 \oplus x^3} \\
-2x^3 - 0x^2 \\
\underline{\overset{+}{\ominus}2x^3 \overset{+}{\ominus} 2x^2} \\
-2x^2 - 3x \\
\underline{\oplus 2x^2 \oplus 2x} \\
-5x - 3 \\
\underline{\oplus 5x \oplus 5} \\
+2
\end{array}
$$

Name _____ Class _____ Date _____

ENRICHMENT ACTIVITY 9-1

Sums and Squares

Study the following patterns:

$1 = 1^2$

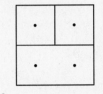

$1^2 + 1 + 2 = 4 = 2^2$

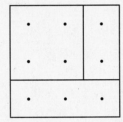

$2^2 + 2 + 3 = 9 = 3^2$

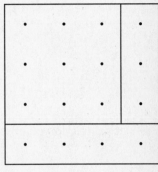

$3^2 + 3 + 4 = 16 = 4^2$

1. Draw a diagram and write an equation that shows that 5^2 can be written as the sum of 4^2 and two consecutive integers.

2. Draw a diagram and write an equation that shows that $(n + 1)^2$ can be written as the sum of n^2 and two consecutive integers.

3. If you know that $20^2 = 400$, what must you add to 400 to find the value of 21^2?

4. Find, without adding, the sum

$$1 + 1 + 2 + 2 + 3 + 3 + 4 + 4 + 5 + 5 + 6 + 6 + 7 + 7 + 8 + 8 + 9 + 9 + 10$$

5. Express, in terms of n, the sum

$$1 + 1 + 2 + 2 + 3 + 3 + 4 + 4 + \ldots + n + n + (n + 1)$$

Name _____ Class _____ Date _____

ENRICHMENT ACTIVITY 9-5

Products, Sums, and Cubes

Study the following pattern:

$$
\begin{aligned}
1(2)(3) + 2 &= 6 + 2 = 8 = 2^3 \\
2(3)(4) + 3 &= 24 + 3 = 27 = 3^3 \\
3(4)(5) + 4 &= 60 + 4 = 64 = ()^3 \\
4(5)(6) + 5 &= 120 + 5 = 125 = ()^3 \\
5(6)(7) + 6 &= 210 + 6 = 216 = ()^3
\end{aligned}
$$

1. What pattern do you observe?

2. How can the value of 7^3 be written using a similar pattern?

3. How can the value of 8^3 be written using a similar pattern?

4. Show that $(n - 1)(n)(n + 1) + n = n^3$.

5. Show that $(n)(n + 1)(n + 2) + (n + 1) = (n + 1)^3$.

SUGGESTED TEST ITEMS (CHAPTER 9)

In 1–18, simplify each expression.

1. $5a^3 - 8a^3$

2. $8x + 7 - 5x - 9$

3. $8x + 7(-5x - 9)$

4. $2x^4 - (5 - 2x^4)$

5. $-ab^2(4a^2b)$

6. $3x^2 - 2x + 5 - x^2 - 7$

7. $7 - 3(x - 5)$

8. $(-3x^2y)^3$

9. $(7y + 3x) - (4x - 7y)$

10. $(2x - 1)(x + 4)$

11. $(2x - 1)^2$

12. $(2x - 1)(2x + 1)$

13. $3r(-4rs^2)^2$

14. $a(a - 1)^2$

15. $12x^2 - [x^2 - (2x^2 - 3)]$

16. $\dfrac{28ab}{4b}$

17. $\dfrac{5^3 \cdot 5^2}{5^4}$

18. $\dfrac{15y^4 - 12y^2}{3y^2}$

19. Divide $x^2 + 5x - 36$ by $x - 4$.

In 20–23, express each number in scientific notation.

20. 3,200

21. 93,000,000

22. 0.054

23. 0.000002

In 24–27, express each number in decimal notation.

24. 8×10^4

25. 1.7×10^9

26. 7.3×10^{-2}

27. 5×10^{-7}

28. The length of a rectangle is represented by $3x - 7$ and the width by $x + 4$.
   a. Represent the perimeter as a polynomial in simplest form.
   b. Represent the area as a polynomial in simplest form.
   c. State a value for x that is not possible.

29. The perimeter of a square is represented by $8a - 12$. Express the area as a polynomial.

30. A mail-order catalog offers shirts for 5 dollars less than the regular price. Shipping charges of 3 dollars are added to every order. Represent in simplest form the cost of ordering four shirts if the regular price of a shirt is x dollars.

In 31–33, select the numeral that precedes the term that best completes the statement.

31. The expression $y^5 + y^5$ is equivalent to which of the following?
   (1) $2y^5$ (2) $2y^{10}$ (3) y^{10} (4) y^{25}

32. The expression $(-3x^4)^3$ is equivalent to which of the following?
   (1) $-27x^7$ (2) $-9x^7$ (3) $-9x^{12}$ (4) $-27x^{12}$

33. What is the value of $8^{-2} \cdot 8^3$?
   (1) 8   (2) -8 (3) $-\dfrac{1}{8}$ (4) $\dfrac{1}{8}$

BONUS: **a.** Determine two consecutive counting numbers whose squares differ by 35.
               b. Is it possible to find two consecutive counting numbers whose squares differ by 24? Explain your answer.

SAT PREPARATION EXERCISES (CHAPTER 9)

I. Multiple-Choice Questions

In 1-11, select the letter of the correct answer.

1. If the base of a triangle is $4x^2$, and the height is $2x^3$, which of the following represents the area?

   (A) $4x^5$ (B) $4x^6$ (C) $4x^3$
   (D) $8x^5$ (E) $8x^6$

2. If the bases of a trapezoid are x and $2x$, and the height is $2x$, which of the following represents the area?

   (A) $6x^3$ (B) $6x^2$ (C) $3x^3$
   (D) $3x^2$ (E) $6x$

3. If Mary drives x^2y^2 miles at a rate of xy^2 miles per hour, which of the following represents the number of hours she drove?

   (A) 1   (B) x (C) x^2y^4
   (D) x^3y^4 (E) $2x^2y^2$

4. If x^2 is the same as $8x$ increased by 50% of $8x$, which of the following could be a value of x?

   (A) 4   (B) 8   (C) 12
   (D) 16   (E) 18

5. The product of $4x$ and $5x$ gives the same result as the sum of $10x^2$ and which of the following?

   (A) $2x^2$ (B) $2x$ (C) $10x^2$
   (D) $10x$ (E) 10

6. How many integers from 95 through 99 can be expressed as xy^2, where x and y are integers greater than 1?

   (A) 4   (B) 3   (C) 2
   (D) 1   (E) 0

7. If $x + 3$ is an even integer, then which of the following is an odd integer?

   (A) $(x + 3)(x + 4)$ (B) $(x + 3)^2$
   (C) $(x + 4)(x + 5)$ (D) $(x + 4)^2$
   (E) None

8. What is the average (arithmetic mean) of $3(5x^2 + 2)$ and $7(5x^2 + 2)$?

   (A) $10x^2 + 20$ (B) $x^2 + 8$
   (C) $25x^2 + 10$ (D) $40x^2 + 16$
   (E) $50x^2 + 20$

9. If $x + y^2 = 6$ and $y = -2$, evaluate $x^2 - y$.

   (A) 6   (B) -6 (C) 2
   (D) -2 (E) 0

10. If x is 10, which of the following has the same value as $2(x^3 + x)$?

    (A) 2.2×10^2 (B) 2.02×10^2
    (C) 2.2×10^3 (D) 2.02×10^3
    (E) 22×10^3

11.

    In the figure above, PR is $4x + 5$, RS is $2x + 3$, and Q is the midpoint of $\overline{PS}$. What is 2 less than the value of QR?

    (A) $6x + 8$ (B) $3x + 4$
    (C) $2x + 2$ (D) $2x - 2$
    (E) $2x - 4$

II. Quantitative Comparison Questions

Questions 12-20 each consist of two quantities, one in Column A and one in Column B. You are to compare the two quantities and choose:

A if the quantity in Column A is greater;
B if the quantity in Column B is greater;
C if the two quantities are equal;
D if the relationship cannot be determined from the information given.

Notes

1. In certain questions, information concerning one or both of the quantities to be compared is centered above the two columns.
2. In a given question, a symbol that appears in both columns represents the same thing in Column A as it does in Column B.
3. Letters such as x, n, and k stand for real numbers.

Column A	*Column B*
12. The sum of x^2 and $4x^2$	The product of $0.1x$ and $50x$

13. x is negative

$(-3x^3)(-2x^2)$ $6x^6 \div 2x^2$

14. $x = y$

$5xy - xy$ y^2 avg $7y^2$

15. $x > 2$

The sum of 2 and $6x$ 12 max $(6x + x)$

16. The width of a rectangle is $3x$ and the area is $27x^2$

The length of the rectangle $9x^2$

17.
$$8(x^2 + x) \qquad 18(x^2 + x)$$
$$+ 9(x^2 + x) \qquad - (x^2 + x)$$

18. $3(x + 3) + 4(x - 1)$ $5x + 2(x + 1)$

19.
$$y = x + 1$$
$$(y + 3)^3 \qquad (x + 4)^3$$

20. $k \neq 0$
$$\frac{9k^3 + 6k^2}{3k^2} \qquad \frac{12k^2 + 12k}{4k}$$

III. Student-Produced Response Questions

In questions 21-24, you are to solve the problem.

21. The measure of one side of a square is $x + 4$. Express in terms of x, a number that is 2 less than the number of square units in the square.

22.

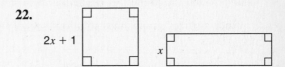

The square and the rectangle above have the same perimeters. What is the area of the rectangle when $x = 0.2$?

23. The side of a rhombus is $x + 5$ and the side of square is $x + 2$. How much is twice the difference between the perimeters of these quadrilaterals when $x = 15$?

24. The area of the rectangle is $x^2 + 6x + 5$ and the length is $x + 1$. Determine the width of the rectangle when $x = 1.7$.

Chapter *10*

First-Degree Equations and Inequalities in One Variable

Aims

- To solve equations that contain parentheses and in which the variable occurs in more than one term.

- To solve equations in which the variable occurs on both sides.

- To use formulas to solve problems.

- To express one variable in terms of another variable.

- To understand the properties of inequalities.

- To find and to graph the solution set of inequalities.

- To use inequalities to solve problems.

A major emphasis in this chapter is the establishment of a sound understanding of algebraic solutions of verbal problems. Such an understanding requires the ability to write and to solve an equation or an inequality based on a verbal description. Many of the examples and exercises involve abstract number problems that allow students to develop the ability to identify number relationships and to translate from words to symbols. Other problems model actual situations within the experience of students to help them appreciate the wide applicability of an algebraic solution to a problem. At the same time, it is desirable, in class discussion, to consider parallel solutions that reinforce students' abilities to apply problem-solving strategies learned earlier in the course and to choose an appropriate method of solution for a particular problem.

10-1 SIMPLIFYING EACH SIDE OF AN EQUATION BEFORE SOLVING

Now that the students have learned to simplify algebraic expressions, they are prepared to solve more difficult equations, such as those containing parentheses and those with similar terms on the same side of the equation.

Have students recall the suggested steps for using an algebraic strategy to solve a problem that were given in Section 6-6. Step 2 of the suggested strategy is to select a variable to represent the number to be found, and step 3 is to write an equation using either a relationship given in the problem or a previously known relationship. Have students identify the facts given in the problem that can be used in this way. In the example on page 306, two facts are identified and two solutions to the problem that use these facts are presented. In one case, fact 1 is used to represent the numbers to be found in terms of the same variable, and fact 2 is used to write an equation. In the second case, the use of the facts is reversed: fact 2 is used to represent the numbers to be found, and fact 1 to write an equation. Encourage students to list the facts in a problem before attempting its solution. Sometimes it is necessary to add to the given facts some other known fact, such as a formula or the value of a coin or bill. After students have found the solution to a problem, ask someone to explain to the class the approach that was used. Ask other students whether they used a different approach, and compare the methods and results obtained.

When beginning to use an algebraic approach to solve problems, students often ask why they must go through all the required steps when they can determine the answer mentally. Remind them that they are learning a procedure, applying it to simple problems at first, that will allow them eventually to solve more difficult problems whose solutions are not easily obtained mentally.

10-2 SOLVING EQUATIONS THAT HAVE THE VARIABLE IN BOTH MEMBERS

An equation often has a variable in both members. Since a variable represents a number, a variable term may be added to or subtracted from both members to obtain an equivalent equation, one that has the same solution set as the given equation.

When there are both variable terms and constants on both sides of an equation, students often find it difficult to decide which opposites are to be added to each side. It may be helpful to some students to identify each term in the equation as a variable or as a constant and to identify which terms are to be retained on each side. For example,

$$\overset{\text{Ⓥ}}{12x} + \overset{\text{C}}{7} = \overset{\text{V}}{2x} - \overset{\text{Ⓒ}}{18}$$

If we choose to retain the variable term on the left and the constant on the right, then the opposite of the constant on the left, -7, and the opposite of the variable term on the right, $-2x$, must be added to each side.

$$
\begin{array}{rcl}
\overset{\text{Ⓥ}}{12x} + \overset{\text{C}}{7} & = & \overset{\text{V}}{2x} - \overset{\text{Ⓒ}}{18} \\
-2x - 7 & & -2x - 7 \\
\hline
10x & = & -25
\end{array}
$$

The solution to the equation can also be found by keeping the variable terms on the right and the constant terms on the left.

$$
\begin{array}{rcl}
\overset{\text{V}}{12x} + \overset{\text{Ⓒ}}{7} & = & \overset{\text{Ⓥ}}{2x} - \overset{\text{C}}{18} \\
-12x + 18 & & -12x + 18 \\
\hline
25 & = & -10x
\end{array}
$$

Students may find it easier to solve the simplified equation $10x = -25$, which has a positive coefficient of x, than to solve $25 = -10x$, which has a negative coefficient of x. Students who have difficulty solving an equation in which both a variable and a constant appear on each side of the equation should be encouraged to always add first, to each side, the opposite of the variable with the smaller coefficient. In Example 1b, method 2 uses this procedure.

In Example 3 two important numerical relationships are given: Emma's share is $500 larger than Clara's share, and the sum of their shares is $5,000. One of these relationships is used to write each girl's share in terms of the same variable; the other, to write the equation. Call attention to the ways in which this information is used in each of the two possible approaches to the solution.

10-3 CONSECUTIVE-INTEGER PROBLEMS

Students are often puzzled to learn that three consecutive even integers and three consecutive odd integers are represented in the same way. Ask why $x, x + 2, x + 4$ can represent a set of consecutive even integers in one problem and a set of odd integers in another.

Emphasize that, for a problem that asks for a set of consecutive integers, an answer that contains a fraction cannot be correct. Thus, if $x, x + 1, x + 2$

are consecutive integers, the domain is the set of integers, and $x = 0.5$ cannot be a solution. If the equation that yielded the fractional result was solved correctly, then either the equation does not correctly represent the conditions of the problem or the problem has no solution.

Use *Enrichment Activity 10-3: Consecutive Integers* to study the sums of consecutive integers. This activity provides an opportunity for students to make discoveries about odd and even numbers.

10-4 SOLVING FOR A VARIABLE IN A FORMULA

A formula is an equation that models a particular situation. Formulas for perimeter, area, and volume are familiar to students, as are rate formulas ($D = rt$ and $I = prt$). Ask such questions as "For the formula $P = 2l + 2w$, how many variables must be known so that the remaining variable or variables can be determined?" Elicit from students that the values of all but one variable must be known unless additional information is available about the problem.

As a counterpart to the solution in the example, you may wish to mention an approach that combines two strategies: first, drawing a diagram that shows the given information, and then working backwards. For example:

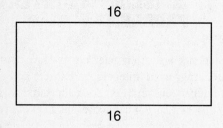

Since the length of the rectangle is 16, the sum of the lengths is 32. Subtract 32 from the perimeter, 48, to obtain 16 as the sum of the widths, and therefore, 8 as the width of one side.

10-5 PERIMETER PROBLEMS

If students have difficulty in remembering the meaning of *perimeter*, point out the word *rim* is contained within the word *perimeter*.

Students should be encouraged to draw and label a diagram for a geometric problem. Call attention to the fact that, in such problems, more than one measure is unknown, but enough information is given to represent all unknown measures in terms of the same variable.

Stress that, since the perimeter is the sum of the measures of the sides, the unit of measure must be the same for each side and for the perimeter.

10-6 SOLVING FOR A VARIABLE IN TERMS OF ANOTHER VARIABLE

The strategy to solve equations containing more than one variable is to use a simpler related problem. Write an equation similar in form to the one to be solved by replacing with constants all variables except the one for which the equation is to be solved. Then, use the same steps to solve the given equation as are needed to solve the simpler equation.

Call attention to the fact that, when solving an equation by adding a term to each side, the sum can sometimes be written as a single term, as in Examples **a** and **c**, but often must be written as the sum of unlike terms, as in Example **b**. When the solution of an equation requires that both sides be divided by a variable term, as in Example **c**, it is necessary that the variable be unequal to 0.

10-7 TRANSFORMING FORMULAS

Although the exercises in this section require that a formula be solved for a particular variable, emphasize that a formula can be solved for any of the variables that it contains. For example, the formula $D = rt$ can be solved not only for D but also for r and for t if these variables are not equal to 0.

$$D = rt \qquad rt = D \qquad rt = D$$

$$\frac{rt}{t} = \frac{D}{t} \qquad \frac{rt}{r} = \frac{D}{r}$$

$$r = \frac{D}{t} \qquad t = \frac{D}{r}$$

Each of the formulas in the exercises should be familiar to students. Ask them to identify the variables in the formulas and to write problems that can be solved by using the formulas.

10-8 PROPERTIES OF INEQUALITIES

Inequalities were introduced in Chapter 1. This section introduces the properties of inequalities and uses these properties to show how equivalent inequalities can be obtained. Ask students to discuss the relationships of positive and negative, greater than 0 and less than 0, and to the right of 0 and to the left of 0 on the number line.

Use *Enrichment Activity 10-8: Graphing an Inequality* to demonstrate graphing an inequality in one variable on a graphing calculator.

10-9 FINDING AND GRAPHING THE SOLUTION OF AN INEQUALITY

Students usually have no problem in solving a first-degree inequality at this level of difficulty but often forget to reverse the inequality when multiplying or dividing by a negative number. Encourage students to check the inequality. The suggested check is based on the fact that the point on the number line that is the graph of the real number a separates the number line into three regions, as seen in these graphs:

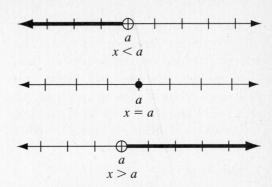

$$a$$
$$x < a$$

$$a$$
$$x = a$$

$$a$$
$$x > a$$

The real number a is the boundary value that separates the values that make $x < a$ true from the values that make $x > a$ true. We call $x = a$ the *corresponding equality* for $x > a$ and $x < a$.

The inequality check should consist of two steps. For example, if the proposed solution is $x < a$:

1. Check the boundary value, a, in the corresponding equality. The number that makes the corresponding equality true separates the numbers on the real number line into those that make the given inequality true and those that make the given inequality false.

2. Check one test value that is less than a, that is, one value to the left of a on the number line.

If the boundary value is correct and the test value makes the inequality true, then the solution is correct. If, however, the boundary value is correct and the test value makes the inequality false, the solution must be reviewed to see whether the sense of the inequality should have been reversed.

When the variable occurs in both members of the equation, division by a negative number can be avoided by adding the opposite of the variable term with the smaller coefficient to both members so that the resulting variable term will have a positive coefficient. If, in the solution, the variable appears on the right side, as in $7 < x$, the inequality can be read from right to left as "x is greater than 7" or rewritten as $x > 7$.

Hands-On Activity

Instructions:

The TEST key on the TI-81 or TI-82 graphing calculator allows the user to test the truth value of any equation or inequality. The calculator assigns the value 1 to any true statement and 0 to any false statement. Therefore, it is possible to graph inequalities and the conjunction or disjunction of inequalities. The graph will display a line at $y = 1$ for all values of x for which the inequality is true, and a line at $y = 0$ for all of the values of x for which the inequality is false. The points at $y = 0$ coincide with the y-axis.

Example: Graph: $x > -1$
$\qquad\qquad\quad x < 2$
$\qquad\qquad\quad (x > -1) \wedge (x < 2)$
$\qquad\qquad\quad (x > -1) \vee (x > 2)$.

Step 1: Set the graphing style to DOT.

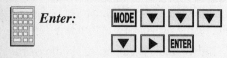

Step 2: Enter $x > -1$ as Y_1.

On the TI-81:

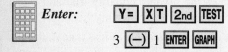

On the TI-82:

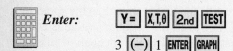

To graph a second inequality on the same graph, enter the inequality as Y_2. Then multiply by some nonzero constant, for example, 0.5, to draw the new graph at a different place from that of the preceding one.

Step 3: Enter $x < 2$ as Y_2.

On the TI-81:

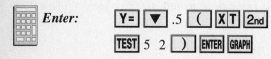

On the TI-82:

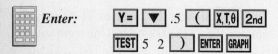

Now the conjunction of the two inequalities must be graphed. To decide on a method to do this, compare the truth table for $Y_1 \wedge Y_2$ with the calculator product $Y_1 Y_2$.

Y_1	Y_2	$Y_1 \wedge Y_2$	Y_1	Y_2	$Y_1 Y_2$
T	T	T	1	1	1
T	F	F	1	0	0
F	T	F	0	1	0
F	F	F	0	0	0

Since the product $Y_1 Y_2$ is 1 whenever the conjunction $Y_1 \wedge Y_2$ is true and 0 whenever the conjunction is false, $Y_1 Y_2$ can be used to graph $Y_1 \wedge Y_2$.

Step 4: With $Y_1 = x > -1$ and $Y_2 = 0.5(x < 2)$, enter $-Y_1 Y_2$ as Y_3 in order to draw the conjunction at -0.5 below the y-axis.

On the TI-81:

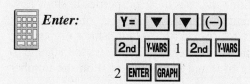

On the TI-82:

An alternative method of graphing the conjunction on the TI-82, which has keys for the logical connectives, is shown below.

To determine a method of graphing the disjunction of two inequalities, compare the truth table for $Y_1 \lor Y_2$ with the calculator expression $Y_1 + Y_2 - (Y_1)(Y_2)$.

Y_1	Y_2	$Y_1 \lor Y_2$
T	T	T
T	F	T
F	T	T
F	F	F

Y_1	Y_2	$Y_1 + Y_2 - Y_1Y_2$
1	1	1
1	0	1
0	1	1
0	0	0

Since $Y_1 + Y_2 - Y_1Y_2$ is 1 whenever the disjunction $Y_1 \lor Y_2$ is true and 0 whenever the disjunction is false, $Y_1 + Y_2 - Y_1Y_2$ can be used to graph $Y_1 \lor Y_2$.

Step 5: With $Y_1 = x > -1$, $Y_2 = 0.5(x < 2)$, and $Y_3 = -Y_1Y_2$, enter $Y_1 + 2Y_2 + Y_1Y_2$ as Y_3 in order to draw the conjunction at -1 below the y-axis. Since the inequality in Y_2 was multiplied by 0.5, every term that has Y_2 as a factor is multiplied by 2 to restore the value 1 for true.

On the TI-81:

 Enter:

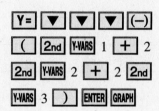

On the TI-82:

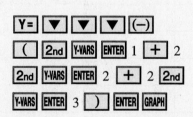

An alternative method of graphing the disjunction on the TI-82, which has keys for the logical connectives, is shown below.

 Enter:

The graph of the union of the two inequalities, that is, the values of x for which $x > -1$ or $x < 2$ is true, is displayed at $y = -1$. Note that this disjunction consists of all real numbers.

Step 6: Repeat Steps 2 through 5 using the inequalities $x \le 3$ and $x < -1$.

10-10 USING INEQUALITIES TO SOLVE PROBLEMS

The text lists some sentences that are used to describe an inequality. Ask students to add to the list.

Students often confuse phrases like "is at least" and "is less than," or "is at most" and "is more than." Give examples to show that, in these pairs, one inequality is the negation of the other. For example, a number that is at least 25 ($x \ge 25$) is a number that is *not* less than 25 ($x \nless 25$) and a number that is at most 25 ($x \le 25$) is a number that is *not* more than 25 ($x \ngtr 25$).

Name _____ Class _____ Date _____

ENRICHMENT ACTIVITY 10-3

Consecutive Integers

1. Study the sums of consecutive integers. Then complete the following table.

Number of Integers	First Integer	Sum	Even or Odd
3	1		
3	4		
3	7		
3	x		
4	1		
4	4		
4	7		
4	x		
5	1		
5	4		
5	7		
5	x		
6	1		
6	4		
6	7		
6	x		
7	1		
7	4		
7	7		
7	x		

Name _____ Class _____ Date _____

2. For each of the following, describe the sum as always even, always odd, or sometimes even and sometimes odd. If the sum is sometimes even and sometimes odd, explain when it is even and when it is odd.

   a. The sum of two consecutive integers

   b. The sum of three consecutive integers

   c. The sum of four consecutive integers

   d. The sum of five consecutive integers

   e. The sum of six consecutive integers

   f. The sum of seven consecutive integers

   g. The sum of an even number of consecutive integers

   h. The sum of an odd number of consecutive integers

3. **a.** What number is always a factor of the sum of three consecutive integers?

   b. What number is always a factor of the sum of five consecutive integers?

   c. What number is always a factor of the sum of seven consecutive integers?

   d. What do you think is true about the sum of an odd number of consecutive integers?

4. **a.** Is 4 a factor of the sum of four consecutive integers?

   b. Describe the sum of four consecutive integers.

5. **a.** Make a table similar to that in part **1** for the sum of consecutive even integers.

   b. What conclusions can you draw about the sums?

6. **a.** Make a table similar to that of part **1** for the sum of consecutive odd integers.

   b. What conclusions can you draw about the sums?

Name _____ Class _____ Date _____

ENRICHMENT ACTIVITY 10-8

Graphing an Inequality

The TEST relations on a TI-81 or TI-82 graphing calculator are used to determine whether an equation or inequality is true or false. If the statement is true, the calculator will display 1 after TEST is pressed; if the statement is false, the calculator will display 0 after TEST is pressed. When an inequality is entered as Y_1, the graph of Y_1 will be a line at $y = 1$ for the values of x for which the inequality is true and a line at $y = 0$ for the values of x for which the inequality is false. Since the $y = 0$ values coincide with the x-axis, only the values for which the inequality is true appear on the graph.

EXAMPLE

Draw the graph of $3x - 1 \leq 8$ using a graphing calculator.

Step 1: Enter the inequality as Y_1.

Enter: [Y=] 3 [X|T] [—] 1 [2nd] [TEST] 6 8 [ENTER]

Step 2: Change the graph from connected to dot mode.

Enter: [MODE] [▼] [▼] [▼] [▼] [▶] [ENTER]

Step 3: Display the graph on the screen.

Enter: [GRAPH]

The display shows that the inequality is true for all values of x that are less than or equal to 3.

EXERCISES

In 1–3, solve each inequality and compare the algebraic solution with its graph on a graphing calculator.

1. $3x - 7 \leq 5$ **2.** $x - 3 \leq 5 - x$ **3.** $\frac{1}{3}x - 5 \geq 2x$

In 4–9, graph each inequality on a graphing calculator and explain the results.

4. $|x| \leq 4$ **5.** $x^2 < 1$ **6.** $x > \sqrt{x}$

7. $x + 1 > x$ **8.** $x < 2x$ **9.** $|x| < 0$

SUGGESTED TEST ITEMS (CHAPTER 10)

1. For any domain, the solution set of $x = x + 1$ is the empty set. Replace the equal sign in the equation with a symbol that will make the statement always true.

In 2–11, solve and check each equation.

2. $a + 3a + 7 = 27$ **3.** $3b - 2(b - 8) = 38$ **4.** $y - (1.4 - y) = 83.6$

5. $5x - 7 = 2x + 8$ **6.** $2n + 8 = 7n + 58$ **7.** $3(a - 4) = 7(9 - a) - 3$

8. $8x + 11 = 6x$ **9.** $c + 0.6c = 14.4$ **10.** $3y + 7 = 14 - (6y + 4)$

11. $0.13x = 17.4 - 0.07x$

12. The length of a rectangle is 5 centimeters less than twice the width. The perimeter is 35 centimeters. What are the dimensions of the rectangle?

13. Solve for h in terms of A and V: $V = \dfrac{1}{3}Ah$.

14. **a.** Solve for C in terms of F: $F = \dfrac{9}{5}C + 32$.

    b. Using the formula obtained in part **a,** determine the Celsius temperature C when the Fahrenheit temperature F is 23°.

15. When Marcy bought some postcards for 40 cents each, she paid a tax of 20 cents. How many postcards did she buy if the total cost of cards including tax was 3 dollars?

In 16–20, evaluate and graph each solution set.

16. $3x < 9$ **17.** $2x - 1 \geq 5$ **18.** $1 - 7x < 15$

19. $(2x > 4) \wedge (3x < -6)$ **20.** $(x + 1 \leq 7) \wedge (x - 1 \geq 0)$

21.
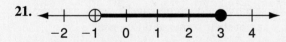

The graph above shows the solution of which inequality?

(1) $-1 \leq x < 3$ (2) $-1 < x \leq 3$ (3) $-1 \leq x \leq 3$ (4) $-1 < x < 3$

22.
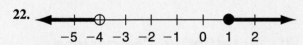

The above graph shows the solution of which inequality?

(1) $(x < -4) \vee (x \geq 1)$ (2) $(x < -4) \wedge (x \geq 1)$ (3) $-4 < x \leq 1$ (4) $(x \leq 1) \vee (x > -4)$

23. Use an algebraic strategy to solve the following problem.

At the auto repair shop, Mrs. Angiers was given an estimate of at most \$255 to repair her car. This estimate included \$60 an hour for labor and \$75 for parts. What is the maximum number of hours that the mechanic expected to spend on the job?

BONUS: Elaine was making favors for a party. She made $\dfrac{1}{3}$ on Monday, $\dfrac{1}{2}$ of the remainder on Tuesday, and $\dfrac{1}{2}$ of those still remaining on Wednesday. She finished on Thursday by making 12. How many favors did she make?

SAT PREPARATION EXERCISES (CHAPTER 10)

I. Multiple-Choice Questions

In 1-10, select the letter of the correct answer.

1. Determine the solution of $3x + k = 9$ when x is zero.

    (A) 0   (B) −3   (C) 3

    (D) −9   (E) 9

2. Solve: $7(x + 3) + 9(x + 3) − 4(x + 3) = 48$.

    (A) 1   (B) 3.5   (C) 4

    (D) 7   (E) 8

3. If $8(x + 4) = 16$, and $y (x + 4) = 24$, determine the value of y.

    (A) 2   (B) −4   (C) 4

    (D) 12   (E) −12

4. If $5(y + 3) = 20$, and $y = x − 3$, determine the value of x.

    (A) 1   (B) 4   (C) −1

    (D) −4   (E) 5

5. If $3(2x − 1) = 30$, evaluate $2x + 1$.

    (A) $4\frac{1}{2}$ (B) $5\frac{1}{2}$ (C) 10

    (D) 12   (E) −12

6. A triangle has an area of $4x + 20$ and a base of $x + 4$. What is the height of the triangle?

    (A) $2x + 10$ (B) $\dfrac{4x + 2}{x + 4}$ (C) $\dfrac{8x + 40}{x + 4}$

    (D) $8x + 10$ (E) $3x − 16$

7. If $3(2x − 1) < 5$, then which of the following is not necessarily true?

    (A) $6x − 3 < 6$ (B) $2x − 1 < 2$
    (C) $3 − 6x > −5$ (D) $1 + 2x > −1$
    (E) $5 > 6x − 3$

8. If $5(x + 5) = 2(x + 1)$, evaluate $\dfrac{x + 5}{3x + 3}$.

    (A) $\dfrac{2}{5}$ (B) $\dfrac{2}{15}$ (C) $\dfrac{2}{3}$

    (D) $\dfrac{6}{5}$ (E) $\dfrac{5}{2}$

9. If the sum of two integers is even, and the product of these integers is odd, then the integers

    (A) are both odd   (B) are consecutive

    (C) are both even   (D) are never equal

    (E) cannot be determined

10. If the average (arithmetic mean) of two consecutive odd integers is 44, what is the product of their sum and difference?

    (A) 176   (B) 88   (C) 45

    (D) 44   (E) 43

II. Quantitative Comparison Questions

Questions 11–20 each consist of two quantities, one in Column A and one in Column B. You are to compare the two quantities and choose:

A if the quantity in Column A is greater;
B if the quantity in Column B is greater;
C if the two quantities are equal;
D if the relationship cannot be determined from the information given.

Notes

1. In certain questions, information concerning one or both of the quantities to be compared is centered above the two columns.
2. In a given question, a symbol that appears in both columns represents the same thing in Column A as it does in Column B.
3. Letters such as x, n, and k stand for real numbers.

Column A	*Column B*

11.
$$x > 2y$$

$2x + 2y$	$6y$

12.
$$x \text{ is an integer}$$

$(x)(x + 2)$	$(x + 1)(x - 1)$

13.
$$x > y > 0$$

$\dfrac{x + y}{x}$	$\dfrac{x + y}{y}$

14.
$$x < 3 < y$$

2 avg $7x$	A solution of $5y > 14 + 4y$

15.
$$x = 3$$

The perimeter of an equilateral triangle with side x	The semi perimeter of a square with side x

16.
$$h > 0, g > 0$$

$h^2 + g^2$	$(h + g)^2$

17.

A solution of $x > 4(x + 6)$	The solution of $-2y = (y + 2) + 8y$

18.

The positive difference between $\dfrac{1}{6}$ and $\dfrac{1}{12}$	The positive difference between $\dfrac{1}{5}$ and $\dfrac{1}{10}$

19.

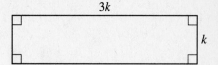

A rectangle has a length that is 3 times its width.

The area of the rectangle when its length is doubled	The area of the rectangle when its width is doubled

20.

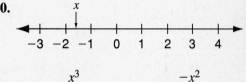

x^3	$-x^2$

III. Student-Produced Response Questions

In questions 21-24, you are to solve the problem.

21. If p represents $x + 1 < 4$ and q represents $x - 1 > -4$, what are the endpoints of the graph of $p \wedge q$?

22. The average of three consecutive integers is 65. What is one less than twice the value of the largest integer?

23. The length of one side of a triangle is twice three more than the shortest, and the third side is nine times five less than the length of the shortest. If the perimeter of the triangle is 57, what is the length of its largest side?

24. What is the largest integral value of y if $x > y + 3x$ when $3(x + 4) = 2 - 3(x + 1)$?

Chapter *11*
Angle Measure in Geometry

Aims

- To formulate good mathematical definitions.
- To use algebra in the solution of geometric problems.
- To derive relationships between angle measures in special pairs of angles.
- To determine the sum of the measures of the angles of triangles.
- To determine the measures of angles in special triangles.

Geometry models the real world. A string stretched between two nails suggests the concept of a straight line determined by two points, which in turn can be used to picture any straight edge.

Students are already familiar with the common geometric figures and with the relationships of size and shape that follow from the definitions of these figures. In this book many of these relationships will be generalized by using algebraic representation. One goal of this course is to prepare students to begin the study of formal proof in Course II with a sense of familiarity concerning most of the theorems to be proved.

From the outset, it is important to use proper symbolism. The difference between $AB = CD$ and $\overline{AB} \cong \overline{CD}$, or between $\angle ABC \cong \angle DEF$ and $m\angle ABC = m\angle DEF$, should be made clear.

Arithmetic as well as algebraic strands are woven together with the geometry throughout this chapter.

There are many opportunities for applications of logic.

11-1 POINTS, LINES, AND PLANES

This opening section begins to lay the groundwork for the study of geometry. Many terms will already be familiar to students, but time should be spent so that precise meanings replace vague concepts.

Ask students what makes a good definition and why good definitions are important. Relate the formulation of a definition to logic by calling attention to the fact that every definition can be expressed as a biconditional. For example, the following conditionals are true:

1. If a point is the midpoint of a line segment, then the point divides the segment into two segments that have the same length.

2. If a point divides a segment into two segments that have the same length, then the point is the midpoint of the line segment.

These two statements can be combined as a biconditional: A point is the midpoint of a line segment if and only if it divides the segment into two segments that have the same length.

The exercises anticipate that students may have some confusion in using the correct notation. You may wish to do some of these exercises orally with the class, and invite such elementary questions as "When is it acceptable to omit dots for points in a diagram?"

11-2 ANGLES, ANGLE MEASURES, AND PERPENDICULARITY

In this section, angles are classified according to their measures. Establish that in this course angle measure will always be expressed in degrees. Also remind students that the "m" notation is understood to refer to degrees. Thus, in an expression such as $m\angle A = 50$, the degree symbol is omitted.

Encourage the use of a protractor both to measure angles and to draw them. Have students use protractors to measure a reflex angle, and discuss the related measures $x°$ and $(360 − x)°$.

Hands-On Activity

Instructions:

Paper folding is an activity that reinforces geometric concepts. Ask students to:

1. Place a dot on a piece of paper.
2. Fold the paper through the dot.
3. With the paper folded, fold the paper again through the dot so that the parts of the first fold on each side of the dot coincide.
4. Open the paper. The two folds form linear pairs of angles that are congruent and therefore right angles. The folds are perpendicular to each other.

Again note that the biconditional statement is applicable to basic definitions in mathematics: for example, "Two lines are perpendicular if and only if the two lines or parts of the lines intersect to form right angles."

11-3 PAIRS OF ANGLES

In addition to the definitions and explanations offered in the text, you may wish to enrich your discussions by considering the following.

Adjacent Angles. The definition given in the text specifies three conditions:

1. The two angles have a common vertex.
2. The two angles have a common side.
3. The two angles do not have any interior points in common.

Offer some diagrams in which only one or two of the conditions are satisfied. For example:

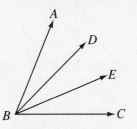

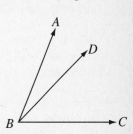

$\angle ABE$ and $\angle DBC$ are not adjacent angles because conditions 2 and 3 fail.

$\angle ABD$ and $\angle ABC$ are not adjacent angles because condition 3 fails.

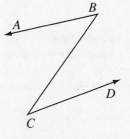

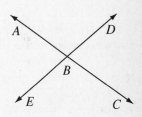

$\angle ABC$ and $\angle BCD$ are not adjacent angles because conditions 1 and 2 fail ($\overline{BC}$ is not $\overline{CB}$). (angles do not share side that comes from common vertex)

$\angle ABE$ and $\angle DBC$ are not adjacent angles because condition 2 fails.

Complementary and Supplementary Angles. We use the same method to find the complement of a given angle, no matter how the original angle is expressed. Consider the following chalkboard arrangement:

Measure of Original Angle	Manner in Which the Complement Is Found	Measure of Complementary Angle
40°	90° − 40°	50°
$x°$	90° − $x°$	$(90° − x)°$
$(2x + 10)°$	90° − $(2x + 10)°$	$(80° − 2x)°$

Emphasize a check based on the condition for a complementary angle (that is, the sum of the measures of the original angle and its complement is 90°).

A similar discussion is applicable to supplementary angles.

Mention that the definitions of complementary and supplementary angles limit the number of angles to two in each case. Thus, in the following diagram, angles 1, 2, and 3 are not supplementary even though the sum of their measures is 180°.

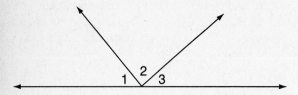

Linear Pair. A linear pair can also be described as two adjacent angles that are supplementary.

The hidden conditional and its converse, formed from this definition, require the use of a conjunction:

$L \rightarrow (A \wedge S)$: If two angles form a linear pair, then they are adjacent and supplementary.

$(A \wedge S) \rightarrow L$: If two angles are adjacent and supplementary, then they form a linear pair.

Students often overlook the conjunction and form false conclusions. Ask for the truth values of the following statements:

$L \rightarrow S$: If two angles form a linear pair, then they are supplementary. (True)

$S \rightarrow L$: If two angles are supplementary, then they form a linear pair. (False)

$L \rightarrow A$: If two angles form a linear pair, then they are adjacent. (True)

$A \rightarrow L$: If two angles are adjacent, then they form a linear pair. (False)

Vertical Angles

Hands-On Activity

Instructions:

Draw line segments on two strips of light cardboard. Join the strips together with a paper fasten-er through a point on each strip near the center of the line segment.

1. Place the strips so that four angles are formed.

2. Measure each pair of the vertical angles. What do you observe?

3. Measure the angles of each linear pair. What do you observe?

4. Change the position of the strips to form new angles and repeat steps 2 and 3.

Discoveries:

When two lines intersect, the vertical angles are congruent and the angles of a linear pair are supplementary.

At this point, the text states that two angles equal in measure are also congruent. Elicit that the converse of this statement is also true.

11-4 ANGLES AND PARALLEL LINES

Use *Enrichment Activity 11-4: Parallel Lines and Angles* before introducing this section. This activity, which deals with the relationships between the measures of the angles of a linear pair and the measures of vertical angles, enables students to easily discover the angle relationships derived in this chapter.

Although a line is in fact parallel to itself, the concept of parallelism is limited here to two or more distinct lines in a plane. Segments and rays are parallel if the lines that contain them are parallel.

When two lines are cut by a transversal, various angles are formed. Alternate interior, alternate exterior, and corresponding angles are pairs of angles that are congruent if and only if the two lines cut by the transversal are parallel.

Make the point that, in a problem accompanied by a diagram, the *Given* (the facts that are stated) become the conditions of the problem. We do not make assumptions based on the appearance of the diagram. Thus, unless lines in a diagram are stated to be parallel, we cannot assume that they are.

Offer the following as a visual aid to help students identify alternate interior angles and corresponding angles:

1. Look for the letter **N** or the letter **Z** in different positions to identify alternate interior angles.
2. Look for the letter **F** in different positions to identify corresponding angles.

Note that alternate interior angles and corresponding angles exist whether or not the lines that form them are parallel.

In this course, the statement about alternate interior angles of parallel lines is treated as a postulate. Simple algebraic proofs concerning other pairs of angles of parallel lines are offered in the text. These proofs help to prepare students for Course II.

11-5 TRIANGLES AND ANGLES

In this section triangles are classified according to their angles. Use the following Hands-On Activity to demonstrate that the triangle is a rigid figure.

Hands-On Activity

Instructions:

Cut four strips of light cardboard of different lengths, and draw a line segment on each. Use paper fasteners to join one endpoint on strip 1 to an endpoint on strip 2, the second endpoint on strip 2 to an endpoint on strip 3, and the second endpoint on strip 3 to the second endpoint on strip 1, forming a triangle.

1. Ask: Can the shape of the triangle be changed without bending the cardboard?
2. Remove one of the strips, and replace it with a strip of a different length.
3. Ask: Can the shape of this new triangle be changed without bending the cardboard?
4. Ask: Is the shape of this new triangle different from the shape of the first one?
5. Insert a fourth strip between strip 1 and strip 3, forming a quadrilateral.
6. Ask: Can the shape of the quadrilateral be changed without bending the cardboard?

7. Ask: Why are triangles often used in building bridges?
8. Ask: Why is a four-sided figure often braced by joining its opposite vertices?

Discoveries:

1. The triangle is a rigid figure, that is, for given lengths of the three sides, only one shape is possible.
2. A quadrilateral is not a rigid figure. For given lengths of the four sides, many different shapes are possible.

The triangle is used in engineering to ensure that a bridge or other structure will retain its shape. A four-sided figure is often braced by inserting a piece that will form two triangles.

This figure can shift to become this figure , but this figure will retain its shape.

Have students measure the angles in very large and in very small triangles to convince themselves that the sum of the angle measures does not depend on the lengths of the sides. After students have had experience with individual triangles, present the informal proof using parallel lines.

An exterior angle of a triangle is defined in terms of the linear pair it forms with one of the interior angles of the triangle. Ask students to describe another method for determining the measure of an exterior angle of a triangle. After several problems, they should realize that the measure of any exterior angle of a triangle is equal to the sum of the measures of the two remote interior angles of the triangle.

11-6 TRIANGLES WITH CONGRUENT ANGLES

In this section triangles are classified according to their sides. Ask questions such as the following:

1. Can a triangle contain two right angles? One right and one obtuse angle? Two obtuse angles?
2. Can a right triangle be isosceles? Equilateral?
3. Can an obtuse triangle be isosceles? Equilateral?
4. Can a base angle of an isosceles triangle be a right angle? An obtuse angle?

Hands-On Activity

Instructions:

1. Draw an angle. Label the vertex *C*.
2. Place point *A* on one ray of the angle. Measure the distance *AC*. Locate point B on the other ray of the angle so that *AC* = *BC*. Draw $\overline{AB}$.
3. Measure ∠*A* and ∠*B*. What do you observe?
4. Draw another angle, and repeat steps 2 and 3.

   Discoveries: Triangle *ABC* is an isosceles triangle, and the measures of ∠*A* and ∠*B* are equal.

Allow sufficient time for treating the properties of an isosceles triangle. When you draw an isosceles triangle on the chalkboard, do not always locate the vertex angle at the top of the diagram and the base angles at the bottom. In the following diagram, ∠*B* is the vertex angle and ∠*A* and ∠*C* are the base angles.

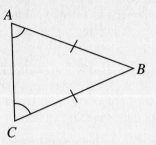

Exterior angles of isosceles triangles provide good exercise material. Using the diagram below, in which m∠*A* = 54 and $\overline{AB} \cong \overline{BC}$, students should be able to find: (1) m∠*ACB* = 54, (2) m∠*ABC* = 72, and (3) m∠*ACD* = 126.

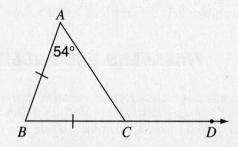

See *Enrichment Activity 11-6: Angle Measures.* This activity combines many of the angle measure relationships studied in this chapter.

Name _____ Class _____ Date _____

ENRICHMENT ACTIVITY 11-4

Parallel Lines and Angles

In the diagram, $\overleftrightarrow{AB} \parallel \overleftrightarrow{CD}$. Transversal $\overleftrightarrow{EF}$ intersects $\overleftrightarrow{AB}$ and $\overleftrightarrow{CD}$. The eight angles formed are labeled 1 through 8 as shown in the diagram.

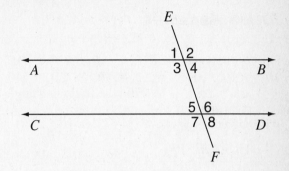

1. Name eight linear pairs of angles.

2. Name four pairs of opposite angles.

3. If the measure of ∠1 is 72° and ∠1 ≅ ∠5, find the measures of the other six angles.

4. If the measure of ∠2 is 115°, and ∠2 ≅ ∠7, find the measures of the other six angles.

5. If the measure of ∠4 is 56°, and ∠4 ≅ ∠5, find the measures of the other six angles.

6. If the measure of ∠3 is 95°, and ∠3 ≅ ∠7, find the measures of the other six angles.

7. Angles 3 and 6 in the diagram are alternate interior angles. When a transversal intersects two parallel lines, the alternate interior angles are congruent. If m∠3 = x, find the measures of the other seven angles in terms of x.

8. What conclusions can you draw about the angles formed by two parallel lines and a transversal?

9. What conclusions can you draw if ∠3 and ∠6 are both right angles?

10. Draw two lines that are not parallel. Then draw a third line that intersects the first two lines. Measure the eight angles formed. Do the conclusions that you formed in step 8 apply when two lines that are not parallel are intersected by a transversal?

Name _____ Class _____ Date _____

ENRICHMENT ACTIVITY 11-6

Angle Measures

1. In polygon *ABCDEF*, $\overline{AB} \parallel \overline{CF} \parallel \overline{DE}$, m∠*A* = 110, m∠*B* = 80, m∠*D* = 140, and m∠*E* = 100. Find the following angle measures:

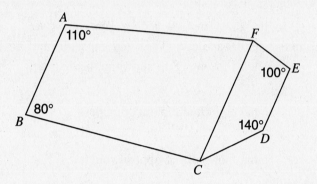

   a. m∠*AFC* =

   b. m∠*BCF* =

   c. m∠*DCF* =

   d. m∠*EFC* =

2. Two line segments *AC* and *EC* are drawn in polygon *ABCDEF* from part **1** so that m∠*BAC* = 70 and m∠*ECF* = 20. (Insert the measures of ∠*AFC* and ∠*EFC* in the diagram.) Use this information and the data from part **1** to find the following angle measures:

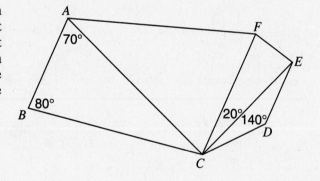

   a. m∠*ACF* =

   b. m∠*FAC* =

   c. m∠*ACB* =

   d. m∠*CED* =

   e. m∠*DCE* =

   f. m∠*CEF* =

Name _____ Class _____ Date _____

3. In **a-e**, name, in each case, all triangles in the diagram of part **2** that fit the given description. If no such triangles exist, write "None."

   a. Isosceles triangles = _____

   b. Equilateral triangles = _____

   c. Scalene triangles = _____

   d. Obtuse triangles = _____

   e. Acute triangles = _____

4. Answer the following questions about the polygon in the diagram of part **2**:

   a. A right angle can be formed by drawing a segment to connect two vertices of the polygon.

   (*1*) The segment is _____

   (*2*) The right triangle is _____

   b. Is $\overline{AF} \parallel \overline{BC}$? Explain your answer.

   _____

   _____

   _____

SUGGESTED TEST ITEMS (CHAPTER 11)

1. In the diagram $\overleftrightarrow{AB} \perp \overleftrightarrow{CD}$, E is the midpoint of $\overline{AB}$, and $BC = AC$.

   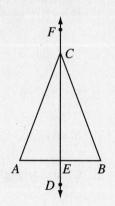

   a. Name the ray that is the opposite of $\overrightarrow{EA}$.

   b. Name a right angle.

   c. Name an acute angle.

   d. Name an obtuse angle.

   e. Name a line segment whose measure is equal to BE.

   f. Name an angle congruent to $\angle CBE$.

   g. Name an angle that is the complement of $\angle CBE$.

2. In the diagram, $\overleftrightarrow{PQ} \parallel \overleftrightarrow{VS}$, and $\overleftrightarrow{TN}$ intersects $\overleftrightarrow{PQ}$ at R and $\overleftrightarrow{VS}$ at A. If m$\angle VAN = 85$, determine:

   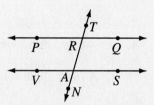

   a. m$\angle SAN$ b. m$\angle SAR$

   c. m$\angle PRA$ d. m$\angle QRA$

3. In $\triangle ABC$, m$\angle A$ is 20 degrees more than m$\angle B$, and m$\angle C$ is 8 degrees less than m$\angle B$. What is the measure of each angle of the triangle?

4. In the diagram, $\overleftrightarrow{AB}$ intersects $\overleftrightarrow{CD}$ at E. If the measure of $\angle AEC$ is represented by $5x - 12$, and m$\angle BED$ is represented by $3x + 40$, determine:

   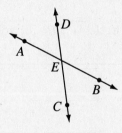

   a. m$\angle AEC$ b. m$\angle BED$

   c. m$\angle AED$ d. m$\angle CEB$

5. In $\triangle PQR$, the measure of the exterior angle at P is 28 degrees less than the measure of $\angle QPR$. What is the measure of the exterior angle at P?

6. The measure of an angle is $\frac{4}{5}$ of the measure of its supplement. What is the measure of the angle and of its supplement?

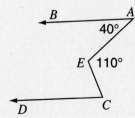

BONUS: In the diagram, $\overleftrightarrow{AB} \parallel \overleftrightarrow{CD}$, m$\angle BAE = 40$, and m$\angle AEC = 110$. Find m$\angle ECD$.

SAT PREPARATION EXERCISES (CHAPTER 11)

I. Multiple-Choice Questions

In 1-8, select the letter of the correct answer.

1.

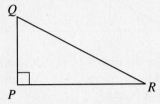

If point *T* (not shown) is a point on an extension through ∠*P*, how many points *T* can be found so that ∠*QTP* ≅ ∠*QRP*?

(A) 1   (B) 2   (C) 3   (D) 4   (E) 5

2. If ∠*X* and ∠*Y* are complementary, and ∠*X* and ∠*Z* are supplementary, which of the following is true?

(A) m∠*X* + m∠*Z* = 270

(B) 2(m∠*X*) = m∠*Y* + m∠*Z*

(C) m∠*Z* − m∠*X* = 90

(D) m∠*Z* − m∠*Y* = 90

(E) m∠*X* + m∠*Z* = 180

3. The length of a tennis court is 10 feet shorter than three times its width, *x*. Express the perimeter of the tennis court in terms of x.

(A) 4*x* − 10   (B) 2*x* − 14   (C) 8*x* + 20

(D) 8*x* + 10   (E) 8*x* − 20

4. The average (arithmetic mean) of the measures of angle *X*, its complementary angle, and its supplementary angle is 80 degrees. What is the measure of the complement of angle *X*?

(A) 30°   (B) 60°   (C) 90°

(D) 120°   (E) 180°

5. What must the complement of the supplement of an obtuse angle be?

(A) an acute angle   (B) a right angle

(C) an obtuse angle   (D) a straight angle

(E) a reflex angle

6.

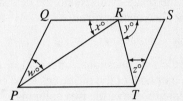

In the figure above, triangle *PRT* shares a side of a parallelogram *PQST*. What is the sum of *w*, *x*, *y*, and *z*?

(A) 135°   (B) 180°   (C) 270°

(D) 360°   (E) 380°

7.

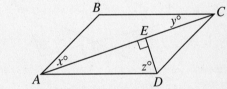

In the figure above, $\overline{DE}$ is perpendicular to a diagonal $\overline{AC}$ of the parallelogram *ABCD*. Which of the following is true?

(A) *x* + *y* + *z* = 180

(B) *x* + *y* + 2*z* = 180

(C) *x* + *z* = 90

(D) *y* + *z* = 90

(E) *x* + *y* = 60

8. If a number is multiplied by 3, the result is the same as 24 decreased by the number. What is the number?

(A) 6 (B) 9 (C) 12 (D) 15 (E) 18

II. Quantitative Comparison Questions

Questions 9–17 each consist of two quantities, one in Column A and one in Column B. You are to compare the two quantities and choose:

A if the quantity in Column A is greater;
B if the quantity in Column B is greater;
C if the two quantities are equal;
D if the relationship cannot be determined from the information given.

Notes

1. In certain questions, information concerning one or both of the quantities to be compared is centered above the two columns.
2. In a given question, a symbol that appears in both columns represents the same thing in Column A as it does in Column B.
3. Letters such as *x, n,* and *k* stand for real numbers.

Column A	*Column B*

9.

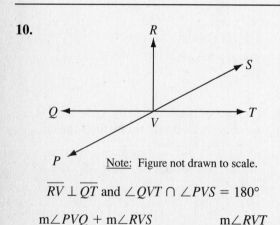

Note: Figure not drawn to scale.

$m\angle P + m\angle Q$ $m\angle R + m\angle S$

10.

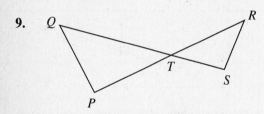

Note: Figure not drawn to scale.

$\overline{RV} \perp \overline{QT}$ and $\angle QVT \cap \angle PVS = 180°$

$m\angle PVQ + m\angle RVS$ $m\angle RVT$

11. Triangle *ABC* is an acute triangle.

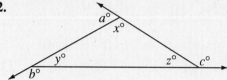

$m\angle A + m\angle B$ $m\angle C$

12.

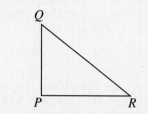

The average (arithmetic mean) of *a, b,* and *c*   The sum of *x, y,* and *z*

13.

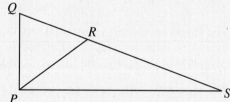

$m\angle P + m\angle Q + m\angle R$ The sum of the measures of an exterior angle at *Q* and an exterior angle at *R*

14.

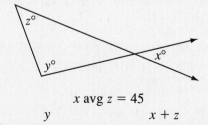

Angle *PRQ* is acute

$m\angle Q + m\angle QPR$ $m\angle S + m\angle SPR$

15.

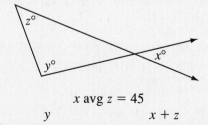

x avg $z = 45$

y $x + z$

16.

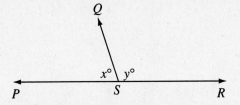

Angle *QSP* is larger than its complement.

$$\frac{x}{y} \qquad\qquad \frac{1}{3}$$

17.

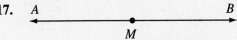

M is the midpoint of $\overline{AB}$. $\overline{AB} = 10$ and *R* (not shown) is a point on *AB*

$$AR \qquad\qquad 5$$

III. Student-Produced Response Questions

In questions 18-22, you are to solve the problem.

18.

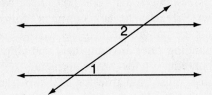

In the figure above, two parallel lines are cut by a transversal. If the m∠1 = 6x + 12 and the m∠2 = 10x + 4, determine m∠1 avg m∠2.

19.

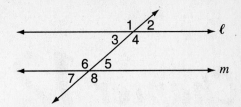

In the figure above, line ℓ is parallel to line *m*. If the measure of ∠1 is 115°, what is the measure of ∠5?

20. In △*ABC*, m∠*A* = 40.5 degrees, and the measure of the exterior angle formed when $\overline{CB}$ is extended through ∠*B* is 110.4 degrees. Determine the sum of the m∠*B* and m∠*C*.

21. If a faulty clock gains six minutes every hour starting at precisely 1:00 pm, what is the correct time when the clock indicates that ten hours have passed?

22.

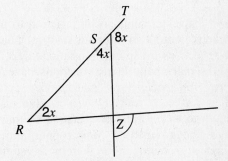

In the figure above, $\overline{RST}$ is a straight line. What is the m∠*R*?

Chapter *12*

Congruence and Transformations

Aims

- To determine the conditions necessary for two triangles to be congruent.
- To study the properties of quadrilaterals.
- To investigate the transformations by which an image is congruent to its preimage.
- To determine when a figure has transformational symmetry.

This chapter presents an introduction to transformations through an informal study of line and point reflections, rotations, translations, and symmetries. Traditionally, transformations have been reserved for higher level mathematics courses. Even at this early stage, however, students are receptive to an informal presentation of transformations and symmetries. Many opportunities to investigate geometric figures from a variety of viewpoints are presented.

12-1   GEOMETRIC FIGURES

Following the discussion in the text about plane geometric figures, curves, and polygons, you may wish to ask questions such as these: Why can't a polygon have fewer than three sides? Why isn't a circle an example of a polygon? How can a square be an example of a simple closed curve?

To enrich the discussion about polygons, ask for commonly used, real-life examples such as the octagonal stop sign. Have students look around the classroom and identify different shapes. Pictures of architectural designs and other art forms are rich in geometric shapes.

The use of graph paper will help students to visualize polygons of different shapes and to identify those that contain parallel and perpendicular lines.

12-2   CONGRUENT TRIANGLES

Before you discuss the concept of congruent triangles, establish the conditions necessary for any two polygons to be congruent. Since two polygons are congruent if and only if all pairs of corresponding sides are congruent and all pairs of corresponding angles are congruent, the same conditions must hold true for any two triangles. The text shows, however, that congruence of all six pairs of corresponding parts of triangles need not be demonstrated. To determine congruence in triangles, it is sufficient to show that three selected pairs of corresponding parts are congruent.

Hands-On Activity

Instructions:

Work as a class or in small groups for this activity.

1. As a group, choose the measures of two sides and of the included angle of a triangle.
2. Have each member of the group use a ruler and protractor to draw a triangle with these measures.

3. Cut out the triangles, and compare their shapes.

4. As a group, choose the measures of two angles and the included side of a triangle. Repeat steps 2 and 3.

5. As a group, choose the measures of three sides of a triangle.

6. Have each member of the group cut three strips of paper or light cardboard to the lengths chosen for the sides of the triangle, and arrange the strips to form a triangle. Fasten the ends of the strips with tape.

7. Compare the shapes of the triangles.

Discoveries:

1. Two triangles are congruent if two angles and the included side of one are congruent to the corresponding parts of the other.

2. Two triangles are congruent if two sides and the included angle of one are congruent to the corresponding parts of the other.

3. Two triangles are congruent if three sides of one are congruent to the corresponding parts of the other.

You may wish to mention that, although triangle congruence cannot generally be established using two pairs of sides and a pair of nonincluded angles (s.s.a. ≅ s.s.a.), these conditions do establish congruence in two right triangles (hyp.leg ≅ hyp.leg).

Also, you might point out that when two pairs of angles are congruent, the third pair of angles must also be congruent. Thus, any side is an included side between two angles congruent to the corresponding angles in the other triangle.

Note that only drawing tools (rulers and protractors) are used in Course I. Formal constructions with straight edge and compasses will be studied in Course II.

12-3 QUADRILATERALS

It is important, especially in this section, to review what constitutes a good mathematical definition. For example, a rectangle is defined as a parallelogram in which all four angles are right angles. What does it mean to say that a rectangle is a parallelogram? This statement means that a rectangle must have all the properties of a parallelogram.

A rectangle must also have some distinguishing feature or features, however, that separate it from the rest of the broader set of parallelograms. Well, a rectangle has four right angles. Then can we define a rectangle as a parallelogram with one right angle? Elicit the properties of a parallelogram that lead to the answer *yes*.

A diagram is helpful in understanding basic definitions.

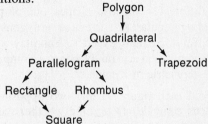

Note how each figure is defined from the figure listed above it.

In Course I, the properties of the family of parallelograms are limited to those mentioned in the text. Properties concerning diagonals will be studied in Course II.

In the exercises, conditional statements are given concerning the special quadrilaterals. The students are asked to determine the truth values of each statement and its converse, inverse, and contrapositive. A background in logic helps students achieve a better understanding of the relationships that exist among quadrilaterals.

The sum of the measures of the angles of any quadrilateral is 360°. Students will see that a quadrilateral can be divided into two triangles, each of whose angle measures has a sum of 180°. How many degrees are in the sum of the measures of the angles of a pentagon? A hexagon? After considering a number of examples, students can arrive at a general formula for the sum of the measures of the angles of any n-sided polygon, namely, $(n - 2)180°$.

12-4 LINE REFLECTIONS AND LINE SYMMETRY

Students should have fun looking at letters and words for symmetry, and finding symmetries in mirror reflections, in prisms, in advertising logos, and in examples from nature and architecture.

They also enjoy hands-on experience in creating symmetric figures by paperfolding or by using a ruler. They should see that when a ruler is laid perpendicular to the line of reflection, the preimage and image points are equidistant from that line.

Hands-On Activity

Instructions:

Cut different geometric shapes out of paper, including regular and irregular polygons with three, four, five, and six sides. You may wish to use graph paper, a straight edge, a compass or other geometric instruments.

1. Fold each figure so that two opposite vertices coincide. Determine whether the fold is a line of symmetry.
2. Fold each figure so that two adjacent vertices coincide. Determine whether the fold is a line of symmetry.
3. Fold each figure so that the two rays of an angle coincide. Determine whether the fold is a line of symmetry.

Discoveries include:

1. All regular polygons have lines of symmetry.
2. For all regular polygons, the perpendicular bisector of each side is a line of symmetry.
3. For regular polygons with an even number of sides, each diagonal joining opposite vertices is also a line of symmetry.
4. Some polygons that are not regular, such as an isosceles triangle, a rectangle, a rhombus, and an isosceles trapezoid, have lines of symmetry.

The use of coordinates to study transformations enables students to visualize the concept and to make connections with arithmetic, algebra, and graphing. The emphasis should be on visualization of the image, rather than on memorization of the relationships of the coordinates.

12-5 POINT REFLECTIONS AND POINT SYMMETRY

When students draw the point reflection of a figure, they are applying the concepts of midpoint and bisector.

Hands-On Activity

Instructions:

Draw any simple geometric figure. Choose any point to be the point of reflection.

1. Use a ruler to draw a line from any point A on the figure to the point of reflection, O.
2. Find point A' on line AO such that $AO = OA'$ and O is the midpoint of AA'.
3. Repeat steps 1 and 2 for other points on the figure.
4. Join the points found in step 2 to draw the figure that is the line reflection of the original figure.
5. Ask: What do you observe when you turn your work upside down?

12-6 TRANSLATIONS

A translation can be thought of as a "slide." The patterns in fabrics are good examples of translational symmetry. Bring to class or ask students to find examples in articles of clothing, draperies, or paper toweling that use translational symmetry. Have students pick out the section that is translated to form the pattern. Call attention to the fact that, since length and angle measure are unchanged, the image is congruent to the original figure.

12-7 ROTATIONS

Hands-On Activity

Instructions:

Draw a large equilateral triangle in the upper right section of a sheet of paper. You may wish to use graph paper, a straight edge, a compass or other geometric instruments. Then, draw a design inside the triangle.

1. Draw a triangle rotated 60° about the vertex closest to the center of the paper, and copy the design.
2. Draw another triangle rotated 60° about the same vertex, and copy the design.

3. Repeat step 2 four more times.
4. Ask: What kind of symmetry does the finished drawing have?

An overhead projector is helpful in discussing transformations. Rotational symmetry, in particular, can be clearly demonstrated by using matching overlays to show what rotation is needed for a figure to coincide with itself. Overlays can also serve

to demonstrate that a rotation of 180° about a point P is equivalent to a point reflection in P.

Since reflections, translations, and rotations all preserve distance and angle measure, a figure is congruent to its image under all of these transformations. A discussion of dilation, a transformation that preserves angle measure but not distance, is presented in Chapter 13 as an application of similarity.

SUGGESTED TEST ITEMS (CHAPTER 12)

1. In the diagram, $\overleftrightarrow{AB} \perp \overleftrightarrow{CD}$, E is the midpoint of $\overline{AB}$, and $\overline{BC} \cong \overline{AC}$.

   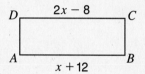

   a. Name a line segment congruent to $\overline{BE}$.

   b. Name a line of symmetry for $\triangle ABC$.

   c. Name the image of A under a reflection in $\overleftrightarrow{CD}$.

   d. Name the image of A under a reflection in E.

   e. Which of the following *cannot* be used to prove $\triangle BEC \cong \triangle AEC$?

       (1) a.s.a $\cong$ a.s.a.   (2) s.a.s. $\cong$ s.a.s.   (3) a.a.a. $\cong$ a.a.a.   (4) s.s.s. $\cong$ s.s.s.

2. In the figure, $ABCD$ is a rectangle. If $AB = x + 12$ and $DC = 2x - 8$, what is the value of x?

3. In parallelogram $ABCD$, $m\angle A = 8 + 2(x + 1)$ and $m\angle C = 5(x - 1)$.

   a. What is the value of x?

   b. Determine the measure of each angle of the parallelogram.

4. Copy the following figures, and draw as many lines of symmetry for each figure as possible.

   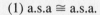

          Rectangle   Isosceles   Regular
                        trapezoid   hexagon

5. Tell whether each of the letters at the right has point symmetry, line symmetry, both point and line symmetry, or neither point nor line symmetry.

   H E A R T S

6. Write the coordinate of the image of point $(5, -4)$ under each transformation.

   a. a reflection in the x-axis

   b. a reflection in the y-axis

   c. a reflection in the origin

   d. a translation that moves the object point 3 units to the left and 6 units up

7. On graph paper, draw $\triangle ABC$ whose vertices are $A(1, 1)$, $B(7, 1)$, and $C(4, 5)$.

   a. Draw $\triangle A'B'C'$, the image of $\triangle ABC$ under a reflection in the y-axis.

   b. Write the coordinates of A', B', and C'.

c. What is the area of $\Delta A'B'C'$?

8. A rectangle that is symmetric with respect to both the x-axis and the y-axis has one vertex at $(-2, 3)$. What are the coordinates of the other vertices?

BONUS: A boy hiking close to a river sees a campfire that was left burning. He runs to the river to get some water and then runs to put out the fire. Copy the sketch and draw in the shortest path the hiker can take to the river and then to the campfire.

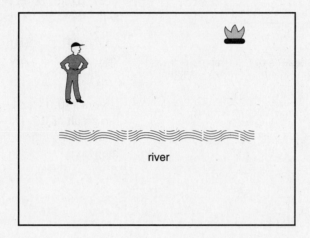

river

SAT PREPARATION EXERCISES (CHAPTER 12)

I. Multiple-Choice Questions

In 1-15, select the letter of the correct answer.

1.

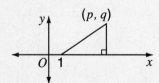

In the figure above, the area of the triangle is 8 and the coordinates of point P are $(0, 4)$. What are the coordinates of point Q?

(A) $(4, 0)$ (B) $(2, 0)$ (C) $(1, 0)$

(D) $\left(\frac{1}{2}, 0\right)$ (E) $\left(0, \frac{1}{2}\right)$

2.

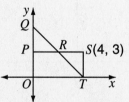

In the figure above, the area of the rectangle $OPST$ equals the area of triangle TQO. What are the coordinates of point R?

(A) $(3, 3)$ (B) $(4, 2)$ (C) $(2, 3)$

(D) $(2, 4)$ (E) $(3, 4)$

3.

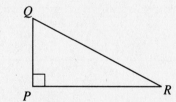

Which of the following represents the area of the triangle shown above?

(A) $\dfrac{q(p-1)}{2}$ (B) $\dfrac{p(q+1)}{2}$

(C) $\dfrac{p(q-1)}{2}$ (D) $\dfrac{q(p+1)}{2}$

(E) $\dfrac{p+q}{2}$

4.

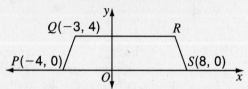

In the figure above, $PQRS$ is an isosceles trapezoid. What are the coordinates of point R?

(A) $(3, 4)$ (B) $(4, 4)$ (C) $(7, 4)$

(D) $(8, 4)$ (E) $(4, 3)$

5. If points $(0, 1)$ and $(3, 7)$ are both points on the graph of line m, which of the following points lies on the reflection of the graph in the y-axis?

(A) $(-3, 7)$ (B) $(1, 0)$ (C) $(3, -7)$

(D) $(3, 8)$ (E) $(7, -3)$

6.

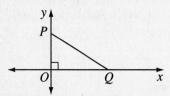

How many points T (not shown) can be found so that $\triangle PQT$ and the triangle above are congruent?

(A) 1   (B) 2   (C) 3

(D) 4   (E) 5

7. The letter S has which of the following symmetries?

  I point symmetry
  II line symmetry
  III rotational symmetry

(A) I only   (B) I and II only

(C) II and III only   (D) I and III only

(E) I, II, and III

8.

The regular octagon shown above has several lines of symmetry. If the image of $\overline{AE}$ is $\overline{GC}$ under a reflection in one of these lines of symmetry, which of the following pairs could be the line of reflection?

(A) $\overline{AG}$ or $\overline{AC}$ (B) $\overline{AG}$ or $\overline{CE}$
(C) $\overline{AE}$ or $\overline{GC}$ (D) $\overline{HD}$ or $\overline{FB}$
(E) $\overline{GC}$ or $\overline{FE}$

9.

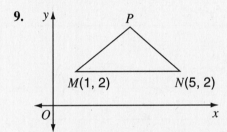

Isosceles triangle MNP has an area of 6, and point P lies on the perpendicular bisector of $\overline{MN}$. What are the coordinates of point P?

(A) $(3, 5)$ (B) $(5, 4)$ (C) $(4, 3)$
(D) $(4, 5)$ (E) $(3, 4)$

10. A pencil lies on graph paper with the eraser at $(-5, 10)$ and the point at $(7, -2)$. If the pencil is moved without changing its direction until the point is at the origin, then the eraser is in which quadrant?

(A) I   (B) II   (C) III
(D) IV   (E) Cannot be determined

11. Which is an equation of the line that passes through $(1, p)$ and the origin?

(A) $y = px$ (B) $y = x + p$
(C) $x = py$ (D) $y = x - p$
(E) $y = px + 1$

12.

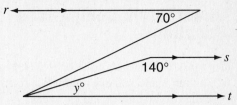

In the figure above, r, s, and t, are parallel lines. What is the measure of angle y?

(A) 20   (B) 30   (C) 40
(D) 50   (E) 70

13. Let $(a, b) \oplus (c, d) = \left(\dfrac{a + c}{2}, \dfrac{b + d}{2} \right)$. For example, $(1, 1) \oplus (3, 5) = (2, 3)$. Which choice is equivalent to $(1, 1) \oplus (5, 9)$?

(A) $(1, 1) \oplus (9, 5)$ (B) $(2, 3) \oplus (4, 5)$
(C) $(4, 6) \oplus (2, 4)$ (D) $(1, 0) \oplus (5, 8)$
(E) $(3, 5) \oplus (1, 1)$

14.

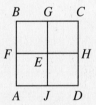

Square $ABCD$ shown above has several lines of symmetry. Under a 90-degree counterclockwise rotation about point E, followed by a translation, the image of $\overline{EG}$ is $\overline{HE}$. Under the same transformations, what is the image of $\overline{BG}$?

(A) $\overline{BF}$ (B) $\overline{JE}$ (C) $\overline{AJ}$
(D) $\overline{FE}$ (E) $\overline{CH}$

15. Which of the following is a reflection of the y-coordinate of point $(1, 5)$ through the origin?

(A) -5 (B) -1 (C) 0
(D) 1 (E) 5

II. Quantitative Comparison Questions

Questions 16-20 each consist of two quantities, one in Column A and one in Column B. You are to compare the two quantities and choose:

  A if the quantity in Column A is greater;
  B if the quantity in Column B is greater;
  C if the two quantities are equal;
  D if the relationship cannot be determined from the information given.

Notes

1. In certain questions, information concerning one or both of the quantities to be compared is centered above the two columns.
2. In a given question, a symbol that appears in both columns represents the same thing in Column A as it does in Column B.
3. Letters such as x, n, and k stand for real numbers.

<u>**Column A**</u>   <u>**Column B**</u>

16.

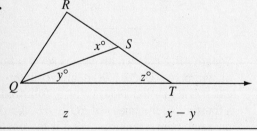

    z $x - y$

17.

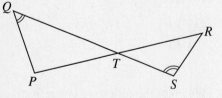

Diagram not drawn to scale

$$\triangle PQT \cong \triangle RST$$
$$\angle Q \cong \angle S$$

  QT ST

18.

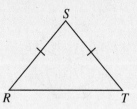

$$RS = 7 \text{ cm}$$

$\overline{RT}$ if the m$\angle S = 50$ $\overline{RT}$ if m$\angle S = 60$

19. Triangle *BED* is inscribed in triangle *AEC* such that $\overline{AE} \cong \overline{CE}$, $\overline{AC} \parallel \overline{BD}$, and m$\angle E = 54°$.

      BD EC

20.

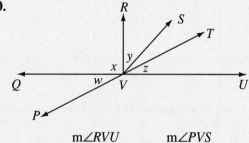

    m$\angle RVU$ m$\angle PVS$

III. Student-Produced Response Questions

In questions 21-25, you are to solve the problem.

21.

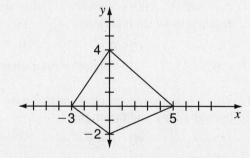

What is the area of the quadrilateral above?

22.

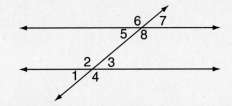

In the figure above, two parallel lines are cut by a transversal. If the m$\angle 3 = 2x - 4$ and the m$\angle 6 = 3x + 44$, evaluate m$\angle 8$.

23. What is the degree measure of the smaller of the two acute angles $2x$ and $3x$ contained in a right triangle?

24.

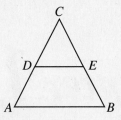

In the accompanying diagram, $\triangle ABC$ is isosceles with $\overline{DE} \parallel \overline{AB}$, and the m$\angle ACB = 70$. What is the m$\angle CED$?

25. What is the area of $\triangle ABC$ whose vertices are $A(1, 1)$, $B(5, 1)$ and $C(3, 8)$?

Chapter 13
Ratio and Proportion

Aims

- To establish the concepts of ratio, proportion, and direct variation.
- To use ratio and proportion in solving verbal problems.
- To introduce similarity of geometric figures.
- To use ratio in comparing perimeters and area of similar figures.

The introductory page of this chapter defines the *golden section,* which, in turn, leads to the golden ratio. Every ratio is a comparison of two numbers. The *golden ratio,* which has the exact value $\dfrac{1 + \sqrt{5}}{2}$, is a comparison of the length to the width of every *golden rectangle,* no matter how large or how small.

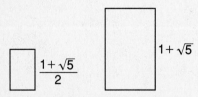

On the introductory page, it is suggested that a calculator be used to find a *rational approximation* for the golden ratio. A ten-digit approximation is shown in the following display:

Enter: (1 + 5 $\sqrt{x}$)
÷ 2 =

Display: 1.618033989

Students should understand that the calculator display of the ratio, length to width, indicates a value that is compared to the number 1. In other words:

$$\text{Golden ratio} = \frac{\text{length}}{\text{width}} = \frac{1 + \sqrt{5}}{2} \approx \frac{1.618033989}{1}$$

The other ratios mentioned in the introduction are reasonably close to the approximation 1.618033989. Each of the following three ratios is formed by comparing two consecutive Fibonacci numbers:

$$\frac{13}{8} = 1.625 \qquad\qquad = \frac{1.625}{1}$$

$$\frac{89}{55} = 1.6\overline{18} \qquad\qquad = \frac{1.618181818}{1}$$

$$\frac{233}{144} = 1.61180\overline{5} \qquad = \frac{1.618055555}{1}$$

See *Enrichment Activity 13 Introduction: Fibonacci Sequence and the Golden Ratio.* Students investigate ratios, each comparing the larger to the smaller of two consecutive terms in the Fibonacci sequence. These ratios converge to the value 1.618033989, which is the rational approximation for the golden ratio, $\dfrac{1 + \sqrt{5}}{2}$.

At present, students lack the algebraic skills needed to show how the equation generated by the golden section, $\dfrac{a}{b} = \dfrac{a + b}{a}$, leads to the golden ratio, $\dfrac{1 + \sqrt{5}}{2}$.

You may wish to review the following solution after presenting the study of quadratic equations with irrational roots in Chapter 21.

142

(1) Given the equation of the golden section:
$$\frac{a}{b} = \frac{a + b}{a}$$

(2) Let $b = 1$:
$$\frac{a}{1} = \frac{a + 1}{a}$$

(3) Cross multiply:
$$a(a) = 1(a + 1)$$

(4) Solve by completing the square or using the quadratic formula:
$$a^2 = a + 1$$
$$a^2 - a - 1 = 0$$
$$a = \frac{1 \pm \sqrt{5}}{2}$$

(5) Disregard the negative value since the variable represents a length:
$$= \frac{1 + \sqrt{5}}{2}$$

The ratio $\frac{a}{b}$ equals $\dfrac{\left(\dfrac{1 + \sqrt{5}}{2}\right)}{1}$ or simply $\dfrac{1 + \sqrt{5}}{2}$, which is the golden ratio.

13-1   RATIO

Since a ratio is a comparison of two numbers expressed as an ordered pair, present the topic of finding a ratio as an example of a binary operation ($a * b = c$). To show that the ratio of terms expressed in the same unit of measure is independent of the unit of measure used, present the following example.

The ratio of 36 inches to 2 yards may be written as $36:72$ using inches, as $3:6$ using feet, or as $1:2$ using yards. Each of these ratios in lowest terms is $1:2$. An understanding that the terms must be in the same unit of measure can be reinforced by a demonstration of cancellation, which can occur only when the units are the same. For example:

$$\frac{36 \text{ inches}}{2 \text{ yards}} = \frac{36 \text{ inches}}{72 \text{ inches}} = \frac{36}{72} = \frac{1}{2}$$

Some students may reduce the ratio $\frac{36}{72}$ to $\frac{18}{36}$ and then stop. They must be reminded to continue reducing until the simplest form (in this case, $\frac{1}{2}$) is reached.

If a calculator is used to determine a ratio, caution students that the calculator displays a decimal value that is compared to the number 1. For example:

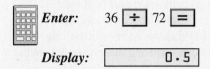

Enter: 36 $\boxed{\div}$ 72 $\boxed{=}$

Display: $\boxed{\quad 0 \cdot 5 \quad}$

The ratio 0.5 must then be expressed in *simplest form* by converting the decimal to a fraction consisting of two whole numbers that have no common factor other than 1:

$$0.5 = \frac{0.5}{1} = \frac{0.5}{1} \times \frac{2}{2} = \frac{1.0}{2} = \frac{1}{2}$$

See ***Enrichment Activity 13-1: Ratio: Estimates and Comparisons.*** Students estimate the ratios of the geographic areas (sizes) of several other nations to the area (size) of the United States in three ways: (1) guessing, based on personal knowledge of world geography; (2) observing a world map and then estimating relative sizes; (3) using data from a current almanac.

13-2   USING A RATIO TO EXPRESS A RATE

A ratio comparing two quantities is not limited to quantities expressed in the same unit. Comparisons of quantities of different types are common and lead to the concept of rate. For example, the ratio of 12 cookies to 4 persons becomes 3 cookies per person.

Use comparison shopping as an application. For example:

Which is a better buy?
a. 8 oz. @ \$0.80   **b.** 12 oz. @ \$1.08

The better buy is choice **b**, since it yields a cost of 9 cents per ounce, while the cost in **a** is 10 cents per ounce.

To show that the ratio of terms comparing quantities expressed in different units is not independent of the units measure, present the following example.

If a car travels 30 miles in 1 hour, it travels 158,400 feet in 3,600 seconds. Therefore, the rate can be expressed as 30:1 or 30 miles per hour. The same rate can also be expressed as 158,400:3,600 or 44:1 or 44 feet per second. Therefore, the units of measure are an important part of the rates.

Extended Task. Students can research unit pricing. Reports should include, but not be limited to, various forms of comparisons such as the following:

- Comparisons of prices for small and large packages of the same product within one store.
- Comparisons of unit prices for the same item from one store to another.
- Comparisons of unit prices for competitive brands of the same type of product (e.g., peanut butter, laundry detergent).

The diverse units of measures used in unit pricing (ounces, grams, fluid ounces, pints, per 100 count, and so on) should also be investigated and noted.

See *Enrichment Activity 13-2: Population Density*. In Part I, three lists of data are given for eight specific states of the United States. Students must match the correct population, area, and population density to each of these states by using logical deductions. A calculator is helpful here.

In Part II, students are given the population density of the United States and then are asked, first, to estimate the population density of each of six other countries and, second, to find this information in an almanac.

13-3 VERBAL PROBLEMS INVOLVING RATIO

Students have been using an algebraic strategy to solve verbal problems. This procedure involves the identification of an unknown (that is, presenting a legend).

When the ratio of two or more numbers is given, that ratio determines the legend. For example, if two numbers are in the ratio 2:3, the legend is written as follows:

Let $2x$ = the smaller number.
Then $3x$ = the larger number.

A common student error is to stop after solving an equation to find the value of x. Remind students

to refer to the legend and to continue until the problem is solved.

The text provides a variety of mathematical and nonmathematical examples involving ratios in realistic settings.

13-4 PROPORTION

In this section, the fundamental principle of proportion is developed: *In any proportion, the product of the means is equal to the product of the extremes.* This concept is often called *cross multiplication.* If this shorter expression is used, be sure students understand that the principle applies only to proportions. Students sometimes incorrectly apply cross multiplication to expressions such as the sum of two fractions.

To emphasize the importance of different strategies in problem solving, four different methods are used to solve Example 1. Here, a statement equating two ratios is shown to be a proportion by:

(1) demonstrating that reduced ratios are equal,

(2) showing that the product of the means equals the product of the extremes,

(3) using a calculator to show that decimal forms of the ratios are equal, and

(4) demonstrating that the difference of the ratios is 0.

In the exercises that follow, students may use cross multiplication to solve equations indicated as proportions. In these exercises, no proportion will yield a second-degree equation. Such quadratic equations are discussed in Chapter 21.

See *Enrichment Activity 13-4: Ratios and Inequalities.* Here, students have an opportunity to discover the concept of cross multiplication applied to inequalities (a topic not discussed in the book at this stage), and to investigate proofs and applications in this area.

13-5 DIRECT VARIATION

Direct variation is a familiar concept even if the terms introduced in this section are unfamiliar.

Direct variation occurs when there is a *constant rate*.

Use Example 3 to show that, in certain situations, we expect a constant rate. In this case, the calories per gram are constant at 4.5, or $\frac{9}{2}$. Point out that the constant rate is the basis for the check; 315 calories is the correct number for 70 grams because the ratio $\frac{315}{70}$ yields the ratio $\frac{9}{2}$, the constant determined from the original condition, $\frac{90}{20}$.

Extended Task. Students can research examples of direct variation in the physical world, providing evidence of such use in a written report. (Many exercises in this section given hints of applications of direct variation: calories, weights, rates, scale drawings, mixtures, recipes, and so on.)

13-6 PERCENT AND PERCENTAGE PROBLEMS

When the base and the rate are given, it is convenient to multiply the base by the rate expressed as a decimal fraction to find the percentage. However, when the percentage is given and either the base or the rate is to be found, the use of a proportion is recommended.

Examples in this section again show a wide variety of approaches in finding solutions. Students may discover still other strategies, such as an alternative algebra approach to Example 2: "If 25% of a number is 80, find the number." Here, the solution can be found by translating the words of the problem into an equation:

Let n = the number.

$$\underbrace{25\% \text{ of a number}}_{0.25n} \underbrace{\text{is}}_{} \underbrace{80.}_{= 80}$$

On scientific calculators, the commutative property holds when using the $\boxed{\%}$ key. For example, to find 20% of 90, both of the methods indicated below produce the correct answer, 18:

Enter: *Method 1:* 90 $\boxed{\times}$ 20 $\boxed{\%}$ $\boxed{=}$

Method 2: 20 $\boxed{\%}$ $\boxed{\times}$ 90 $\boxed{=}$

Display: $\boxed{\qquad 18.}$

Caution students that these two methods do not, however, produce the same result when used on a basic four-function calculator. To find 20% of 90 using a basic calculator, a definite order must be followed. In most cases, the order is as follows:

Enter: 90 $\boxed{\times}$ 20 $\boxed{\%}$

Display: $\boxed{\qquad 18.}$ Correct

On the other hand:

Enter: 20 $\boxed{\%}$ $\boxed{\times}$ 90 $\boxed{=}$

Display: $\boxed{\qquad 1800.}$ Incorrect

Again, this example demonstrates the need for good estimation skills when using a calculator.

Extended Task. Students can investigate compound interest. Frequently used variables related to this topic include, but are not limited to, the following:

p = principal (money) invested
r = rate of interest, usually per year
t = time, usually in years
n = number of interest periods per year
I = interest earned on the investment
A = accumulated total: principal plus interest

Formulas for simple interest now serve merely as a means of broad estimations:

$$I = prt; \quad A = p + prt; \quad A = p(1 + rt)$$

The basic formula for an accumulated total under compound interest is

$$A = p\left(1 + \frac{r}{n}\right)^{nt}$$

What is the difference between the annual percentage rate or yield (APR) and the yearly rate of interest being compounded?

13-7 SIMILAR POLYGONS

When a picture is enlarged, we want the enlargement to be proportional to the original so that the figure(s) will not be distorted. Pictures that have been enlarged or reduced in size are familiar examples of similar polygons.

Remind students of the notational difference between $\overline{AB}$ (a line segment) and AB (the measure of the line segment). Note that when we write ratios or proportions, we are dealing with measures.

In the exercises, students are asked if two rectangles must be similar. They are also asked about other types of quadrilaterals. After discussing these figures, ask students to explain why equilateral triangles must be similar. Elicit a statement concerning the similarity of any two polygons with the same number of sides. (Any two *regular* polygons with the same number of sides are similar.)

Continue to encourage students to draw diagrams for problems involving geometric figures. Similar triangles or other polygons need not be drawn exactly to a given ratio, but a reasonably accurate sketch can often help the student to avoid errors.

13-8   SIMILAR TRIANGLES

This section contains a development, starting with a specific example and leading to a general conclusion, that a.a. $\cong$ a.a. is a condition by which we can state that two triangles are similar.

Most numerical and algebraic exercises concerning similar triangles lead to the writing and solution of proportions. Students frequently have difficulty setting up a correct proportion because they do not pay attention to which angles correspond or they ignore the fact that corresponding sides are found opposite congruent angles. Exercises 1–4 are intended to help students develop this sense. You might have students mark their diagrams to show congruent angles. For example, the diagram for Exercise 19 could be marked as shown below:

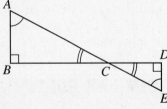

In this exercise, angles B and D are given as right angles. The intersecting line segments $\overline{AE}$ and

$\overline{BD}$ should lead students to recognize a pair of vertical angles. Encourage students to write the vertices of the triangles in the order of their correspondence ($\triangle ABC \sim \triangle EDC$ or $\triangle CAB \sim \triangle CED$). Corresponding sides can thus be easily identified.

In a problem relating to a physical situation, such as finding the height of a tree, students should be sure to write the unit of measure in the answer. Even when the unit is unspecified, as is the case in Exercise 12, students may write an answer in the form "$DF = 8$ units," and should understand that "units" refers to linear units.

13-9   DILATIONS

After establishing a.a. $\cong$ a.a. as a condition for similarity of two triangles, a fourth type of transformation, dilation, is introduced as an application.

Ask students for other examples of dilation. You might begin by mentioning that a doctor dilates (enlarges) the pupils of the eyes during a detailed eye examination.

Proportions are used to solve for the unknown lengths of sides in similar triangles.

In part **a** of the example in this section you might show students that reducing a ratio can simplify the arithmetic:

$$\frac{x}{18} = \frac{16}{24}$$
$$\frac{x}{18} = \frac{2}{3}$$
$$3x = 36$$
$$x = 12$$

Students may write an incorrect proportion because they mistakenly use only part of a side of a triangle. Have them look again at the diagram for the example in this section after the answer to part **a** has been obtained:

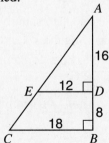

Emphasize that, for instance $\frac{16}{12} \neq \frac{8}{18}$. Since segment $\overline{BD}$ is not a side of either triangle, its measure, 8, cannot be a term of any correct ratio.

13-10 RATIO OF PERIMETERS AND RATIO OF AREAS OF SIMILAR POLYGONS

After a numerical development of the relationship between the ratio of the perimeters of similar triangles and the ratio of the measures of the corresponding sides, you may wish to show students algebraic proof.

The key to the proof that follows is in the setup. We set up two similar triangles so that the ratio of the measures of the corresponding sides, which is known to be constant, can be specified.

Given: $\triangle ABC \sim \triangle A'B'C'$

Let the measures of the sides of $\triangle ABC$ be called as_1, as_2, and as_3.

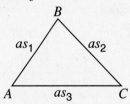

Let the measures of the sides of $\triangle A'B'C'$ be called bs_1, bs_2, and bs_3.

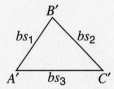

Show: The ratio of the perimeters is equal to the ratio of the measures of the corresponding sides.

Proof:

(1) $\dfrac{\text{Sides of } \triangle ABC}{\text{Sides of } \triangle A'B'C'} = \dfrac{as_1}{bs_1} = \dfrac{as_2}{bs_2} = \dfrac{as_3}{bs_3} = \dfrac{a}{b}$

(2) Perimeter of $\triangle ABC = as_1 + as_2 + as_3$
$$= a(s_1 + s_2 + s_3)$$

(3) Perimeter of $\triangle A'B'C' = bs_1 + bs_2 + bs_3$
$$= b(s_1 + s_2 + s_3)$$

(4) $\dfrac{\text{Perimeter of } \triangle ABC}{\text{Perimeter of } \triangle A'B'C'} = \dfrac{a(s_1 + s_2 + s_3)}{b(s_1 + s_2 + s_3)}$
$$= \dfrac{a}{b}$$

(5) Therefore, from steps 1 and 4:
$$\dfrac{\text{Perimeter of } \triangle ABC}{\text{Perimeter of } \triangle A'B'C'} = \dfrac{\text{sides of } \triangle ABC}{\text{sides of } \triangle A'B'C'}$$

You may wish to offer an algebraic proof for the statement that the ratio of the areas of similar triangles is the square of the ratio of the measures of the corresponding sides.

As with the proof offered above for perimeter, the key to the area proof that follows is in the setup. Again, we set up two similar triangles so that the ratio of the measures of corresponding sides, which is known to be constant, can be specified. We begin by establishing that the corresponding altitudes have the same ratio as the corresponding sides.

Given: $\triangle ABC \sim \triangle A'B'C'$ with altitudes $\overline{BD}$ and $\overline{B'D'}$.

Let the ratio of corresponding sides be $a:b$.

Show: The ratio of the areas is equal to the square of the corresponding sides.

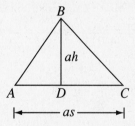

Proof:

(1) To establish that corresponding altitudes of similar triangles have the same ratio as the corresponding sides, first consider triangle ABD and $A'B'D'$, for which the altitudes of triangles $\triangle ABC$ and $\triangle A'B'C'$ are sides.

Since $\triangle ABD \sim \triangle A'B'D'$ (a.a. $\cong$ a.a.), $\dfrac{BD}{B'D'} = \dfrac{AB}{A'B'}$, where $\dfrac{AB}{A'B'}$ represents the ratio of the corresponding sides of the original similar triangles.

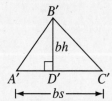

(2) In the original triangles, let the measures of the bases and the altitudes to these bases be as follows:

base $AC = as$ base $A'C' = bs$
altitude $BD = ah$ altitudes $B'D' = bh$

(3) Substitute into the formula for the area of a triangle:

$$\text{Area of } \Delta = \frac{1}{2}(\text{base} \times \text{altitude})$$

$$\text{Area of } \Delta ABC = \frac{1}{2}(as)(ah)$$

$$= \frac{1}{2}a^2(sh)$$

$$\text{Area of } \Delta A'B'C' = \frac{1}{2}(bs)(bh)$$

$$= \frac{1}{2}b^2(sh)$$

(4) Write the ratio:

$$\frac{\text{Area of } \Delta ABC}{\text{Area of } \Delta A'B'C'} = \frac{\frac{1}{2}a^2(sh)}{\frac{1}{2}b^2(sh)} = \frac{a^2}{b^2}$$

(5) Therefore, $\dfrac{\text{area of } \Delta ABC}{\text{area of } \Delta A'B'C'}$

$$= \frac{a^2}{b^2} = \left(\frac{a}{b}\right)^2 = \left(\frac{\text{sides of } \Delta ABC}{\text{sides of } \Delta A'B'C'}\right)^2$$

If you have previously mentioned to students that reducing a ratio can simplify the arithmetic in the solution of a proportion, you must remind them now to be careful as they reduce ratios that are perfect squares. For example, demonstrate with the ratio $16:36$. The simplest form of $\frac{16}{36}$ is $\frac{4}{9}$, not $\frac{2}{3}$.

$$\frac{16 \div 4}{36 \div 4} = \frac{4}{9} \qquad \sqrt{\frac{16}{36}} = \frac{4}{6} = \frac{2}{3}$$

Note that the exercises for perimeter require students to work on either side of the proportion. In other words, they are asked either to find a perimeter or to find a side. The exercises for area, however, are limited to one side of the proportion, finding area. The reason is that finding a side, as in the example presented below, leads to a simple *quadratic* equation if a straightforward algebraic solution is pursued.

You may wish to suggest the following examples as a challenge question. Even if students cannot solve the equation, they may find an answer by guessing and checking.

Example: The areas of two similar triangles are in the ratio $16:25$. If the length of a side of the smaller triangle is 8 centimeters, find the length of the corresponding side of the larger triangle.

Algebraic Solution:

Let $x =$ the length of the side of the larger triangle. Then:

$$\frac{\text{Area of small } \Delta}{\text{Area of large } \Delta} = \left(\frac{\text{side of small } \Delta}{\text{side of large} \Delta}\right)^2$$

$$\frac{16}{25} = \left(\frac{8}{x}\right)^2$$

$$\frac{16}{25} = \frac{64}{x^2}$$

$$16x^2 = 1{,}600$$

$$x^2 = 100$$

$$x = \pm 10$$

Answer: The side of the larger triangle measures 10 centimeters.

Note that in the preceding solution we took the square root of each member of the equation as a final step. It is also possible to simplify the equation by taking the square root of each member as an initial step:

$$\frac{16}{25} = \left(\frac{8}{x}\right)^2$$

$$\pm\frac{4}{5} = \frac{8}{x}$$

$$\pm 4x = 40$$

$$x = \pm 10$$

In considering ratios of perimeters and areas, there are several reasons for paying particular attention to units of measure.

For example,

(1) the solution may sometimes go from a ratio (no unit) to a length (linear unit), or vice versa;

(2) in working with areas, an additional distinction must be made: ratio of areas (no unit), measures of areas (square units), and measures of sides (linear units).

Name _____ Class _____ Date _____

ENRICHMENT ACTIVITY 13-INTRODUCTION

Fibonacci Sequence and the Golden Ratio

The Fibonacci sequence starts with the numbers 1 and 1. Then, by adding the last two consecutive Fibonacci numbers, the next term in the sequence is obtained.

Since $1 + 1 = 2$, the third term is 2:   1, 1, 2
Since $1 + 2 = 3$, the fourth term is 3:   1, 1, 2, 3
Since $2 + 3 = 5$, the fifth term is 5:   1, 1, 2, 3, 5
The Fibonacci sequence continues in this pattern: 1, 1, 2, 3, 5, 8, 13, 21, 34, 55, . . .

Part 1. Copy the first ten numbers of the Fibonacci sequence, shown above, and continue the sequence until 26 terms are obtained.

Part 2. Each of the ratios shown below compares the *larger* of *two consecutive Fibonacci* numbers to the *smaller.* Each ratio is then converted to a decimal approximation.

$(1, \underline{1}, \underline{2}, 3, 5, 8, . . .)$ $(1, 1, \underline{2}, \underline{3}, 5, 8, . . .)$ $(1, 1, 2, \underline{3}, \underline{5}, 8, . . .)$ $(1, 1, 2, 3, \underline{5}, \underline{8}, . . .)$

$$\frac{2}{1} = \frac{2.0}{1} \qquad\qquad \frac{3}{2} = \frac{1.5}{1} \qquad\qquad \frac{5}{3} = \frac{1.666666666}{1} \qquad\qquad \frac{8}{5} = \frac{1.6}{1}$$

Continue this new pattern. Write each ratio as a fraction of two consecutive Fibonacci numbers (larger to smaller), and then as a decimal compared to 1, using all the Fibonacci numbers given in Part 1. (*Note*: You need to find 20 ratios in all.)

$$\frac{13}{8} = \qquad\qquad\qquad \frac{21}{13} = \qquad\qquad\qquad \frac{34}{21} =$$

Part 3. As you have learned, the golden ratio, which is a comparison of *length ℓ* to *width w* in every golden rectangle, equals the ratio $\frac{1 + \sqrt{5}}{2}$. Write an observation to show the connection between the Fibonacci numbers and the golden ratio.

Name _____ Class _____ Date _____

ENRICHMENT ACTIVITY 13-1

Ratio: Estimates and Comparisons

In this three-step process, each ratio that is written shows a comparison of the geographic area (size) of another nation in our world to the area (size) of the United States.

If country X is 2 times the size of the United States and country Y is about one-third the size of the United States, then the ratios comparing the sizes of these countries are written as shown at the right.

	Ratio of Size
Country X	2.0
United States	1.0
Country Y	0.3

Fill in the table below as follows:

Column 1: Estimate, to the *nearest tenth,* each ratio of size using *no* resources.

Each estimate is a guess, based on your general knowledge of world geography. The ratio of the United States is 1. Write these ratios in column 1.

Column 2: Estimate, to the *nearest tenth,* each ratio of size using a world map.

Based on your observation of a world map from a source such as an atlas, write a new ratio in column 2 for each given nation. Notice the changes in your estimates.

Column 3: Find, to the *nearest hundredth,* the actual ratio of size for each nation.

Obtain the true geographic area for each nation listed by using a source such as an almanac. Then compare each area (size) to the area of the United States and write the actual ratio in column 3. Were your estimation skills on target or way off?

	Column 1 Estimated Ratio of Size Using No Resources	Column 2 Estimated Ratio of Size Using a World Map	Column 3 Estimated Ratio of Size Using True Areas (Almanac)
Australia			
Brazil			
Canada			
China			
India			
Japan			
Mexico			
Russia			
Spain			
United States	1.0	1.0	1.00

BONUS: On a separate piece of paper, compare the area of each nation listed above to the area of Mexico. Write (**a**) one observation to show how this new list of ratios is different from column 3 above, and (**b**) another observation to show how the new list is the same as column 3 above.

Name _____ Class _____ Date _____

ENRICHMENT ACTIVITY 13-2

Population Density

Population density is a *rate* in which the total population of an area is compared to its geographic size. For example, using 1995 estimates from the U.S. Census Bureau, the population density of the United States is as follows:

$$\frac{263,814,032 \text{ people}}{3,679,192 \text{ sq mi}} = 72 \text{ people/sq mi} \quad \textit{(nearest whole number)}$$

Part 1. The three lists of numbers given below are based on 1995 population estimates and known geographic areas for eight specific states in the United States. These data are given in numerical order from smallest to largest but *not* necessarily in the order of the states as listed in the table that follows.

State Population	Area (sq mi)	Population Density
606,276	8,722	1
856,047	53,821 ✔	6
7,069,836 ✔	54,471	68
7,903,925	65,756	131 ✔
13,952,714	147,046	192
18,169,051	163,707	212
18,378,185	268,601	334
31,430,697	656,424	906

Use logical deductions and a calculator to place each set of numbers from these lists in its correct position in the following table. As an example, the data for North Carolina, indicated by ✔ marks in the lists above, have been correctly placed in the table.

Name _____ Class _____ Date _____

	State Population	*Area (sq mi)*	*Population Density*
Alaska			
California			
Florida			
Montana			
New Jersey			
New York			
North Carolina	7,069,836	53,821	131
Texas			

Part 2. The population density of the United States is 72 people per square mile.

   a. For each of the following six countries, estimate (guess) its population density:

   Canada _____   China _____   India _____

   Japan _____   Mexico _____   Russia _____

   b. Use an almanac to find the actual population density (to the *nearest whole number* of people per square mile) of the six countries listed in part **a.**

   Canada _____   China _____   India _____

   Japan _____   Mexico _____   Russia _____

Name _____ Class _____ Date _____

ENRICHMENT ACTIVITY 13-4

Ratios and Inequalities

If two ratios are unequal, a proportion does *not* exist between them. Certain relationships, however, can be stated. Consider these two approaches to inequalities.

Multiply each inequality by the least common denominator. Here, the L.C.D. = (5)(4) or 20.	Change the ratios to fractions with common denominators. Then compare the numerators.
$$\frac{2}{5} < \frac{3}{4}$$ $$\frac{2}{\cancel{5}} \, (\cancel{5})(4) < \frac{3}{\cancel{4}} \, (5)(\cancel{4})$$ $$2(4) < 3(5)$$ $$8 < 15$$	$$\frac{2}{5} < \frac{3}{4}$$ $$\frac{2}{5}\left(\frac{4}{4}\right) < \frac{3}{4}\left(\frac{5}{5}\right)$$ $$\frac{8}{20} < \frac{15}{20}$$ $$8 < 15$$

In the exercises on this page, all variables represent positive numbers.

1. Use either approach shown above to prove this statement:

$$\text{If } \frac{a}{b} < \frac{c}{d}, \text{ then } ad < bc. \qquad (a, b, c, d > 0)$$

2. Fill in the blank to make each statement true.

   a. If $\frac{a}{b} > \frac{c}{d}$, then _____.   **b.** If $\frac{a}{b} \leq \frac{c}{d}$, then _____.

   c. If $\frac{1}{b} < \frac{1}{d}$, then _____.   **d.** If $\frac{1}{b} > \frac{c}{d}$, then _____.

Name _____ Class _____ Date _____

3. If $b > 0$, which must be true: $\dfrac{1}{b} < \dfrac{1}{b+1}$ or $\dfrac{1}{b} > \dfrac{1}{b+1}$ or $\dfrac{1}{b} = \dfrac{1}{b+1}$?
   Explain your answer.

4. If $\dfrac{a}{b} > \dfrac{b}{a}$, where $a > 0$, $b > 0$, which is true: $\dfrac{a}{b} > 1$ or $\dfrac{a}{b} < 1$ or $\dfrac{a}{b} = 1$? Why?

5. If $\dfrac{a}{b} > \dfrac{a+c}{b+c}$ ($a, b, c > 0$), which is true: $a > b$ or $a < b$ or $a = b$? Why?

In 6–9, $x > 0$ and $y > 0$. In each case: **a.** Tell whether the sentence is true or false. **b.** Explain your answer to part **a.**

6. $\dfrac{x}{y} < \dfrac{x}{y+1}$

7. $\dfrac{x}{y} < \dfrac{x+1}{y}$

8. $\dfrac{x+y}{y} < \dfrac{x}{y}$

9. $\dfrac{x+1}{y} < \dfrac{x}{y}$

10. If $\dfrac{a}{b} < \dfrac{c}{d}$ (variables > 0), how does the ratio $\dfrac{a+c}{b+d}$ relate to $\dfrac{a}{b}$ and $\dfrac{c}{d}$?

   (*Hint:* Try several numerical examples before stating a general conclusion.)

SUGGESTED TEST ITEMS (CHAPTER 13)

In 1–4, express each ratio in simplest form.

1. $15:45$

2. $18:3$

3. $\dfrac{1}{3}:\dfrac{5}{12}$

4. 10 grams to 4 kilograms

5. A machine takes 5 minutes to fill 360 cereal boxes. Express the rate, in boxes per second, at which the machine works.

6. If a car used 16 gallons of gasoline to travel 512 miles, how far can the car travel on 12 gallons of gasoline?

In 7–10, in each case, solve and check.

7. $\dfrac{2}{9} = \dfrac{x}{36}$

8. $\dfrac{a+1}{7} = \dfrac{a-1}{5}$

9. $\dfrac{y}{y-3} = \dfrac{6}{5}$

10. $\dfrac{1}{3} = \dfrac{2x-3}{5x}$

11. A cup of lemonade is made by mixing a can of frozen lemonade concentrate with water in the ratio of $1:3$. How many cans of concentrate are needed to prepare 12 cups of lemonade?

12. The measure of the angles of a triangle are in the ratio $2:2:5$. What is the measure of each angle of the triangle?

13. A baseball team won 30 games and lost 10. What percent of the games that the team played did they lose?

14. What is the missing value for x in the table if y varies directly as x?

x	12	15	?
y	8	10	14

15. Mr. Carter found that 32% of the persons who work in his office come to work by bus. How many persons work in Mr. Carter's office if eight come to work by bus?

16. In the diagram, $\triangle ABC \sim \triangle ADE$, $DE = 7$, $BC = 10$, and $DB = 6$. What is the length of AD?

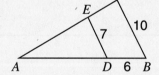

17. The perimeters of two triangles are in the ratio $3:8$. The lengths of the sides of the smaller triangle are 12 centimeters, 15 centimeters, and 21 centimeters. What are the lengths of the sides of the larger triangle?

BONUS I: If 20 typists can type 20 pages in 20 minutes, how many typists are needed to type 40 pages in 40 minutes? How many pages can 10 typists type in 10 minutes?

BONUS II: Separate the polygon in the diagram into four congruent polygons each of which is similar to the original.

SAT PREPARATION EXERCISES (CHAPTER 13)

I. Multiple-Choice Questions

In 1-14, select the letter of the correct answer.

1.

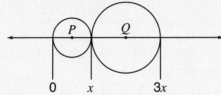

What is the ratio of the circumference of circle P to that of circle Q in the above figure?

(A) $\frac{1}{2}$ (B) $\frac{x}{2}$ (C) $\frac{1}{4}$

(D) $\frac{x}{4}$ (E) 4

2. The ratio of the length of a rectangle to its width is $4:1$. What percent of the perimeter is the width?

(A) 75%   (B) $33\frac{1}{3}\%$ (C) 25%

(D) 20%   (E) 10%

3. The area of a circle is 9π and the perimeter of a square is 12. Which of the following drawings correctly shows the relative sizes of the circle and the square?

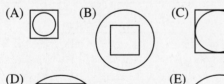

4. If $ax = 6$ and $bx = 8$, evaluate x^2.

(A) $48ab$ (B) $\frac{48}{ab}$ (C) $\frac{ab}{48}$

(D) $\frac{6b}{8a}$ (E) $\frac{36}{48}$

5. $1x^{100}y^4,\ 3x^{97}y^6,\ 5x^{94}y^8,\ 7x^{91}y^{10}, \ldots$

If the pattern above is continued, what would be the 21st term?

(A) $41x^{40}y^{44}$ (B) $41x^{37}3y^{44}$

(C) $43x^{40}y^{44}$ (D) $43x^{37}3y^{44}$

(E) $43x^{40}y^{37}$

6.

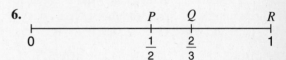

On the number line above, what is the ratio of PQ to QR?

(A) $\frac{1}{2}$ (B) $\frac{1}{3}$ (C) $\frac{2}{3}$

(D) $\frac{3}{4}$ (E) $\frac{5}{6}$

7. If $2x + 7 = 12$, then the ratio of $2x$ to $2x + 5$ is

(A) $\frac{1}{2}$ (B) $\frac{2}{3}$ (C) $\frac{3}{4}$

(D) $\frac{4}{5}$ (E) 2

8. If the continued ratio $x:y:z$ is $2:3:k$, and y is 75% of z, then x is what percent of z?

(A) 75%   (B) $66\frac{2}{3}\%$ (C) 50%

(D) $33\frac{1}{3}\%$ (E) 25%

9.

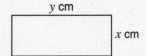

If the ratio of x to y in the rectangle above is $2:3$, which of the following represents twice the area of the rectangle?

(A) $\frac{x^2}{3}$ cm^2 (B) $3x^2$ cm^2 (C) $6x^2$ cm^2

(D) $6xy$ cm^2 (E) $9x^2$ cm^2

10. What is the ratio of the average (arithmetic mean) of 3, 5, and x to the sum of 3, 5, and x if x is a positive integer?

(A) $\dfrac{1}{3}$ (B) $\dfrac{8+x}{15x}$ (C) $\dfrac{8+x}{3}$

(D) $\dfrac{3x}{8+x}$ (E) $\dfrac{2(8+x)}{3}$

11. In a certain class, $\dfrac{4}{5}$ of the students have pencils and $\dfrac{3}{4}$ of them have pens. If there are 20 students in the class, what is the smallest number of them who might have both pens and pencils?

(A) 15 (B) 11 (C) 5

(D) 4 (E) 1

12. In a triangle, side x is $\dfrac{1}{2}$ of side y and side z is $\dfrac{3}{4}$ of side y. Then side y is what fractional part of the perimeter of the triangle?

(A) $\dfrac{2}{3}$ (B) $\dfrac{1}{3}$ (C) $\dfrac{3}{8}$

(D) $\dfrac{4}{9}$ (E) $\dfrac{9}{4}$

13.

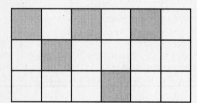

How many more squares in the figure above must be shaded so that the ratio of the shaded squares to the unshaded squares is the same as the ratio of the length of the shorter side of the rectangle to the length of the longer side?

(A) 4 (B) 3 (C) 2

(D) 1 (E) 0

14. What is the ratio of $2(2^{200})$ to $(2^{200})^2$?

(A) $\dfrac{1}{2}$ (B) $\dfrac{1}{2^{100}}$ (C) $\dfrac{1}{2^{199}}$

(D) $\dfrac{1}{2^{200}}$ (E) 2

II. Quantitative Comparison Questions

Questions 15-24 each consist of two quantities, one in Column A and one in Column B. You are to compare the two quantities and choose:

A if the quantity in Column A is greater;
B if the quantity in Column B is greater;
C if the two quantities are equal;
D if the relationship cannot be determined from the information given.

Notes

1. In certain questions, information concerning one or both of the quantities to be compared is centered above the two columns.
2. In a given question, a symbol that appears in both columns represents the same thing in Column A as it does in Column B.
3. Letters such as x, n, and k stand for real numbers.

Column A	*Column B*
15. $\dfrac{1 \text{ millimeter}}{1 \text{ centimeter}}$	$\dfrac{1 \text{ centimeter}}{1 \text{ meter}}$
16. $2 + \dfrac{1}{2 + \frac{1}{2}}$	$2\dfrac{1}{2}$

17.

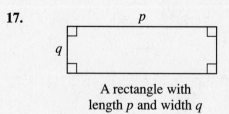

A rectangle with length p and width q

One-fourth the perimeter of the rectangle	The average of p and q

18. The distance traveled in one hour at a rate of 10 km in 15 minutes	The distance traveled in one hour at a rate of 12 km in 20 minutes

19.

$$x > 0; y > 0$$

$$\frac{x}{y} \qquad\qquad \frac{y}{x}$$

20.

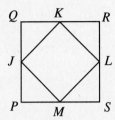

Square *JKLM* is formed
by joining the midpoints
of the sides of square *PQRS*.

Area of *PQRS*   Area of *JKLM*
when its length and
width are doubled.

---

21.   *X* and *Y* are consecutive even integers
$$(0 < X < Y)$$

    X + 50% of Y Y + 50% of X

---

22.   The longest side of   50% of the perimeter
a given triangle   of a given triangle

---

23.   *X* and *Y* are consecutive
positive odd integers, in order.

    50% of Y 20% of $(X + Y)$

---

24.   *X*, *Y*, and *Z* are the measures
of the sides of a triangle,
in descending order of length.

    X 50% of $(Y + Z)$

III. Student-Produced Response Questions

In questions 25-33, you are to solve the problem.

25. If *x* varies directly as *y* and $x = 5$ when $y = 3$, what is the value of *x* when $y = 7$.

26. What is the ratio of 8 inches to 5 feet?

27. At a certain time of the day, a vertical yardstick casts a 15-inch shadow. What is the height in feet of a flagpole that casts a shadow 20 feet long at the same time of the day?

28. A board is cut into lengths in the ratio of $1:2:5$. If the smallest length is 10 feet, what is the length in feet of the original board?

29. If the ratio of $r:s$ is $2:3$ and the ratio of $s:t$ is $1:2$, what is the ratio of $r:t$?

30. 20 is 40% of what number?

31. Gina got two consecutive discounts of 20%. If the original cost of the item was $1,000, what was the final price?

32. If the ratio of the perimeters of two similar triangles is $2:3$, determine the ratio of their corresponding areas.

33. Ten seconds is what fractional part of two hours? Write the answer in lowest terms.

Chapter *14*
Probability

Aims

- To introduce empirical and theoretical probability.

- To evaluate simple probabilities applied to fair objects by the theoretical rule.

- To determine the probabilities of compound events by using the counting principle, tree diagrams, listings of ordered elements, and graphs.

- To define and evaluate permutations, using factorial notation, formulas, and the scientific calculator.

- To solve probability problems in which items are chosen at random either without replacement or with replacement.

Originally developed to answer questions that arose in games of chance, the principles of probability are now applied to important questions that arise in education, science, industry, and the social sciences. Encourage students to research some of these uses.

From the outset, the text establishes a link between the topics of probability and statistics. Empirical probability requires the collection of data. Thus, some vocabulary of statistics is introduced in the first section. The text then uses empirical probability to lead into theoretical probability, reserving further discussion of the presentation of data for Chapter 15.

Probability and permutations are topics that may have been introduced to and investigated by students in earlier grades. However, a more thor-

ough presentation should be made at this time. Students although able to obtain correct answers to simple probability problems, often lack a true understanding of the meaning of these answers and an appreciation of when certain rules do or do not apply.

In addition to standard types of probability problems, some problems that use an algebraic solution are included in this chapter.

14-1 EMPIRICAL PROBABILITY

It is important that students perform an empirical study in probability before they are introduced to the rule for theoretical probability. For one reason, the theoretical rule can be applied only to fair objects, that is, objects for which each singleton outcome is equally likely to occur. Too often, students will want to treat every situation as if this is the case, but the differences between biased and fair objects must be recognized.

Perform an experiment in class. Collect the data, organize them in a table that includes cumulative relative frequency, and construct a graph of the cumulative relative frequency as the number of trials increases. Students may toss coins, as outlined in the text, or roll dice. By starting with a fair object, students will see why we assign certain probabilities such as P (head on a coin) $= \frac{1}{2}$ and P (4 on a die) $= \frac{1}{6}$. They will also be able to compare their guesses for the probability of an event with the cumulative relative frequency found in the experiment. Once the experiment is performed, the definition of empirical probability will make sense: probability is a guess of the cumulative relative frequency of an event, but that guess is based on careful and accurate gathering of data in a scientific experiment.

The text introduces a folded index card as an example of a biased object. After performing an experiment with a fair coin or a fair die, ask what probability may be assigned to each of the three outcomes obtained by tossing the biased folded card. Is the probability of each outcome $\frac{1}{3}$? The answer is no. Some students may say that there are two ways for the card to fall on its side, two ways for the card to fall on its edge, and only one way for the card to land as a tent. Then can we say P (side) = $\frac{2}{5}$, P (edge) = $\frac{2}{5}$, and P (tent) = $\frac{1}{5}$? Again, the answer is no. The fallacy in reasoning lies in an attempt to apply the rule for theoretical probability to a biased object, for which each singleton outcome is *not* equally likely to occur.

There is only one way to determine the probabilities: perform an empirical study. Let the students toss folded cards at home and collect the data in class the following day. The results will show that no particular probability can be assigned since the likelihood of achieving a certain outcome depends on other factors, such as the size of the card used and the manner in which the card was tossed.

Compare the result of generating random integers within some range on a computer with the result of asking a group of people to each select an integer within the same range. Is each integer equally likely to occur in both cases? Studies have shown that, in large numbers of trials, a computer will produce the integers within the selected range with equal frequencies. People, however, evincing natural human biases, will not.

The exercises offer suggestions for other experiments, using both fair and biased objects. As students answer questions dealing with probability, a sense of theoretical probability should emerge.

Extended Task: Have students define a situation or an activity with different possible outcomes. Perform a study or an experiment to determine, by empirical methods, the probabilities to be assigned to those possible outcomes.

14-2 THEORETICAL PROBABILITY

After introducing terms such as *outcome, sample space,* and *event,* we define the theoretical probability of an event as the number of ways that the event can occur divided by the total number of possibilities, or $P(E) = \frac{n(E)}{n(S)}$. In other words, theoretical probability is a ratio that can be written without performing an experiment. Why, then, did we do the experiments in Section 14-1? We did them because the rule for theoretical probability can be applied only to fair objects, whereas the empirical approach can be used with any object— fair or biased.

If each outcome of sample space has an equal chance of occurring, this sample space is said to have *uniform probability*. Ask whether a weighted coin or loaded dice have uniform probability.

Any selection of objects made without looking or without being able to influence the result is referred to as a *random selection*. Ask students to imagine that 20 sealed envelopes are lying on a table. Each of 19 envelopes contains a $1 bill; the twentieth envelope has a $100 bill. If any one envelope can be chosen, the probability of selecting the $100 bill is $\frac{1}{20}$. Would the probability change if a selection that is not random were used? Now suppose the bills were not in envelopes, but were openly displayed on a table. If any one bill can be chosen, is the probability of selecting the $100 bill still $\frac{1}{20}$?

Exercise 22 uses geometric figures in a probability problem to review some important properties of polygons.

14-3 EVALUATING SIMPLE PROBABILITIES

To write any simple probability, it is necessary to determine the number of ways the specific event can occur, where the set of outcomes in the event is a subset of the sample space. Emphasize that the probability of any event E must be equal to or greater than 0 (the impossible case) and less than or equal to 1 (the certain case).

In rolling a fair die, the probability that an even number will appear is $\frac{3}{6}$, or $\frac{1}{2}$. Since $\frac{1}{2} = .5$, or 50%, we can say that P (even number) $= \frac{1}{2}$, or .5, or 50%. Thus, the probability of an event can be expressed as a fraction, as a decimal, or as a percent. Probabilities are usually stated in fractional form. Although the text also shows fractions reduced to simplest form, there is no need to require that students do this. You may even prefer that students leave fractional answers in an unreduced form to reflect their thought processes about the problems.

Example 11, as well as Exercises 18–21, involve an algebraic solution to a simple probability problem.

See **Enrichment Activity 14-3: Probability and a Digital Clock.** This activity combines patterns and counting techniques with probability. When you look at the time on a digital clock, certain digits are visible. For example, the digits 0, 3, and 7 are in the display 3:07. If you look at a digital clock for a series of random times, which digit appears most often? What is the probability of seeing that digit at any one random time?

14-4 THE PROBABILITY OF (A AND B)

Suppose we agree to meet at Main Street *and* Second Avenue. How exact is that location? What word would you use to describe our meeting place? It is the *intersection* of two streets.

Ask, "Where else have we used the word *and* in our study of mathematics this year?" More than one student should recall the study of logic.

There is a natural integration of probability, logic, and sets within this section. In addition to discussing the concept from many viewpoints, note the similarities in the symbols used:

In sets, (A and B) is written $A \cap B$.
In logic, (p and q) is written $p \wedge q$.

14-5 THE PROBABILITY OF (A OR B)

Suppose we agree to meet at Main Street *or* Second Avenue. How exact is that location? Not very exact; we could easily miss each other by being anywhere on Main Street or anywhere on Second Avenue. In terms of sets, students will recognize the *union*. Their study of *or* in logic will help them understand the use of this connective in probability. Again, note the similarities in the symbols used:

In sets, (A or B) is written $A \cup B$.
In logic, (p or q) is written $p \vee q$.

A Venn diagram is an important aid in understanding the meaning of the rule:

$$P(A \text{ or } B) = P(A) + P(B) - P(A \text{ and } B)$$
$$P(A \cup B) = P(A) + P(B) - P(A \cap B)$$

Once this rule is understood, you may wish to study the probability of a union from a different viewpoint, by considering three disjoint sets. For example:

If $P(A) = .8$, $P(B) = .4$, and
$P(A \cap B) = .3$, find $P(A \cup B)$.

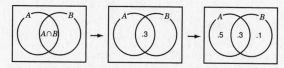

Draw a Venn diagram as shown above, and write .3 in the intersection to represent $P(A \cap B)$. Since $P(A) = .8$ and $P(A \cap B) = .3$ what probability can be assigned to the crescent-shaped region of A that does not include the intersection? Students will see that $.8 - .3 = .5$ or, by addition, that $.3 + .5 = .8$. [This region, which need not be formally defined, is called "(A less B)," written symbolically as A/B. Thus, $P(A/B) = .5$.] In a similar manner, the crescent-shaped region of B is $.4 - .3 = .1$. [More formally, the region is "(B less A)," written symbolically as B/A, and $P(B/A) = .1$.]

The probability of the union is the sum of the probabilities of the three disjoint sets, that is:

$$P(A \cup B) = .5 + .3 + .1 = .9$$

Compare this answer to the one found by the more familiar approach:

$$P(A \cap B) = P(A) + P(B) - P(A \cap B)$$
$$= .8 + .4 - .3 = .9$$

14-6 THE PROBABILITY OF (NOT A); PROBABILITY AS A SUM

Working with the probability that an event does occur to determine the probability that the event does *not* occur is an indirect approach and, in complex situations, can be more efficient than a direct approach. Acknowledge with students, however, that a direct approach for many of these simple situations is not only possible, but also is sometimes more efficient. In Example 1, for instance, we can go directly to the required event; there are two ways to roll a number that is not less than 5, namely, rolling a 5 and rolling a 6. Therefore, $P(\text{not less than } 5) = \frac{2}{6}$.

Take advantage of any opportunity to apply the rules of probability to real-life situations. For example, in Exercise 2 explore what it means to say that there is a 30% chance of rain. Elicit that past experience has shown that, given certain atmospheric conditions, rain has occurred on about 30 of 100 such days. Elicit also that fixing a probability for rain is complex, taking into account an array of variable factors; the question is not simply one of "Will it rain or will it not rain?"

The General Exercises at the end of this section represent a summary of all the probability concepts presented to this point.

See *Enrichment Activity 14-6: Probability and Area: And, Or, Not.* One or more regions are drawn within a 5 by 5 grid. The area of each region or the number of enclosed square units is determined by counting boxes. Probabilities are then found based on these areas, such as $P(D)$, $P(\text{not } D)$, $P(A \text{ and } B)$, and $P(A \text{ or } B)$.

14-7 THE COUNTING PRINCIPLE AND SAMPLE SPACES

When problems involve two or more activities, the number of outcomes can be obtained by actually displaying and counting the possibilities. A tree diagram, a set of ordered pairs, and a graph are ways of displaying the outcomes of two activities. If three or more activities are involved, however, a graph is not feasible. A tree diagram is recommended for most problems.

When preparing a tree diagram, students sometimes mistakenly include the number of trials; for example, for three tosses of a coin, they may start the tree with three branches: 1, 2, 3. Emphasize that only outcomes appear in a tree diagram.

The counting principle is a multiplication procedure that gives the number of outcomes without displaying them. It can be applied to any sample space, including those that result from three or more activities. The counting principle should be used to check the number of outcomes displayed when a tree diagram is prepared; it is also used when the number of possible outcomes makes a tree diagram impracticable.

14-8 PROBABILITIES AND THE COUNTING PRINCIPLE; PREDICTING OUTCOMES

If two dice are rolled, students can accept the fact that the outcomes on these dice are *independent* of each other. However, if a single die is rolled twice, some students erroneously believe that the outcome of the first roll has some influence on the outcome of the second. Elicit that this is not so; the outcome of the second roll is independent of the first.

Note with the class that the counting principle allows us to determine only the number of ways in which two or more activities can occur. A tree diagram, a listing, or a graph, on the other hand, shows the actual outcomes.

Here, in section 14-8, a counting principle for probability is stated. The counting principle provides a method for determining a probability ratio for compound events that are independent, without reference to the particular outcomes.

In section 14-9, the sample space is illustrated by drawing a tree diagram or listing a set of ordered elements. Unlike the counting principle, which is limited to compound events that are independent, such illustrations of the sample space allow us to view the actual outcomes and to determine probabilities for all compound events, whether they are independent or not.

Section 14-8 also presents the use of a proportion as a way of obtaining a relatively meaningful expectation based on past records. Note that in some of the given situations the compound events are clearly independent, as in consecutive tosses of a coin or in consecutive rolls of a die. However, in Exercise 11, for example, although the radios are individual items, the manufacturing process consists of a series of related events. Elicit reasons for the occurrence of a defect, such as the fatigue factor: the longer an operator works without rest, the more prone he or she is to error. Elicit also that, as with any theoretical probability, a prediction becomes more reliable as the number of trials increases. Thus, although we may not find exactly one defective radio in the first set of 400, or exactly two in the first set of 800, we are likely to find about 25 defective radios in the total set of 10,000.

14-9 PROBABILITIES WITH TWO OR MORE ACTIVITIES

In this section, a sample space, listed as a set of ordered elements or shown as a tree diagram, should be established before probabilities of compound events are found. In many instances, students prefer a tree diagram. Note that a tree diagram also helps students to write a listing of ordered elements.

Point out the relationship to logic here. Show how the listings in a truth table correspond to the branches of a tree diagram and to a listing of ordered elements. Use two variables and three variables.

Emphasize that a tree diagram depicts a definite pattern that makes it easier to list the elements in the sample space.

For larger sample spaces, such as the 36 elements obtained when two dice are rolled, a tree diagram is awkward to draw. Nevertheless, you may wish students to draw one such diagram and, therefore, will assign Exercise 6a. Even if you don't ask students to complete the diagram, they should be

encouraged to draw a few parts so that they can see how the diagram is related to the listing of ordered pairs. You should assign Exercise 6b, which requires a listing for this sample space, so that students will have a handy reference when working out other problems involving dice.

For this same sample space, in which two standard dice are rolled, a compact graph of ordered pairs that displays the sample space is given in Example 3. Ask students to make some observations about the graph. Their responses may include some of the following facts:

1. All the points representing a sum of 8 fall on a straight line.

2. If a point is on that line, that point represents a way to obtain a sum of 8.

3. If a point is not on that line, that point does not represent a way to obtain a sum of 8.

4. All the points "above" that line represent sums greater than 8.

5. All the points "below" that line represent sums less than 8.

Note how such observations prepare students for graph work with linear open sentences in the coordinate plane, which will be presented in Chapter 16.

As enrichment now, you might have students try to write the observations symbolically. For example:

Let x represent a possible outcome for the first die.

Let y represent a possible outcome for the second die.

Then (x, y) represents a possible outcome for two dice.

1. $\{(x, y) \mid x + y = 8\}$ falls on a straight line.

2. If a point is on that line, then, for that point, $x + y = 8$.

3. If a point is not on that line, then, for that point, $x + y \neq 8$.

4. For all the points "above" that line, $x + y > 8$.

5. For all the points "below" that line, $x + y < 8$.

Note that, since the domains for these variables x and y are each limited to the set $\{1, 2, 3, 4, 5, 6\}$, the set of ordered pairs (x, y) has exactly 36 elements, or points. Within this limited portion of the coordinate plane, called a *lattice of points,* we are considering the line $x + y = 8$, which has only five discrete points on it. Later, when the line $x + y = 8$ is presented in the full coordinate plane, the line will have an infinite number of points, and these points will not be discrete (there will be an infinite number of points between any two points on the line).

See *Enrichment Activity 14-9: Probability on a Dart Board.* Students determine the area of the bull's-eye and the area of each ring on a dart board, establish probabilities for random throws of a dart, and answer a series of questions related to events that may happen when one or two darts are thrown at the board.

14-10 PERMUTATIONS

In this section, students learn how to count the number of ways in which arrangements can be ordered. Factorial notation, introduced as representing the permutation of n objects taken n at a time, where n is a natural number, serves as a simple representation of the factors of this product.

At this point, students may not yet realize just how large some of these numbers can become. For example, 9 persons can be seated in a row 9! ways. Ask, "If a new arrangement was achieved every second, how long would it take to represent every possible arrangement?" Since

$$9! = 9 \cdot 8 \cdot 7 \cdot 6 \cdot 5 \cdot 4 \cdot 3 \cdot 2 \cdot 1 = 362,880$$

362,880 seconds would be required. Since there are 86,400 seconds in a day, exactly 4.2 days (4 days, 4 hours, 48 minutes) would be needed to rearrange just 9 persons in a row in every possible order. How long would it take to rearrange 13 persons in a row? (72,072 days, or almost 200 years.)

Many permutations that once required lengthy computation can now be evaluated quickly by using a calculator. Both the factorial key, $\boxed{x!}$, and the use of repeated multiplication are discussed in this section. The more general permutation key found on many scientific calculators is introduced in the next section, along with the concept of $_nP_r$.

When using a calculator to evaluate factorials and permutations, students must have a clear knowledge of scientific notation. When the number of digits in a factorial or a permutation exceeds the number of places in a calculator display, the calculator will shift from standard decimal notation to scientific notation.

Take the time to show why:

$$2! + 4! \neq 6!$$
$$\frac{4!}{2!} \neq 2! \qquad 8! - 6! \neq 2! \qquad 2! \cdot 3! \neq 6!$$

Demonstrate also how to simplify a division containing factorials. For example:

$$\frac{100!}{98!} = \frac{100 \cdot 99 \cdot \cancel{98!}}{\cancel{98!}} = 100 \cdot 99 = 9,900$$

This technique can be used in the next section when determining the permutation of n things taken r at a time.

As an alternative approach to the solution of many permutation problems, you may wish to introduce a diagraming technique. For instance, re-examine Example 2, which asks for the number of possible arrangements of the letters in $\{N, O, W\}$.

Solution:

(1) There are three spaces to be filled: ____ ____ ____

(2) Any of the three letters can be used to fill the first space: 3   ____ ____

(3) After the first space has been filled, two choices remain for the second space: 3 · 2 ____

(4) After the second space has been filled, only one choice remains for the third space: 3 · 2 · 1

Answer: There are $3 \cdot 2 \cdot 1$, or 6 ways: **NOW; NWO; ONW; OWN; WNO; WON.**

You may also wish to introduce a challenge by asking students to consider the same problem with the additional condition that the first letter must be a vowel.

Solution:

(1) There are three spaces to be filled: _____ _____ _____

(2) Since there is only one vowel, **O**, there is only one way to fill the first space: __1__ _____ _____

(3) After **O** has been used, two choices, **N** and **W**, remain for the second space: __1__ · __2__ _____

(4) After a letter has been used in the second space, only one letter remains for the third space: __1__ · __2__ · __1__

Answer: There are 1 · 2 · 1, or 2 ways: **ONW; OWN.**

Note that students can check this answer by referring to part **b** of the solution to Example 2, where all possible arrangements are listed.

You can continue with the original problem and different additional conditions. For example, in how many arrangements will the last letter be a consonant?

Solution:

(1) There are two ways to fill the last space, either with **N** or with **W**: _____ _____ __2__

(2) After the last space has been filled, we turn to the first space. There are two choices, **O** and one consonant, remaining for this choice: __2__ _____ __2__

(3) After the first space has been filled, one letter remains for the second space: __2__ · __1__ · __2__

Answer: There are 2 · 1 · 2, or 4 ways: **OWN; WON; NOW; ONW.**

14-11 MORE ABOUT PERMUTATIONS

In considering arrangements, we do not always include all of the given objects every time. In such cases, when n objects are taken r at a time ($r \leq n$), the counting principle is also applicable. For example, in how many ways can two students be chosen for president and vice president from a class of 30 students? By the counting principle, there are 30 · 29 or 870 possible selections. This can also be written as $_{30}P_2$.

In the text, the general formula for arranging n things r at a time is written as:

$$_nP_r = \frac{n(n-1)(n-2)\ldots}{r \text{ factors}}$$

The general formula for $_nP_r$ can also be written:

$$_nP_r = \frac{n!}{(n-r)!}.$$

Thus, an alternative way of evaluating $_{30}P_2$ is:

$$_{30}P_2 = \frac{30!}{(30-2)!} = \frac{30!}{28!} = \frac{30 \cdot 29 \cdot 28!}{28!}$$
$$= 30 \cdot 29 = 870$$

In this section, three methods are presented whereby permutation can be evaluated on a calculator:

1. Using the multiplication key, $\boxed{\times}$

2. Using the factorial key, $\boxed{x!}$

3. Using the permutation key, $\boxed{_nP_r}$

Although the permutation key is found on many scientific calculators, be aware that it is not a standard feature on all calculators. Students should, however, become familiar with all three methods.

Some mention of the term *combination* might be made at this point, only to show the difference between a combination and a permutation. An in-depth study of combinations is presented in Course II.

14-12 PROBABILITY WITHOUT REPLACEMENT; PROBABILITY WITH REPLACEMENT

Some problems in this section specifically mention *without* replacement or *with* replacement. In some instances, however, no mention is made about replacement. If this is the case, as in Exercise 9, common sense should prevail. Students should be able to determine whether or not replacement occurs in a problem even though this information is not specified.

The evaluation of probabilities with two or more activities is handled in the same manner in these exercises as it was in Sections 14-8 and 14-9, when the concept was introduced.

See *Enrichment Activity 14-12: Expectation.* Expectation, a topic not typically studied at this level, is explained through a simple game. By multiplying each payoff or result by the probability of its occurrence, and then finding the sum of these products, students determine a single ratio. This ratio indicates the amount that a player may expect to win (positive) or lose (negative) over a given number of turns. At first, students experience a losing game. A second game is played using new rules. Eventually, students are asked to write their own rules so that a winning game may occur in a specific number of moves.

Name _____ Class _____ Date _____

ENRICHMENT ACTIVITY 14-3

Probability and a Digital Clock

Each time displayed on a digital clock appears for *exactly 1 minute*. For example, 3:07 is on view for 1 full minute before the time changes.

<u>A 1-Hour Interval</u>   (Beginning at 3:00)

If you look at a digital clock sometime during the hour that begins at 3:00, what is the probability that you will see certain digits in the display? During this hour:

$P(7) = \dfrac{6}{60} = \dfrac{1}{10} = .1$ because the digit 7 appears for exactly 6 of the 60 minutes in this hour (3:07, 3:17, 3:27, 3:37, 3:47, 3:57).

$P(5) = \dfrac{15}{60} = \dfrac{1}{4} = .25$ because the digit 5 appears for exactly 15 of the 60 minutes in this hour (3:05, 3:15, 3:25, 3:35, 3:45, 3:50, 3:51, 3:52, 3:53, 3:54, 3:55, 3:56, 3:57, 3:58, 3:59).

$P(3) = \dfrac{60}{60} = 1$ because 3 is in every digital display for the hour starting at 3:00.

(*These probabilities may be different for an hour starting at a different time.*)

<u>A 24-Hour Interval</u>

Imagine that you look at a digital clock at any random time, day or night.

1. Before you attempt to solve the problems in Exercise 2, answer the following questions by *guessing:*

    a. Which of the ten digits (0, 1, 2, 3, 4, 5, 6, 7, 8, 9) will appear most often in a display on a digital clock? _____

    b. What is the probability that the digit named in part **a** appears in the display? _____

    c. Which digit appears the second most often in the clock display? _____

    d. What is the probability that the digit named in part **c** appears in the display? _____

2. Use *patterns and counting techniques* to find each probability in this exercise. If you look at a digital clock at any time over a period of 24 hours, what is the probability that the given digit is in the display?

    a. $P(0) =$ _____   b. $P(1) =$ _____   c. $P(2) =$ _____   d. $P(3) =$ _____   e. $P(4) =$ _____

    f. $P(5) =$ _____   g. $P(6) =$ _____   h. $P(7) =$ _____   i. $P(8) =$ _____   j. $P(9) =$ _____

3. Write some observations based on your answers to Exercise 2. (How good were the guesses you made in Exercise 1 when compared to your answers in Exercise 2?)

4. If you use *any* 12-hour interval of time rather than a 24-hour period, will your answers to Exercise 2 be different? If yes, explain how. If no, explain why.

Name _____ Class _____ Date _____

Probability and Area: And, Or, Not

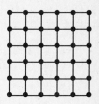

When a grid of 25 small squares is drawn, as shown at the right, the vertical and horizontal lines intersect to form lattice points. Regions can be drawn within this grid, and the areas of these regions can be found. The grid itself contains an *infinite* number of points.

In 1–3, a shaded region, *D*, is drawn on each grid. Find the probability, in each case, that *any* point within this grid: **a.** lies in region *D*, written as *P(D)* **b.** does not lie in region *D*, written *P(not D)*.

1.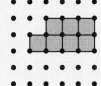

   a. *P(D)* _____

   b. *P(not D)* _____

2.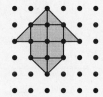

   a. *P(D)* _____

   b. *P(not D)* _____

3.

   a. *P(D)* _____

   b. *P(not D)* _____

4. Write two observations about the regions in Exercises 1–3 and the probabilities you found.

_____

_____

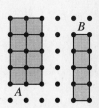

For the grid of lattice points at the right, $P(A) = \dfrac{8}{25}$ and $P(B) = \dfrac{4}{25}$.

Since these regions are disjoint, we see that:

$$P(A \text{ and } B) = 0, \quad \text{and} \quad P(A \text{ or } B) = \frac{12}{25}$$

Name _____ Class _____ Date _____

In 5-7: **a.** Draw regions A and B so that $P(A) = \dfrac{8}{25}$, $P(B) = \dfrac{4}{25}$, and the given value of $P(A$ and $B)$ is true. **b.** Find the value of $P(A$ or $B)$.

5. a. $P(A$ and $B) = \dfrac{2}{25}$

b. $P(A$ or $B) =$

6. a. $P(A$ and $B) = \dfrac{3}{25}$

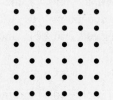

b. $P(A$ or $B) =$

7. a. $P(A$ and $B) = \dfrac{4}{25}$

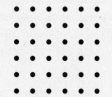

b. $P(A$ or $B) =$

8. Describe two different ways to find $P(A$ and $B)$ in Exercises 5–7.

_____

_____

9. For the grid of 25 squares, shown at the right, if $P(A) = \dfrac{8}{25}$ and $P(B) = \dfrac{4}{25}$, is it possible for $P(A$ and $B) > .16$? If yes, draw the regions. If no, explain why.

_____

Name _____ Class _____ Date _____

ENRICHMENT ACTIVITY 14-9

Probability on a Dart Board

A dart board, consisting of concentric circles that overlap, has a diameter of 10 inches. The center circle, called the bull's-eye, has a diameter of 2 inches, and the width of each ring is 1 inch.

The total area of the dart board equals $\pi r^2 = \pi(5)^2 = 25\pi$.

1. Find, in terms of π, the area of the:

   a. bull's-eye _____   **b.** small white ring _____

   c. small black ring _____   **d.** large white ring _____   **e.** largest black ring _____

   (*Hint:* The sum of these five areas must equal 25π.)

2. A person with poor aim throws a dart at the board. The probability that the dart lands randomly in a region is defined as the ratio of the area of that region to the total area of the dart board. Express, either as a fraction in simplest form or as a decimal, each of the following probabilities:

   a. $P(\text{bull's-eye}) =$ _____   **b.** $P(\text{small white ring}) =$ _____

   c. $P(\text{small black ring}) =$ _____   **d.** $P(\text{large white ring}) =$ _____

   e. $P(\text{large black ring}) =$ _____

Use the probabilities found in Exercise 2 to answer Exercises 3 and 4.

3. A dart is thrown at the board and lands in the region described. Find the probability of each event.

   a. $P(\text{any white ring}) =$ _____   **b.** $P(\text{any black ring}) =$ _____

   c. $P(\text{any black region}) =$ _____   **d.** $P(\text{not in the bull's-eye}) =$ _____

   e. $P(\text{not in either of the two large rings}) =$ _____

4. Our friend with poor aim throws two darts that land in the regions described. Find the probability of each event.

   a. $P(\text{both in white rings}) =$ _____   **b.** $P(\text{both in black rings}) =$ _____

   c. $P(\text{both in the bull's-eye}) =$ _____   **d.** $P(\text{neither in the bull's-eye}) =$ _____

   e. $P(\text{both in the largest ring}) =$ _____   **f.** $P(\text{neither in the largest ring}) =$ _____

   g. $P(\text{at least one in the bull's-eye}) =$ _____

   h. $P(\text{neither in the two largest rings}) =$ _____

Name _____ Class _____ Date _____

ENRICHMENT ACTIVITY 14-12

Expectation

Play the game described here for six or more turns before answering any question on this sheet.

   Materials needed: A marker (such as paper clip) and a standard die.

   Rules: • Place the marker in the box labeled START.
   • With each turn, first guess the number (1, 2, 3, 4, 5, or 6) that will appear when you roll the die.
   • Roll the die.
   • If the number you guessed appears, move three spaces to the right (positive direction). If your number does not appear, move one space to the left (negative direction).

LOSE							START							WIN

After you have played the game, answer these questions.

1. For each roll: **a.** Did you expect to move to the right or to the left?
   b. In which direction did you move?

2. To find the **expectation** in this game, written E(game), fill in the missing parts of the formula for expectation, and perform the arithmetic.

   E(game) = P(correct guess) $\times$ (+3) + P(incorrect guess) $\times$ (−1)

    = (   ) (+3) + (   ) (−1)

    =

   E(game) =

3. To understand what expectation means, consider an example. An expectation of $\frac{+4}{6}$ means that, in most cases, you could expect to move four places in a positive direction for every six turns taken. What does the expectation for the game just played indicate?

   _____

4. Let's change the rules. If you make a correct guess, you can now move five spaces to the right. If you make an incorrect guess, you still move one space to the left.

   a. What is the expectation using these rules? **b.** What does this expectation mean?

5. Write some new rules so that a player of this game would *expect to win* in an average of 24 turns, not in fewer turns and not in more turns.

SUGGESTED TEST ITEMS (CHAPTER 14)

1. Evaluate each of the following:
   a. $4!$ **b.** $7!$ **c.** $_5P_5$ **d.** $_5P_3$ **e.** $\dfrac{9!}{8!}$

2. If the probability that it will snow tomorrow is 30%, what is the probability that it will *not* snow?

3. Two students from a class of 12 boys and 8 girls are chosen at random. What is the probability that the students chosen are:
   a. both boys?   **b.** both girls?   **c.** a boy and a girl?

4. In how many different orders can six persons line up to board a bus?

5. Marcy has a reading list of 12 books. In how many different orders can she choose three of the books?

6. Marcy has a reading list of 12 biographies and five historical novels. In how many different ways can she choose two books, one biography and one historical novel from the list?

7. Two cards are drawn at random from a standard deck of 52 cards. What is the probability that both cards are aces?

8. In how many ways can the letters of the word EQUALITY be arranged?

9. If $P(A) = .7$, $P(B) = 5$, and $P(A \cap B) = .3$, what is the value of $P(A \cup B)$?

10. If two fair six-sided dice are tossed, what is the probability that the faces that turn up show a sum of 9?

11. Four fair coins are tossed simultaneously.
    a. Show the sample space by a tree diagram or by listing.
    b. What is the total number of outcomes in the sample space?
    c. What is the probability of the coins showing two heads and two tails?
    d. What is the probability of the coins showing at least one head?

12. The probability of drawing a red marble from a sack that contains only red and green marbles is $\dfrac{1}{4}$. After 10 red marbles are removed from the sack, the probability of drawing a red marble from the sack is $\dfrac{1}{6}$. How many red and how many green marbles were in the sack before the red marbles were removed?

13. Adam, Bert, Clara, Doris, Elaine, and Flora are members of the school choir. One will be chosen at random to sing the opening solo, and a second to sing the closing solo, at the spring concert. Each is equally likely to be chosen for the solos.
    a. Draw a tree diagram or list the sample space of possible pairs of choir members who could be chosen.
    b. What is the probability that two boys are chosen?
    c. What is the probability that one boy and one girl are chosen?
    d. What is the probability that Bert is *not* chosen?

14. The letters of the word BEGIN are arranged at random.
    a. How many arrangements are possible?
    b. How many arrangements that begin with a vowel are possible?
    c. What is the probability that an arrangement chosen at random begins with a vowel?

BONUS: Grace is playing a game in which she needs to advance exactly 15 spaces in order to win. The number of spaces that she must advance is determined by rolling a die. What is the probability that she will win in three turns?

SAT PREPARATION EXERCISES (CHAPTER 14)

I. Multiple-Choice Questions

In 1-12, select the letter of the correct answer.

1. In Central High, there is one administrator for 10 teachers and one teacher for 25 students. If k represents the number of students, which of the following represents the number of administrators?

    (A) $\dfrac{25k}{10}$ (B) $250k$ (C) $\dfrac{k}{250}$

    (D) $\dfrac{10k}{25}$ (E) $\dfrac{10}{25k}$

2. A bowl contains only red and black marbles. There are x red marbles, with 2 more black marbles than red. If a marble is selected at random, what is the probability that it will be black?

    (A) $\dfrac{2}{x}$ (B) $\dfrac{x}{x+2}$ (C) $\dfrac{x}{2x+2}$

    (D) $\dfrac{x+2}{2x+2}$ (E) $\dfrac{2}{x+2}$

3. Set P is $\{2, 3, 5\}$ and set Q is $\{6, 10, 15\}$. If one element is selected at random from set P and another from set Q, what is the probability that the element from set P will be a divisor of the element from set Q?

    (A) 1 (B) $\dfrac{1}{6}$ (C) $\dfrac{2}{3}$

    (D) $\dfrac{1}{2}$ (E) $\dfrac{1}{3}$

4. A student answers 3 multiple-choice questions by random guessing. Each question has 1 correct answer and 3 incorrect answers. What is the probability that the student will get all three questions wrong?

    (A) $3\left(\dfrac{3}{4}\right)$ (B) $\left(\dfrac{1}{4}\right)^3$ (C) $3\left(\dfrac{3}{4}\right)^3$

    (D) $\left(\dfrac{3}{4}\right)^3$ (E) $\left(\dfrac{1}{3}\right)^3$

5. There are 3 black marbles in a bowl containing a total of x marbles. If one marble is drawn at random, not replaced, and another is drawn at random, what is the probability that both marbles will be black?

    (A) $\dfrac{6}{x^2-x}$ (B) $\dfrac{3x}{x^2-x}$ (C) $\dfrac{x}{3x-3}$

    (D) $\dfrac{2x}{3x-3}$ (E) $\dfrac{x}{3(x-3)}$

6. If each operation is performed at random without a calculator in evaluating the numerical expression $3 + (5)(10) - 4$, what is the probability that the answer obtained will be correct?

    (A) $\dfrac{1}{6}$ (B) $\dfrac{1}{3}$ (C) $\dfrac{1}{2}$

    (D) $\dfrac{2}{3}$ (E) $\dfrac{1}{4}$

7. A red spinner has consecutive integers from x to $x + 3$ inclusive, and a blue spinner has consecutive integers from y to $y + 4$. Each spinner is equally likely to land on any numbered space. How many elements are in the sample space representing the number pairs possible using one number from each spinner?

    (A) 9 (B) 12 (C) 15

    (D) 20 (E) $(x + 3)(y + 4)$

8. A car travels a distance of 60 miles; the first half at 30 mph and the second half at 60 mph. If a headlight is equally likely to burn out at any time during the trip, what is the probability that it will burn out during the first 30 miles?

    (A) $\dfrac{1}{4}$ (B) $\dfrac{1}{3}$ (C) $\dfrac{1}{2}$

    (D) $\dfrac{2}{3}$ (E) 1

9.

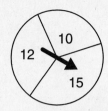

The three regions on the spinner above are *unequal* in size. Let x represent the number of the region on which the arrow lands in a single spin. If $P(x$ is a multiple of 3$) = \dfrac{4}{5}$, and $P(x$ is a multiple of 5$) = \dfrac{3}{5}$, determine $P(x$ is a multiple of 2$)$.

(A) $\dfrac{1}{5}$ (B) $\dfrac{2}{5}$ (C) $\dfrac{3}{5}$

(D) $\dfrac{4}{5}$ (E) $\dfrac{7}{5}$

10.

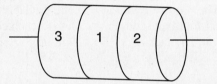

The wheels above rotate independently on an axis, and each wheel is divided into three equal sections labeled with the digits 1, 2, and 3. If the spinning wheels are stopped at random to form a 3-digit number, what is the probability that the number will be a multiple of three?

(A) $\dfrac{1}{9}$ (B) $\dfrac{2}{9}$ (C) $\dfrac{3}{9}$

(D) $\dfrac{4}{9}$ (E) 1

11. If a number P is selected at random from $\{4, 5, 6\}$ and another number Q is selected at random from the remaining numbers in the set, what is the probability that $x^2 = Px + Q$ can be factored into two binomials when x represents any real number?

(A) 0   (B) $\dfrac{1}{2}$ (C) $\dfrac{1}{3}$

(D) $\dfrac{1}{4}$ (E) $\dfrac{1}{6}$

12. A number x is selected at random from:
$\{2, 3, 4, 5, 6, 8, 9, 10, 11, 12\}$
The probability that x is a multiple of 3 is twice as great as which of the following?

(A) $P(x$ is even)   (B) $P(x$ is odd)

(C) $P(x$ is prime)   (D) $P(x$ is square)

(E) $P(x$ is negative)

II. Quantitative Comparison Questions

Questions 13-20 each consist of two quantities, one in Column A and one in Column B. You are to compare the two quantities and choose:

A if the quantity in Column A is greater;

B if the quantity in Column B is greater;

C if the two quantities are equal;

D if the relationship cannot be determined from the information given.

Notes

1. In certain questions, information concerning one or both of the quantities to be compared is centered above the two columns.

2. In a given question, a symbol that appears in both columns represents the same thing in Column A as it does in Column B.

3. Letters such as x, n, and k stand for real numbers.

Column A	*Column B*
13.	A single card is selected at random from a standard deck of cards.
The probability that the card selected will be a king	The probability that the card selected will be a heart

14.   A fair six-sided die is tossed.

| The probability that the number 4 will be obtained with one toss | The probability that the same numbers will be obtained with two tosses |

---

15. P(both heads), if two fair coins are tossed   P(all heads), if three fair coins are tossed

---

16.   A bank containing only quarters and nickels is shaken until a coin falls out.

| The probability a 25¢ coin falls out | The probability a 5¢ coin falls out |

17.

2   3   5   7

At random, 2 of the 4 cards above are selected. The product of the numbers is recorded.

P(product is even)   P(product is odd)

18.

The spinner above has three equal regions: 1, 2, 3. The arrow is spun *twice* and the sum of the numbers is recorded.

P(sum is even)   P(sum is odd)

19.

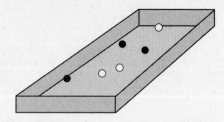

| The probability of drawing a black marble after one black marble has been removed | The probability of drawing a white marble after one black marble has been added |

---

20.   An urn contains 5 white balls and 7 black balls. Four balls are drawn at random.

| The probability that all four balls chosen will be black | The probability that two of each color will be chosen |

III. Student-Produced Response Questions

In 21-25, you are to solve the problem.

21. If $P(x)$ equals the probability that a number x is drawn at random from the set $\left\{0, \frac{1}{4}, \frac{1}{2}, \frac{3}{4}\right\}$, evaluate $P(x)$ when $P(x) = P\left(\frac{1}{2}\right) + P\left(\frac{1}{4}\right)$.

22. If a bowl contains 5 white and 7 black balls and one is drawn from the bowl, what is the probability that the ball is green?

23. Marie first chooses one of four numbers from the set $\{1, 2, 3, 6\}$, at random. She then chooses one of two numbers from the set $\{1, 5\}$, at random. What is the probability that she will choose the same number on both tries?

24. A display of 10 yellow, 5 red, and 25 blue lights is tested for longevity. Each light is equally likely to burn out first. What is the probability that the first light to burn out will be yellow?

25. A number is selected at random from the set {1, 2, 3, 4, 5, 6, 7, 8, 9}. What is the probability that the number chosen will be either less than 4 or an odd number?

Chapter 15
Statistics

Aims

- To determine the steps necessary to conduct a statistical study.
- To organize data using tables.
- To present data graphically using a histogram or a whisker-box plot.
- To determine measures of central tendency.
- To understand the meaning of quartiles and percentiles.

The sections of this chapter lead the student through the steps of a statistical study. As each step is studied, this manual suggests that students participate in an actual statistical study by collecting, organizing, and presenting in tables and graphs data related to some topic of their choice. At each step of the process, classroom discussion should be used as a means of helping the students to understand the implications of their study.

Although the use of data to predict future trends and to assess the reliability of a sample may be discussed, the statistical procedures for such analysis are not studied at this course level.

15-1   COLLECTING DATA

In this section, students are introduced to the first step of any statistical study, the collection of data. Ask students if they have ever taken part in a survey. Were the data collected carefully and accurately? Can we trust statistical reports in which no mention is made of the collection of data?

In the exercises, the difference between fair and biased sampling is highlighted. A discussion of these exercises should lead to an understanding of the reliability of data in particular cases.

The following activity is the first step of an ongoing project that can be used as the assessment tool for this chapter. The project can be done individually, in groups of three to five students, or as a project for the entire class.

Hands-On Activity (Part 1)

Instructions:
Collect data for a statistical study.

1. Decide the nature of the study. What data will you collect?
2. Decide how the data are to be collected. What will be the source(s) of the data?
   a. Questionnaires
   b. Personal interviews
   c. Telephone interviews
   d. Published material such as almanacs and newspapers.
3. Collect the data. How many data values are necessary to obtain reliable information?

Students should select their own topics for this activity. However, if students have difficulty in making a selection, the following list of suggestions may be helpful.

1. How accurately can the ordinary person estimate 1 inch?

   Ask each respondent to draw, without the
   use of a measurement device, a line 1 inch
   long. Measure the lines drawn, and record
   the lengths to the nearest tenth or to the
   nearest quarter of an inch.

2. What is the average high temperature for the
   place in which you live or in some large city
   for a given period of time?

   Record daily high temperatures for a given
   number of days, or use the temperatures
   recorded in the newspaper or on TV.

3. How much television does the ordinary person
   watch in 1 week?

   Use in your survey persons of all ages, or
   choose a particular age bracket to study.

4. How many movies does the ordinary person
   watch in 1 month?

   Use in your survey persons of all ages, or
   choose a particular age bracket to study.

5. How many points does the best basketball
   player on your school team score in a game?

   Record the number of points that the star
   player scores in every game.

15-2 ORGANIZING DATA

Once the data of a statistical study have been
carefully collected, they must be organized into a
table or a stem-and-leaf diagram. Discuss the rules
for grouping data, and explain that there are many
ways to set up tables for the same set of data values.

Many students have difficulty in determining
the intervals to use in grouping data. Let students
suggest ways to group a set of data, and write their
suggestions on the chalkboard. Have the class
examine these methods by applying such criteria
as the following: Has the range been covered?
Does it matter whether we arrange the intervals in
ascending or descending order? Are there too
many intervals? Too few? Which of the suggested
methods display the data most effectively?

Hands-On Activity (Part 2)

Instructions:
Organize the data collected in Part 1.

1. Organize the data into a frequency table.
   a. The following questions will guide you in
      selecting intervals.
      How many intervals will be used?
      What will be the length of each interval?
      What are the starting and ending points of
      each interval?
      Do these intervals overlap?
      Are the intervals equal in size?
      Does every data value fall into one
      interval?
   b. Tally the data values.
   c. List the frequency of each interval.
   d. Check that the total frequency equals the
      number of data values in the data collected.

2. Organize the data into a stem-and-leaf
   diagram.
   a. Decide what will be used as the stems.
   b. Decide what will be used as the leaves.
   c. Construct the diagram.
   d. Check that the number of leaves in the
      diagram equals the number of data values
      in the data collected.

3. Decide which method of organization is better for your data. Explain your answer.

15-3 THE HISTOGRAM

A histogram is a bar graph in which the height of
the bar represents the frequency. Other types of
graphs or diagrams can display data in a similar
manner.

For example, dots can be used to show the number of times the letter "e" occurs in English words.
Ask each student to open a book, choose a line of
type at random, and count the number of times that
the letter "e" occurs in that line. Draw a horizontal
axis on a large sheet of paper, and list, at evenly
spaced intervals, the integers from 0 to the largest
number of occurrences. Then have each student
place a gummed paper dot above the number of *e*'s in

his/her line, arranging those that represent the same number of *e*'s one above another in a vertical display. The resulting diagram shows the frequency distribution of the data and can easily be made to resemble a histogram by enclosing the dots with bars.

Graphing calculators have the ability to draw a histogram. For example, use a graphing calculator to construct a histogram for the heights, in inches, shown below.

Height (inches)	Frequency
75 – 79	8
70 – 74	14
65 – 69	32
60 – 64	27
55 – 59	11
50 – 54	8

On the TI-81:
First clear previous data.

Enter:

Enter the data shown in the table. Use the midpoint of each interval as the typical height for that interval. Enter the midpoint as *x* and the frequency as *y*.

Enter: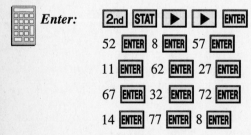

After the data have been entered, set the range. In order to leave some space before and after the histogram, add an extra interval at the beginning and end of the heights. Set the minimum value of *x* at 45 and the maximum value of *x* at 84. Since the bars are to be of width 5, set Xscl at 5. Set the minimum value of *y* at -1 and the maximum value of *y* at 35

or any number larger than the greatest frequency, 32. Set Yscl at 1. Then draw the histogram.

Enter:

On the TI-82:
First clear previous data from the lists.

Enter: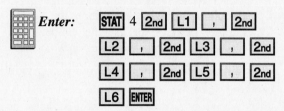

Enter the data values in list 1. Use the midpoint of each interval as the typical height for that interval. Enter the frequency in list 2.

Enter: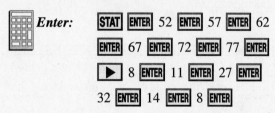

Now turn on plot 1, select the histogram logo, L1 for Xlist, and L2 for frequency.

Enter: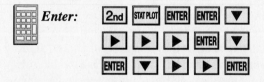

Finally, set the window to appropriate values as described for the TI-81, and graph the histogram.

Enter:

When the ungrouped data are entered, accept 1 as the *y* value after each *x* value on the TI-81 or highlight 1 for frequency on the TI-82.

Hands-On Activity (Part 3)

Instructions:

Use the organized data from Part 2 to draw a histogram.

1. Choose for the horizontal axis a scale that will allow you to display each interval of your data.

2. Mark the endpoints of the intervals, and label each interval with its value or range of values.

3. Place a title under the horizontal axis to tell what the values of the intervals represent.

4. Choose for your vertical axis a scale that will allow you to display the largest frequency.

5. Label the vertical axis with the scale and the title "Frequency."

6. Draw the bar to represent the frequency of each interval.

15-4 THE MEAN, THE MEDIAN, AND THE MODE

Because of broad popular use of the word *average* and confusion about its meaning, more precise terms are used in the study of statistics. In this section three measures of central tendency are introduced: the mean, the median, and the mode. As students learn the procedures to determine each of these measures for a given set of data, they should discuss the question of when one measure of central tendency may prove to be more representative than another for the data presented.

The sets of data in the text are deliberately kept small in order to provide simple exercises. Students should understand that, for such sets of data, the mode is not considered a significant measure of central tendency.

Graphing calculators, as well as some scientific calculators, have the capability of finding the mean of a set of numbers. Suppose, for example, that the problem is to find the mean of the following set of numbers: 12, 9, 15, 8, 13, 5, 16, 10, 6, 14.

On the TI-30X:

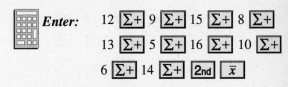

Enter: 12 $\boxed{\Sigma+}$ 9 $\boxed{\Sigma+}$ 15 $\boxed{\Sigma+}$ 8 $\boxed{\Sigma+}$ 13 $\boxed{\Sigma+}$ 5 $\boxed{\Sigma+}$ 16 $\boxed{\Sigma+}$ 10 $\boxed{\Sigma+}$ 6 $\boxed{\Sigma+}$ 14 $\boxed{\Sigma+}$ $\boxed{2nd}$ $\boxed{\bar{x}}$

Display: | 10.8 |

On the TI-81:
First clear previous data.

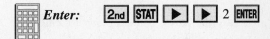

Enter: $\boxed{2nd}$ $\boxed{STAT}$ $\boxed{\blacktriangleright}$ $\boxed{\blacktriangleright}$ 2 $\boxed{ENTER}$

Then enter the new data. Enter the data values as x and the frequencies as y. Since each data value occurs only once, accept the value 1, which is already entered, as the value of y.

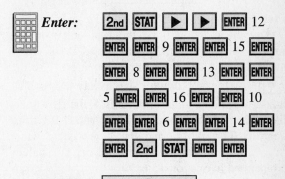

Enter: $\boxed{2nd}$ $\boxed{STAT}$ $\boxed{\blacktriangleright}$ $\boxed{\blacktriangleright}$ $\boxed{ENTER}$ 12 $\boxed{ENTER}$ $\boxed{ENTER}$ 9 $\boxed{ENTER}$ $\boxed{ENTER}$ 15 $\boxed{ENTER}$ $\boxed{ENTER}$ 8 $\boxed{ENTER}$ $\boxed{ENTER}$ 13 $\boxed{ENTER}$ $\boxed{ENTER}$ 5 $\boxed{ENTER}$ $\boxed{ENTER}$ 16 $\boxed{ENTER}$ $\boxed{ENTER}$ 10 $\boxed{ENTER}$ $\boxed{ENTER}$ 6 $\boxed{ENTER}$ $\boxed{ENTER}$ 14 $\boxed{ENTER}$ $\boxed{ENTER}$ $\boxed{2nd}$ $\boxed{STAT}$ $\boxed{ENTER}$ $\boxed{ENTER}$

Display: | $\bar{x} = 10.8$ |

Note that the symbol for mean is $\bar{x}$ and that this is just one of the statistical results displayed on the screen. The display also tells us that the sum of the data values is 108 ($\Sigma x = 108$) and that there are 10 data values ($n = 10$). The other values listed on this screen are useful in more advanced statistics courses.

On the TI-82:
First clear previous data from the lists.

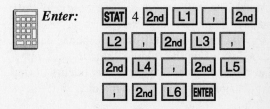

Enter: $\boxed{STAT}$ 4 $\boxed{2nd}$ $\boxed{L1}$ $\boxed{,}$ $\boxed{2nd}$ $\boxed{L2}$ $\boxed{,}$ $\boxed{2nd}$ $\boxed{L3}$ $\boxed{,}$ $\boxed{2nd}$ $\boxed{L4}$ $\boxed{,}$ $\boxed{2nd}$ $\boxed{L5}$ $\boxed{,}$ $\boxed{2nd}$ $\boxed{L6}$ $\boxed{ENTER}$

Enter the data in list 1.

Enter: STAT ENTER 12 ENTER 9 ENTER 15

ENTER 8 ENTER 13 ENTER 5 ENTER 16

ENTER 10 ENTER 6 ENTER 14 ENTER

Set up the use of the information by identifying Xlist as L1 and Freq as 1.

Enter: STAT ▶ 3 ENTER ▼ ENTER

Now, use the keys listed below to calculate (Calc) one-variable statistics (1-Var Stats).

Enter: STAT ▶ ENTER ENTER

Display: $\bar{x} = 10.8$

The mean ($\bar{x}$) will be the first entry on the screen. At the bottom of the screen is an arrow indicating that there is more information. Use the

▼ key to scroll down. The display tells us that the smallest data value (minX) is 5, the first quartile (Q1) is 8, the median (Med) is 11, the third quartile (Q3) is 14, and the largest data value (maxX) is 16. The first and third quartile values are studied in Section 15-6.

See ***Enrichment Activity 15-4: Locating the Median Value.***

15-5 MEASURES OF CENTRAL TENDENCY AND GROUPED DATA

The mean of grouped data in intervals of length greater than 1 has not been addressed in the text. The true mean can be obtained only from raw data. For large sets of data, however, an approximate value for the mean can be obtained by using the middle value in each interval in place of each data value that occurs in that interval. For example, given the data in the first

two columns of the following table, the mean can be determined as shown below.

Interval	Frequency, f	Midpoint, x	fx		
16–19	5	17.5	5(17.5)	=	87.5
20–23	11	21.5	11(21.5)	=	236.5
24–27	8	25.5	8(25.5)	=	204.0
28–31	5	29.5	5(29.5)	=	147.5
32–35	7	33.5	7(33.5)	=	234.5
36–39	3	37.5	3(37.5)	=	112.5
40–43	1	41.5	1(41.5)	=	41.5
	$N = 40$			Sum	= 1,064

$$\text{Approximate mean} = \frac{1{,}064}{40} = 26.6$$

A spreadsheet (see the following examples) offers a convenient way of performing this computation. Enter the lower endpoint of each interval in column A, the upper endpoint in column B, and the frequency in column C. Next, enter in column D a formula to compute x (the midpoint of column A and column B) and in column E a formula to compute fx (the product of column C and column D). Then sum the entries in column C and the entries column E. The mean is the sum of column E divided by the sum of column C, which can be displayed in column F.

The formats for entering the sum formulas may vary on different spreadsheets. On most spreadsheets, after the formulas have been entered in D2 and E2, they can be copied into the rows below, with the spreadsheet automatically adjusting the row reference. The following spreadsheet displays the formulas.

	A	B	C	D	E	F
1	Lower Endpoint	Upper Endpoint	Frequency f	Midpoint x	fx	Mean
2	16	19	5	(A2 + B2)/2	C2 • D2	
3	20	23	11	(A3 + B3)/2	C3 • D3	
4	24	27	8	(A4 + B4)/2	C4 • D4	
5	28	31	5	(A5 + B5)/2	C5 • D5	
6	32	35	7	(A6 + B6)/2	C6 • D6	
7	36	39	3	(A7 + B7)/2	C7 • D7	
8	40	43	1	(A8 + B8)/2	C8 • D8	
9			SUM(C2..C8)		SUM(E2..E8)	E9/C9

When the formulas are replaced by the numerical values, the spreadsheet displays the results of the computations.

	A	B	C	D	E	F
1	Lower Endpoint	Upper Endpoint	Frequency f	Midpoint x	fx	Mean
2	16	19	5	17.5	87.5	
3	20	23	11	21.5	236.5	
4	24	27	8	25.5	204.0	
5	28	31	5	29.5	147.5	
6	32	35	7	33.5	234.5	
7	36	39	3	37.5	112.5	
8	40	43	1	41.5	41.5	
9			40		1064.0	26.6

The spreadsheet provides a simple way of investigating how the mean changes when the frequencies change or when new data values are added. For example, have students consider the following: How is the mean affected if every frequency is doubled? If every data value is doubled? If 10 new data values are added to the 40–43 interval? If 10 new data values are added to the 24–27 interval?

Hands-On Activity (Part 4)

Instructions:
Find the mean, median, and mode for your grouped data from Part 2.

1. Use the number of values in your data to determine how far from either end of the data the median lies.
   a. If your data are organized into intervals of length 1, find the median.
   b. If your data are organized into intervals of a length other than 1, find the interval in which the median lies.

2. Find the interval with the largest frequency.
   a. If your data are organized into intervals of length 1, find the mode.
   b. If your data are organized into intervals of a length other than 1, find the modal interval.

3. Find the mean.
   a. If your data are organized into intervals of length 1, find the mean by using the data value for each interval.
   b. If your data are organized into intervals of a length other than 1, find the mean by using the midpoint of each interval as the typical data value for that interval.

15-6 QUARTILES, PERCENTILES, AND CUMULATIVE FREQUENCY

Students have taken many different standardized tests in school, such as achievement tests and IQ tests. The scores for these tests are reported in terms of student performance relative to that of other students who took the same test. Students should understand the meaning of these scores. What does it mean if a student's score is at the lower quartile or the 85th percentile?

Quartile scores and percentile scores, as determined by the standard method, are not always the same. For large sets of data, the first quartile and the 25th percentile are usually the same, as are the third quartile and the 75th percentile. However, for small sets of data, such as the ones with which we work in this chapter, and for sets of data in which one value occurs a large number of times, the number that is the first quartile may not be the 25th percentile and the number that is the third quartile may not be the 75th percentile. This happens because the method of determining quartile values is not the same as the method of determining percentile rank.

For example, consider the following set of numbers: 0, 1, 1, 1, 1, 1, 1, 2, 3, 5. The median is 1 because 50% of the scores are 1 or less. The lower quartile is also 1 because 25% of the scores are 1 or less than 1. To have an exact percentile rank for 1, we include exactly half of the six 1's in the lower set and half in the upper set when determining percentile rank. Thus there are four data values in the lower set: 0 and three of the 1's. Since $\frac{4}{10} = 0.4$, the percentile rank of 1 is 40.

Hands-On Activity (Part 5)

Instructions:
For your grouped data from Part 2:

1. Prepare a cumulative frequency table.
2. Draw a cumulative frequency histogram.
3. Find the lower quartile value.
4. Find the upper quartile value.
5. Draw a whisker-box plot.

Name _____ Class _____ Date _____

ENRICHMENT ACTIVITY 15-4

Locating the Median Value

A set of five data values is arranged in order: 17, 24, 25, 38, 95.

When you count from the smallest value up, the median is the 3rd number:

17,　24,　㉕,　38,　95

1　　2　　3　　4　　5

When you count from the largest value down, the median is the 3rd number:

17,　24,　㉕,　38,　95

5　　4　　3　　2　　1

Thus, for five data values arranged in numerical order, the median is the 3rd value whether counting from the smallest number up or the largest number down.

Now, imagine that another set of data is arranged in numerical order. Counting from the smallest value up or from the largest value down, tell which value is the median if the set contains:

a. 7 values _____　　**b.** 9 values _____　　**c.** 15 values _____

d. 39 values _____　　**e.** 81 values _____　　**f.** 237 values _____

g. N values (where N is odd) _____

A set of six data values is arranged in order: 9, 11, 12, 14, 25, 38.

When you count from the smallest value up, the median is the mean (average) of the 3rd and 4th numbers:

9,　11,　12,　14,　25,　38

1　　2　　3　　4　　5　　6

$$\text{Median} = \frac{12 + 14}{2} = 13$$

When you count from the largest value down, the median is the mean (average) of the 3rd and 4th numbers:

9,　11,　12,　14,　25,　38

6　　5　　4　　3　　2　　1

$$\text{Median} = \frac{12 + 14}{2} = 13$$

Thus, for six data values in numerical order, the median is the mean of the 3rd and 4th values whether counting from the smallest number up or the largest number down.

Name _____ Class _____ Date _____

Now, imagine that another set of data is arranged in numerical order. Counting from the smallest value up or from the largest value down, tell which values are averaged to obtain the median if the set contains:

h. 8 values _____   **i.** 10 values _____   **j.** 18 values _____

k. 42 values _____   **l.** 88 values _____   **m.** 230 values _____

n. N values (where N is even) _____

Finally, write a rule for finding the median of a set of N numbers in numerical order. Your rule should have two parts, one for when N is odd and the other for when N is even.

SUGGESTED TEST ITEMS (CHAPTER 15)

1. The weights, in grams, of 10 apples are 123, 134, 127, 130, 127, 129, 127, 128, 137, and 128.
   Determine: **a.** the mean **b.** the median **c.** the mode

2. The mean of five consecutive odd integers is 55. What are the integers?

3. Amanda's scores on four spelling tests were 85, 93, 88, and 81. What was her score on a fifth test if the mean of the five scores was 86?

4. A butcher prepared 12 packages of ground beef that had a mean weight of 1.2 pounds. How much ground beef did he use?

5. What is the mode for the following set of numbers: 2, 5, 4, 5, 3, 6, 5, 2, 3, 6, 7, 5, 3, 5, 7, 6, 5?

6. What is the value of x if the mean and the mode of the following set of numbers are equal: 12, 15, 13, 15, 17, 15, x?

7. Express, in terms of a, the mean of $3a - 1$, $5a + 2$, and $a - 7$.

8. The students in Mrs. Collin's class were absent the following numbers of days during a 5 week period: 0, 2, 1, 4, 1, 6, 1, 0, 1, 5, 0, 5, 0, 4, 5, 4, 1, 0, 2, 1, 1, 0, 0, 1, 3.

   a. Organize the data into a table showing frequency and cumulative frequency. Use intervals of 1 day, starting with 0.

   b. Draw a frequency histogram. **c.** Draw a cumulative frequency histogram.

   d. What is the median number of days absent? **e.** What is the mean number of days absent?

   f. What is the number of days that is the lower quartile?

   g. What is the number of days that is the upper quartile?

   h. What is the probability that a student chosen at random from this class was absent for 5 days?

   i. What is the probability that a student chosen at random from this class was absent for 3 days?

   j. What is the probability that a student chosen at random from this class was absent fewer than 10 days?

9. Borje has recorded the number of calories in the food that he ate during the last 40 days. The table at the right shows his data.

   a. Construct a cumulative frequency histogram.

   b. In what interval does the median lie?

   c. In what interval does the lower quartile lie?

   d. In what interval does the upper quartile lie?

Calories	Frequency
1,950–1,999	2
1,900–1,949	9
1,850–1,899	11
1,800–1,849	7
1,750–1,799	3
1,700–1,749	5
1,650–1,699	2
1,600–1,649	0
1,550–1,599	1

SAT PREPARATION EXERCISES (CHAPTER 15)

I. Multiple-Choice Questions

In 1-13, select the letter of the correct answer.

1. Fifty chickens can lay 1,000 eggs in 30 days. At the same rate, how long would it take 25 chickens to lay 500 eggs?

   (A) 15 days (B) 20 days (C) 30 days

   (D) 60 days (E) 80 days

2. If the mean of x and y is z, and the mean of p and q is r, what is the mean of x, y, p, and q?

   (A) $2(z + r)$ (B) $z + r$ (C) $\dfrac{z + r}{2}$

   (D) $\dfrac{z + r}{4}$ (E) $\dfrac{2zr}{4}$

Questions 3 and 4 refer to the following graph.

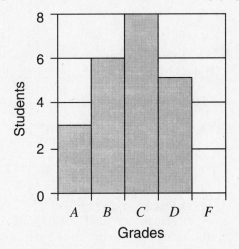

3. The partially completed graph above is a frequency distribution for students that received passing grades A, B, C, and D on a mathematics test. If the class contained 25 students, how many students received a failing grade?

   (A) 4 (B) 3 (C) 2

   (D) 1 (E) 0

4. If a student is selected at random from those with a passing grade, what is the probability that the student will receive a B or higher?

   (A) $\dfrac{6}{25}$ (B) $\dfrac{6}{22}$ (C) $\dfrac{9}{25}$

   (D) $\dfrac{9}{22}$ (E) $\dfrac{8}{25}$

5. Select the set of scores for which the following is true:
   mode < mean, and mean < median

   (A) 80, 80, 80, 82, 83

   (B) 80, 80, 82, 82, 82

   (C) 80, 80, 82, 83, 84

   (D) 80, 82, 82, 82, 83

   (E) 80, 80, 80, 82, 84

Questions 6 and 7 refer to the following graph.

CUMULATIVE FREQUENCY HISTOGRAM

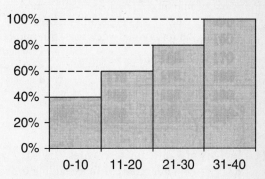

6. Based on the cumulative frequency histogram above, which interval contains the median?

   (A) 0-10 (B) 11-20 (C) 21-30

   (D) 31-40 (E) 21-40

7. A teacher assigned letter grades based on the number of questions each student answered incorrectly on a test. If values in the interval 0-10 are assigned the grade A, values in 11-20 are assigned B, 21-30 assigned C, and 31-40 assigned D, what grade is the mode?

   (A) A (B) B (C) C

   (D) D (E) Cannot be determined

8. The average (arithmetic mean) of 80, 83, 89, and x is the same as the average of 80, 83, and 86. What is the average of 82 and x?

   (A) 80   (B) 81   (C) 82

   (D) 83   (E) 84

9. The average (arithmetic mean) of 3 positive numbers x, y, and z is 15. If $y = 10$, what is the value of $x + z$?

   (A) 5   (B) 15   (C) 35

   (D) 45   (E) 50

10. A list of numbers 2, 4, 8, . . . is formed by doubling each of the preceding numbers. What is the remainder when the 15th number is divided by 6?

    (A) 0   (B) 2   (C) 4

    (D) 6   (E) 8

11. In a list of 7 different test scores, 75, 80, ____, 82, ____, 89, 90, arranged in ascending order, two scores have been erased. Which of the following can *not* be the average (arithmetic mean)?

    (A) 82   (B) $82\frac{6}{7}$ (C) 83

    (D) $83\frac{1}{7}$ (E) $83\frac{4}{7}$

Questions 12 and 13 refer to the following table and information.

	John	Jack	Jane
Running	3	0	1
Biking			
Swimming			

The score card above shows the scores for a running competition. The scores for the biking and swimming competitions have not yet been determined. Each of the three athletes competed in all three competitions. Winning a competition earns 3 points and second place earns 1 point.

12. The points for each of the three competitions were added together to determine each athlete's total score. Which of the following represents an impossible total score for any of the three athletes?

    (A) 1   (B) 4   (C) 5

    (D) 8   (E) 9

13. If Jane does better than John in biking, and John does best in swimming, which of the following could be the totals for John, Jack, and Jane, respectively?

    (A) 4, 5, 3   (B) 4, 3, 5   (C) 6, 2, 4

    (D) 7, 2, 3   (E) 9, 7, 3

14. p: The average of x, y, and 8 is 5.
         q: The sum of x and y is 8.
    Based on statements p and q above, which of the following must be true for all values of x and y?

        I. $p \rightarrow q$
        II. $p \rightarrow \sim q$
        II. $\sim p \rightarrow q$

    (A) I only   (B) II only

    (C) III only   (D) II and III only

    (E) I, II and III

II. Quantitative Comparison Questions

Questions 15-19 each consist of two quantities, one in Column A and one in Column B. You are to compare the two quantities and choose:

A if the quantity in Column A is greater;
B if the quantity in Column B is greater;
C if the two quantities are equal;
D if the relationship cannot be determined from the information given.

Notes

1. In certain questions, information concerning one or both of the quantities to be compared is centered above the two columns.
2. In a given question, a symbol that appears in both columns represents the same thing in Column A as it does in Column B.
3. Letters such as x, n, and k stand for real numbers.

Column A	*Column B*

15.

$$3 + x = y$$

The average (arithmetic mean) of 3, 4, and x	The average (arithmetic mean) of 8, 9, and y

---

16. 30, 40, 50, 30, 30

mode	arithmetic mean

17.

Three times the average (arithmetic mean) of two positive numbers	The sum of the same two numbers

18.

$$p \text{ and } q > 0$$
$$p + q = 14$$

average of p and q	$\dfrac{p + q + 13}{3}$

19.

$$r = 4 - s$$

$\dfrac{r + s}{2}$	$\dfrac{1}{2}$

III. Student-Produced Response Questions

In questions 20 and 21, you are to solve the problem.

20.

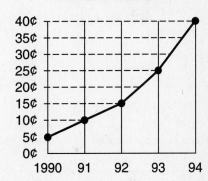

ANNUAL CHARGES

Which year did charges increase by the greatest percent?

21.

Grade	A	B	C	D	F
Students	4		10	8	4

The chart above shows how some students in a class performed on a test. If 90% of the class passed (got a D or better), then how many more students received a B than an A?

Chapter *16*

Graphing Linear Functions and Relationships

Aims

- To find ordered pairs of numbers that are solutions of an algebraic equation or inequality in two variables.
- To graph a linear equation using solutions of the equation or the slope and the y-intercept of the equation.
- To represent direct variation graphically.
- To write an equation of a line by using one point and the slope of the line, or by using two points.
- To graph linear inequalities.
- To graph equations involving absolute value.

This chapter connects algebra and geometry by showing how a line can be used to display the solution set of a linear equation in two variables. The concept of function is introduced in an intuitive manner to indicate that the value of one variable is determined by or is dependent on the value of the other. A more formal definition of function will be presented in more advanced courses.

The chapter introduction presents a common situation arising when we make use of a service. Cost, which is the sum of a basic fee plus an additional charge, depends on the length of time for which we made use of the service. Students should be able to provide other examples in which the value of one quantity depends on that of another.

While it is important that students be able to graph a linear function using paper and pencil, the graphing calculator presents a unique opportunity

for students to explore relationships. Many of the Hands-On Activities for this chapter suggest ways of using the calculator for this purpose.

16-1   SOLUTIONS OF OPEN SENTENCES IN TWO VARIABLES

Students are familiar with procedures for finding the solution set of an open sentence in one variable. Most of the equations they have solved have been first-degree equations in one variable with one element in the solution set. Now, the solution sets of open sentences in two variables, in which each solution can be written as an ordered pair, are examined. The solution set may contain an infinite or a finite number of ordered pairs, depending on the replacement set required by the conditions of the problem.

When finding solutions of an open sentence in two variables, it is recommended that the sentence be transformed into an equivalent one that has y alone on one side (that is, that the sentence be solved for y). This approach makes it easier to use substitution for each element of the replacement set.

Students need to be reminded that multiplication or division of both sides of an inequality by a negative number reverses the inequality. Encourage students to check some ordered pairs of the solution set in the original equation or inequality.

Hands-On Activity

Instructions:

Use a TI-82 calculator to make a table of solutions for an equation in two variables.

1. Solve the equation for y, and enter the expression in terms of x as Y_1 in the $\boxed{Y=}$ menu.

2. Choose a starting value for x and some positive value by which to change (or increment) the values of x. Enter these values as TblMin and ΔTbl in the $\boxed{\text{TblSet}}$ menu. Highlight Auto for both Indpnt and Depend in this menu.

3. Press $\boxed{\text{2nd}}$ $\boxed{\text{TABLE}}$ keys to display a table of values for x and y.

4. Use the $\boxed{\blacktriangledown}$ and $\boxed{\blacktriangle}$ keys to scroll to larger and smaller values of x.

For example, to display a table of ordered pairs in the solution set of $3x + y = 17$, proceed as follows:

1. Solve the equation for y:
$$3x + y = 17$$
$$y = 17 - 3x$$

2. *Enter:* $\boxed{Y=}$ 17 $\boxed{-}$ 3 $\boxed{\text{X,T,}\theta}$ $\boxed{\text{ENTER}}$

3. *Enter:* $\boxed{\text{2nd}}$ $\boxed{\text{TblSet}}$ 1 $\boxed{\text{ENTER}}$
   0.5 $\boxed{\text{ENTER}}$ $\boxed{\blacktriangledown}$ $\boxed{\text{ENTER}}$

4. *Enter:* $\boxed{\text{2nd}}$ $\boxed{\text{TABLE}}$

   Display:

X	Y_1	
1	14	
1.5	12.5	
2	11	
2.5	9.5	
3	8	
X = 1		

5. Ordered pairs of the solution set are shown with the values of x in the first column and the values of y in the second column. Use $\boxed{\blacktriangledown}$ and $\boxed{\blacktriangle}$ to scroll to other pairs of values.

16-2 GRAPHING LINEAR FUNCTIONS USING THEIR SOLUTIONS

In this section, students are introduced to the graphs of first-degree equations in two variables that can be written in the form $Ax + By + C = 0$. Although two points determine a line, stress that it is advisable to plot three or more points to be sure the graph is correct.

Again, it is recommended that an equivalent equation with y alone on one side be used to construct the table of values. Remind students that, when the domain is the set of signed numbers, any signed number may be used as a value for x. However, it is convenient to choose values of x so that both numbers in the resulting solution will be integral. For example, when finding solutions of the equation $y = \frac{3}{4}x - 2$, choose multiples of 4 for x in order that the corresponding values of y will be integral.

Hands-On Activity

Instructions:

Use a graphing calculator to draw a graph, and compare the calculator screen with a hand-drawn graph.

1. Solve the equation for y, and enter the expression in terms of x and Y_1 in the $\boxed{Y=}$ menu.

2. Set the range or window, that is, the maximum and minimum values of x and of y that will appear on the screen. On the TI-81, an Xmin of -4.7 and an Xmax of 4.8 will display the values of x in tenths. Set the Ymin at -3.1, and the Ymax at 3.1. On the TI-82, use an Xmin of -4.7, an Xmax of 4.7, and a Ymax of 3.1. On the TI-82, this window will be set automatically by choosing 4: ZDecimal in the $\boxed{\text{ZOOM}}$ menu.

3. Graph the function.

4. Use [TRACE] with [▶] and [◀] to display coordinates of the points on the line.

For example, to display the graph of $2x + y = 2$, proceed as follows:

1. Solve the equation for y:
$$3x + y = 2$$
$$y = 2 - 3x$$

2. *Enter:* [Y=] 2 [−] 3 [X,T,θ] [ENTER]

3. On the TI-82,

   Enter: [ZOOM] 4

   On the TI-81,

   Enter: [RANGE] [(−)] 4.7 [ENTER] 4.8
   [ENTER] 1 [ENTER] [(−)] 3.2
   [ENTER] 3.2 [ENTER] 1 [ENTER]

4. *Enter:* [GRAPH]

   Display:

   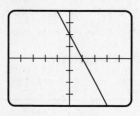

5. *Enter:* [TRACE]

   (Use [◀] and [▶] to move to different points on the graph.)

What if, after following these steps, no graph appears on the screen? For example, to display the graph of $y = 14 - 2x$, in step 2:

Enter: [Y=] 14 [−] 2 [X,T,θ] [ENTER]

Do steps 3 and 4 as shown above. No graph will be displayed on the screen, however, because the graph is outside the window of the calculator. Do step 5, pressing [▶] until the graph begins to appear on the screen.

Note the new range or window of the graph. The Xmin and Xmax will have changed to larger values of x. Change the Ymax to larger values of y.

On the TI-82,

Enter: [WINDOW] [ENTER] [(−)] 0.7 [ENTER]
8.7 [ENTER] 1 [ENTER] [(−)] 3.2
[ENTER] 16 [ENTER] 2 [ENTER]

On the TI-81,

Enter: [WINDOW] [ENTER] [(−)] 0.7 [ENTER]
8.7 [ENTER] 1 [ENTER] [(−)] 3.2
[ENTER] 16 [ENTER] 2 [ENTER]

Now, repeat steps 4 and 5.

Display:

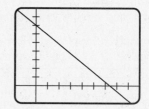

16-3 GRAPHING A LINE PARALLEL TO AN AXIS

In earlier chapters, an equation such as $x = 2$ was graphed as a point on a number line. If we wish to graph such an equation in the coordinate plane, any point whose abscissa is 2 satisfies the equation, since no restriction has been placed on y, and y can have any value. Thus, the graph of $x = 2$ is an infinite set of points, a vertical line 2 units to the right of the y-axis.

Since every point that lies on the x-axis has an ordinate of 0, the equation of the x-axis is $y = 0$. Similarly, since the abscissa of each point is 0 on the y-axis, the equation of the y-axis and $x = 0$.

Elicit that an equation of the line that passes through (3, 5) and (−2, 5), for example, is $y = 5$, and that such a line, one in which the ordinate of every point is the same, is parallel to the x-axis.

You might present some of the exercises in another form, and even extend them. For example, another way to present Exercise 16a is: Write an equation of the line that is parallel to the x-axis and that passes through point $(0, 1)$. Then extend this problem from a point that is on an axis to a point that is in the plane: Write an equation of the line that is parallel to the x-axis and that passes through point $(2, 1)$. Note with the class that the same equation, $y = 1$, is an answer for the original question and the two related questions.

16-4 THE SLOPE OF A LINE

Students should recognize the various expressions that represent the slope of a line, such as m, $\frac{\Delta y}{\Delta x}$, and $\frac{y_2 - y_1}{x_2 - x_1}$. They should be able to use the given definition of slope, the ratio of the vertical change to the horizontal change, to compute slopes, and they should be able to identify lines that have positive slopes, negative slopes, zero slope, and no slope.

Remind students, especially when they are working with negative values in computing slopes, that the subtractions to obtain Δy and Δx must be performed in the same order. Either of the two given points may be selected as the first point, and the other as the second point. Thus, the slope of the line containing $(-1, 4)$ and $(7, -3)$, for example, can be computed in either of the following ways:

$$\frac{4 - (-3)}{-1 - 7} = \frac{4 + 3}{-8} = \frac{7}{-8}$$

$$\frac{-3 - 4}{7 - (-1)} = \frac{-7}{7 + 1} = \frac{-7}{8}$$

Point out that $\frac{7}{-8}$ and $\frac{-7}{8}$ are each equivalent to $-\frac{7}{8}$.

The equivalence of fractions is particularly important for students to recognize when they are trying to graph a line by the point-slope method. Example 2 shows that, starting at point $(2, -1)$, we draw the line whose slope is $\frac{3}{2}$ by moving 3 units upward and 2 units to the right to obtain another point on the line. Since $-\frac{3}{2}$ is equivalent to $\frac{-3}{-2}$, we

could also get from one point to another on this line by moving 3 units downward and 2 units to the left.

16-5 THE SLOPE-INTERCEPT FORM OF A LINEAR EQUATION

Given the equation $2y = 4x - 6$, students sometimes state that the slope is 4 and the y-intercept is 6. The equation must be solved for y in terms of x so that it is in slope-intercept form, however, before we can read the slope and y-intercept directly from the equation.

After some practice with nonzero slopes, ask for the general form of a linear equation whose slope is 0. Show that $y = mx + b$, or $y = 0 \cdot x + b$, becomes $y = b$ for such an equation. Can a line with no slope, such as the graph of $x = 5$, be represented by an equation of the form $y = mx + b$? Note that this slope-intercept form cannot be used when the slope m is undefined.

The statement that two lines are parallel if and only if their slopes are equal is presented without proof. This case was investigated in Exercise 29 in Section 16-4. A graphing calculator can be used to demonstrate the truth of the statement.

Hands-On Activity

Instructions:
Use a graphing calculator to draw the graphs of several equations that have the same slope.

1. On a graphing calculator, graph four equations that have the same slope. For example, use $y = 2x - 3$, $y = 2x - 1$, $y = 2x + 1$, and $y = 2x + 3$. Do the graphs appear to be parallel?

2. On a graphing calculator, graph another four equations that have the same slope. For example, use $y = -x - 3$, $y = -x - 1$, $y = -x + 1$, and $y = -x + 3$. Do the graphs appear to be parallel?

3. On a graphing calculator, graph four equations that do *not* have the same slope. For example, use $y = 2x - 3$, $y = x - 1$,

$y = -2x + 1$, and $y = -x + 3$. Do the graphs appear to be parallel?

4. Does it appear that lines are parallel if and only if their slopes are equal?

16-6 GRAPHING LINEAR FUNCTIONS USING THEIR SLOPES

The use of the slope-intercept method of graphing an equation reinforces the meaning of the terms *slope* and *y-intercept*.

Remind students that, when the slope is an integer, it can be written as a ratio with a denominator of 1. For example, a slope of 3 can be written as the ratio $\frac{3}{1}$, as well as equal ratios $\frac{6}{2}$, $\frac{9}{3}$, etc.

Mention again that a negative ratio can be considered to be the ratio of a positive number to a negative one, or the ratio of a negative number to a positive one. For example, $-\frac{2}{3}$ can be thought of as $\frac{-2}{3}$ or as $\frac{2}{-3}$. Have students use both forms to convince themselves that the use of either form will give points on the same line.

Since the y-intercept of the graph of a linear function is not always an integer, the use of the slope-intercept method can result in inaccurate graphs. Exercises 25–27 are designed to help students see that sometimes a point other than the y-intercept can be the starting point for this method of graphing an equation.

Students should be encouraged to check their work by choosing some point on the graph and substituting its coordinates in the given equation.

16-7 WRITING AN EQUATION OF A LINE

The slope and the y-intercept can be used to write an equation of a line. In Section 16-5 these two values were given. In this section, either the slope and some point on the line other than the y-intercept, or two points on the line, are given.

Students are required to write an equation of a line parallel to a given line and passing through a particular point. Slopes of perpendicular lines are not considered at this level.

In Exercises 16 and 17, information is given that can be written as the coordinates of two points on the line that is the graph of the required equation. Have students use the coordinates of these two points and the method of this section to write the equation.

16-8 GRAPHING DIRECT VARIATION

The graph of two variables that vary directly is a straight line through the origin. Simple, familiar examples of direct variation are used in this section to show how slope and the constant of variation are related. (The topic of direct variation was first considered in Section 13-5.)

The equations $\frac{y}{x} = 3$ and $y = 3x$ are not always equivalent. Although all of the solutions of $\frac{y}{x} = 3$ are also solutions of $y = 3x$, $(0, 0)$ is a solution of $y = 3x$ but not of $\frac{y}{x} = 3$.

Discuss with students when $(0, 0)$ is or is not a solution for a problem. For example, when the number of cups of lemonade (y) that can be made from x cups of frozen concentrate can be expressed as $y = 3x$, the set of non-negative numbers is a reasonable domain and range. One possible solution is that 0 cup of lemonade can be made from 0 cup of concentrate. However, when $y = 3x$ describes the relationship between the perimeter of an equilateral triangle (y) and the measure of one of its sides (x), the set of positive numbers is a reasonable domain and range. The solution set does not include $(0, 0)$.

The text stresses that it is important to be aware of the unit being used in a relationship. Note that, since a ratio compares two quantities that are measured in the *same unit*, the resulting ratio is independent of the unit used (lemonade problem: ratio is 3). However, since a rate compares two quantities of different types, the rate changes with the unit used (cereal-box problem:

rate can be expressed as $\frac{1}{6}$ carton/second or as 10 cartons/minute). Elicit how cancellation can be used to convert 10 cartons per minute to $\frac{1}{6}$ carton per second:

$$\frac{10 \text{ cartons}}{\text{minute}} \cdot \frac{1 \text{ minute}}{60 \text{ seconds}} = \frac{10}{60} \frac{\text{cartons}}{\text{seconds}} = \frac{1}{6} \frac{\text{carton}}{\text{second}}$$

16-9 GRAPHING FIRST-DEGREE INEQUALITIES IN TWO VARIABLES

The graph of any equation in the form $y = mx + b$ divides the coordinate plane into three sets of points: the set of points on the line, the set of points in the half-plane above the line, and the set of points in the half-plane below the line. Therefore, a half-plane that is the graph of $y > mx + b$ must lie above the line $y = mx + b$ for the given values of m and b.

What above the graph of $x > -2$? Since the plane divider, the graph of $x = -2$, is a vertical line, the solution set is the half-plane to the right. The half-plane to the left represents the graph of $x < -2$.

Stress that a test point should be selected to check whether the correct half-plane had been chosen. Make sure that the test point is not on the line. It is convenient to choose (0, 0) as the test point because it simplifies the computation. Before students shade in the appropriate half-plane, have them check to see whether the plane divider belongs to the graph of the open sentence (solid line) or does not belong to the graph (dashed line).

Hands-On Activity

Instructions:
Use a graphing calculator to display the graph of a linear inequality.

1. Enter the equation of the line that is the plane divider as Y_1 in the `Y=` menu.

2. Select 7: Shade (in the `2nd` `DRAW` menu.

3. Since Shade (will be copied to the home screen, follow left parentheses by at least two restraints. The first restraint is the lower

boundary, and the second restraint is the upper boundary, of the area to be the shaded. To shade the area below the plane divider, enter some constant value that is less than Ymin as the first restraint and Y_1, the plane divider, as the second restraint. To shade the area above the plane divider, enter Y_1, the plane divider, as the first restraint and some constant value that is greater than Ymax as the second restraint.

4. Enter an optional Xres, a whole number from 1 to 8, to vary the distance between lines of shading. The default value if this number is not included is 1, which fills in the entire region.

For example, to draw the graph of $y > 2x - 3$, proceed as follows:

On the TI-81,

Enter: `Y=` 2 `X T` `—` 3 `ENTER`

Enter: `2nd` `DRAW` 7

Enter: `2nd` `Y-VARS` `ENTER` `ALPHA` `,` 10 `ALPHA` `,` 2 `)` `ENTER`

On the TI-82,

Enter: `Y=` 2 `X,T,θ` `—` 3 `ENTER`

Enter: `2nd` `DRAW` 7

Enter: `2nd` `Y-VARS` `ENTER` `ENTER` `,` 10 `,` 2 `)` `ENTER`

Display:

To draw the graph of $y < 2x - 3$, replace the third line shown above for each calculator as follows:

On the TI-81,

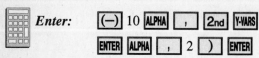

Enter: (−) 10 ALPHA , 2nd Y-VARS
ENTER ALPHA , 2) ENTER

On the TI-82,

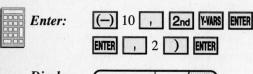

Enter: (−) 10 , 2nd Y-VARS ENTER
ENTER , 2) ENTER

Display:

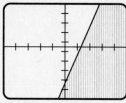

16-10 GRAPHS INVOLVING ABSOLUTE VALUE

This section presents some absolute-value equations for which the graphs consist of rays or segments of lines. This material may be considered optional.

Enrichment Activity 16-10: Graphing Step Functions introduces a common pricing situation in which cost is based on an integral value of time or weight. When this is the case, a graph that shows cost consists of a series of horizontal lines. Ask students to suggest other, similar situations. For example, the cost of mailing a letter depends on the weight of the letter rounded up to the next ounce, and the library fine for an overdue book depends on the number of days the book is overdue, with the number of days always considered to be an integer.

Name _____ Class _____ Date _____

ENRICHMENT ACTIVITY 16-10

Graphing Step Functions

In the city parking garage, the following rates are in effect:
$4.00 for the first hour or part of an hour.
$2.00 for each additional hour or part of an hour.
The maximum charge for 24 hours is $40.00.

a. Complete the following table showing the costs for 12 cars each of which left the parking garage after the given number of hours.

Hours	Cost	Hours	Cost	Hours	Cost
$\frac{1}{4}$		2		$17\frac{3}{4}$	
$\frac{2}{3}$		$2\frac{1}{4}$		18	
1		6		19	
$1\frac{1}{2}$		$12\frac{1}{2}$		$20\frac{1}{3}$	

b. Complete the following table showing the costs for 8 cars that went in and out of the parking garage at the given times.

Time In	Time Out	Cost	Time In	Time Out	Cost
9:15 A.M.	9:50 A.M.		10:00 A.M.	2:30 P.M.	
9:30 A.M.	10:29 A.M.		10:10 A.M.	10:00 P.M.	
9:30 A.M.	10:35 A.M.		12:15 P.M.	8:00 A.M.	
10:00 A.M.	12:45 P.M.		12:45 P.M.	11:00 A.M.	

c. Draw a graph to show the cost, y, of parking a car for x hours ($0 < x < 24$). (*Hint:* The graph will consist of a series of horizontal segments that look like this: ○———●.)

d. How would the graph change if, after the first hour, a person was charged a fractional part of $2.00 for a fractional part of an hour—if, for example, parking for $1\frac{3}{4}$ hours cost $4.00 + \frac{3}{4}$ ($2.00)?

SUGGESTED TEST ITEMS (CHAPTER 16)

1. Is $(3, -1)$ a solution of the equation $2x - y = 5$?

2. What is the value of k such that $(-1, k)$ is a point on the graph of $2x - y = 3$?

3. Graph each of the following equations:
   a. $y = -2x + 4$ **b.** $x - 2y = 6$ **c.** $x = 3$ **d.** $y = -4$

4. Write an equation of the line whose slope is 3 and whose y-intercept is -1.

5. The perimeter (y) of a regular pentagon varies directly as the length of one side (x).
   a. What is the constant of variation if $y = 10$ when $x = 2$?
   b. Using the result of part **a**, write an equation for y in terms of x.
   c. Draw the graph of the equation written in part **b**.
   d. What is the slope of the line drawn in part **c**?

6. Determine the slope and y-intercept for each of the following equations:
   a. $y = 2x + 1$ **b.** $x + y = 7$ **c.** $x - 2y = 6$ **d.** $y = 3$

7. Write an equation of the line through the point $(0, 2)$ that is parallel to the line whose equation is $y = 3x - 1$.

8. Write an equation of the line through points $(-2, 3)$ and $(-2, 0)$.

9. The sum of the ordinate and twice the abscissa of a point is greater than or equal to 2.
   a. Write the sentence as an inequality.
   b. Graph the inequality written in part **a**.

10. What is the slope of the line through points $(2, 2)$ and $(4, -4)$?

11. **a.** Graph points $A(-1, 0)$, $B(5, 0)$, and $C(2, 4)$ and draw $\triangle ABC$.
    b. If $\overline{CD}$ is the altitude to $\overline{AB}$, what are the coordinates of D?
    c. What is the length of AB?
    d. What is the length of CD?
    e. What is the area of $\triangle ABC$?
    f. What is an equation of the line of symmetry of $\triangle ABC$?

12. The population, y, of a small town is increasing each year by a constant number of people. Let x equal the number of years from the present year. Two years ago $(x = -2)$, the population was 210 $(y = 210)$. This year $(x = 0)$ the population is 220 $(y = 220)$.
    a. Write an equation that can be used to find the population of the town at any time x years from now.
    b. Draw the graph of the equation in part **a** from $x = -10$ (10 years ago) to $x = 10$ (10 years in the future).
    c. Assume that the population change has been consistent over the past 10 years. Then:
    (1) What was the population 5 years ago?
    (2) When did the town have a population of 175?
    d. Assume that the population change continues in the future. Then:
    (1) What will be the population of the town in 8 years?
    (2) When will the population reach 275?

13. Sketch the graph of $|y| = |x + 2|$.

BONUS: One vertex of a rectangle is at $(1, 2)$, and the point of intersection of the diagonals is at $(5, 4)$. What are the coordinates of the other vertices of the rectangle if two sides of the rectangle are parallel to the x-axis?

SAT PREPARATION EXERCISES (CHAPTER 16)

I. Multiple-Choice Questions

In 1–10, select the letter of the correct answer.

1. If $(0, 1)$ and $(3, 7)$ are both points on the graph of line m, which of the following points also lies on the graph of line m?

(A) $(3, 8)$ (B) $(3, 1)$ (C) $(2, 6)$

(D) $(2, 4)$ (E) $(1, 3)$

2. Line k passes through the point $(3, 7)$. If line k has no slope, then k must pass through which of the following points?

(A) $(7, 3)$ (B) $(3, 0)$ (C) $(0, 7)$

(D) $(0, 0)$ (E) $(-3, -7)$

3.

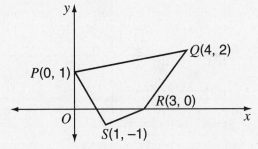

In the figure above, which segment has the greatest slope?

(A) $\overline{PQ}$ (B) $\overline{QR}$ (C) $\overline{RS}$

(D) $\overline{PS}$ (E) Cannot be determined

4. The triangle formed by the intersection of lines $x = 1$, $y = -2$ and $x + y = 5$ can be classified as which one of the following?

(A) acute and scalene
(B) obtuse and scalene
(C) acute and isosceles
(D) right and isosceles
(E) equilateral

5. Which is an equation of the line that passes through $(1, p)$ and the origin?

(A) $x = py$ (B) $y = px$

(C) $y = x + p$ (D) $y = x - p$

(E) $y = px + 1$

6.

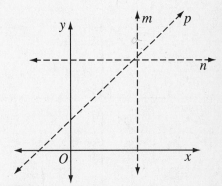

In the figure above, the equation of m is $x = 3$, and the equation of n is $y = 4$, which of the following could *not* be the equation of line p?

(A) $x = y - 2$ (B) $x - y = -1$

(C) $y = \dfrac{2x}{3} + 2$ (D) $y = 2x - 2$

(E) $2y = x + 5$

7. If $(2, 3)$ is a point on the graph of $3x + ky = -9$, then which of the following points is also on the line?

(A) $(-3, 1)$ (B) $(0, -3)$ (C) $(3, 2)$

(D) $(4, 6)$ (E) $(7, 6)$

8. Triangle ABC is isosceles, with A at $(1, 1)$ and B at $(5, 1)$. Which of the following could *not* be point C?

(A) $(1, -3)$ (B) $(1, 5)$ (C) $(3, -2)$

(D) $(3, 3)$ (E) $(5, -5)$

9. Quadrilateral *ABCD* is a square with vertex *A* at (2, 3).

> *p:* The area of *ABCD* is 25.
> *q:* Point *C* is (7, 8).

Based on the statements above, which of the following must be true?

(A) $p \wedge q$ (B) $p \rightarrow q$ (C) $p \rightarrow \sim q$

(D) $p \leftrightarrow q$ (E) $q \rightarrow p$

Notes

1. In certain questions, information concerning one or both of the quantities to be compared is centered above the two columns.

2. In a given question, a symbol that appears in both columns represents the same thing in Column A as it does in Column B.

3. Letters such as *x*, *n*, and *k* stand for real numbers.

10.

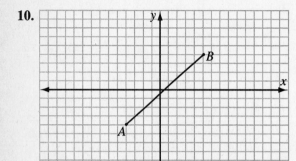

In the figure above, points *A, B* and *C* (not shown) form a triangle. The slope of line segment *AC* is $\frac{1}{3}$ and the slope of line segment *BC* is -2. What are the coordinates of point *C*?

(A) (6, −2)   (B) (5, 0)   (C) (3, −5)

(D) (3, −7)   (E) (0, 6)

II. Quantitative Comparison Questions

Questions 11–17 each consist of two quantities, one in Column A and one in Column B. You are to compare the two quantities and choose:

A if the quantity in Column A is greater;
B if the quantity in Column B is greater;
C if the two quantities are equal;
D if the relationship cannot be determined from the information given.

	<u>*Column A*</u>	<u>*Column B*</u>

11. $y - 3x = 2$

The slope of the equation above	The *y*-intercept of the equation above

12.

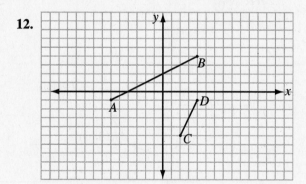

The slope of line segment *AB*	The slope of line segment *CD*

13. | The slope of the line that passes through the points (7, 2) and (4, 1) | 1 |
|---|---|

14. $2y = -3x + 1$

The slope of the equation above	The *y*-intercept of the equation above

15.

$$x = 1$$
$$y = -2$$
$$x + y = 5$$

| The area of the tri-angle formed by the three lines above | 15 |

16.

$$s > t$$

| The absolute value of $s - t$ | The absolute value of $t - s$ |

17.

$$x > z$$
$$z < y$$

| x | y |

III. Student-Produced Response Questions

In 18– 23, you are to solve the problem.

18.

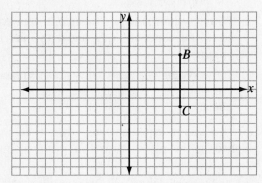

In the figure above, points A (not shown), B, and C form a triangle. The slope of line segment AC is zero and the slope of line segment AB is $\frac{3}{4}$. What is the length of line segment AB?

19.

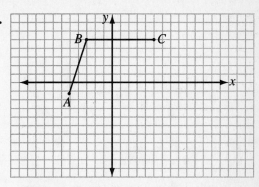

In the figure above, points A, B, C and D (not shown) form a quadrilateral. The slope of line segment AD is zero and the slope of line segment CD is -3. What is the area of the quadrilateral?

20. If $x^2 < 4$ and $x > 0$, what is one possible value of x?

21. If a 32-meter pole is broken into two parts at a ratio of 3 to 5, what is the measure, in meters, of the longer of the two parts?

22. Charlie can mow the lawn in 24 minutes, and Sally can mow the same lawn in 15 minutes. How many minutes will it take them to mow the lawn together?

23. The recipe Jeanmarie uses to make bread requires rice flour and whole wheat flour in the ratio 1:3. How many cups of rice flour would she need if she decides to use 12 cups of whole wheat flour?

Chapter 17

Systems of Linear Open Sentences in Two Variables

Aims

- To solve linear systems in two variables, graphically and algebraically.

- To graph the solution sets of systems of inequalities.

- To solve verbal problems by using a pair of simultaneous equations in two variables.

This chapter introduces linear systems of equations and inequalities and presents both graphic and algebraic approaches to the solution of a system. The text presents simple systems of two equations and inequalities in two unknowns.

Students are presented first with a graphic approach to a solution. As the need for a more exact method of solution becomes apparent, the algebraic methods of addition and substitution are examined. Verbal problems, in which two variables can be identified, are solved using systems of equations.

17-1 USING A GRAPH TO SOLVE A SYSTEM OF LINEAR EQUATIONS

Students should understand that the solution set of a system of linear equations may have one ordered pair (consistent equations, represented by two lines that intersect), no ordered pairs (inconsistent equations, represented by two parallel lines), or an infinite number of ordered pairs (dependent equations, represented by two lines that coincide).

You may wish to encourage students to rewrite each equation in the form $y = mx + b$. In this way, the type of solution set that will be obtained should become apparent before the lines are graphed:

1. If the system is a pair of consistent equations, the slopes are unequal.

2. If the system is a pair of inconsistent equations, the slopes are equal and the y-intercepts are unequal.

3. If the system is a pair of dependent equations, the slopes are equal and the y-intercepts are equal.

Only consistent equations will then need to be graphed in the plane to determine the point of intersection.

You may want to teach Section 17-5 next, in order to complete the work with graphic solutions before considering algebraic solutions.

Hands-On Activity

Instructions:
Use a TI-81 or TI-82 calculator to graph a system of linear equations in two variables.

1. Solve each equation for y, and enter the first expression in terms of x as Y_1 and the second expression in terms of x as Y_2 in the $\boxed{Y=}$ menu.

2. Choose an appropriate range of values for x and y, and enter these values as Range on the TI-81 or Window on the TI-82.
3. Graph the equations.
4. Use Trace to find the coordinates of the solution.

For example, to find the solution of this system:
$$3x + y = 9$$
$$x - 2y = -4$$
proceed as follows:

1. Solve each equation for y in terms of x:
$$3x + y = 9 \quad \text{and} \quad x - 2y = -4$$
$$y = 9 - 3x \qquad -2y = -x - 4$$
$$y = \frac{1}{2}x + 2$$

 Enter: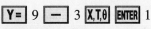

2. On the TI-81,

Enter: [RANGE] [(−)] 4.7 [ENTER] 4.8 [ENTER]
1 [ENTER] [(−)] 4 [ENTER] 10 [ENTER]

On the TI-82,

Enter: [WINDOW] [ENTER] [(−)] 4.7 [ENTER] 4.7
[ENTER] 1 [ENTER] [(−)] 4 [ENTER] 10 [ENTER]

3. *Enter:* [GRAPH]

4. *Enter:* [TRACE]

Use [▶] and [◀] to move to the point of intersection of the two graphs. Read the coordinates at the bottom of the screen.

Display:

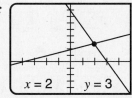

$x = 2 \qquad y = 3$

For additional practice, now graph the system of equations: $y - x = 2$ and $2x + y = 8$ (previously solved graphically on page 604) using steps 1–4 in the instructions above.

17-2 USING ADDITION TO SOLVE A SYSTEM OF LINEAR EQUATIONS

The example in the text in which the solution set of a system of equations is not an ordered pair of integers makes it clear that at times the solution is difficult to read from a graph. In this section, the system of equations is solved algebraically by an addition method: the two equations are written in equivalent forms that have additive inverses as the coefficients of one of the variables. These equations are then added to obtain one equation with one variable.

Mention that this is just one algebraic procedure for solving a system of equations. In the next section, the substitution method is discussed.

Regardless of the method used, the basis of solution is to treat the two equations in two variables simultaneously so that one equation in one variable emerges.

Enrichment Activity 17-2: Determinants and Cramer's Rule explain the use of these concepts to solve a linear system of two equations in two variables.

17-3 USING SUBSTITUTION TO SOLVE A SYSTEM OF LINEAR EQUATIONS

In this section, students learn to solve a system of equations by using the substitution method to eliminate one of the variables. This method is easily applied when a coefficient of one of the variables is 1 or −1. The substitution method appears in a variety of problems studied in Courses II and III, particularly for systems involving equations beyond the first degree.

After students have practiced using the substitution method, they have the opportunity, in Exercises 21–36, to decide which of the two algebraic methods to apply. When going over the homework in class, you may wish to have two different solutions shown for one system.

Enrichment Activity 17-3: Systems with Three Variables requires students to solve systems of three linear equations in three unknowns.

17-4 USING SYSTEMS OF EQUATIONS TO SOLVE VERBAL PROBLEMS

Sometimes it is easier to solve a verbal problem by using two variables rather than one variable. Once a verbal problem is translated into a system of linear equations, the methods used to solve linear systems are applied.

Number problems, geometry problems, and business problems are stressed in this section. Other verbal problems concerning motion, investment, coins, mixture, and the like may also be considered.

Some of the problems presented in Chapter 3 to be solved by a trial-and-error strategy can be easily solved by an algebraic strategy using a system of linear equations. You may want to have students compare the two strategies.

17-5 GRAPHING THE SOLUTION SET OF A SYSTEM OF INEQUALITIES

In Section 16-9, students learned how to graph a linear inequality in two variables. This concept is now extended to graph the solution set of a system of inequalities.

It is helpful to graph a system of inequalities by using either chalk of different colors or shading in different directions to distinguish the regions. Students should be careful when determining boundaries to use a dashed line when the boundary is not included in the region. The coordinates at the intersection of two boundary lines are a pair of the solution set only when both boundaries are solid lines, that is, are included in the solution of the inequalities. Test points should always be points in the interior of the region, not on a boundary line.

If time permits, you may wish to introduce some basic ideas of linear programming as an application of graphing. This area of mathematics is used to solve problems in science and industry.

Hands-On Activity

Instructions:

Use a graphing calculator to display the graph of a system of linear inequalities.

1. Follow the procedure outlined in the Hands-On Activity in Section 16-9 to graph the first inequality, using 2 for the Xres.
2. Follow the same procedure to graph the second inequality, entering the plane divider as Y_2 and using 3 for the Xres.

The graph will show the solution set for each inequality. The shading lines for the first inequality will be more closely spaced than those for the second. The common solution will be the irregularly shaded region.

For example, to graph the common solution of
$$y \geq x - 4$$
$$y \leq -x + 4$$
proceed as follows:

On the TI-81,

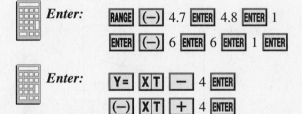

Enter: RANGE (−) 4.7 ENTER 4.8 ENTER 1 ENTER (−) 6 ENTER 6 ENTER 1 ENTER

Enter: Y= X|T − 4 ENTER (−) X|T + 4 ENTER

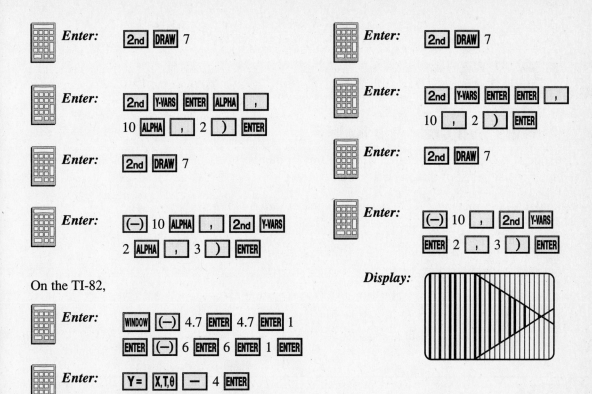

Enter: `2nd` `DRAW` 7

Enter: `2nd` `Y-VARS` `ENTER` `ALPHA` `,`
10 `ALPHA` `,` 2 `)` `ENTER`

Enter: `2nd` `DRAW` 7

Enter: `(−)` 10 `ALPHA` `,` `2nd` `Y-VARS`
2 `ALPHA` `,` 3 `)` `ENTER`

On the TI-82,

Enter: `WINDOW` `(−)` 4.7 `ENTER` 4.7 `ENTER` 1
`ENTER` `(−)` 6 `ENTER` 6 `ENTER` 1 `ENTER`

Enter: `Y=` `X,T,θ` `−` 4 `ENTER`
`(−)` `X,T,θ` `+` 4 `ENTER`

Enter: `2nd` `DRAW` 7

Enter: `2nd` `Y-VARS` `ENTER` `ENTER` `,`
10 `,` 2 `)` `ENTER`

Enter: `2nd` `DRAW` 7

Enter: `(−)` 10 `,` `2nd` `Y-VARS`
`ENTER` 2 `,` 3 `)` `ENTER`

Display:

Name _____ Class _____ Date _____

ENRICHMENT ACTIVITY 17-2

Determinants and Cramer's Rule

A determinant is a number associated with an array of numbers arranged in equal numbers of rows and columns. The simplest of these is a 2×2 array.

In general, the determinant $\begin{vmatrix} a & b \\ c & d \end{vmatrix}$ equals the number $(ad - bc)$.

For example: $\begin{vmatrix} 3 & -2 \\ 5 & 1 \end{vmatrix} = 3(1) - (-2)(5) = 3 + 10 = 13$

$\begin{vmatrix} -5 & 4 \\ 2 & -9 \end{vmatrix} = -5(-9) - (4)(2) = 45 - 8 = 37$

$\begin{vmatrix} 6 & 2 \\ 9 & 3 \end{vmatrix} = 6(3) - (2)(9) = 18 - 18 = 0$

EXAMPLE

Use determinants to solve the following system: $\quad 3x + y = 9$
$\qquad\qquad\qquad\qquad\qquad\qquad\qquad\qquad x - 2y = -4$

Solution:

(1) Write each equation in the form $ax + by = c$.

(2) Evaluate determinant D, whose entries are the coefficients of x and y:

$$D = \begin{vmatrix} 3 & 1 \\ 1 & -2 \end{vmatrix} = 3(-2) - (1)(1) = -6 - 1 = -7$$

(3) Evaluate determinant D_x by replacing the first column of D, the coefficients of x, by the constant terms:

$$D_x = \begin{vmatrix} 9 & 1 \\ -4 & -2 \end{vmatrix} = 9(-2) - (1)(-4) = -18 + 4 = -14$$

(4) Evaluate determinant D_y by replacing the second column of D, the coefficients of y, by the constant terms:

$$D_y = \begin{vmatrix} 3 & 9 \\ 1 & -4 \end{vmatrix} = 3(-4) - (9)(1) = -12 - 9 = -21$$

(5) Use D, D_x, and D_y to find the solution of the system:

$$x = \frac{D_x}{D} = \frac{-14}{-7} = 2 \qquad y = \frac{D_y}{D} = \frac{-21}{-7} = 3$$

Answer: $\quad -x = 2, y = 3$

Name _____ Class _____ Date _____

The use of determinants to solve a system of linear equations is an application of Cramer's Rule.

For a system of two linear equations in two variables:

$$ax + by = e$$
$$cx + dy = f$$

$$\text{Let } D = \begin{vmatrix} a & b \\ c & d \end{vmatrix}, \quad Dx = \begin{vmatrix} e & b \\ f & d \end{vmatrix}, \quad Dy = \begin{vmatrix} a & e \\ b & f \end{vmatrix}$$

$$x = \frac{Dx}{D}, \quad y = \frac{Dy}{D}$$

Cramer's Rule can be used to solve a system of n equations in n variables. However, as n increases, the complexity of evaluating the determinants increases. Some calculators will evaluate higher order determinants.

EXERCISES

Use determinants to solve the following systems:

1. $2x + y = 5$
$2x - 3y = 1$

2. $x + y = 5$
$x - y = -7$

3. $3x + 2y = 10$
$5x - 3y = 23$

4. $x - 8y = -43$
$7x - y = -26$

5. a. Use determinants to solve the following system: $6x + 2y = 9$
$9x + 3y = 2$

b. What conclusion can you draw about the system in part **a**?

Investigate the solution of a system of three equations in three variables using 3 by 3 determinants. How is a 3 by 3 determinant evaluated using paper and pencil? How is a 3 by 3 determinant evaluated using a calculator?

Name _____ Class _____ Date _____

ENRICHMENT ACTIVITY 17-3

Systems With Three Variables

A system of three linear equations in three variables that has a solution can be solved by using addition, substitution, or a combination of addition and substitution. Study the following solutions.

EXAMPLE

Solve the following system:

$$x + y + z = 5 \quad [A]$$
$$3x - y + z = 11 \quad [B]$$
$$5x + 2y - z = 4 \quad [C]$$

Solution:

(1) Use equations [A] and [B] to write an equation in two variables by eliminating z. To do this, multiply equation [A] by -1 and add the new equation to equation [B]. The resulting equation, [D], is an equation in two variables.

$$-1(x + y + z = 5) \quad [A] \times -1$$
$$\underline{\begin{aligned} -x - y - z &= -5 \\ 3x - y + z &= 11 \quad [B] \end{aligned}}$$
$$2x - 2y = 6 \quad [D]$$

(2) Use equations [B] and [C] to write another equation in two variables by eliminating z. To do this, add equation [B] to equation [C]. The resulting equation, [E], is another equation in two variables.

$$\begin{aligned} 3x - y + z &= 11 \quad [B] \\ \underline{5x + 2y - z} &= \underline{4} \quad [C] \\ 8x + y &= 15 \quad [E] \end{aligned}$$

(3) Solve equations [D] and [E], which are a system of two equations in two variables, for x and y:

$$\frac{1}{2}(2x - 2y = 6) \quad [D] \times \frac{1}{2}$$
$$\begin{aligned} x - y &= 3 \\ \underline{8x + y} &= \underline{15} \quad [E] \\ 9x &= 18 \\ x &= 2 \\ y &= -1 \end{aligned}$$

Name _____ Class _____ Date _____

(4) Substitute the values of x and y in one of the original equations to find the value of z.

$$x + y + z = 5 \qquad [A]$$
$$2 + (-1) + z = 5$$
$$1 + z = 5$$
$$z = 4$$

Answer: $x = 2$, $y = -1$, $z = 4$ or $(2, -1, 4)$

Alternative Solution:

(1) Solve [A] for z in terms of x and y:

$$x + y + z = 5 \qquad [A]$$
$$z = 5 - x - y \quad [D]$$

(2) Substitute the result of step 1 for z in equation [B]:

$$3x - y + z \qquad\quad = 11 \qquad [B]$$
$$3x - y + (5 - x - y) = 11$$
$$3x - y + 5 - x - y = 11$$
$$2x - 2y = 6$$
$$x - y = 3$$
$$x = 3 + y \quad [E]$$

(3) Substitute the result of step 2 for x in equation [D]:

$$z = 5 - x \qquad\quad - y \quad [D]$$
$$= 5 - (3 + y) - y$$
$$= 5 - 3 - y \quad - y$$
$$= 2 - 2y \qquad\qquad [F]$$

(4) Substitute the value of x in terms of y from equation [E] and the value of z in terms of y from equation [F], and solve the resulting equation, [C], for y:

$$5x + 2y - z \qquad\quad = 4 \quad [C]$$
$$5(3 + y) + 2y - (2 - 2y) = 4$$
$$15 + 5y + 2y - 2 + 2y \quad = 4$$
$$9y = -9$$
$$y = -1$$

Name _____ Class _____ Date _____

(5) Substitute the value of y in equations [E] and [F] to find the values of x and z:

$$x = 3 + y \qquad [E]$$
$$= 3 + (-1)$$
$$= 2$$

$$z = 2 - 2y \qquad [F]$$
$$= 2 - 2(-1)$$
$$= 4$$

Answer: $x = 2$, $y = -1$, $z = 4$, or $(2, -1, 4)$

EXERCISES

Solve the following systems:

1. $\quad x + y + z = 10$
$\quad\ 2x - y + z = 3$
$\quad\ 4x + y - z = 15$

2. $\quad x + 2y + 2z = 1$
$\quad\ x - y + z = 5$
$\quad\ x + 2y - z = -5$

3. $\quad 2x + 3y - z = 9$
$\quad\ 3x - 2y + z = 2$
$\quad\ x + 2y - 3z = 10$

4. $\quad x - y - 2z = 0$
$\quad\ x - y + 4z = 3$
$\quad\ 2x - 3y - 8z = -5$

5. $\quad 2x - y - z = 10$
$\quad\ 3x - y + z = 34$
$\quad\ x + 2y - z = 9$

6. $\quad x + y + z = 0$
$\quad\ 4x + 6y + z = 2$
$\quad\ 2x - 2y - z = -22$

SUGGESTED TEST ITEMS (CHAPTER 17)

1. Solve graphically and check:

$$3x - y = 5$$
$$x - y = 1$$

2. **a.** Graph the following system of inequalities:

$$y \geq 2x - 2$$
$$x + 2y < 4$$

   b. From the solution set drawn in part **a,** select the pair of integers having the largest sum.

3. Solve algebraically and check:

   a. $2x - 5y = 16$ **b.** $4x + 3y = 0$
        $7x + 4y = 13$ $y = 2x + 20$

4. **a.** Solve algebraically and check.

$$2x + y = 8$$
$$y = 2x - 2$$

   b. Solve graphically the same system of equations.

5. Write one value of a for which the equations of the following system are inconsistent:

$$2x + y = a$$
$$4x = 7 - 2y$$

6. Write the value of m for which the equations of the following system are dependent:

$$y = mx + 3$$
$$x + 2y = 6$$

7. Last year, Albert planted a rectangular garden with a perimeter of 34 feet. This year, he made his garden half as long and twice as wide. The perimeter of the new garden is 26 feet. What are the dimensions of each garden?

8. At the first meeting of the Chess Club, 12 students were present. After efforts were made to increase interest in the club, there were twice as many girls and 3 times as many boys that attended the second meeting than those that attended the first. If there were 29 students at the second meeting, how many boys and how many girls attended each meeting?

BONUS: Of the spectators at a basketball game, all but 36 were students, all but 70 were parents, and all but 82 were faculty. **a.** How many spectators were there at the game? **b.** How many of the spectators were students, how many were parents, and how many were faculty?

SAT PREPARATION EXERCISES (CHAPTER 17)

I. Multiple-Choice Questions

In 1–10, select the letter of the correct answer.

1.

$$\underset{P \qquad\qquad Q \quad R \qquad S}{\longleftrightarrow}$$

In the above diagram, Q is the midpoint of $\overline{PS}$, $PQ = x$, and $QR = y$. Which of the following represents the length of RS?

(A) $x - y$ (B) $x + y$ (C) $2x - y$

(D) $2x + y$ (E) $2y - x$

2. If $x + y = 3 + k$ and $2x + 2y = 10$, what is the value of k?

(A) 7   (B) 6   (C) 4

(D) 3   (E) 2

3. If $2x + 3y = k$ and $4x = 7y$, which of the following represents the value of y in terms of k?

(A) $\dfrac{k}{10}$ (B) $k - 6\dfrac{1}{2}$ (C) $\dfrac{2k}{10}$

(D) $\dfrac{2k}{13}$ (E) $\dfrac{10k}{13}$

4.

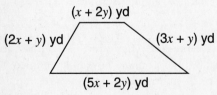

(x + 2y) yd

(2x + y) yd   (3x + y) yd

(5x + 2y) yd

The quadrilateral above is to be enclosed in fencing that can be purchased in rolls of $(2x + y)$ yards each. How many rolls should be purchased to build the fence?

(A) 6   (B) 5   (C) 4

(D) 3   (E) 2

5. If $x + y = 3$ and $x^2 - y^2 = 6$, what is the value of the reciprocal of $\dfrac{1}{x - y}$?

(A) $\dfrac{1}{6}$ (B) $\dfrac{1}{3}$ (C) $\dfrac{1}{2}$

(D) 2   (E) 3

6. Which of the following are the coordinates of a point in the solution set of the system of inequalities shown below?
$$x > 3$$
$$x + y < 2$$

(A) $(4, -1)$ (B) $(4, -3)$ (C) $(3, -3)$

(D) $(5, 1)$ (E) $(-5, 4)$

7. If $2x + 5y = 5$ and $x - 2y = 7$, what is the average (arithmetic mean) of x and y?

(A) 12   (B) 10   (C) 6

(D) 4   (E) 2

8. If $2x + 3y = 7$ and $x + 5y = -9$, what is the value of $2(3x + 8y)$?

(A) 8   (B) 4   (C) 2

(D) -2 (E) -4

9. If $2x + 3y = 3$ and $x + 2y = 1$, then $x + y$ is what percent of $3x + 5y$?

(A) 25   (B) $33\dfrac{1}{3}$ (C) 50

(D) $66\dfrac{2}{3}$ (E) 75

10. If $3x + 2y = 7$ and $kx - y = 5$, which of the following represents the value of x in terms of k?

(A) $\dfrac{12}{3 + 2k}$ (B) $\dfrac{17}{3 + 2k}$ (C) $\dfrac{12}{3 + k}$

(D) $\dfrac{17}{3 + k}$ (E) $\dfrac{2}{3 + k}$

II. Quantitative Comparison Questions

Questions 11–17 each consist of two quantities, one in Column A and one in Column B. You are to compare the two quantities and choose:

A if the quantity in Column A is greater;
B if the quantity in Column B is greater;
C if the two quantities are equal;
D if the relationship cannot be determined from the information given.

Notes

1. In certain questions, information concerning one or both of the quantities to be compared is centered above the two columns.
2. In a given question, a symbol that appears in both columns represents the same thing in Column A as it does in Column B.
3. Letters such as x, n, and k stand for real numbers.

Column A	*Column B*
11.	$2x + y = -3$
$|x|$ when $y = 3$	$|y|$ when $x = 0$

12. The graph of $2x - 3y = 12$

The measure of the acute angle the above line makes with the x-axis	The measure of the acute angle the above line makes with the y-axis

13. $x + y = 5$
$x - y = 2$

$x^2 + x - y - y^2$	10

14. $2x + y = 4$
$3x + 2y = 6$

$x + y$	$x - y$

15. $3x + 2y = 7$
$-x - 4y = 2$

$x - y$	4

16. $2x + 3y + 2k = 30$
$x + y + k = 10$

y	$10 + k$

17. $2x + y = 6$
$x + y = 2$

$x + (6 - 2x)$	$2(2 - y) + y$

III. Student-Produced Response Questions

In questions 18–25, you are to solve the problem.

18. A woman is five times as old as her daughter. In five years, she will be three times as old as her daughter. How old is her daughter?

19. A number is 5 less than twice another, and their sum is 100. What is the larger of the two numbers?

20. The length of a rectangle is 5 times its width, and the perimeter is 72 feet. If the area of the rectangle is equal to the area of a square, what is the measure of a side of the square to the nearest foot?

21. A number is 4 more than another number. If four times the smaller number is decreased by twice the larger number, the result is 12. Determine the value of the larger number.

22. Two angles are supplementary. The larger of the two is 9 more than twice the other. Determine the measure of the larger of the two angles.

23. Alex invested $3,900, part at 5% and the rest at 6%. If the total annual income from the two investments was $215, what was the amount invested at 6%?

24. What is the y value of the solution of the following system of equations?

$$6x + 2y = 14$$
$$3x + 2y = 8$$

25. A chemist has 30 cc of a 12% solution of acid. He wishes to add enough water to make a 4% solution of acid. How many cc of water must be added to the acid solution?

Chapter *18*

Special Products and Factoring

Aims

- To use the prime factorization of a positive integer to determine the greatest common factor of two or more integers.
- To reexamine special products such as the square of a monomial, the product of the sum and difference of two terms, and the product of two binomials.
- To factor polynomial expressions that have monomial and binomial factors.

A polynomial may consist of a single term or the sum of two or more terms. Factoring a polynomial of two or more terms allows us to express the polynomial as a product rather than as a sum. Since the process of factoring reverses the process of multiplication, the multiplication of binomials is reviewed before the process of factoring a polynomial is introduced.

18-1 FACTORS AND FACTORING

Every nonzero real number is a factor of every other nonzero real number. For example, 6 is a factor of 5 since $6\left(\dfrac{5}{6}\right) = 5$. However, when we factor an integer or a polynomial with integral coefficients, we are usually looking for factors that are integers or polynomials with integral coefficients. When two integers have no common factor other than 1, the integers are *relatively prime*.

To find the greatest common factor (GCF) of two or more given integers, such as 32 and 60, alternative approaches may be shown.

Method 1

List all the factors of 32 and 60.

32: 1, 2, 4, 8, 16, 32

60: 1, 2, 3, 4, 5, 6, 10, 12, 15, 20, 30, 60

Common factors = 1, 2, 4

GCF = 4

Method 2

Express 32 and 60 as products of primes.

$$32 = 2 \cdot 2 \cdot 2 \cdot 2 \cdot 2 \text{ or } 2^5$$
$$\downarrow \; \downarrow$$
$$60 = 2 \cdot 2 \cdot 3 \cdot 5 \quad \text{ or } 2^2 \cdot 3 \cdot 5$$
$$\downarrow \; \downarrow$$
$$\text{GCF} = 2 \cdot 2 \qquad \qquad = 2^2 \text{ or } 4$$

Note that the GCF of one positive and one negative coefficient is positive. For example, the GCF of 32 and -60 is 4. Later, when students use factoring in solutions of equations, there may be a particular reason to use the negative of the GCF when writing a monomial factor.

Be sure students understand that, for parts **c** and **e** of Exercise 27, the second factors must be negative since the given factors are negative and the product, 144, is positive.

Use ***Enrichment Activity 18-1: Finding Primes—the Sieve of Eratosthenes*** to find the primes that are less than 200.

18-2 COMMON MONOMIAL FACTORS

When factoring a polynomial whose terms have a common monomial factor, remind students to check their work by multiplying the factors. The product should be the original polynomial.

Impress on students that the *greatest* monomial factor is to be found. For example:

$$12x^2y + 24xy^3 = 6xy(2x + 4y^2)$$

Note, however, that $2x + 4y^2$ can be factored further. Thus:

$$12x^2y + 24xy^3 = 6xy(2x + 4y^2)$$
$$= 6xy \cdot 2(x + 2y^2)$$
$$= 12xy(x + 2y^2)$$

In doing this type of factoring, students sometimes find it easier to think in terms of multiplying rather than dividing. An alternative approach to the example in this section is as follows:

$3cd$ is the GCF of $6c^3d$, $12c^2d^2$, and $3cd$.

To find the other factor, write the GCF as

$$3cd(\qquad)$$

and ask, "By what must I multiply $3cd$ to get *each* of the original terms?"

By what must I multiply $3cd$ to get $6c^3d$?

$$3cd(2c^2 \qquad)$$

By what must I multiply $3cd$ to get $-12c^2d^2$?

$$3cd(2c^2 - 4cd \qquad)$$

By what must I multiply $3cd$ to get $3cd$?

$$3cd(2c^2 - 4cd + 1)$$

This method may help students to remember the final term of 1, which many tend to omit.

18-3 THE SQUARE OF A MONOMIAL

Squaring a monomial means using the monomial twice as a factor, that is, multiplying the monomial by itself. The examples in the text use several steps to find the squares of the given monomials. After students understand the properties used in squaring a monomial and observe the pattern that emerges, they should be able to write the square using only one written step.

The relevant observations are as follows:

1. The operation of squaring is distributed over each factor of the product. In general, when a and b are signed numbers and m and n are positive integers:

$$(ambn)^2 = a^2mb^2n$$

2. When a monomial is a square, its numerical coefficient is a square.

3. When a monomial is a square, the exponent of each variable is an even number, as exemplified by

$$(am)^2 = a^2m.$$

18-4 MULTIPLYING THE SUM AND THE DIFFERENCE OF TWO TERMS

When we multiply the sum of two terms by the difference of the same two terms, the sum of the middle terms of the product is zero, so that the product is the square of the first term minus the square of the second term. For example:

$$(x + y)(x - y) = x^2 - xy + xy - y^2 = x^2 - y^2$$

Students should be able to find these products mentally. Fractions and decimals are included in the exercises to reinforce skills in these areas.

An interesting arithmetic application of these special algebraic products is to calculate the product of two numbers by writing each of the two numbers in terms of their average. For example:

$$(21)(19) = (20 + 1)(20 - 1)$$
$$= 20^2 - 1^2 = 400 - 1 = 399$$
$$(56)(64) = (60 - 4)(60 + 4)$$
$$= 60^2 - 4^2 = 3,600 - 16 = 3,584$$

As students become adept, you can extend the calculations to include fractions and decimals. For example:

$$\left(3\frac{1}{4}\right)\left(2\frac{3}{4}\right) = \left(3 + \frac{1}{4}\right)\left(3 - \frac{1}{4}\right)$$
$$= 3^2 - \left(\frac{1}{4}\right)^2 = 9 - \frac{1}{16} = 8\frac{15}{16}$$
$$(9.8)(10.2) = (10 - 0.2)(10 + 0.2)$$
$$= 10^2 - (0.2)^2$$
$$= 100 - 0.04 = 99.96$$

All of the arithmetic problems shown here fit a general pattern. Any product $a \cdot b$, where $a \neq b$, can be converted to the sum of the two terms multiplied by the difference of the same two terms as follows:

$$a \cdot b = \left(\frac{a+b}{2} + \frac{a-b}{2}\right)\left(\frac{a+b}{2} - \frac{a-b}{2}\right)$$

In each binomial, notice that the first term is the average of a and b, and the second term is one-half of the difference of a and b.

18-5 FACTORING THE DIFFERENCE OF TWO SQUARES

By reversing the thought process established in Section 18-4, students should recognize how to factor the difference of two squares.

Students can use a calculator to determine whether a number is a perfect square.

Enter: 1,369 $\boxed{\sqrt{x}}$

Display: $\boxed{\qquad 37.}$

Enter: 1.69 $\boxed{\sqrt{x}}$

Display: $\boxed{\qquad 1.3}$

Enter: 2,784 $\boxed{\sqrt{x}}$

Display: $\boxed{52.763624}$

Since the square root of 1,369 is an integer and the square root of 1.69 is an exact decimal value, 1,369 and 1.69 are perfect squares. The value that the calculator displays as the square root of 2,784, however, is an approximate value. Therefore, 2,784 is not a perfect square.

It is useful for students to know the squares of the integers from $1^2 = 1$ to $15^2 = 225$. They should also recognize that $1.44 = \frac{144}{100}$ and therefore

$$1.44 = \frac{144}{100} = \frac{12^2}{10^2} = 1.2^2$$

Call attention also to the fact that, when a number has one digit after the decimal point (tenths), its square has two digits after the decimal point (hundredths): $1.5^2 = 2.25$.

18-6 MULTIPLYING BINOMIALS

Multiplication of two binomials was introduced in Section 9-5. Now, students are asked to find the product of two binomials mentally. When presented with an example such as $(x + 5)^2$, some students will immediately answer $x^2 + 25$, disregarding the middle term. Emphasize that:

$$\begin{aligned}(x + 5)^2 &= (x + 5)(x + 5) \\ &= x^2 + 5x + 5x + 25 \\ &= x^2 + 10x + 25\end{aligned}$$

Here is a good place to reintroduce geometric interpretations of these products, such as were presented in Chapter 9. For example, to demonstrate the value of $(x + 5)^2$:

1. Begin with a square of side x and area x^2.

2. Increase the length of side x to $x + 5$.

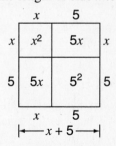

3. Note that the new square contains *four* parts, with areas x^2, $5x$, $5x$, and 5^2, not just the two parts x^2 and 5^2.

18-7 FACTORING TRINOMIALS

As students learn the procedure for factoring trinomials of the form $ax^2 + bx + c$, certain relationships become apparent:

1. If the leading coefficient (as in this case of the x^2 term) is 1 ($a = 1$), then the coefficient of the first term of each binomial is 1.
2. If the sign of the third term is negative ($c < 0$), then the sign of the last term of one binomial is positive, while the sign of the last term of the other binomial is negative.
3. If the sign of the third term is positive ($c > 0$), we consider the middle term, bx:
   a. If b is positive, then the sign of the last term in each binomial factor must be positive.
   b. If b is negative, then the sign of the last term in each binomial factor must be negative.

Note: Knowing these relationships will reduce the number of possible pairs of factors to list and to test.

When factoring trinomials where the coefficient of the x^2 term is a number other than 1, students should list the possible pairs of factors. Once students become familiar with factoring techniques, however, certain possible pairs of factors can be eliminated immediately. For example:

Factor $2x^2 - x - 6$.
There are eight possible pairs of factors:

$(2x + 6)(x - 1)$	$(2x - 6)(x + 1)$
$(2x + 2)(x - 3)$	$(2x - 2)(x + 3)$
$(2x + 1)(x - 6)$	$(2x - 1)(x + 6)$
$(2x + 3)(x - 2)$	$(2x - 3)(x + 2)$

In four of these pairs, the first binomial is not prime and these pairs should be rejected:

$(2x + 6)(x - 1)$	$(2x - 6)(x + 1)$
$(2x + 2)(x - 3)$	$(2x - 2)(x + 3)$

In two other pairs, the coefficient of the middle term is either too large or too small. These pairs should also be rejected:

$$(2x + 1)(x - 6) \qquad (2x - 1)(x + 6)$$

This leaves only two pairs of factors to consider:

$$(2x + 3)(x - 2) \qquad (2x - 3)(x + 2)$$

In actuality, these two pairs should be tested first. After multiplying the factors, the student will see that the correct factors of $2x^2 - x - 6$ are $(2x + 3)(x - 2)$.

Every expression that is the product of two factors is also the product of the opposites of these factors. For example:

$$2x^2 - x - 6 = (2x + 3)(x - 2)$$
$$= (-2x - 3)(-x + 2).$$

However, the factors with positive coefficients of the first terms are commonly used.

An alternative factoring process that does not rely on trying possible pairs of factors is outlined in ***Enrichment Activity 18-7: Factoring Trinomials.***

18-8 FACTORING A POLYNOMIAL COMPLETELY

When the instruction is to factor a polynomial *completely*, the process of factoring continues until all factors other than monomial factors are prime. Students should look first for the greatest common factor, if there is one, so that any remaining factoring may be made easier.

Two types of errors in this area are:

1. Students find binomial factors that are not prime because they have forgotten to first factor the greatest common monomial term. For example:

$$100x^2 - 36y^2 = (10x + 6y)(10x - 6y)$$
$$\text{not prime}$$

This can be corrected by additional factoring:

$$= 2(5x + 3y) \cdot 2(5x - 3y)$$
$$= 4(5x + 3y)(5x - 3y)$$

2. Students correctly find the greatest common monomial factor and/or one pair of binomial factors, but they forget to check each binomial to see whether it is factored completely. For example:

$64x^2 - 4x^2y^4$
$= 4x^2(16 - y^4)$ still factorable
$= 4x^2(4 + y^2)(4 - y^2)$ still factorable
$= 4x^2(4 + y^2)(2 + y)(2 - y)$

To test understanding of this section, ask for the factors of $x^2 + 36$. Some responses may be $(x + 6)(x - 6)$ and $(x + 6)(x + 6)$, but neither of these pairs of factors has a product equal to $x^2 + 36$. The binomial $x^2 + 36$ cannot be factored over the set of integers.

Name _____ Class _____ Date _____

ENRICHMENT ACTIVITY 18-1

Finding Primes—The Sieve of Eratosthenes

The search for a method of determining primes is of ancient origin. One method, called a *sieve,* is said to have been used by Eratosthenes (277–194 B.C.). The sieve consists of an organized method of crossing out composite numbers so that the remaining numbers must be primes.

(1) Write a list of whole numbers from 2 to any reasonable limit, say 200.

	2	3	4	5	6	7	8	9	10
11	12	13	14	15	16	17	18	19	20
21	22	23	24	25	26	27	28	29	30
31	32	33	34	35	36	37	38	39	40
41	42	43	44	45	46	47	48	49	50
51	52	53	54	55	56	57	58	59	60
61	62	63	64	65	66	67	68	69	70
71	72	73	74	75	76	77	78	79	80
81	82	83	84	85	86	87	88	89	90
91	92	93	94	95	96	97	98	99	100
101	102	103	104	105	106	107	108	109	110
111	112	113	114	115	116	117	118	119	120
121	122	123	124	125	126	127	128	129	130
131	132	133	134	135	136	137	138	139	140
141	142	143	144	145	146	147	148	149	150
151	152	153	154	155	156	157	158	159	160
161	162	163	164	165	166	167	168	169	170
171	172	173	174	175	176	177	178	179	180
181	182	183	184	185	186	187	188	189	190
191	192	193	194	195	196	197	198	199	200

(2) Circle the first number, 2, and cross out every multiple of 2.

(3) Circle the next number that has not been crossed out, 3, and cross out every multiple of 3. Some of these numbers, for example, 6 and 12, will already be crossed out.

(4) Circle the next number that has not been crossed out, and cross out every multiple of this number that was not crossed out in step 2 or 3.

(5) Repeat step (4) until every number less than 15 is either circled or crossed out.

(6) Circle the remaining numbers that are not crossed out. The circled numbers are the primes that are less than 200.

Name _____ Class _____ Date _____

1. When you cross out 119 because it is a multiple of 7, you have crossed out the multiple of what prime that is greater than 15?

2. Why can you stop crossing out numbers in this list when you have crossed out all multiples of primes less than 15?

3. If the table listed the numbers up to 400, what is the largest prime whose multiples need to be crossed out in order that all the remaining numbers will be prime?

4. The search for a formula for primes has been unsuccessful. However, the formula $x^2 - x + 41$ seems to yield only primes when whole numbers are substituted for x.

   a. Use the formula to find 10 prime numbers.

   b. Find a value of x for which the formula yields a composite number.

Name _____ Class _____ Date _____

ENRICHMENT ACTIVITY 18-7

Factoring Trinomials

The usual process for factoring a trinomial of the form $ax^2 + bx + c$ into two binomials is a guess-and-check approach. There is, however, a process for factoring a trinomial that exactly reverses the steps of multiplying two binomials.

When two binomials are multiplied, we first obtain four terms:
$$(2x + 3)(5x - 2) = 2x(5x - 2) + 3(5x - 2)$$
$$= 10x^2 - 4x + 15x - 6$$

The two middle terms are similar terms and can be combined:
$$(2x + 3)(5x - 2) = 2x(5x - 2) + 3(5x - 2)$$
$$= 10x^2 - 4x + 15x - 6$$
$$= 10x^2 + 11x - 6$$

In reversing this multiplication to factor $10x^2 + 11x - 6$, the last step is the one that seems to be most difficult to reverse since there are infinitely many pairs of terms whose sum is $11x$. However, we note that, when the product is expressed as the sum of four terms, $10x^2 - 4x + 15x - 6$, the product of the first and last terms is equal to the product of the two middle terms:
$$10x^2(-6) = -60x^2 \quad \text{and} \quad -4x(15x) = -60x^2$$
We can apply this fact to reverse the steps used to multiply two binomials.

EXAMPLES

1. Factor $6x^2 - 5x - 4$.

(1) Multiply the first and last terms: $\qquad\qquad\qquad 6x^2(-4) = -24x^2$

(2) Write all pairs of factors of $-24x^2$ whose sum is a term in x with a negative coefficient. Choose the pair whose sum is $-5x$.

$+1x$	$-24x$
$+2x$	$-12x$
$+3x$	$-8x$
$+4x$	$-6x$

(3) Using this pair of terms, write the trinomial as the sum of four terms: $\qquad 6x^2 + 3x - 8x - 4$

(4) Factor out the common monomial factor of the first two terms and of the last two terms, using the sign of the first term of each pair as the sign of the greatest common factor: $\qquad 3x(2x + 1) - 4(2x + 1)$

(5) Factor out the common binomial factor: $\qquad\quad (2x + 1)(3x - 4)$

Name _____ Class _____ Date _____

2. Factor $18x^2 - 9x + 1$.

    (1) Multiply the first and last terms:

                                                          $18x^2(+1) = +18x^2$

    (2) Write all pairs of factors of $+18x^2$ whose
           sum is a term in x with a negative coefficient.
           The two terms must have the same sign and
           must therefore both be negative. Choose the
           pair whose sum is $-9x$.

$$-1x \qquad -18x$$
$$-2x \qquad -9x$$

$$-3x \qquad -6x$$

    (3) Using this pair of terms, write the trinomial
           as the sum of four terms:

$$18x^2 - 3x - 6x + 1$$

    (4) Factor out the common monomial factor of
           the first two terms and of the last two terms,
           using the sign of the first term of each pair
           as the sign of the greatest common factor.
           Note that 1 is the greatest common factor
           of the last two terms.

$$3x(6x - 1) - 1(6x - 1)$$

    (5) Factor out the common binomial factor:

$$(6x - 1)(3x - 1)$$

EXERCISES

1. Follow the steps given below to factor $4x^2 + 3x - 10$.

    (1) Write the product of the first and last terms:

                                          $4x^2(-10) = $ _____

    (2) Write all possible pairs of terms that have
           the product found in step 1. The terms must
           have opposite signs and must have a positive
           sum. Select the pair that has a sum of $+3x$.

    (3) Use the pair of terms that you selected to
           write the polynomial as the sum of four terms:

                                          $4x^2 + $ ____ $-$ ____ -10

    (4) Factor the greatest common factor from the
           first two terms and from the last two terms.

    (5) Write the common binomial factor. Write the
           other binomial factor as the sum of the common
           factors found in step 4.

2. Use this procedure to factor the following trinomials:

a. $2x^2 + 9x + 10$

b. $4x^2 - 9x - 9$

c. $3x^2 - 16x + 5$

d. $3x^2 - 10x - 8$

e. $6x^2 - 13x + 6$

f. $12x^2 + 13x - 4$

g. $8x^2 - 37x - 15$

h. $5x^2 + 27x + 10$

i. $7x^2 + 20x - 3$

SUGGESTED TEST ITEMS (CHAPTER 18)

1. Write the prime factorization of 495.

2. List all of the whole numbers that are factors of 90.

3. What is the greatest common factor of $12a^2b$ and $42ab^2$?

In 4–7, write, in each case, an equivalent expression without parentheses.

4. $(5ab^2)^2$ **5.** $(2x - 1)^2$ **6.** $(x + 3)(2x - 3)$ **7.** $(y - 7)(y + 7)$

In 8–19, factor each polynomial completely.

8. $12a^2 - 6ab$ **9.** $a^2 - 5a + 6$ **10.** $s^2 - 25$ **11.** $8r^3 - 2r^2$

12. $x^2 + 8x - 20$ **13.** $y^2 + 6y + 9$ **14.** $2x^2 - x - 6$ **15.** $4b^2 + 15b + 9$

16. $4c^2 + 16$ **17.** $9b^2 - 16$ **18.** $5y^2 - 20$ **19.** $5x^2 - 10x + 5$

20. Express the area of a rectangle as a trinomial if the length is represented by $(3x - 1)$ and the width by $(2x + 1)$.

21. Express the length of one side of a square in terms of s, if the area of the square is represented by $4s^2 - 12s + 9$.

BONUS I: **a.** Show that the product of two consecutive odd integers is always 1 less than the square of their average.   **b.** Is this true also for consecutive even integers?

BONUS II: Show that any nonzero integer that is 1 less than a perfect square can be factored into two consecutive even or two consecutive odd integers.

SAT PREPARATION EXERCISES (CHAPTER 18)

I. Multiple-Choice Questions

In 1–13, select the letter of the correct answer.

1. Evaluate $(6 + 2)(2)(5) - (2)(4)(12 - 2)$.

(A) 0   (B) 2   (C) 40

(D) 80   (E) 160

2. Which of the following has the same value as $(95)(83)$?

(A) $(90)(80) + (5)(3)$

(B) $(90)(80) + (5)(80) + (3)(90)$

(C) $90^2 - (2)(90) - (5)(7)$

(D) $90^2 - (5)(7)$

(E) $80(15) + 80(3)$

3.

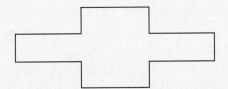

In the figure above, if each vertical segment is of length y, and each horizontal segment is of length x, which of the following represents its perimeter?

(A) $2(3x + 3y)$

(B) $(3x)(3y)$

(C) $2(3x + y)$

(D) $12(x + y)$

(E) $36xy$

4.

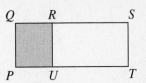

In rectangle $PQST$ above, the areas of the shaded and unshaded regions are $x^2 + 3x$ and $6x + 18$, respectively. If $PQ > QR$ and $PQ \neq RS$, then for all values of $x > 0$, which of the following represents the perimeter of rectangle $PQST$?

(A) $2x + 9$ (B) $4x + 18$

(C) $2x^2 + 9x$ (D) $4x^2 + 18x$

(E) $x^2 + 9x + 18$

5.

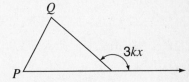

In the figure above, $m\angle P = (3x^2)$, and $m\angle Q = (6x)$. If the measure of the exterior angle is $(3kx)$, which of the following expressions represents the value of k?

(A) $x + 2$ (B) $x^2 + 3x$

(C) $3x^2 + 3x$ (D) $9x^4 + 18x^2$

(E) $-3x$

6. If $4x^2 = (2)(6)$, and $3y^2 = (3)(6)$, what is the value of $(x + y)(x - y)$?

(A) 3   (B) 0   (C) -3

(D) 6   (E) 9

7. If $x = y + 5$, what is the value of $x^2 - 2xy + y^2$?

(A) 100   (B) 50   (C) 25

(D) 10   (E) 5

8. If $x^2 + y^2 = 5$ and $xy = 5$, what is the value of $(x + y)^2$?

   (A) 15   (B) 20   (C) 25

   (D) 30   (E) 50

9.

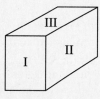

Rectangular Box

In the figure above, for all values of $x > 1$, the area of face I is $x^2 - 1$, and the area of face II is $x^2 + 3x + 2$. Which of the following represents the area of face III?

   (A) $x^2 + 3x + 1$

   (B) $x^2 - 3x + 2$

   (C) $2x^2 + 3x + 1$

   (D) $x^2 + x - 2$

   (E) $x^2 - 2x - 2$

10.

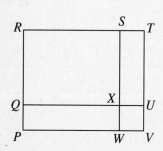

In the figure above, $RS = PR = y$ and $UV = VW = 2$. Which of the following rectangles has an area of $y^2 - 4$?

   (A) $PQXW$

   (B) $PRSW$

   (C) $PRTV$

   (D) $QRSX$

   (E) $QRTU$

11.

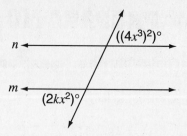

In the figure above, lines m and n are parallel. Use the degree measures shown in the diagram to find an expression for k.

   (A) $2x^3$ (B) $4x^2$ (C) $4x^4$

   (D) $8x^2$ (E) $8x^4$

12.

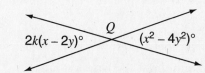

In the figure above, two lines intersect at Q. Use the degree measures shown in the diagram to find an expression for k.

   (A) $x + 2y$ (B) $x - 2y$

   (C) $\dfrac{x + 2y}{2}$ (D) $\dfrac{x - 2y}{2}$

   (E) $x + y$

13.

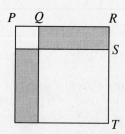

In the figure above, if $PR = RT = x$ and $QR = ST = y$, what is the sum of the areas of the shaded rectangles?

   (A) $x^2 - y^2$ (B) $2xy - y^2$

   (C) $2xy - 2y^2$ (D) $x^2 - xy$

   (E) $2xy$

II. Quantitative Comparison Questions

Questions 14–19 each consist of two quantities, one in Column A and one in Column B. You are to compare the two quantities and choose:

A if the quantity in Column A is greater;
B if the quantity in Column B is greater;
C if the two quantities are equal;
D if the relationship cannot be determined from the information given.

Notes

1. In certain questions, information concerning one or both of the quantities to be compared is centered above the two columns.
2. In a given question, a symbol that appears in both columns represents the same thing in Column A as it does in Column B.
3. Letters such as x, n, and k stand for real numbers.

Column A	*Column B*
14. $(a - b)^2$	$(b - a)^2$

15. x is an integer.

$x(x + 2)$	$(x + 1)(x - 1)$

16. $(x^2 - y^2)(x + y)$ $(x - y)(x^2 + 2xy + y^2)$

17. $k \neq 0$

$x^2 + k^2$	$(x + k)(x - k)$

18. $h > 0, g > 0$

$h^2 + g^2$	$(h + g)^2$

19. $y = x + 2$

$y^2 - 8y + 15$	$x^2 - 4x + 3$

III. Student-Produced Response Questions

In questions 20–26, you are to solve the problem.

20. The product of two monomials is $-9x^4y^5$. If the first factor is $-9xy$, what is the second factor when $x = 1$ and $y = -2$?

21. Determine the area of a rectangle when $x = 1\frac{1}{2}$ if its dimensions are $(2x + 1)$ and $(2x - 1)$.

22. What is the value of $-2ab^3c^2$ if $a = 1$, $b = -2$ and $c = 3$?

23. If the volume of a cube is 125, what is the value of an edge?

24.

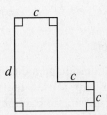

Determine the perimeter of the adjoining figure if $c = 2$ and $d = 6$.

25. If $x = -1$, what is the value of $x(x^3 + x^4)$?

26. What is the number of cubic units in the volume of a cube with a surface area of 96 square units?

Chapter 19

Algebraic Fractions, and Equations and Inequalities Involving Fractions

Aims

- To teach the fundamental operations with algebraic fractions, including reducing to lowest terms.
- To solve equations containing fractional coefficients, as well as fractional equations.
- To extend these processes to the solution of literal equations.

Throughout this chapter, the operations on algebraic fractions are related to the corresponding operations on arithmetic fractions.

The work of this chapter may be limited to fractions with monomial denominators. It is important that you do not spend an inordinate amount of time to achieve mastery of all of the material in this chapter. Students should review their work with arithmetic fractions and apply those principles to algebraic fractions. All of the work with fractions, equations involving fractions, and fractional equations will be considered again in Courses II and III.

CHAPTER OVERVIEW

In the problem on the introductory page, some Ukrainian eggs designed by Andrea were shared with members of her family: one-fifth to grandparents; one-fourth of those remaining to parents;

one-third of those then left to an aunt; and one-half of the remainder to her brother. Six eggs were left for Andrea.

There are many ways to approach the problem of determining how many eggs Andrea designed, including the strategies of working backward, of solving an algebraic equation, and of using guess-and-check. Each lead to the correct solution: Andrea designed 30 eggs.

Working Backward:

Andrea had 6 eggs left.

If Andrea gave $\frac{1}{2}$ of the eggs she had to her brother and kept 6, then her brother was given 6 eggs. The total of 6 (brother) + 6 (Andrea) = 12.

If Andrea gave $\frac{1}{3}$ of the eggs she had at the time to her aunt and had 12 left for her brother and herself, then those 12 eggs represent $\frac{2}{3}$ of the total at that time, indicating that $\frac{1}{3}$ must equal 6 eggs. The total of 6 (aunt) + 6 (brother) + 6 (Andrea) = 18.

If Andrea gave $\frac{1}{4}$ of the eggs she had at the time to her parents and had 18 eggs left, then those 18 eggs represent $\frac{3}{4}$ of the total at that time, indicating that $\frac{1}{4}$ must equal 6 eggs. The total of 6 (parents) + 6 (aunt) + 6 (brother) + 6 (Andrea) = 24.

If Andrea gave $\frac{1}{5}$ of the eggs she designed to her grandparents and had 24 eggs left for others, then those 24 eggs represent $\frac{4}{5}$ of the total, and $\frac{1}{5}$ must equal 6 eggs. The total number of eggs designed is 30, as seen here:

$$6 \text{ (grandparents)} + 6 \text{ (parents)} + 6 \text{ (aunt)}$$
$$+ 6 \text{ (brother)} + 6 \text{ (Andrea)} = 30$$

(See *Check* below.)

Solving an Algebraic Equation:

Let x = number of eggs at start.

Then $\frac{4}{5}x$ = number of eggs left after giving $\frac{1}{5}x$ to grandparents,

$\frac{3}{4}\left(\frac{4}{5}x\right)$ = number of eggs left after giving $\frac{1}{4}\left(\frac{4}{5}x\right)$ to parents,

$\frac{2}{3}\left[\frac{3}{4}\left(\frac{4}{5}x\right)\right]$ = number of eggs left after giving $\frac{1}{3}\left[\frac{3}{4}\left(\frac{4}{5}x\right)\right]$ to aunt, and

$\frac{1}{2}\left\{\frac{2}{3}\left[\frac{3}{4}\left(\frac{4}{5}x\right)\right]\right\}$ = number of eggs left after giving $\frac{1}{2}\left\{\frac{2}{3}\left[\frac{3}{4}\left(\frac{4}{5}x\right)\right]\right\}$ to brother.

The number of eggs remaining	equals	six for Andrea.
$\frac{1}{2}\left\{\frac{2}{3}\left[\frac{3}{4}\left(\frac{4}{5}x\right)\right]\right\}$	=	6
$\frac{1}{2}\left\{\frac{2}{3}\left[\frac{3}{4}\left(\frac{4}{5}x\right)\right]\right\}$	=	6
$\frac{1}{5}x$	=	6
x	=	30

(See *Check* below.)

Guess-and-Check:

Since $\frac{1}{5}$ of the total number of eggs designed were given to Andrea's grandparents, the total number must be a multiple of 5. By following the sequence given in the problem and using multiples of 5, the following solutions are found:

With a total of 5 eggs:
  1 to grandparents; 1 to parents; 1 to aunt; 1 to brother; 1 to Andrea (too few; Andrea must have 6 eggs left).

With a total of 10 eggs:
  2 to grandparents; 2 to parents; 2 to aunt; 2 to brother; 2 to Andrea (again, too few).

With a total of 15 eggs:
  each party gets 3 eggs (too few).

With a total of 20 eggs:
  each party gets 4 eggs (too few).

With a total of 25 eggs:
  each party gets 5 eggs (still too few).

With a total of 30 eggs:
  each party, including Andrea, gets 6 eggs (correct).

When any multiple of 5 greater than 30, is used, it can be shown that Andrea will have more than 6 eggs remaining for herself. Thus, we see that there is only one correct solution.

Check: This check can be applied to any strategy used. Start with 30 eggs. Then:

$$30 - \frac{1}{5}(30) = 30 - 6$$
$$= 24 \text{ remain (6 to grandparents)}$$

$$24 - \frac{1}{4}(24) = 24 - 6$$
$$= 18 \text{ remain (6 to parents)}$$

$$18 - \frac{1}{3}(18) = 18 - 6$$
$$= 12 \text{ remain (6 to aunt)}$$

$$12 - \frac{1}{2}(12) = 12 - 6$$
$$= 6 \text{ remain (6 to brother)}$$
$$(6 \text{ for Andrea})$$

It is interesting that, in this case, each of the parties received the same number of eggs. This may not always be the case when a total is distributed among many people. However the concept of *sharing* often involves equal amounts for all parties involved. For example, if a company issues shares of stock, each share is worth the same amount as every other share. The lessons learned in early childhood from our parents and elementary school teachers about sharing were also based on equal amounts for all.

19-1 THE MEANING OF AN ALGEBRAIC FRACTION

An algebraic fraction, or rational expression, is a quotient of polynomials. Every rational expression, such as $\frac{8}{2}$, corresponds to a division problem, here $8 \div 2$. Since division by 0 is not possible, a rational expression is undefined (has no meaning) when its denominator equals 0. Thus, the expression $\frac{x+8}{x+2}$ is undefined if $x + 2 = 0$ or $x = -2$. Recall that, when $\frac{a}{b} = c$, $bc = a$. Then:

1. When -2 is substituted for x in $\frac{x+8}{x+2}$, the expression becomes $\frac{-2+8}{-2+2}$, or $\frac{6}{0}$.
   If $\frac{6}{0} = c$, then $0 \cdot c = 6$. But there is no value of c for which $0 \cdot c = 6$. Therefore, $\frac{6}{0}$ has no value, or is undefined.

2. When -8 is substituted for x in $\frac{x+8}{x+2}$, the expression becomes $\frac{-8+8}{-8+2} = \frac{0}{-6} = 0$.
   If $\frac{0}{-6} = c$, then $-6c = 0$. This equation is true when $c = 0$. Therefore, $\frac{0}{-6} = 0$, a defined value.

19-2 REDUCING FRACTIONS TO LOWEST TERMS

A fraction, whether arithmetic or algebraic, is said to be reduced to lowest terms when its numerator and denominator have no common factor other than 1 or -1. In this section, we show alternative ways to reduce fractions to lowest terms. One method uses the division property of a fraction; another method, which is preferred by most students, uses factoring techniques and cancellation.

Help students to remember that cancellation of factors represents division by writing the quotient 1 when a factor is divided by itself. This tactic will help students to avoid the following error:

$$\frac{3x+6}{6x+12} = \frac{\overset{1}{\cancel{3}}\overset{1}{\cancel{(x+2)}}}{\underset{2}{\cancel{6}}\underset{1}{\cancel{(x+2)}}} = 2$$

At this point, you may consider some situations where cancellation is not possible. For example, in the expression $\frac{x+2}{x}$ the x terms cannot be canceled since x is not a factor in the numerator. Suppose the x terms were canceled. The fraction would then become $\frac{1+2}{1}$, or $\frac{3}{1}$. Show that this is not equal to the value of $\frac{x+2}{x}$ by substituting a numerical value for x. Letting $x = 3$ gives

$$\frac{3+2}{3} = \frac{5}{3} \neq \frac{3}{1}.$$

Emphasize that cancellation is valid only for a factor of the *entire* numerator and denominator.

It is good practice for a teacher to indicate all values of variables for which a fraction is not defined. This procedure is used in examples in the book.

It must be recognized, however, that students often experience difficulty in working with algebraic fractions. For this reason, it is more important to emphasize the algebraic skills needed to perform operations with algebraic fractions than to demand that students always indicate values for which the fraction is undefined. In time, the concept of identifying these values will be understood by students through examples seen in class, questions that you ask, and occasional exercises in this chapter.

See *Enrichment Activity 19-2: Is It Magic or Is It Math?* Students begin with any positive fraction and then, by following some simple rules, generate new fractions that converge to a specific value. The more fractions formed, the more specific the value becomes. After working with numerical values, students are asked to examine algebraic fractions, which, in turn, lead to proofs of the numerical discoveries made.

19-3 MULTIPLYING FRACTIONS

When multiplying fractions, it is preferable to use the cancellation method to reduce the form of the product before applying the general rule, thus simplifying the arithmetic. For example, it is easier to treat $\frac{14}{15} \cdot \frac{5}{21}$ as $\frac{\cancel{7} \cdot 2}{3 \cdot \cancel{5}} \cdot \frac{\cancel{5}}{\cancel{7} \cdot 3} = \frac{2}{9}$ than to multiply first.

The same procedures are used when multiplying algebraic fractions. Emphasize the need to factor binomial and trinomial numerators and denominators. Also, remind students that they must have one factor in the numerator and the identical factor in the denominator before they can cancel. Thus, in the following example, it would not be valid to cancel the factor $(x + 1)$, which appears only in the numerator of each fraction:

$$\frac{2x + 2}{x + 3} \cdot \frac{x^2 + 4x + 3}{4}$$

$$= \frac{2(x + 1)}{x + 3} \cdot \frac{(x + 1)(x + 3)}{4}$$

$$= \frac{(x + 1)^2}{2} \text{ (where } x \neq -3) \quad Answer$$

Note that the factored form, $\frac{(x + 1)^2}{2}$, and the expanded form, $\frac{x^2 + 2x + 1}{2}$, are both acceptable answers. Unless there is a particular reason to expand, answers can be left in the factored form.

19-4   DIVIDING FRACTIONS

To perform the operation of division, we multiply the dividend of a quotient by the reciprocal of the divisor. At times, students will cancel before taking the reciprocal of the divisor. This type of error can be avoided by suggesting that students follow a definite procedure:

(1) Write the division problem:
$$\frac{4x + 8}{3} \div \frac{4}{9}$$

(2) Write an equivalent problem using multiplication:
$$= \frac{4x + 8}{3} \cdot \frac{9}{4}$$

(3) Factor and cancel common factors:
$$= \frac{4(x + 2)}{3} \cdot \frac{9}{4}$$

(4) Write the final product:
$$= 3(x + 2) \quad Answer$$

19-5   ADDING OR SUBTRACTING FRACTIONS THAT HAVE THE SAME DENOMINATOR

A comparison between the rules for addition and subtraction of simple arithmetic fractions and the rules for algebraic fractions is again helpful. Students seem to have more difficulty with subtraction than they do with addition. For example, a common error is to write:

$$\frac{3x + 2}{4} - \frac{2x + 5}{4} = \frac{3x + 2 - 2x + 5}{4}$$

Stress the use of parentheses as a means of showing that the entire numerator, $2x + 5$, is being subtracted:

$$\frac{3x + 2}{4} - \frac{2x + 5}{4} = \frac{(3x + 2) - (2x + 5)}{4}$$

$$= \frac{3x + 2 - 2x - 5}{4}$$

$$= \frac{x - 3}{4}$$

19-6   ADDING OR SUBTRACTING FRACTIONS THAT HAVE DIFFERENT DENOMINATORS

To add or subtract fractions with different denominators, we must first transform the fractions into equivalent fractions that have a common denominator. For this purpose we use the lowest common denominator (L.C.D.).

Methods for finding the L.C.D. have been presented in previous mathematics courses. One such method involves prime factorization. For example, we can find the L.C.D. of the denominators $8x^2y$ and $10xy^2$ in the following manner:

$$8x^2y = 2 \cdot 2 \cdot 2 \quad \cdot x \cdot x \cdot y \quad = \quad (2^3) \quad \cdot (x^2) \cdot y$$

$$10xy^2 = 2 \quad \cdot 5 \cdot x \mid \cdot y \cdot y = \quad \left(2 \cdot (5) \cdot x \mid \cdot (y^2) \right.$$

$$\text{L.C.D.} = 2 \cdot 2 \cdot 2 \cdot 5 \cdot x \cdot x \cdot y \cdot y = \quad 2^3 \cdot 5 \cdot \quad x^2 \cdot y^2$$

$$= \quad 40x^2y^2 \quad Answer$$

Note that the L.C.D. is the least common multiple of the algebraic expressions.

For each prime factor, we find the highest power of that factor to appear in any of the denominators. The L.C.D. is the product of these highest powers.

Encourage students to determine mentally the L.C.D. in the exercises. Also, remind them to reduce answers to lowest terms.

See **Enrichment Activity 19-6: Operations with Fractions.** Students find the sum, difference, product, and quotient of two sets of algebraic fractions. Then, by comparing various algebraic results in which one of two expressions is given as larger, or in which the expressions are given as equal, students are asked to determine possible numerical values for the variables. Multiple variables must be handled simultaneously in these exercises. Solutions are found by using algebraic methods or problem-solving strategies.

19-7 SOLVING EQUATIONS CONTAINING FRACTIONAL COEFFICIENTS

In Chapter 10, some of the first-degree equations studied contained fractional coefficients. At that point, both the additive and multiplicative inverses were used to solve the equations. Now that students are familiar with finding the L.C.D., equations that contain fractional coefficients can be solved by multiplying both sides of the equation by the L.C.D. Thus, an equivalent equation without fractional coefficients is formed.

For example, solve for x in the equation

$$\frac{2x}{3} - 4 = \frac{x}{2}$$

Method 1

$$\frac{2x}{3} - 4 = \frac{x}{2}$$

$$\frac{2}{3}x - 4 = \frac{1}{2}x$$

$$-\frac{2}{3}x \qquad = -\frac{2}{3}x$$

$$-4 = -\frac{1}{6}x$$

$$-6(-4) = -6\left(-\frac{1}{6}x\right)$$

$$24 = x$$

Method 2

$$\frac{2x}{3} - \frac{4}{1} = \frac{x}{2}$$

$$6\left(\frac{2x}{3} - \frac{4}{1}\right) = 6\left(\frac{x}{2}\right)$$

$$2(2x) - 6(4) = 3(x)$$

$$4x - 24 = 3x$$

$$-4x \qquad = -4x$$

$$-24 = -x$$

$$24 = x$$

To solve an equation such as $\frac{3x-5}{7} - \frac{2x+4}{5} = 4$, it should become obvious that Method 2 is preferred.

For equations that are in the form of a proportion, a third method, using the products of the means and extremes, can be used. Point out that this method is the same as multiplying both sides of the equation by the product of the denominators, which is the L.C.D., or a multiple of the L.C.D. Stress that, in order to cross multiply, there can be only one term in each member of the equation. Thus, only Exercises 1–6 and 13–18 can be solved by this method.

After learning to solve equations by multiplying both members by the L.C.D. to obtain an equivalent equation, students often confuse the process with that of finding the sum or difference of two algebraic fractions. Show the difference between the following exercises:

Add: $\frac{x}{3} + \frac{x}{4}$.

$$\frac{x \cdot 4}{3 \cdot 4} + \frac{x \cdot 3}{4 \cdot 3} = \frac{4x}{12} + \frac{3x}{12}$$

$$= \frac{7x}{12} \quad Answer$$

Solve: $\frac{x}{3} + \frac{x}{4} = 21$.

$$12\left(\frac{x}{3} + \frac{x}{4}\right) = 12(21)$$

$$4x + 3x = 252$$

$$7x = 252$$

$$x = 36 \quad Answer$$

Ask students to list some differences between the two procedures, their justifications, and their results. For example:

1. When adding two fractions, we use the L.C.D. to change the fractions to equivalent fractions with like denominators.

2. The sum of two fractions is a fraction (even if later reducible to one with a denominator of 1).

3. When solving an equation with fractional coefficients, we use the L.C.D. to write an equivalent equation that does not contain fractions.

4. The equivalent equation we show in our work is actually the result of applying the multiplication property of equality to an equation, all of whose terms have like denominators:

$$\frac{x}{3} + \frac{x}{4} = 21$$

$$\frac{4x}{12} + \frac{3x}{12} = \frac{252}{12}$$

$$12\left(\frac{4x}{12} + \frac{3x}{12}\right) = 12\left(\frac{252}{12}\right)$$

$$4x + 3x = 252$$

Each member of the equation $4x + 3x = 252$ is 12 times each member of the equation $\frac{x}{3} + \frac{x}{4} = 21$.

The text offers a variety of settings in which a verbal problem can lead to an equation involving fractions. In keeping with the problem-solving philosophy established at the beginning of the text, these problems are offered primarily as a resource that should not be presented in its entirety on consecutive days.

Example 4 establishes that the procedure for clearing an equation of fractions is applicable also to clearing an equation of decimals. You might suggest that students show their work as follows:

$$0.05x + 0.25(3x) + 0.10(x + 5) = 3.20$$
$$0.05\,x + 0.25\,(3x) + 0.10\,(x + 5) = 3.20$$

When the terms of an equation involve different numbers of decimal places, thinking of an L.C.D. can help remind students that the number of places they must move the decimal point in every term is determined by the greatest number of decimal places in any term. Thus, in Exercise 31, for example, we move the decimal point two places to the right because the L.C.D. is 100:

$$0.03y - 1.2 = 8.7$$
$$0.03\,y - 1.20 = 8.70$$

19-8 SOLVING INEQUALITIES CONTAINING FRACTIONAL COEFFICIENTS

Students generally feel comfortable in applying for inequalities the procedures they learned for equations. Ask students to recall what operations change the order of an inequality and what operations leave the order unchanged.

Graphing the solution set for an inequality reminds students of the difference between an infinite solution set, which they often obtain when they solve an inequality, and a finite solution set, which they usually obtain when they solve an equation. Then, each verbal problem in this section requires that students select, from the infinite solution set for the inequality set up to solve the problem, the particular value that satisfies all the conditions of the problem.

Many of the verbal problems in this section parallel the settings of the verbal problems from Section 19-7 in which equations were solved. Thus, students have another opportunity to start from a familiar experience and accept a new challenge. The major difference, of course, is that the relationship is now inequality, rather than equality.

19-9 SOLVING FRACTIONAL EQUATIONS

The text distinguishes between an equation with fractional coefficients and a fractional equation, in which the variable appears in a denominator. In both cases, the procedure for solution involves using the L.C.D. to clear the equations of fractions.

Stress that, for an expression or equation involving a variable in a denominator, the domain of definition is limited to values of the variable that do not yield a denominator of 0.

When both sides of an equation are multiplied by some number, that number must be nonzero in order that the resulting equation will be equivalent to the original equation. When a fractional equation is multiplied by the L.C.D., which contains a variable, we must exclude all values of the variable that would make the denominators, and therefore the L.C.D., equal to 0. The solution set of the equation cannot contain values of the variable that make one or more of the denominators equal to 0.

To emphasize this requirement, you might ask students to tell, before they try to solve a fractional equation, for which values of the variable a particular equation is not defined. Example **b** shows that, when the only possible candidate for solution of a fractional equation is a value of the variable for which the equation is not defined, the solution set is empty.

It is necessary that students check the possible candidates for an answer before they write a solution set. Some of the fractional equations in the exercises have no solution. Students will be aware of this situation in Exercises 25–28, where they are asked to explain why there is no solution. They must continue to check their results, however, to spot other equations that have no solutions.

Emphasize that the check is to be done in the original equation, and that the method of solution is not repeated in the check. Instead, we work out the arithmetic separately for the left and right sides of the equation, as shown in Examples **a** and **b**.

Some of the fractional equations in the exercises can be solved as proportions, obtaining the products of the means and extremes. Ask students to recall the definition of a proportion as an equation in which each side is a ratio.

Exercises 31 and 32 appear to lead to second-degree equations. If the equations are solved correctly, however, the square terms cancel.

Note that fractional inequalities are not included in this course. You may want to mention to students the complexity of solving a fractional inequality. Because the L.C.D. contains a variable, we must consider two separate cases in the solution to a fractional inequality: when we are multiplying by a positive number (and the order of the inequality remains unchanged), and when we are multiplying by a negative number (and the order of the inequality changes).

19-10 EQUATIONS AND FORMULAS INVOLVING SEVERAL VARIABLES

Literal equations, including formulas, can be solved for any indicated variable. At the outset, it is helpful to relate the solution of a literal equation to the solution of a corresponding equation in which numbers replace all but the indicated variable. This procedure is shown in the Example, and should be reviewed in class before students attempt to answer the exercises.

See **Enrichment Activity 19-10: Fractions Between Fractions.** Students apply a simple rule to two unequal positive fractions to find a third fraction that lies somewhere *between* them. Students should discover that this fraction is not the average of the other two. By examining a series of cases where denominators are equal, the rule for the average of two such fractions can be found. (This activity can be extended for students who seek a true challenge by asking them to discover the rule for the average of the general fractions $\frac{a}{b}$ and $\frac{c}{d}$, where $b > 0, d > 0$.)

Name _____ Class _____ Date _____

ENRICHMENT ACTIVITY 19-2

IS IT MAGIC OR IS IT MATH?

A mathemagician said, "Write any positive fraction and follow these steps."

Step 1. To form a new fraction, let the new numerator = the old denominator, and let the new denominator = the sum of the old numerator and the old denominator.

Step 2. Repeat Step 1, using the new fraction to form yet another fraction. Continue repeating this process until you have <u>six</u> fractions, including your original fraction.

Example: $\dfrac{4}{1} \to \dfrac{1}{5} \to \dfrac{5}{6} \to \dfrac{6}{11} \to \dfrac{11}{17} \to \dfrac{17}{28}$

The mathemagician said, "I know the sixth fraction, to the *nearest tenth,* equals 0.6." It can be shown that $\dfrac{17}{28} = 0.6$ to the *nearest tenth,* so the mathemagician is correct.

1. Follow the mathemagician's rules, using each fraction shown below, until you have six fractions. In each case, does the sixth fraction, to the *nearest tenth,* equal 0.6?

   a. $\dfrac{3}{5} \to$

   b. $\dfrac{2}{13} \to$

2. Write three fractions of your choice, and try the rules using each of these fractions. In each case, does the sixth fraction, to the *nearest tenth,* equal 0.6?

   a.

   b.

   c.

3. Follow the mathemagician's rules using the algebraic fraction $\dfrac{x}{y}$ ($x > 0, y > 0$).

   $\dfrac{x}{y} \to$

4. The following statement is true for all positive values of *a, b, c,* and *d*:

   $$\text{If } \frac{a}{b} < \frac{c}{d}, \qquad \text{then} \qquad \frac{a}{b} < \frac{a+c}{b+d} < \frac{c}{d}$$

   Apply this statement to the <u>sixth</u> algebraic fraction formed in Exercise 3 to show why the mathemagician is always correct.

5. Apply the mathemagician's rules to form <u>seven</u> fractions instead of six. Expand the examples in Exercises 1 and 2, or try some new examples.

   a. What is the value, to the *nearest hundredth,* of the seventh fraction?

   b. Use algebraic methods to show that your answer to part **a** is correct.

Name _____ Class _____ Date _____

ENRICHMENT ACTIVITY 19-6

OPERATIONS WITH FRACTIONS

All variables on this page represent positive numbers: $x > 0, y > 0, w > 0.$

In 1 and 2, A and B represent given fractions. In each case, find the sum, difference, product, and quotient of the given fractions.

	A	B	$A + B$	$A - B$	$A \cdot B$	$A \div B$
1.	$\dfrac{x}{y}$	$\dfrac{w}{y}$				
2.	$\dfrac{x}{y}$	w				

3. If the product in Exercise 1 is greater than the product in Exercise 2, which of the following is a possible value for y?

   (1) 0   (2) $\dfrac{2}{3}$ (3) 1   (4) $\dfrac{3}{2}$

4. If the quotient in Exercise 1 is greater than the quotient in Exercise 2, which of the following is a possible value for y?

   (1) 0   (2) $\dfrac{2}{3}$ (3) 1   (4) $\dfrac{3}{2}$

5. If the difference in Exercise 1 is greater than the difference in Exercise 2, which of the following is a possible value for y?

   (1) 0   (2) $\dfrac{4}{7}$ (3) 1   (4) $\dfrac{7}{4}$

6. If the sum in Exercise 1 is greater than the sum in Exercise 2, which of the following is a possible value for y?

   (1) 0   (2) $\dfrac{4}{7}$ (3) 1   (4) $\dfrac{7}{4}$

7. If the quotients in Exercises 1 and 2 are equal, what is the value of y?

8. Explain why the sum in Exercise 1 *cannot* equal the difference in Exercise 1.

9. If the sum in Exercise 1 is equal to the product in Exercise 1, can $x = 1$ and $y = 1$ at the same time? Explain your answer.

In 10–12, the sum in Exercise 1 is equal to the product in Exercise 1, and the values of two variables are given. In each case, find the value of the third variable.

10. If $x = 2$ and $y = 1$, find the value of w.

11. If $y = 1$ and $w = 5$, find the value of x.

12. If $x = 1$ and $w = 2$, find the value of y.

Name _____ Class _____ Date _____

ENRICHMENT ACTIVITY 19-10

FRACTIONS BETWEEN FRACTIONS

If two positive fractions are unequal, it is always possible to find a fraction that lies somewhere *between* them by applying this rule:

Let the numerator of the new fraction = the sum of the numerators, and the denominator of the new fraction = the sum of the denominators.

Example: $\frac{1}{4} < \frac{2}{5}$. Then, $\quad \frac{1}{4} < \frac{1+2}{4+5} < \frac{2}{5} \quad$ or $\quad \frac{1}{4} < \frac{3}{9} < \frac{2}{5}$

Convert the fractions to decimals as a check: $0.25 < 0.\overline{33} < 0.40$.

1. In each case, demonstrate the rule shown above by using the given fractions. As a check, convert each fraction displayed in the last step to decimal form.

   a. $\frac{2}{3} < \frac{4}{5}$ **b.** $\frac{9}{4} < \frac{14}{5}$ **c.** $\frac{7}{8} < \frac{19}{20}$

2. Demonstrate and check the rule using three examples of your choice.

   a.   **b.**   **c.**

3. The rule stated above can be written in general terms as follows:

   > If $\frac{a}{b} < \frac{c}{d}$, then $\frac{a}{b} < \frac{a+c}{b+d} < \frac{c}{d}$ $(a > 0,\ b > 0,\ c > 0,\ d > 0)$

   Is the fraction $\frac{a+c}{b+d}$ the average of $\frac{a}{b}$ and $\frac{c}{d}$? Explain your answer.

4. Test and check the rule again using examples where the denominators are equal.

   a. $\frac{3}{4} < \frac{9}{4}$ **b.** $\frac{1}{6} < \frac{5}{6}$ **c.** $\frac{9}{2} < \frac{10}{2}$

5. **a.** Write a new rule in general terms for the examples from Exercise 4. (Let $d = b$.)

   b. Does the rule from part **a** always find the average of two fractions whose denominators are equal? Explain your answer.

SUGGESTED TEST ITEMS (CHAPTER 19)

1. For what value of x is the fraction $\dfrac{2x-5}{x+4}$ undefined?

In 2–5, express each fraction as an equivalent fraction in lowest terms.

2. $\dfrac{9x^2y}{27xy^2}$ **3.** $\dfrac{3a+3b}{6}$ **4.** $\dfrac{9c^3-3c^2}{9c^4}$ **5.** $\dfrac{4xy+2y}{20xy}$

In 6–14, perform each indicated operation and express the answer in lowest terms.

6. $\dfrac{5x^2}{6}\cdot\dfrac{12}{25x}$ **7.** $\dfrac{6y-12}{8}\cdot\dfrac{4y}{3y^2}$ **8.** $12x^2\div\dfrac{4x}{3}$

9. $3x\cdot\dfrac{1}{5x}$ **10.** $3x+\dfrac{1}{5x}$ **11.** $\dfrac{x-5}{3}+\dfrac{2x+3}{5}$

12. $\dfrac{2}{3x}\div\dfrac{6}{4x}$ **13.** $\dfrac{a+2}{5a}-\dfrac{a+5}{2a}$ **14.** $\dfrac{a}{6}\div\dfrac{7a}{12}$

15. If the length of a rectangle is represented by $\dfrac{3b}{4}$ and the width is represented by $\dfrac{2b}{5}$, represent the perimeter of the rectangle in lowest terms.

In 16–21, solve and check each equation:

16. $\dfrac{3x-7}{5x}=\dfrac{1}{4}$ **17.** $\dfrac{1}{2}a-\dfrac{1}{3}a=\dfrac{5}{6}$ **18.** $\dfrac{y}{3}+12=\dfrac{5y}{9}$

19. $\dfrac{x-3}{2}=\dfrac{x+5}{3}$ **20.** $\dfrac{3b}{4}-\dfrac{b+4}{6}=\dfrac{5}{3}$ **21.** $0.2d+1=0.24d$

In 22 and 23, use an algebraic solution to solve each problem.

22. When 9 is added to $\dfrac{2}{3}$ of a number, the result is $\dfrac{7}{6}$ of the number. What is the number?

23. A child's bank contains 22 coins. There are twice as many dimes as nickels, and the remaining coins are quarters. What is the greatest possible number of quarters in the bank if the value of the coins is at most $3.50?

BONUS: Of a group of persons questioned, two-thirds said that they read newspapers and three-fourths said that they listened to the news on television. One-tenth said that they neither read newspapers nor listened to the news on television.

         a. What fractional part of the group questioned both read newspapers and listened to the news on television?

         b. What is the least number of persons that could have been surveyed?

SAT PREPARATION EXERCISES (CHAPTER 19)

I. Multiple-Choice Questions

In 1–10, select the letter of the correct answer.

1. If $\frac{x}{3} + \frac{y}{4} = 10$ and y is twice x, what is the average (arithmetic mean) of $\frac{x}{3}$ and $\frac{y}{4}$?

    (A) 20   (B) 18   (C) 12

    (D) 10   (E) 5

2. If $\frac{x}{3} + \frac{y}{4} + \frac{z}{5} = 1\frac{1}{4}$, what is the value of $20x + 15y + 12z$?

    (A) 30   (B) 45   (C) 75

    (D) 105   (E) $47xyz$

3. If PQ is $\frac{2}{3}$ of PR and PR is $\frac{3}{4}$ of PS, then PQ is what fraction of PS?

    (A) $\frac{6}{7}$ (B) $\frac{7}{8}$ (C) $\frac{8}{9}$

    (D) $\frac{9}{10}$ (E) $\frac{1}{2}$

4. If the product of two monomials is $-9x^4y^5$ and one of the factors is $-9xy$, which of the following is the other factor?

    (A) $-x^3y^4$ (B) x^3y^4 (C) $9x^3y^4$
    (D) $81x^4y^5$ (E) $81x^5y^6$

5. If $\frac{1}{xy} + \frac{1}{yz} + \frac{1}{xz} = P$, and twice the reciprocal of P is xyz, what is the value of $x + y + z$?

    (A) 1   (B) 2   (C) $\frac{1}{2}$

    (D) 0   (E) $2P$

6. Which of the following represents $\frac{3x + 5}{7} - \frac{2 - 3x}{7}$ in the simplest form?

    (A) 1   (B) $\frac{3}{7}$ (C) $\frac{6x + 3}{14}$

    (D) $\frac{6x + 7}{14}$ (E) $\frac{6x + 3}{7}$

7. Determine the value of $\frac{3x - 1}{2x - 2} + \frac{9}{2x - 2}$ when $x = -1$.

    (A) $\frac{5}{4}$ (B) $\frac{-5}{4}$ (C) $\frac{13}{4}$

    (D) $\frac{-13}{4}$ (E) Undefined

8. The lengths of the sides of a triangle are in the ratio of $\frac{1}{3} : \frac{1}{2} : \frac{1}{4}$. If the perimeter is 130, determine the length of the shortest side.

    (A) 27   (B) 30   (C) 32.5

    (D) 33   (E) 42

9. Which of the following represents the width of a rectangle if the area is $x^2 - 5x + 6$ and its length is $4x - 12$?

    (A) $\frac{(x + 2)(x + 3)}{4(x + 3)}$

    (B) $\frac{(x + 6)(x + 1)}{4x - 12}$

    (C) $\frac{(x - 2)(x + 3)}{4(x - 3)}$

    (D) $\frac{(x + 6)(x - 1)}{4x - 12}$

    (E) $\frac{(x - 2)}{4}$

10. The numerator of a fraction is ten less than its denominator. If the value of the fraction is $\frac{8}{9}$, which of the following is the fraction?

(A) $\frac{6}{16}$ (B) $\frac{10}{17}$ (C) $\frac{26}{36}$

(D) $\frac{80}{90}$ (E) $\frac{71}{81}$

II. Quantitative Comparison Questions

Questions 11–17 each consist of two quantities, one in Column A and one in Column B. You are to compare the two quantities and choose:

   A if the quantity in Column A is greater;
   B if the quantity in Column B is greater;
   C if the two quantities are equal;
   D if the relationship cannot be determined from the information given.

Notes

1. In certain questions, information concerning one or both of the quantities to be compared is centered above the two columns.
2. In a given question, a symbol that appears in both columns represents the same thing in Column A as it does in Column B.
3. Letters such as x, n, and k stand for real numbers.

Column A	*Column B*

11. $\frac{10}{20} + \frac{2}{4}$ $\frac{10+2}{20+4}$

---

12. $\quad\quad 1 < \frac{x}{y} < 2$

y x

---

13. $\quad\quad 0 < x < y < 1$

xy $x + y$

14.

5 in.   5 in.

2 in. | **I**   2 in. | 60° **II**

The area of rectangle **I**   The area of parallelogram **II**

---

15. $\quad\quad x \neq 0 \text{ and } y \neq 0$

$\frac{5}{x^2y} + \frac{5y}{2x}$ $\frac{5y + 2x}{x^2y^2}$

---

16. $\frac{2a+5}{3} - \frac{a-2}{4}$ $\frac{5a+26}{12}$

---

17. $\quad\quad y > x$

$y + \frac{x}{2}$ $x + \frac{y}{2}$

III. Student-Produced Response Questions

In questions 18–22, you are to solve the problem.

18. The average (arithmetic mean) of a number and 2 is $\frac{17}{15}$. Determine the value of the number.

19. One pipe fills a tank in 40 minutes and another pipe fills it in an hour. A third pipe empties the tank in 30 minutes. In how many minutes will the tank be filled if all three pipes are opened at the same time?

20. What is the ratio of acid to the total volume of a solution containing 12 ml of acid in 16 ml of water?

21. For what positive value of the variable x is $\frac{x^2}{16 - x^2}$ not defined?

22. What was the percent of discount if a $15.00 item was purchased for $12.00? Express the discount as a percent.

Chapter 20
Operations with Radicals

Aims

- To define a radical, and to distinguish between radicals that are rational and those that are irrational.
- To study procedures involving square-root radicals and rational approximations on a calculator.
- To demonstrate the fundamental operations with square-root radicals

The introductory page of this chapter serves as a reminder to students of the role played by rational approximations for irrational numbers. This concept was first introduced in Chapter 1 and has been reinforced by calculator exercises throughout the book.

Students will discover that many radicals are irrational and that care must be taken when performing operations with these numbers on a calculator. In later sections of this chapter, as the fundamental operations with radicals are presented, the role of the calculator should be minimized so that students will learn procedures to find exact solutions expressed in simplest radical form.

20-1 RADICALS AND THE RATIONAL NUMBERS

The operations of squaring a number and of finding the square root of a positive number, mentioned briefly in Chapter 1, serve as the starting

point for the study of radicals. Students are again reminded of the calculator keys for these operations, and are asked to determine which sequence of key strokes will produce correct values when a specific calculator is used.

A key idea presented here is that the square root of every perfect square is a rational number. Examples and exercises in this section are limited to radicals that are rational.

It is important that students understand the symbolism associated with square roots.

1. The principal or positive square root is expressed by using no sign or by using $+$, as in $\sqrt{36} = +\sqrt{36} = 6$.

2. The negative square root is expressed by using $-$, as in $-\sqrt{36} = -6$.

3. The two square roots, positive and negative, are expressed by using both signs, $\pm$, as in $\pm\sqrt{36} = \pm 6$.

Special care must be taken when using the sign-change key, $\boxed{+/-}$, to find the negative root of a number on a calculator. Again, students are asked to determine which sequence of key strokes will produce a correct value when using this key on a specific calculator.

The roots of an equation of the form $x^2 = a$, where a is positive, are the two square roots of a,

241

that is, $\pm\sqrt{a}$. Therefore, the solution set of $x^2 = 36$ is $\{-6, 6\}$ or $\{\pm 6\}$.

Discuss the square root of a negative number. Students should understand that the square root of a negative number does not exist in the set of real numbers.

Students are introduced briefly to other roots of a number in the general form $\sqrt[n]{b}$, where n is the index of the radical and b is the radicand. Be sure that students understand that, when no index is written, the index is understood to be 2. Compare even and odd roots of negative numbers.

Be sure that students understand the following: $\sqrt{-4}$ does not exist in the set of real numbers since the product of two equal factors cannot be -4.

$\sqrt[3]{-8} = -2$ since $-2(-2)(-2) = -8$.

$\sqrt[4]{-16}$ does not exist in the set of real numbers since the product of four equal factors cannot be -16.

$\sqrt[5]{-32} = -2$ since $-2(-2)(-2)(-2)(-2) = -32$.

It is useful for students to memorize the list of perfect squares from $1^2 = 1$ to $25^2 = 625$.

Point out that in Exercise 74, to evaluate $\sqrt{(-9)^2}$, we must carry out the squaring process first to obtain a number that is defined for the set of real numbers, that is, the square root of a positive number. Thus, $\sqrt{(-9)^2} = \sqrt{81} = 9$. Note that we cannot apply the definition of inverse operations here because the operation of square root is not defined for a negative number in the set of real numbers.

To evaluate $\sqrt{(9)^2}$, we can apply the definition of inverse operations, thus obtaining 9. Of course, we can also square first.

20-2 RADICALS AND THE IRRATIONAL NUMBERS

Once students understand that the square root of a perfect square is a rational number, it is natural for them to see that the square root of a positive number that is not a perfect square is irrational. Remind students that a calculator displays a *rational approximation* for every irrational number entered.

There are hints that help us to identify certain numbers as rational or irrational, whether or not we use a calculator. Suppose, for example, that we need to determine whether $\sqrt{3}$ is rational or irrational. We use a calculator as follows:

Enter: 3 $\boxed{\sqrt{x}}$

Display: $\boxed{\text{1.7320508}}$

In this section, a procedure is established whereby the display is cleared and the resulting number is then squared, demonstrating that $(1.7320508)^2 \neq 3$.

Enter: 1.7320508 $\boxed{x^2}$

Display: $\boxed{\text{2.9999999}}$

If we consider the ending or last digit of a number obtained by squaring:

$0^2 = 0$	$1^2 = 1$	$2^2 = 4$	$3^2 = 9$
$4^2 = 16$, ending in 6		$5^2 = 25$, ending in 5	
$6^2 = 36$, ending in 6		$7^2 = 49$, ending in 9	
$8^2 = 64$, ending in 4		$9^2 = 81$, ending in 1	

we see that the last nonzero digit of a perfect square must be 1, 4, 5, 6, or 9.

Therefore, since $3 = 3.00000000\ldots$, the last nonzero digit of this number is 3. But no digit, when squared, ends in 3, indicating that the number 3 is not a perfect square and that $\sqrt{3}$ must be irrational.

For the same reason, any whole number whose ending or units digit is 2, 3, 7, or 8 cannot be a perfect square, and its square root must be an irrational number.

The general rules stated in this section for working with radicals apply to all radicals, whether rational or irrational. The first rule, which typically applies to radicals that are irrational, is the most important, namely, it is best to state the *exact* answer in radical form. Other rules are given as aids when students use estimation or rounded values to express radical numbers. Estimation does play an important role when working with radicals that are irrational, as seen in Example 1 in this section.

See *Enrichment Activity 20-2: Square Root: Divide and Average.* An algorithm is presented to approximate the square root of a number using the basic operations of division and finding an average. Students are led through an example and are then asked to find a series of square roots using the procedure that has been illustrated. The square-root key on the calculator is *not* to be used when doing this activity.

20-3 FINDING THE PRINCIPAL SQUARE ROOT OF A MONOMIAL

Students often write $\sqrt{a^9}$ as a^3. Show that if this result is true, then $a^3 \cdot a^3 = a^9$ must also be true. But, since we add exponents when powers of like bases are multiplied, $a^3 \cdot a^3 = a^6$, not a^9. Similarly, ask why the square root of any monomial in the form $\sqrt{a^n}$, where n is a positive even integer, is computed as $\left| a^{\frac{n}{2}} \right|$.

In this section, all radicands in the exercises are perfect squares.

20-4 SIMPLIFYING A SQUARE-ROOT RADICAL

Starting with this section, you should stress algebraic manipulation rather than calculator usage. As seen in the demonstration in the text, the calculator is used only in checking. If both the original radical and its simplified form produce the same calculator display, we are reasonably certain that the radical has been simplified correctly.

Often, when simplifying a radical, students do not find the largest perfect square factor. Therefore, the radical is not expressed in simplest form. In this case, remind students to make sure that the remaining radicand has no perfect square factor other than 1. The process may have to be repeated, especially when the largest perfect square factor is not easily recognizable (example: $\sqrt{180}$). Note that this process is similar to reducing fractions to lowest terms.

We now have a method of simplifying a square-root radical in the form $\sqrt{a^n}$, where n is a positive odd integer (example: $\sqrt{a^5} = \sqrt{a^4}\sqrt{a} = a^2\sqrt{a}$).

Remind students with numerical examples that the square root of the sum or difference of nonnegative numbers is not equal to the respective sum or difference of the square roots of the numbers. For example:

$$\sqrt{36} + \sqrt{64} \neq \sqrt{36 + 64}$$
$$\sqrt{36} + \sqrt{64} \neq \sqrt{100}$$
$$6 + 8 \neq 10$$
$$14 \neq 10$$

In the same way, use a calculator to demonstrate this concept with radicals that are irrational:

$$\sqrt{2} + \sqrt{5} \neq \sqrt{2 + 5}$$
$$\sqrt{2} + \sqrt{5} \neq 7$$
$$1.4142136 + 2.2360680 \neq 2.6457513$$
$$3.6502816 \neq 2.6457513$$

20-5 ADDITION AND SUBTRACTION OF RADICALS

Compare the addition and subtraction of radicals to the same operation involving fractions or monomials.

Like fractions:

$$\frac{8}{9} + \frac{7}{9} = (8 + 7)\frac{1}{9} = \frac{15}{9}$$

Like monomials:

$$8x + 7x = (8 + 7)x = 15x$$

Like radicals:

$$8\sqrt{2} + 7\sqrt{2} = (8 + 7)\sqrt{2} = 15\sqrt{2}$$

Unlike fractions can always be changed to like fractions and combined:

$$\frac{1}{10} + \frac{1}{3} = \frac{3}{30} + \frac{10}{30} = \frac{13}{30}$$

Unlike monomials cannot be changed to like monomials unless some special relationship exists among the variables. For example, if we know that $y = 5x$, then $2x + 3y$ can be expressed as a monomial, $17x$. Otherwise, the binomial $2x + 3y$ is in simplest form.

It may or may not be possible to combine unlike radicals. For example, $2\sqrt{2} + 3\sqrt{3}$ is in simplest form. On the other hand, the following unlike radicals can be combined after they are simplified:

$$\sqrt{50} + \sqrt{8} = 5\sqrt{2} + 2\sqrt{2} = 7\sqrt{2}$$

20-6 MULTIPLICATION OF SQUARE-ROOT RADICALS

Just as

$$(5x)(3y) = (5 \cdot 3)(xy) = 15xy$$

so also

$$(5\sqrt{2})(3\sqrt{3}) = (5 \cdot 3)(\sqrt{2 \cdot 3}) = 15\sqrt{6}.$$

Students should recognize that like and unlike square-root radicals can be multiplied.

Ask what happens when any square-root radical is multiplied by itself. For example:

1. $\sqrt{7} \cdot \sqrt{7} = \sqrt{49} = 7$

2. $\sqrt{24} \cdot \sqrt{24} = \sqrt{576} = 24$

As students realize that $(\sqrt{a})^2 = a$ when $a \geq 0$, they will discover that it is not necessary to multiply the radicands to find the product.

20-7 DIVISION OF SQUARE-ROOT RADICALS

Be sure students apply the following property of square-root radicals correctly:

$$\sqrt{\frac{a}{b}} = \frac{\sqrt{a}}{\sqrt{b}} \qquad \text{and} \qquad \frac{\sqrt{a}}{\sqrt{b}} = \sqrt{\frac{a}{b}}$$

Some students will try to divide and simplify in cases where the property does not apply. For example, $\frac{\sqrt{12}}{2} \neq \sqrt{6}$. If this error occurs, ask students to check by multiplying. Does $2\sqrt{6} = \sqrt{12}$? Since $\sqrt{24} = \sqrt{4} \cdot \sqrt{6} = 2\sqrt{6}$, and $\sqrt{24} \neq \sqrt{12}$, we know that $2\sqrt{6} \neq \sqrt{12}$. How can we simplify $\frac{\sqrt{12}}{2}$? The correct procedure:

$$\frac{\sqrt{12}}{2} = \frac{\sqrt{4} \cdot \sqrt{3}}{2} = \frac{2\sqrt{3}}{2} = \sqrt{3}$$

can lead into a discussion of the cancellation laws.

The process of rationalizing the denominator is formalized in Course III.

See *Enrichment Activity 20-7: Operations with Radicals.* The 25 parts of Exercise 1, which include all basic operations with radicals, form the basis for a puzzle. If all the parts of Exercise 1 are performed without error, students will appreciate the answer to both parts of Exercise 3.

Name _____ Class _____ Date _____

ENRICHMENT ACTIVITY 20-2

SQUARE ROOT: DIVIDE AND AVERAGE

Principle 1: If the divisor of a number and the resulting quotient are equal, then the square root of the number is either the divisor or the quotient. (See example at right.)

$$12\overline{)144} \begin{smallmatrix}12\\ \end{smallmatrix} \to \sqrt{144} = 12$$

Principle 2: If a divisor and a quotient of a number are unequal, then the square root of the number is between the divisor and the quotient. (See example at right.)

$$9\overline{)144} \begin{smallmatrix}16\\ \end{smallmatrix} \to \sqrt{144} \text{ is between 9 and 16}$$

The two principles shown above lead us to a method to approximate the square root of a number. This method, called ***divide and average,*** can be used when you have lost your calculator or its square-root key is broken.

EXAMPLE

Use the divide and average method to find $\sqrt{14}$ to the *nearest hundredth*.

(1) Guess the square root. Divide the number by your guess. Extend the quotient to one more decimal place than the divisor:

$$4\overline{)14.0} \begin{smallmatrix}3.5\\ \end{smallmatrix}$$

(2) Since the square root is between the divisor and the quotient, find the average of the divisor and the quotient:

$$\frac{4 + 3.5}{2} = \frac{7.5}{2} = 3.75$$

Keep repeating steps 1 and 2, but each time use the average as the new divisor.

(3) Divide:

$$3.75\overline{)14.00,000} \begin{smallmatrix}3.733\\ \end{smallmatrix}$$

(4) Average:

$$\frac{3.75 + 3.733}{2} = \frac{7.483}{2} = 3.7415$$

(5) At this point, round the average to the nearest hundredth and state the result:

$$\sqrt{14} \approx 3.74 \quad \textit{Answer}$$

Note: The more times you repeat the steps, the closer the divisor and quotient become. If steps 1 and 2 are repeated using the average 3.7415, the square root becomes more precise.

Divide: $3.7415\overline{)14.0000,00000} \begin{smallmatrix}3.74181\\ \end{smallmatrix}$ Average: $\dfrac{3.7415 + 3.74181}{2} = \dfrac{7.48331}{2} = 3.741655$

(Actually, $\sqrt{14} = 3.7416$ to the *nearest ten thousandth,* which is close to the average above.)

Name _____ Class _____ Date _____

In 1–12, in each case, use the ***divide and average*** method to find the square root to the *nearest hundredth*. (You may use a calculator to divide and to find an average, but do *not* use the square-root key $\boxed{\sqrt{x}}$ on the calculator.)

1. $\sqrt{50}$ _____   **2.** $\sqrt{40}$ _____   **3.** $\sqrt{6}$ _____   **4.** $\sqrt{88}$ _____

5. $\sqrt{108}$ _____   **6.** $\sqrt{290}$ _____   **7.** $\sqrt{11}$ _____   **8.** $\sqrt{529}$ _____

9. $\sqrt{614}$ _____   **10.** $\sqrt{0.6}$ _____   **11.** $\sqrt{0.3}$ _____   **12.** $\sqrt{2,525}$ _____

13. Which numbers in Exercises 1–12, if any, are rational? Explain your answer.

14. Use the divide and average method to find $\sqrt{10}$ to the *nearest thousandth*.

15. Use the divide and average method to find $\sqrt{102}$ to the *nearest thousandth*.

Name _____ Class _____ Date _____

ENRICHMENT ACTIVITY 20-7

OPERATIONS WITH RADICALS

1. For each of the 25 parts of this exercise, perform the indicated operation(s) and write the answer in simplest radical form. (*Note:* Many answers will match, and these will be used to answer Exercises 2 and 3, which follow.)

a. $\sqrt{18}$ _____   **b.** $\sqrt{704}$ _____

c. $\dfrac{3}{2}\sqrt{8}$ _____   **d.** $\sqrt{108} + \sqrt{45}$ _____

e. $\sqrt{10} + \dfrac{1}{2}\sqrt{40}$ _____   **f.** $\sqrt{25} - \sqrt{12}$ _____

g. $\sqrt{8}(\sqrt{34}) - 2\sqrt{68}$ _____   **h.** $\sqrt{180} - \sqrt{80}$ _____

i. $2\sqrt{48} - \sqrt{12} - 2\sqrt{27}$ _____   **j.** $(4 + \sqrt{3})(2 - \sqrt{3})$ _____

k. $5\sqrt{3} \cdot 2\sqrt{2}$ _____   **l.** $(1 + \sqrt{3})(1 + \sqrt{3})$ _____

m. $\sqrt{11} \cdot \sqrt{77}$ _____   **n.** $3\sqrt{12} + 3\sqrt{5}$ _____

o. $\sqrt{7} + \sqrt{63} + \sqrt{343}$ _____   **p.** $(\sqrt{6})^2 - (\sqrt{3})^2$ _____

q. $\sqrt{54} + 7\sqrt{6}$ _____   **r.** $\dfrac{18\sqrt{15}}{9\sqrt{3}}$ _____

s. $\sqrt{45} \div \sqrt{9}$ _____   **t.** $\sqrt{2}(\sqrt{8} + \sqrt{6})$ _____

u. $\sqrt{1100} - 2\sqrt{11}$ _____   **v.** $(-\sqrt{30})(\dfrac{1}{2}\sqrt{6})$ _____

w. $(\sqrt{5} + \sqrt{2})(\sqrt{5} - \sqrt{2})$ _____   **x.** $\sqrt{20} - \sqrt{125}$ _____

y. $\sqrt{32} - \sqrt{2} + \sqrt{8}$ _____

Name _____ Class _____ Date _____

2. Of the 25 answers obtained in Exercise 1, exactly 11 answers match 11 other answers. In the table that follows, write the letters of the answers that match and indicate each common answer. For example, parts **a** and **c** match because each value equals $3\sqrt{2}$.

Matches	Common Answer		Matches	Common Answer
a − c	$3\sqrt{2}$			

3. Of the 25 answers obtained in Exercise 1, exactly three answers have no match.

   a. Multiply the three answers that have no match, and write the product in simplest form. _____

   b. Arrange the letters that designate these three answers to form a commonly used word, and write that word here. _____

SUGGESTED TEST ITEMS (CHAPTER 20)

1. State whether each number is rational or irrational.
   a. 7
   b. $\sqrt{7}$
   c. $\sqrt{98}$
   d. $\sqrt{169}$
   e. 0.73
   f. $0.\overline{73}$
   g. $2 + \sqrt{2}$

2. Simplify each of the following:
   a. $\sqrt{3} + \sqrt{27}$
   b. $\sqrt{98} - \sqrt{32}$
   c. $3\sqrt{2}(4\sqrt{3})$
   d. $5\sqrt{5}(3\sqrt{5})$
   e. $\sqrt{\dfrac{64}{4}}$
   f. $\sqrt{\dfrac{125}{5}}$
   g. $\dfrac{\sqrt{72}}{3}$

3. Simplify each of the following. Assume that all variables represent positive numbers.
   a. $\sqrt{121a^4}$
   b. $\sqrt{0.36x^2}$
   c. $\left(\sqrt{3y^3}\right)^2$
   d. $\sqrt{a}(3\sqrt{a})$

4. What is the approximate value of $\sqrt{20}$ to the *nearest tenth*?

5. Solve and check:
   a. $x^2 = 1.44$
   b. $5x^2 = 245$

6. Evaluate each expression by using a calculator.
   a. $\sqrt[3]{50{,}653}$
   b. $-\sqrt{36.9664}$
   c. $\sqrt[4]{33.1776}$

7. Between which two consecutive integers is $\sqrt{250}$?

In 8–9, for each irrational number, write a rational approximation: **a.** as shown on a calculator display **b.** rounded to four significant digits

8. $\sqrt{92}$

9. $-\sqrt{2{,}200}$

In 10 and 11, select the numeral preceding the expression that best completes the statement.

10. Which of the following numerical expressions is an irrational number?
    (1) $(\sqrt{2})^2$
    (2) $(2 + \sqrt{2})(2 - \sqrt{2})$
    (3) $(2 + \sqrt{2})^2$
    (4) $\sqrt{2})(\sqrt{8})$

11. The largest number in $\{1.\overline{3},\ 1.31,\ 1.\overline{31},\ 1.3\overline{1}\}$ is
    (1) $1.\overline{3}$
    (2) 1.31
    (3) $1.\overline{31}$
    (4) $1.3\overline{1}$

12. The length of the rectangle at the right is $5\sqrt{10}$ inches, and the width is $4\sqrt{15}$ inches.

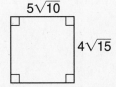

$5\sqrt{10}$

$4\sqrt{15}$

   a. Which side is greater: the length or the width?

   b. Express the perimeter of the rectangle
      (1) in simplest radical form
      (2) rounded to the *nearest hundredth*

   c. Express the area of the rectangle
      (1) in simplest radical form
      (2) rounded to the *nearest hundredth*

SAT PREPARATION EXERCISES (CHAPTER 20)

I. Multiple-Choice Questions

In 1–13, select the letter of the correct answer.

1. The area of a rectangle is 64 and the base is $4\sqrt{2}$. What is the perimeter of the rectangle?

    (A) $32\sqrt{2}$ (B) $24\sqrt{2}$ (C) $16\sqrt{2}$

    (D) $12\sqrt{2}$ (E) $8\sqrt{2}$

2.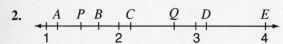

    In the figure above, P is located at $\sqrt{2}$ and Q is located at $\sqrt{8}$. Which of the following points is located closest to the average (arithmetic mean) of $\sqrt{2}$ and $\sqrt{8}$?

    (A) A (B) B (C) C

    (D) D (E) E

3. If $\dfrac{\sqrt{x}}{\sqrt{y}} = k$, where k is a whole number,

    which of the following ordered pairs does *not* satisfy the equation above?

    (A) $(100, 25)$ (B) $(36, 9)$ (C) $(12, 9)$

    (D) $(54, 6)$ (E) $(135, 15)$

4. If $\sqrt{36x^6} = 48$, evaluate $\sqrt{36x^2}$.

    (A) 6   (B) 12   (C) 16

    (D) 24   (E) 32

5. If $x + \sqrt{2} = \sqrt{4}$ and $y + \sqrt{8} = \sqrt{16}$, what is the ratio of x to y?

    (A) $\dfrac{\sqrt{2}}{\sqrt{16}}$ (B) $\dfrac{1}{4}$ (C) $\dfrac{1}{\sqrt{2}}$

    (D) $\dfrac{1}{2}$ (E) $\dfrac{1}{3}$

6. If $x\sqrt{8} - y\sqrt{3} = 1$, which of the following does *not* lie on the graph of the line?

    (A) $(\sqrt{2}, \sqrt{3})$ (B) $(-\sqrt{8}, -\sqrt{27})$

    (C) $(-1, \sqrt{3})$ (D) $(4\sqrt{2}, 5\sqrt{3})$

    (E) $\left(\dfrac{\sqrt{2}}{4}, 0\right)$

7.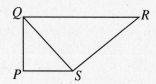

    $\triangle QPS \sim \triangle RSQ$

    In the figure above, if $QS = 6$, $SR = 6\sqrt{2}$, and $QR = 12$, what is the value of QP?

    (A) 6   (B) 3   (C) $3\sqrt{2}$

    (D) $\sqrt{2}$ (E) 2

8.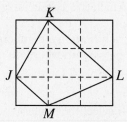

    The square above is divided by the dashed lines into 9 one-foot squares. What is the perimeter, in feet, of the quadrilateral *JKLM* inscribed in the square?

    (A) $8\sqrt{2}$ (B) $4\sqrt{5} + 3\sqrt{2}$

    (C) $2\sqrt{2} + 2\sqrt{5}$ (D) $3\sqrt{2} + 2\sqrt{5}$

    (E) $4\sqrt{5}$

9. Let $a \mathbf{\ T\ } b = \sqrt{a^2 + b^2}$ for all real numbers a and b. Which of the following is *not* equal to $4 \mathbf{\ T\ } 5$?

    (A) $(4 \mathbf{\ T\ } 4) \mathbf{\ T\ } 3$ (B) $2\sqrt{10} \mathbf{\ T\ } 1$

    (C) $(6 \mathbf{\ T\ } 2) \mathbf{\ T\ } 1$ (D) $(3 \mathbf{\ T\ } 3) \mathbf{\ T\ } 5$

    (E) $(0 \mathbf{\ T\ } 1)(5 \mathbf{\ T\ } 4)$

10.

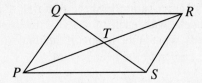

In parallelogram *PQRS* above, m∠*PQS* = 90°, *PQ* = 4, and *PT* = 5. What is the length of *QR*?

(A) $2\sqrt{13}$ (B) 6   (C) 8

(D) $3\sqrt{5}$ (E) 10

11. What is the distance from point $(1, -1)$ to point $(6, 11)$?

(A) 13   (B) 12   (C) 11

(D) 10   (E) 9

12.

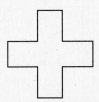

Each segment in the figure above has a length of 1 centimeter and each angle measures 90°. What is the greatest number of segments of length $\sqrt{2}$ centimeter that can be drawn lying in the interior of the figure with both endpoints on the border of the figure?

(A) 2   (B) 4   (C) 6

(D) 8   (E) 10

13.

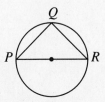

In the figure above, *PQ* = 6 and *QR* = 8. What is the area of the circle?

(A) 25π (B) 36π (C) 64π

(D) 100π (E) 128π

II. QUANTITATIVE COMPARISON QUESTIONS

Questions 14–18 each consist of two quantities, one in Column A and one in Column B. You are to compare the two quantities and choose:

A if the quantity in Column A is greater;
B if the quantity in Column B is greater;
C if the two quantities are equal;
D if the relationship cannot be determined from the information given.

Notes

1. In certain questions, information concerning one or both of the quantities to be compared is centered above the two columns.
2. In a given question, a symbol that appears in both columns represents the same thing in Column A as it does in Column B.
3. Letters such as *x*, *n*, and *k* stand for real numbers.

Column A	*Column B*
14. $\dfrac{1}{5}$	$\sqrt{\dfrac{1}{24}}$

15. The area of a square whose side measures $\dfrac{3\sqrt{2}}{2}$ The area of a square whose side measures $\dfrac{1}{2}\sqrt{18}$

16.

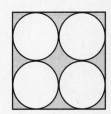

The squares have equal areas.

The shaded area above   The shaded area above

17. | The diameter of a circle with a circumference of 8π | The diameter of a circle with an area of 17π

---

18. $\qquad x = \sqrt{5}, y = \sqrt{3}$

$\qquad$ 3 $\qquad\qquad (x+y)(x-y)$

III. STUDENT-PRODUCED RESPONSE QUESTIONS

In questions 19–24, you are to solve the problem.

19. What is the approximate integral value of a side of a square whose area is 3 square units?

20. What is the integral value of n such that $n < \sqrt{5} < n + 1$?

21. If a garden is in the shape of a right isosceles triangle with each of the legs measuring 10 yards, what is the length of the longest side of the garden to the nearest yard?

22. Determine the perimeter of a square to the nearest hundredth if the diagonal of the square is $2\sqrt{2}$.

23. If a rectangular sheet of paper is 8 inches by 11 inches, how long is a side of a square sheet having the same area?

24. A stay wire that is fastened to a telephone pole reaches the ground 9 feet from the foot of the pole. If the wire is attached to the pole at a point which is 12 feet above the ground, what is the length, in feet, of the wire?

Chapter *21*
Quadratic Equations

Aims

- To solve quadratic equations of the form $ax^2 + bx + c = 0$ $(a \neq 0)$ by factoring, and to solve incomplete quadratic equations of the form $ax^2 + c = 0$ $(a \neq 0)$.

- To use the quadratic formula.

- To introduce verbal problems involving quadratic relationships, including the Pythagorean Theorem.

- To graph quadratic equations of the form $y = ax^2 + bx + c$ $(a \neq 0)$.

This chapter introduces the terminology and techniques necessary to solve second-degree equations in one variable and to graph quadratic functions. Some of this material, in particular the Pythagorean Theorem, will be familiar to students. All of it will be studied in detail in Course II. However, it is useful to have students discuss and work with the concepts presented here, which will enable them to approach familiar ideas from a new viewpoint.

21-1 THE STANDARD FORM OF A QUADRATIC EQUATION

Review with students the definition of a *polynomial* and the way in which we determine the degree of a polynomial. In this section the standard form of a second-degree polynomial equation or quadratic equation is defined since this is the form most often used to find the solution.

Call attention to the fact that an expression such as $\frac{x^2}{2} - \frac{x}{4} + 3$ which is the same as $\frac{1}{2}x^2 - \frac{1}{4}x + 3$ is a polynomial but $x - 5 + \frac{6}{x}$ is not a polynomial. However, the equation $x - 5 + \frac{6}{x} = 0$ can be transformed into the equivalent equation $x^2 - 5x + 6 = 0$ which is a polynomial equation.

Procedures for solving equations containing fractional coefficients should be reviewed before transforming an equation such as $\frac{x^2}{2} - 3 = \frac{x}{4}$ into the standard form.

21-2 SOLVING A QUADRATIC EQUATION BY FACTORING

The procedure for solving a quadratic equation by factoring rests on the multiplication property of 0 that allows us to apply the principle $ab = 0$ if and only if $a = 0$ or $b = 0$. Once students have been introduced to this application, they sometimes try incorrectly to apply the principle in solving an equation such as $x^2 - 5x = 6$ by factoring to get $x(x - 5) = 6$, and then setting each factor equal to 6. Emphasize that in order to apply the principle, one member of the equation must be 0.

Remind students that, in general, the check to be applied for a quadratic equation, has two parts, a check for each root. When both roots are the same number, that value should be written only once in the solution set. This situation exists when the left member of $ax^2 - bx + c = 0$ represents a perfect square trinomial. For example, the solution set of $x^2 - 2x + 1 = 0$ is {1} since $x^2 - 2x + 1 = (x - 1)^2$.

Students may need to discuss Example 4 in order to fully understand the answer. Have them find the height of the ball at each $\frac{1}{4}$ second from $t = 0$ to $t = \frac{3}{2}$, that is, when the ball has been in the air $0, \frac{1}{4}, \frac{1}{2}, \frac{3}{4}, 1, \frac{5}{4},$ and $\frac{3}{2}$ seconds. Ask "How is the height of the ball changing during the first $\frac{3}{4}$ seconds that the ball is in the air?" and "How is the height of the ball changing after $\frac{3}{4}$ seconds in the air?" It may be helpful to draw a graph that shows this data. Ask students to find the height of the ball after $\frac{7}{4}$ seconds. About how long was the ball in the air before it hit the ground? (If the ground is represented by a height of 0, the ball must have hit the ground after it had been in the air for a little less than $\frac{7}{4}$ seconds.)

21-3 SOLVING INCOMPLETE QUADRATIC EQUATIONS

An incomplete quadratic equation (pure quadratic equation) can be written in the form $ax^2 + c = 0$, where $a \neq 0$. Since the first-degree term is not present, this quadratic equation always has an equivalent equation of the form $x^2 = n$ where $n = \frac{-c}{a}$. At this level, n is restricted to a non-negative real number. Since every positive real number has two real square roots, then $x = \sqrt{n}$ or $x = -\sqrt{n}$. The solution set may contain roots that are rational numbers or irrational numbers.

Ask students to solve $x^2 + 36 = 0$. Why does this equation have no solution in the set of real

numbers? (The square of every real number is positive or 0.) Ask students whether an incomplete quadratic equation can have one rational root and one irrational root. (No, $\sqrt{n}$ and $-\sqrt{n}$ are both rational when n is a perfect square or both irrational when n is not a perfect square.)

21-4 SOLVING A QUADRATIC EQUATION BY USING THE QUADRATIC FORMULA

This section may be considered optional since the quadratic formula is studied in Course II. However, teachers may wish to introduce it here if students ask about the solution of an equation in which the polynomial in standard form is not factorable. Students should understand that only equations with rational roots can be solved by factoring in the set of integers but that the quadratic formula can be used to solve any quadratic equation.

You may wish to show students the derivation of the quadratic formula. In the two approaches that follow, the second avoids fractions until the last step.

Approach 1

Given the general quadratic equation:
$$ax^2 + bx + c = 0 \ (a \neq 0)$$

(1) Divide by a to obtain a leading coefficient of 1:
$$x^2 + \frac{bx}{a} + \frac{c}{a} = 0$$

(2) Transform the equation, keeping only variable terms on the left.
$$x^2 + \frac{bx}{a} = -\frac{c}{a}$$

(3) Form a perfect-square trinomial on the left by adding $\left(\frac{b}{2a}\right)^2$ or $\frac{b^2}{4a^2}$; add the same value on the right:
$$x^2 + \frac{bx}{a} + \left(\frac{b}{2a}\right)^2 = \left(\frac{b}{2a}\right)^2 - \frac{c}{a}$$
$$x^2 + \frac{bx}{a} + \frac{b^2}{4a^2} = \frac{b^2}{4a^2} - \frac{c}{a}$$

(4) Factor the left member, simplify the right:

$$\left(x + \frac{b}{2a}\right)^2 = \frac{b^2}{4a^2} - \frac{4ac}{4a^2}$$

$$= \frac{b^2 - 4ac}{4a^2}$$

(5) Take the square root of each member.

$$x + \frac{b}{2a} = \pm\sqrt{\frac{b^2 - 4ac}{4a^2}}$$

$$= \frac{\pm\sqrt{b^2 - 4ac}}{2a}$$

(6) Add $\frac{-b}{2a}$ to both members:

$$x = \frac{-b}{2a} \pm \frac{\sqrt{b^2 - 4ac}}{2a}$$

(7) Combine terms on the right:

$$= \frac{-b \pm \sqrt{b^2 - 4ac}}{2a}$$

Approach 2

Given the general quadratic equation:

$$ax^2 + bx + c = 0 \quad (a \neq 0)$$

(1) Multiply by $4a$:

$$4a^2x^2 + 4abx + 4ac = 0$$

(2) Transform the equation.

$$4a^2x^2 + 4abx = -4ac$$

(3) Form a perfect square. Since $(2ax + b)^2 = 4a^2x^2 + 4abx + b^2$, add b^2 to both members:

$$4a^2x^2 + 4abx + b^2 = b^2 - 4ac$$

(4) Factor the left member.

$$(2ax + b)^2 = b^2 - 4ac$$

(5) Take the square root of each member.

$$2ax + b = \pm\sqrt{b^2 - 4ac}$$

(6) Add $-b$ to both members:

$$2ax = -b \pm \sqrt{b^2 - 4ac}$$

(7) Divide both members by $2a$:

$$x = \frac{-b \pm \sqrt{b^2 - 4ac}}{2a}$$

21-5 THE THEOREM OF PYTHAGORAS

Similar triangles are used to demonstrate the truth of the Pythagorean Theorem. Although many students may find this demonstration difficult, it provides a review of many of the ideas developed earlier in the course.

Another demonstration of the Theorem of Pythagoras that you may wish to present to the class uses the areas of two congruent squares, as shown below.

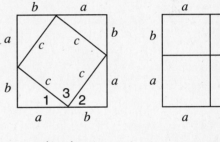

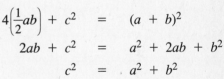

$$4\left(\frac{1}{2}ab\right) + c^2 = (a + b)^2$$
$$2ab + c^2 = a^2 + 2ab + b^2$$
$$c^2 = a^2 + b^2$$

In presenting this demonstration, ask the students how we know that the quadrilateral with four sides of length c inscribed in the figure at the left is a square. (The sum of the measures of $\angle 1$, $\angle 2$, and $\angle 3$ is $180°$ and the sum of the measures of $\angle 1$ and $\angle 2$ is $90°$. Therefore, $\angle 3$ is a right angle.)

In addition to these two proofs for the Pythagorean Theorem, hundreds of others exist. Ask students to research some other proofs.

Use ***Enrichment Activity 21-5: Pythagorean Triples*** to examine some interesting number patterns related to the right triangle.

21-6 USING QUADRATIC EQUATIONS TO SOLVE PROBLEMS

Frequently, verbal problems involving geometric figures or number relationships can be solved by an algebraic strategy that uses a quadratic equation. This important section gives students problem-solving experience as well as practice in finding the roots of quadratic equations. Make sure that students understand that often one of the roots of the equation written to solve a problem is not an answer to the problem.

21-7 THE GRAPH OF A QUADRATIC EQUATION

This section may be considered optional. However, it is helpful for students to see the difference between the graph of a first-degree equation (a straight line) and the graph of a second-degree equation (a curve—in this case, a parabola).

Present in class at least one equation where the coefficient of x^2 is negative. Be sure that students understand that in order to evaluate $-x^2$ for some value of x, we must first square the value of x and then take the opposite of that square. Since the square of any real number is nonnegative, its opposite is always nonpositive; that is, the value of $-x^2$ is always negative or 0.

Since graphs of second-degree equations are studied in detail in Course II, competence should not be expected at this level.

Name _____ Class _____ Date _____

ENRICHMENT ACTIVITY 21-5

Pythagorean Triples

A *Pythagorean triple* is a set of positive integers that when substituted for a, b, and c in the equation $a^2 + b^2 = c^2$, make the equation true. To form a Pythagorean triple choose any two positive integers U and V, $U > V$.

Let $a = U^2 - V^2$,
$\qquad b = 2UV$,
$\qquad c = U^2 + V^2$,

Copy the following chart, letting $U : 2, 3, 4, 5 \ldots$ and $V = 1$, then, for each value of U calculate $U^2 - V^2$, $2UV$, and $U^2 + V^2$, and fill in the appropriate column.

U	V	$U^2 - V^2$	$2UV$	$U^2 + V^2$
2	1	3	4	5
3	1			
4	1			
5	1			
...	1			

1. Study the Pythagorean triples that you wrote. What patterns do you observe?

Make a new chart, starting with $U = 3$ and letting $V = U - 1$.

U	V	$U^2 - V^2$	$2UV$	$U^2 + V^2$
3	2	5	12	13
4	3			
5	4			
6	5			
...	...			

2. Study the Pythagorean triples that you wrote. What patterns do you observe?

Name _____ Class _____ Date _____

Make a new chart, starting with $U = 4$ letting $V = U - 2$.

U	V	$U^2 - V^2$	$2UV$	$U^2 + V^2$
4	2	12	16	20
5	3			
6	4			
7	5			
...	...			

3. Study the Pythagorean triples that you wrote. What patterns do you observe?

4. Consider the numbers 51, 140, 149, which form a Pythagorean triple. What values of U and V will give this triple?

5. Write a Pythagorean triple in which the middle number is 56.

6. Write a Pythagorean triple in which the smallest number is 69.

7. Answer the following questions about Pythagorean triples:

   a. Is it possible to write a Pythagorean triple in which all of the numbers are even? Give an example of such a triple, or explain why no triple is possible.

   b. Is it possible to write a Pythagorean triple in which all of the numbers are odd? Give an example of such a triple, or explain why no triple is possible.

   c. Is it possible to write a Pythagorean triple in which two of the numbers are odd and one is even? Give an example of such a triple, or explain why no triple is possible.

   d. Is it possible to write a Pythagorean triple in which two of the numbers are even and one is odd? Give an example of such a triple, or explain why no triple is possible.

SUGGESTED TEST ITEMS (CHAPTER 21)

In 1–6, in each case, solve and check.

1. $x^2 - 7x + 12 = 0$

2. $x^2 - 5x = 6$

3. $a^2 - 25 = 0$

4. $y^2 - 5y = 0$

5. $b(2b + 1) = 36$

6. $\dfrac{x + 1}{16} = \dfrac{2}{x - 3}$

7. The sum of the squares of two consecutive integers is 145. What are the integers? (There are two solutions.)

8. What is the length of the hypotenuse of a right triangle if the lengths of the legs are 24 inches and 7 inches?

9. What is the length of the longer leg of a right triangle if the length of the hypotenuse is 41 centimeters and the length of the shorter leg is 9 centimeters?

10. The dimensions of a rectangle are 5 inches by 4 inches. What is the length of a diagonal:
   a. in radical form?   **b.** to the *nearest tenth* of an inch?

11. The base of a triangle is 4 centimeters longer than the altitude. The area of the triangle is 30 square centimeters.
   a. What is the length of the base?   **b.** What is the length of the altitude?

12. A baseball diamond is a square that measures 90 feet between bases. At a point 20 feet from third base on the line between second and third base, the third baseman catches the ball and throws it to first base. How far was the ball thrown? Express the answer to the *nearest tenth* of a *foot*.

13. Use the quadratic formula to find the roots $x^2 - 4x + 1 = 0$.
   a. Express the roots in the simplest radical form.
   b. Express the roots to the *nearest hundredth*.

14. Sketch the graph of $y = x^2 - 2x - 1$ from $x = -2$ to $x = 4$.

BONUS I: Vertex O of rectangle $OBCD$ is at the center of circle O and vertex C is on the circle. Point B is on radius $\overline{OA}$, $OA = BD = 13$, and $BA = 8$.
   a. What is the area of the rectangle?
   b. What is the area of the circle?

BONUS II: Solve graphically and check: $y = x^2 - 4x + 1$
$y = 2x - 4$

SAT PREPARATION EXERCISES (CHAPTER 21)

I. Multiple-Choice Questions

In 1–11, select the letter for the correct answer.

1.

In the figure above, each side of the square is the same length as each side of the equilateral triangle. What percent of the perimeter of the square is the perimeter of the equilateral triangle?

(A) 75%   (B) 50%   (C) $33\frac{1}{3}$%

(D) 25%   (E) 10%

2. Which of the following equations represents the statement: the square of a number increased by 2 more than the number is 60.

(A) $x^2 + 2x = 60$
(B) $(x + 2)^2 + x = 60$
(C) $x^2 + x + 2 = 60$
(D) $x^2 + (x + 2)^2 = 60$
(E) $(x + 2x)^2 + 2 = 60$

3.

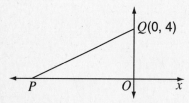

In triangle PQO above, the slope of $\overline{PQ} = \frac{1}{2}$. What is the length of PQ?

(A) 8   (B) $4\sqrt{5}$ (C) 9

(D) $3\sqrt{10}$ (E) 10

4. If $\frac{x^2}{6} = \frac{3}{2}$, what is the sum of the two roots of the equation?

(A) 0   (B) 3   (C) 6

(D) 9   (E) 12

5.

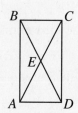

In the figure above, quadrilateral $ABCD$ is a rectangle. Diagonals $\overline{AC}$ and $\overline{BD}$ intersect at E. If $AB = 12$ and $AD = 5$, what is the length of AE?

(A) 5   (B) 6.5   (C) 8.5

(D) 13   (E) 17

6.

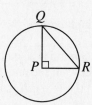

In the figure above, $QR = 8\sqrt{2}$. What is the area of circle P?

(A) 8π (B) 16π (C) 32π

(D) 64π (E) 128π

7.

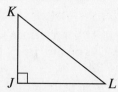

If the area of $\triangle JKL$ above is 2 and JL is 2.5, what is the length of JK?

(A) 0.625   (B) 0.8   (C) 1.25

(D) 1.6   (E) 5

8.

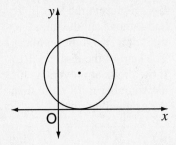

If the circumference of the circle above is 16π, which of the following could be the coordinates of the center of the circle?

(A) $(16, 8)$ (B) $(8, 16)$ (C) $(8, 8)$

(D) $(8, 4)$ (E) $(4, 8)$

9.

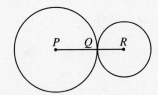

Circles P and Q above intersect at point Q and no other point. If $PR = x$ and the circumference of circle P is 6π, which of the following represents the circumference of circle R?

(A) $(x - 3)\pi$ (B) $(x - 6)\pi$

(C) $2(x - 3)\pi$ (D) $2(x - 6)\pi$

(E) $2(x - 9)\pi$

10.

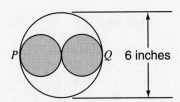

In the figure above, the two shaded circles touch each other at the center of the large circle, and touch the large circle at points P and Q. What is the ratio of the shaded area to the unshaded area?

(A) $\dfrac{1}{1}$ (B) $\dfrac{1}{2}$ (C) $\dfrac{1}{3}$

(D) $\dfrac{1}{4}$ (E) $\dfrac{1}{5}$

11. Six congruent isosceles right triangles are arranged in five different ways as shown below. Which of the following arrangements has the least perimeter?

(A)   (B)

(C)   (D)

(E)

II. Quantitative Comparison Questions

Questions 12–19 each consist of two quantities, one in Column A and one in Column B. You are to compare the two quantities and choose:

   A if the quantity in Column A is greater;
   B if the quantity in Column B is greater;
   C if the two quantities are equal;
   D if the relationship cannot be determined from the information given.

Notes

1. In certain questions, information concerning one or both of the quantities to be compared is centered above the two columns.

2. In a given question, a symbol that appears in both columns represents the same thing in Column A as it does in Column B.

3. Letters such as x, n, and k stand for real numbers.

Column A	*Column B*
12. $\sqrt[3]{9}$	2
13. $\dfrac{\sqrt{3} + \sqrt{3}}{\sqrt{3}}$	$\dfrac{\sqrt{5} + \sqrt{5}}{\sqrt{5}}$

14.

$$x^2 - 25$$

| The value of x | 25 |

_____

15.

$$2x \leq 4$$
$$2y + 2 \leq 12$$

| x | y |

_____

16.

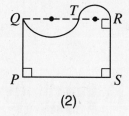

(1)   (2)

$PQ = 5$, $QT = 5$, $TR = 3$

| The perimeter of the solid-bordered figure in (1) | The perimeter of the solid-bordered figure in (2) |

_____

17.

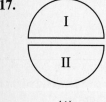 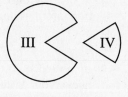

(1)   (2)

Two circles of equal areas are cut to form figures I, II, III, and IV.

| The sum of the perimeters of figures I and II | The sum of the perimeters of figures III and V |

_____

18. The slope of a line whose equation is $3x + 4y = 12$ | The slope of a line whose equation is $y = 3x + 4$

19. Let t represent the tens digit and u represent the units digit of a two-digit number. The sum of the digits is 10. If the digits are reversed, the new number is 18 more than the original number.

| The digit t of the original number | The digit u of the original number |

III. Student-Produced Response Questions

In questions 20–25, you are to solve the problem.

20. If $x = \sqrt{3}$, what is the value of $6(\sqrt{x})^4 + (6\sqrt{x})^2$?

21.

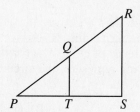

In the figure above, QT is parallel to RS. If $PT = 2$, $TS = 1$, and $RS = 4$, what is the length of PQ?

22. If $x^{2y}x^3 = x^{30}$, what is the value of y?

23. If $(x - 6)^2 = 64$, what is the value of x^2?

24.

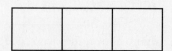

In the figure above, a rectangle is composed of three equal squares as shown. If the area of the rectangle is 12 square inches, what is the perimeter, in inches, of the rectangle?

25. What is the value of w if $\dfrac{\sqrt{w + 2}}{2} = 5$?

ANSWERS FOR ENRICHMENT ACTIVITY EXERCISES

Enrichment Activity 1-3A: Repeating Decimals

$\frac{1}{9} = 0.111 \ldots = 0.\overline{1}$

$\frac{2}{9} = 0.222 \ldots = 0.\overline{2}$

$\frac{3}{9} = 0.333 \ldots = 0.\overline{3}$

$\frac{4}{9} = 0.444 \ldots = 0.\overline{4}$

$\frac{5}{9} = 0.555 \ldots = 0.\overline{5}$

$\frac{6}{9} = 0.666 \ldots = 0.\overline{6}$

$\frac{7}{9} = 0.777 \ldots = 0.\overline{7}$

$\frac{8}{9} = 0.888 \ldots = 0.\overline{8}$

$\frac{1}{11} = 0.0909 \ldots = 0.\overline{09}$

$\frac{2}{11} = 0.1818 \ldots = 0.\overline{18}$

$\frac{3}{11} = 0.2727 \ldots = 0.\overline{27}$

$\frac{4}{11} = 0.3636 \ldots = 0.\overline{36}$

$\frac{5}{11} = 0.4545 \ldots = 0.\overline{45}$

$\frac{6}{11} = 0.5454 \ldots = 0.\overline{54}$

$\frac{7}{11} = 0.6363 \ldots = 0.\overline{63}$

$\frac{8}{11} = 0.7272 \ldots = 0.\overline{72}$

$\frac{9}{11} = 0.8181 \ldots = 0.\overline{81}$

$\frac{10}{11} = 0.9090 \ldots = 0.\overline{90}$

$\frac{1}{7} = 0.\overline{142857}$

$\frac{2}{7} = 0.\overline{285714}$

$\frac{3}{7} = 0.\overline{428571}$

$\frac{4}{7} = 0.\overline{571428}$

$\frac{5}{7} = 0.\overline{714285}$

$\frac{6}{7} = 0.\overline{857142}$

$\frac{1}{14} = 0.0\overline{714285}$

$\frac{2}{14} = 0.\overline{142857}$

$\frac{3}{14} = 0.2\overline{142857}$

$\frac{4}{14} = 0.\overline{285714}$

$\frac{5}{14} = 0.3\overline{571428}$

$\frac{6}{14} = 0.\overline{428571}$

$\frac{7}{14} = 0.5\overline{0}$

$\frac{8}{14} = 0.\overline{571428}$

$\frac{9}{14} = 0.6\overline{428571}$

$\frac{10}{14} = 0.\overline{714285}$

$\frac{11}{14} = 0.7\overline{857142}$

$\frac{12}{14} = 0.\overline{857142}$

$\frac{13}{14} = 0.9\overline{285714}$

Pattern: Multiples of $0.\overline{1}$. (also, multiples of $0.\overline{11}$, like products in the 11 times table)

Pattern: Multiples of $0.\overline{09}$ (similar to products in the 9 times table)

Pattern: Every decimal repeats the same digits, in the same order, but starts at a different place: 0.142857142857....

Pattern: Similar to the repeating digits in the $\frac{1}{7}$ table, but six fractions here begin with a non-repeating digit in the tenths place, and one fraction repeats 0: $\left(\frac{7}{14} = \frac{1}{2} = 0.5\overline{0} = 0.5\right)$

Challenge

$\frac{1}{13} = 0.\overline{076923}$

$\frac{2}{13} = 0.\overline{153846}$

$\frac{3}{13} = 0.\overline{230769}$

$\frac{4}{13} = 0.\overline{307692}$

$\frac{5}{13} = 0.\overline{384615}$

$\frac{6}{13} = 0.\overline{461538}$

$\frac{7}{13} = 0.\overline{538461}$

$\frac{8}{13} = 0.\overline{615384}$

$\frac{9}{13} = 0.\overline{692307}$

$\frac{10}{13} = 0.\overline{769230}$

$\frac{11}{13} = 0.\overline{846153}$

$\frac{12}{13} = 0.\overline{923076}$

Pattern: Six fractions $\left(\dfrac{1}{13}, \dfrac{3}{13}, \dfrac{4}{13}, \dfrac{9}{13}, \dfrac{10}{13}, \dfrac{12}{13}\right)$ repeat the same series of digits but start at a different place (0.076923076923...). The other six fractions behave in a similar way with a different set of digits (0.153846153846...).

Enrichment Activity 1-3B: Fraction-Decimal Multiples

1. $\dfrac{1}{8} = 0.125$ $\dfrac{3}{8} = 0.375$ $\dfrac{5}{8} = 0.625$ $\dfrac{7}{8} = 0.875$

$\dfrac{2}{8} = 0.250 = 0.25$ $\dfrac{4}{8} = 0.500 = 0.5$ $\dfrac{6}{8} = 0.750 = 0.75$ $\dfrac{8}{8} = 1.000 = 1$

2. $\dfrac{1}{20} = 0.05$ $\dfrac{1}{40} = 0.025$ $\dfrac{1}{16} = 0.0625$ $\dfrac{1}{3} = 0.333... = 0.\overline{3}$

$\dfrac{7}{20} = 0.35$ $\dfrac{17}{40} = 0.425$ $\dfrac{9}{16} = 0.5625$ $\dfrac{2}{3} = 0.666... = 0.\overline{6}$

$\dfrac{19}{20} = 0.95$ $\dfrac{29}{40} = 0.725$ $\dfrac{12}{16} = 0.7500 = 0.75$ $\dfrac{3}{3} = 0.999... = 0.\overline{9}$

3. a. 10 times the number $= 9.9999...$
Subtract the number $\quad -0.9999...$
9 times the number $= \overline{9.0000... = 9}$

Divide by 9 to find the original number. $\dfrac{9}{9} = 1$
b. $0.9999... = 0.\overline{9} = 1$

4. $\dfrac{1}{40} = 0.025$ $\dfrac{1}{16} = 0.0625$ $\dfrac{1}{32} = 0.03125$ $\dfrac{1}{21} = 0.\overline{047619}$

$+\dfrac{7}{40} = 0.175$ $+\dfrac{7}{16} = 0.4375$ $+\dfrac{7}{32} = 0.21875$ $+\dfrac{6}{21} = 0.\overline{285714}$

$\dfrac{8}{40} = 0.200$ $\dfrac{8}{16} = 0.5000$ $\dfrac{8}{32} = 0.25000$ $\dfrac{7}{21} = 0.\overline{333333}$

$\left(\text{or } \dfrac{1}{5} = 0.2\right)$ $\left(\text{or } \dfrac{1}{2} = 0.5\right)$ $\left(\text{or } \dfrac{1}{4} = 0.25\right)$ $\left(\text{or } \dfrac{1}{3} = 0.\overline{3}\right)$

$\dfrac{1}{11} = 0.\overline{09}$ $\dfrac{1}{7} = 0.\overline{142857}$ $\dfrac{1}{30} = 0.0333...$ $\dfrac{1}{12} = 0.08333...$

$\dfrac{2}{11} = 0.\overline{18}$ $\dfrac{2}{7} = 0.\overline{285714}$ $+\dfrac{2}{30} = 0.0666...$ $+\dfrac{2}{12} = 0.16666...$

$+\dfrac{3}{11} = 0.\overline{27}$ $+\dfrac{4}{7} = 0.\overline{571428}$ $\dfrac{3}{30} = 0.0999...$ $\dfrac{3}{12} = 0.24999...$

$\dfrac{6}{11} = 0.\overline{54}$ $\dfrac{7}{7} = 0.\overline{999999}$ $\left(\text{or } \dfrac{1}{10} = 0.1\right)$ $\left(\text{or } \dfrac{1}{4} = 0.25\right)$

    $\left(\text{or } \dfrac{7}{7} = 1\right)$

c. Conclusion: A pattern of 9's that continues without end can be replaced by adding 1 to the place value *immediately to the left* of the pattern of 9's, and then dropping all the 9's. For example:

$0.999...$ $0.24999...$ $0.35999...$ $0.49999...$
$= 1.$ $= 0.25$ $= 0.36$ $= 0.5$

Enrichment Activity 2-1: Operations with Fractions

A. 1   K. 11
B. 4   L. 14
C. 7   M. 17
D. 10   N. 20
E. 13   O. 3
F. 16   P. 6
G. 19   Q. 9
H. 2   R. 12
I. 5   S. 15
J. 8   T. 18

Enrichment Activity 2-4: Clock Arithmetic

a.

+	1	2	3	4	5	6	7	8	9	10	11	12
1	2	3	4	5	6	7	8	9	10	11	12	1
2	3	4	5	6	7	8	9	10	11	12	1	2
3	4	5	6	7	8	9	10	11	12	1	2	3
4	5	6	7	8	9	10	11	12	1	2	3	4
5	6	7	8	9	10	11	12	1	2	3	4	5
6	7	8	9	10	11	12	1	2	3	4	5	6
7	8	9	10	11	12	1	2	3	4	5	6	7
8	9	10	11	12	1	2	3	4	5	6	7	8
9	10	11	12	1	2	3	4	5	6	7	8	9
10	11	12	1	2	3	4	5	6	7	8	9	10
11	12	1	2	3	4	5	6	7	8	9	10	11
12	1	2	3	4	5	6	7	8	9	10	11	12

b. 1. Yes 2. Yes 3. Yes 4. 12

5.

1	2	3	4	5	6	7	8	9	10	11	12
11	10	9	8	7	6	5	4	3	2	1	12

Enrichment Activity 2-5: Digital Addition; Digital Multiplication

1.

⊕	0	2	4	6	8
0	0	2	4	6	8
2	2	4	6	8	0
4	4	6	8	0	2
6	6	8	0	2	4
8	8	0	2	4	6

3.

⊗	0	2	4	6	8
0	0	0	0	0	0
2	0	4	8	2	6
4	0	8	6	4	2
6	0	2	4	6	8
8	0	6	2	8	4

2. a. Yes   **b.** Yes
c. Yes   **d.** 0
e. Number ⊕ Inverse = Identity

$$0 \oplus 0 = 0$$
$$2 \oplus 8 = 0$$
$$4 \oplus 6 = 0$$
$$6 \oplus 4 = 0$$
$$8 \oplus 2 = 0$$

4. a. Yes   **b.** Yes
c. Yes   **d.** 6
e. Number ⊗ Inverse = Identity

$$2 \otimes 8 = 6$$
$$4 \otimes 4 = 6$$
$$6 \otimes 6 = 6$$
$$8 \otimes 2 = 6$$

5. Yes
Conclusion: This is a field; all 11 properties hold.

Enrichment Activity 3-4: Elimination by Pairs

a. and b.

Number of Eligible Teams	Number of Games Needed
4	3
5	4
6	5
7	6
8	7
9	8
n	$n - 1$

c. Compare the numbers in the unordered list by pairs. Choose the larger of each pair. Repeat until the largest number in the list is selected. For example:

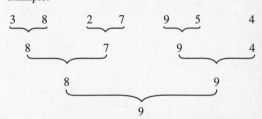

d. An alternative method would be to compare the first two numbers, select the larger, and compare it with the third number in the list. Again, select the larger and compare it with the fourth in the list. Continue the process until comparison is made with the last number in the list. This method uses the same number of steps as in the example above.

Enrichment Activity 3-6: Guessing a Number by Bisection

a. 10   **b.** 8
c. A maximum of 11 guesses would be needed to locate a number between 1 and 2,000 since 1 guess would be required to know that the number 1,000 was between 1 and 999, or was between 1,001 and 2,000. Then, if the number was not 1,000, a maximum of 10 guesses would be sufficient to find the number. Note that each guess divides the possible numbers into two equal sets.

Use a simpler related problem to find a general solution.

Range of Numbers	Maximum Number of Guesses	
From 1 to 3	2	First guess would be 2. If 2 is not the number, the next guess would be the correct one.
From 1 to 7	3	First guess would be 4. If 4 is not the number, the number must be one of a set of 3 possible numbers, and at most 2 more guesses are needed.
From 1 to 15	4	First guess would be 8. If 8 is not the number, the number must be one of a set of 7 possible numbers, and at most 3 more guesses are needed.

Set of Numbers	Maximum Number of Guesses	Powers of 2
From 1 to 3	2	$2^2 = 4$
From 1 to 7	3	$2^3 = 8$
From 1 to 15	4	$2^4 = 16$
From 1 to 31	5	$2^5 = 32$
From 1 to 63	6	$2^6 = 64$
From 1 to 127	7	$2^7 = 128$
From 1 to 255	8	$2^8 = 256$

If $2n - 1 \le$ the number of integers in the set from which the chosen number is selected, n is the maximum number of guesses needed to identify the number.

To find a word in a dictionary, choose a middle word and ask if the chosen word comes after or before the word for which you are searching. Continue the process. To find a name on a list, choose a middle name and continue the process.

Enrichment Activity 3-7: Arrangements

a. The diagram appears to show two arrangements, one clockwise and the other counterclockwise.

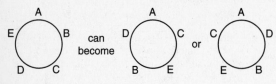

Since, in both new arrangements, each person is sitting between the same two persons, only one different arrangement is possible.
b. No such arrangement is possible.
c. It is easier to find different arrangements as more people are added to the group.

Enrichment Activity 4-1: Number Play

Columns 2 and 3 can vary. The answers for columns 1 and 4 are shown here.

	Col. 1	Col. 4
1.	15	n
2.	30	$2n$
3.	38	$2n + 8$
4.	3,800	$200n + 800$
5.	3,600	$200n + 600$
6.	360	$20n + 60$
7.	400	$20n + 100$
8.	20	$n + 5$
9.	15	n

Conclusion: The result on line 9 will always equal the starting number on line 1.

Enrichment Activity 4-7: Surface Area

1. **a.** 1,676.7 cm^2
   b. $SA = 2\ell w + 2\ell h + 2wh$
   or
   $SA = 2(\ell w + \ell h + wh)$

2. **a.** 218π cm^2
   b. $SA = \pi r^2 + \pi r^2 + \pi dh$
   or
   $SA = 2\pi r^2 + 2\pi rh$
   or
   $SA = 2\pi r(r + h)$

3. Larger-looking, flat boxes allow for more advertising on the surface of the box and appear to contain more cereal.

Enrichment Activity 4-8: Shaded Areas

Figure 1
   a. $128 - 20\pi$ **b.** 65.17
Figure 2
   a. 27π **b.** 84.82
Figure 3
   a. $36 + 18\pi$ **b.** 92.55
The shaded region in Figure 3 has the greatest area.

Enrichment Activity 5-3: Adding Signed Numbers

a.

$(+2) + (+3)$ *Answer:* __+5__

$(-4) + (-1)$ *Answer:* __−5__

$(-3) + (-5)$ *Answer:* __−8__

$(-2) + (-3)$ *Answer:* __−5__

$(-4) + (-2)$ *Answer:* __−6__

$(-2) + (-1)$ *Answer:* __−3__

$(-5) + (+2)$ *Answer:* __−3__

$(+1) + (-3)$ *Answer:* __−2__

$(+4) + (-3)$ *Answer:* __+1__

$(-4) + (+3)$ *Answer:* __−1__

$(-1) + (+4)$ *Answer:* __+3__

$(-5) + (+6)$ *Answer:* __+1__

$(+5) + (-8)$ *Answer:* __−3__

b. (*1*) Add the absolute values. (*2*) Positive (*3*) Negative
c. (*1*) Find the difference of the absolute values.
   (*2*) Sign of the number with the larger absolute value

Enrichment Activity 5-8: Graphing Ordered Pairs of Numbers

a.

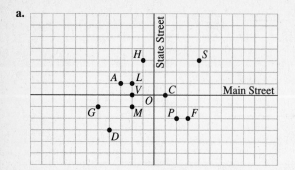

b. M is 2 blocks west and 1 block south of O $(-2, -1)$

c. The first number gives the number of blocks east or west of O, the center of town. If the number is positive, the position is east of O; if the number is negative, the position is west of O. The second number gives the number of blocks north or south of O. If the number is positive, the position is north of O; if the number is negative, the position is south of O.

Enrichment Activity 6-1: Finding Solution Sets

Storing Values of the Domain

1. $\{2\}$ 2. $\{-4\}$ 3. $\{-3\}$
4. $\{-3, 3\}$ 5. $\{-2, 2\}$ 6. $\{0\}$

Using Tables

1. $\{3\}$ 2. $\emptyset$ or $\{\ \}$ 3. $\{-5\}$
4. $\{-2, 2\}$ 5. $\{-3, 3\}$ 6. $\emptyset$ or $\{\ \}$
7. $\{-3\}$ 8. $\{5\}$ 9. $\{-4, 4\}$

Enrichment Activity 7-3: Conjunction with Three Variables

2. a. Row 4   **b.** Row 1   **c.** Row 5
d. Rows 7, 8   **e.** Rows 3, 4   **f.** Rows 2, 6
3. $(p \wedge q) \wedge r$ and $(p \wedge r) \wedge q$ and $(q \wedge r) \wedge p$ all have the same truth value.

Conclusion: The order of the variables is not important when using conjunction.

Enrichment Activity 7-4A: Breakfast at the Diner: *Not, And, Or*

	Bacon	Eggs	Pancakes	Juice	Coffee
Aleyda	✓	✓		✓	
Belva	✓		✓	✓	
Caron	✓	✓			✓
Donnelle		✓	✓		✓
Eudora			✓	✓	✓

1. Caron ordered bacon and eggs (clue 3).
2. Aleyda did not order coffee (clue 4), so she had juice (clue 2.)
3. Since Aleyda had eggs or pancakes, not both (clue 5), she had to have ordered bacon (clue 1: everyone ordered three items).
4. Eudora and Belva both ordered juice (clue 6). Therefore, Caron and Donnelle did not have juice (only three juices were ordered).
5. It follows that Caron and Donnelle had coffee (clue 2), and that Caron's order is now complete with three items (clue 1). Eliminate pancakes for Caron.
6. Belva must have ordered bacon and pancakes (clue 7), and she now has three items. Eliminate eggs and coffee for Belva.
7. The third coffee must go to Eudora, and bacon can be eliminated for Donnelle and Eudora since the others have accounted for three orders of bacon.
8. Since Eudora did not order eggs (clue 8), she ordered pancakes.
9. Both Aleyda and Donnelle must have ordered eggs, since Belva and Eudora did not. This completes Aleyda's order of three items, and pancakes complete Donelle's order.

1.

p	q	r	$p \wedge q$	$p \wedge r$	$q \wedge r$	$(p \wedge q) \wedge r$	$(p \wedge r) \wedge q$	$(q \wedge r) \wedge p$
T	T	T	T	T	T	T	T	T
T	T	F	T	F	F	F	F	F
T	F	T	F	T	F	F	F	F
T	F	F	F	F	F	F	F	F
F	T	T	F	F	T	F	F	F
F	T	F	F	F	F	F	F	F
F	F	T	F	F	F	F	F	F
F	F	F	F	F	F	F	F	F

Enrichment Activity 7-4B: Conjunction Disjunction, and the Distributive Principle

1.

					Col. 5			Col. 8
p	q	r	$q \wedge r$	$p \vee (q \wedge r)$	$p \vee q$	$p \vee r$	$(p \vee q) \wedge (p \vee r)$
T	T	T	T	T	T	T	T
T	T	F	F	T	T	T	T
T	F	T	F	T	T	T	T
T	F	F	F	T	T	T	T
F	T	T	T	T	T	T	T
F	T	F	F	F	T	F	F
F	F	T	F	F	F	T	F
F	F	F	F	F	F	F	F

Conclusion: Disjunction is distributive over conjunction as seen in the truth values of the statements that head columns 5 and 8.

2.

					Col. 5			Col. 8
p	q	r	$q \vee r$	$p \wedge (q \vee r)$	$p \wedge q$	$p \wedge r$	$(p \wedge q) \vee (p \wedge r)$
T	T	T	T	T	T	T	T
T	T	F	T	T	T	F	T
T	F	T	T	T	F	T	T
T	F	F	F	F	F	F	F
F	T	T	T	F	F	F	F
F	T	F	T	F	F	F	F
F	F	T	T	F	F	F	F
F	F	F	F	F	F	F	F

Conclusion: Conjunction is distributive over disjunction, as seen in Col. 5 and Col. 8, where all truth values match.

Enrichment Activity 8-1: Number Puzzles

Introduction

1. 6   **2.** 6   **3.** 7
4. 5   **5.** 9   **6.** 12
7. 12   **8.** 13

Observation: The sum of the five digits equals 15 in every row and in every column.

Puzzle 1

	1	2	3	4	5
R	3	5	1	2	4
S	5	2	4	1	3
T	1	4	2	3	5
V	2	3	5	4	1
W	4	1	3	5	2

Puzzle 2

	1	2	3	4	5
J	4	3	2	1	5
K	2	5	4	3	1
L	5	4	1	2	3
M	3	1	5	4	2
N	1	2	3	5	4

Enrichment Activity 8-5: Logical Equivalents with Three Variables

a. (1) $(h \wedge a) \to s$
(2) $(h \wedge s) \to a$
(3) $(h \wedge \sim a) \to \sim s$
(4) $(a \wedge s) \to h$

b.

h	a	s	$h \wedge a$	$h \wedge s$	$(h \wedge a) \to s$	$(h \wedge s) \to a$
T	T	T	T	T	T	T
T	T	F	T	F	F	T
T	F	T	F	T	T	F
T	F	F	F	F	T	T
F	T	T	F	F	T	T
F	T	F	F	F	T	T
F	F	T	F	F	T	T
F	F	F	F	F	T	T

h	a	s	$\sim a$	$\sim s$	$h \wedge \sim a$	$a \wedge s$	$(h \wedge \sim a) \to s$	$(a \wedge s) \to h$
T	T	T	F	F	F	T	T	T
T	T	F	F	T	F	F	T	T
T	F	T	T	F	T	F	F	T
T	F	F	T	T	T	F	T	T
F	T	T	F	F	F	T	T	F
F	T	F	F	T	F	F	T	T
F	F	T	T	F	F	F	T	T
F	F	F	T	T	F	F	T	T

c. Sentences (2) and (3) are logical equivalents. The truth tables show, line by line, that they have the same truth value.

Enrichment Activity 9-1: Sums and Squares

1. $4^2 + 4 + 5 = 25 = 5^2$

2.

$$n^2 + n + (x + 1) = n^2 + 2n + 1$$
$$= (n + 1)(n + 1)$$
$$= (n + 1)^2$$

3. $20^2 + 20 + 21 = 400 + 20 + 21 = 441$

4. $10^2 = 100$ **5.** $(n + 1)^2$

Enrichment Activity 9-5: Products, Sums, and Cubes

1. $3(4)(5) + 4 = \ 60 + 4 = \ 64 = 4^3$
$4(5)(6) + 5 = 120 + 5 = 125 = 5^3$
$5(6)(7) + 6 = 210 + 6 = \ 16 = 6^3$

The product of three consecutive integers plus the middle integer is equal to the cube of the middle integers.

2. $6(7)(8) + 7 = 336 + 7 = 343 = 7^3$

3. $7(8)(9) + 8 = 504 + 8 = 512 = 8^3$

4. $(n - 1)(n)(n + 1) = (n^2 - n)(n + 1)$
$$= n^3 + n^2 - n^2 - n$$
$$= n^3 - n$$

$(n - 1)(n)(n + 1) + n = n^3 - n + n = n^3$

5. $(n)(n + 1)(n + 2) + (n + 1) \stackrel{?}{=} (n + 1)^3$
$n(n^2 + 3n + 2) + (n + 1) \stackrel{?}{=} (n + 1)(n + 1)(n + 1)$
$(n^3 + 3n^2 + 2n) + (n + 1) \stackrel{?}{=} (n + 1)(n^2 + 2n + 1)$
$n^3 + 3n^2 + 3n + 1 = n^3 + 3n^2 + 3n + 1$

Enrichment Activity 10-3: Consecutive Integers

1.

Number of Integers	First Integer	Sum	Even or Odd
3	1	6	even
3	4	15	odd
3	7	24	even
3	x	$3x+3$	even or odd
4	1	10	even
4	4	22	even
4	7	34	even
4	x	$4x+6$	even
5	1	15	odd
5	4	30	even
5	7	45	odd
5	x	$5x+10$	even or odd
6	1	21	odd
6	4	39	odd
6	7	57	odd
6	x	$6x+15$	odd
7	1	28	even
7	4	49	odd
7	7	70	even
7	x	$7x+21$	even or odd

2. Let x be the first consecutive integer.
   a. Odd; $2x + 1$ is the sum of an even number and an odd number.
   b. Even if x is odd; $3x + 3$ is the sum of two odd numbers.
   Odd if x is even; $3x + 3$ is the sum of an even number and an odd number.
   c. Even; $4x + 6$ is the sum of two even numbers.
   d. Even if x is even; $5x + 10$ is the sum of two even numbers.
   Odd if x is odd; $5x + 10$ is the sum of an odd number and an even number.
   e. Odd; $6x + 15$ is the sum of an even number and an odd number.
   f. Even if x is odd; $7x + 21$ is the sum of two odd numbers.
   Odd if x is even; $7x + 21$ is the sum of an even number and an odd number.
   g. Even when the number of integers divided by 2 is even.
   Odd when the number of integers divided by 2 is odd.
   h. Even when the first integer is even and the number of integers after the first, divided by 2, is even.
   Odd when the first integer is odd and the number of integers after the first, divided by 2, is even.
   Even when the first integer is odd and the number of integers after the first, divided by 2, is odd.

Odd when the first integer is even and the number of integers after the first, divided by 2, is odd.

3. a. 3 b. 5 c. 7
   d. The sum always has the number of integers as a factor. It is always the number of integers times the middle integer.
4. a. No
   b. It is 6 more than 4 times the first integer.
   It is twice the sum of the second and third integers.
   It is 6 less than 4 times the last integer.
5. a. Student tables.
   b. The sum of even integers is always even.
6. a. Student tables.
   b. The sum of odd integers is even if there is an even number of integers and odd if there is an odd number of integers.

Enrichment Activity 10-8: Graphing and Inequality

1.
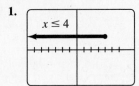

2.
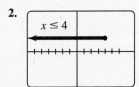

3.
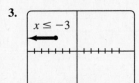

4.
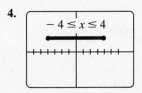

All real numbers between −4 and 4.

5.
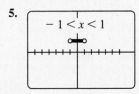

All real numbers between −1 and 1.

271

6.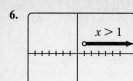

All real numbers greater than 1. Since there is no real number that is the square root of a negative number, the inequality is meaningless for $x < 0$.

7.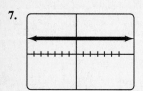

All real numbers.

8.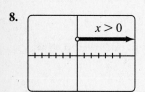

All positive real numbers.

9.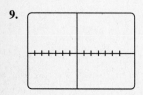

Since $|x|$ is always positive, there is no real number that makes this inequality true.

Enrichment Activity 11-4A: Parallel Lines and Angles

1. $\angle 1$ and $\angle 2$, $\angle 2$ and $\angle 4$, $\angle 4$ and $\angle 3$, $\angle 3$ and $\angle 1$, $\angle 5$ and $\angle 6$, $\angle 6$ and $\angle 8$, $\angle 8$ and $\angle 7$, $\angle 7$ and $\angle 5$
2. $\angle 1$ and $\angle 4$, $\angle 2$ and $\angle 3$, $\angle 5$ and $\angle 8$, $\angle 6$ and $\angle 7$
3. $m\angle 2 = 108$, $m\angle 3 = 108$, $m\angle 4 = 72$, $m\angle 6 = 108$, $m\angle 7 = 108$, $m\angle 8 = 72$
4. $m\angle 1 = 65$, $m\angle 3 = 115$, $m\angle 4 = 65$, $m\angle 5 = 65$, $m\angle 6 = 115$, $m\angle 8 = 65$
5. $m\angle 1 = 56$, $m\angle 2 = 124$, $m\angle 3 = 124$, $m\angle 6 = 124$, $m\angle 7 = 124$, $m\angle 8 = 56$
6. $m\angle 1 = 85$, $m\angle 2 = 95$, $m\angle 4 = 85$, $m\angle 5 = 85$, $m\angle 6 = 95$, $m\angle 8 = 85$
7. $m\angle 1 = 180 - x$, $m\angle 2 = x$, $m\angle 4 = 180 - x$, $m\angle 5 = 180 - x$, $m\angle 6 = x$, $m\angle 7 = x$, $m\angle 8 = 180 - x$
8. Alternate interior angles are congruent.
   Corresponding angles are congruent.
   Alternate exterior angles are congruent.
   Interior angles on the same side of the transversal are supplementary.
   Exterior angles on the same side of the transversal are supplementary.
9. All of the angles are right angles. The transversal is perpendicular to each of the parallel lines.
10. Student drawing; measurements. No.

Enrichment Activity 11-6: Angle Measures

1. **a.** 70 **b.** 100 **c.** 40 **d.** 80
2. **a.** 70 **b.** 40 **c.** 30 **d.** 20 **e.** 20 **f.** 80
3. **a.** $\triangle ACF$, $\triangle CEF$, $\triangle DCE$ **b.** None **c.** $\triangle ACB$
   d. $\triangle DCE$ **e.** $\triangle ACB$, $\triangle ACF$, $\triangle FCE$
4. **a.** (1) $\overline{AE}$ (2) Right $\triangle AEC$
   b. No. Let $\overline{AC}$ be a transversal that intersects $\overline{AF}$ and $\overline{BC}$. Since the alternate interior angles ($\angle FAC$ and $\angle ACB$) are not equal in measure, $\overline{AF}$ is not parallel to $\overline{BC}$.

Enrichment Activity 13-I: Introduction: (Fibonacci Sequence and the Golden Ratio)

Part 1. To ease reading, the terms of the Fibonacci sequence are written below from smallest to largest in three-column format:

1	55	4,181
1	89	6,765
2	144	10,946
3	233	17,711
5	377	28,657
8	610	46,368
13	987	75,025
21	1,597	121,393
34	2,584	

Part 2.

$$\frac{13}{8} = \frac{1.625}{1} \qquad \frac{21}{13} = \frac{1.615384615}{1}$$

$$\frac{34}{21} = \frac{1.619047619}{1} \qquad \frac{55}{34} = \frac{1.617647059}{1}$$

$$\frac{89}{55} = \frac{1.618181818}{1} \qquad \frac{144}{89} = \frac{1.617977528}{1}$$

$$\frac{233}{144} = \frac{1.618055556}{1} \qquad \frac{377}{233} = \frac{1.618025751}{1}$$

$$\frac{610}{377} = \frac{1.618037135}{1} \qquad \frac{987}{610} = \frac{1.618032787}{1}$$

$$\frac{1,597}{987} = \frac{1.618034448}{1} \qquad \frac{2,584}{1,597} = \frac{1.618033813}{1}$$

$$\frac{4,181}{2,584} = \frac{1.618034056}{1} \qquad \frac{6,765}{4,181} = \frac{1.618033963}{1}$$

$$\frac{10,946}{6,765} = \frac{1.618033999}{1} \qquad \frac{17,711}{10,946} = \frac{1.618033985}{1}$$

$$\frac{28,657}{17,711} = \frac{1.61803399}{1} \qquad \frac{46,368}{28,657} = \frac{1.618033988}{1}$$

$$\frac{75,025}{46,368} = \frac{1.618033989}{1} \qquad \frac{121,393}{75,025} = \frac{1.618033989}{1}$$

Part 3. As the terms of the Fibonacci sequence increase, the ratio comparing the greater of two consecutive Fibonacci numbers to the smaller approaches the value of the golden ratio: $\dfrac{1 + \sqrt{5}}{2} \approx \dfrac{1.618033989}{1}$

Enrichment Activity 13-1: Ratio: Estimates and Comparisons

Columns 1 and 2 vary according to student estimates.

	Column 3 Actual Ratio of Size	Source for Teacher: Area (sq mi)
Australia	0.81	2,966,200
Brazil	0.89	3,286,500
Canada	1.05	3,849,674
China	1.00	3,696,100
India	0.33	1,222,243
Japan	0.04	145,850
Mexico	0.21	756,066
Russia	1.79	6,592,800
Spain	0.05	194,898
United States	1.00	3,679,192

BONUS:	Actual Ratio of Size
Australia	3.92
Brazil	4.35
Canada	5.09
China	4.89
India	1.62
Japan	0.19
Mexico	1.00
Russia	8.72
Spain	0.26
United States	4.87

a. Observations (Differences)
  1. With Mexico's area used as the base of comparison, its ratio changes from 0.21 to 1.00. In turn, the ratio of size for every nation becomes almost 5 times as large as the ratio in the original problem.
  2. In the original problem, both China and the United States have a ratio of 1.00, indicating that the two nations are equal in area. In the Bonus question, with a ratio of 4.89 for China and 4.87 for the United States, it is clear that China has a larger geographic area.

b. Observations (Sameness)
  1. The ratios in both the original problem and in the Bonus question (with the exception of China and the United States) show the relative sizes of the nations: Japan is the smallest in area; Spain is the next larger; and so on up to the largest nation in area, Russia.
  2. Similar comparisons can be made using the ratios in both lists. For example:
     a. The area of the United States is approximately 3 times the area of India.
     b. If the area of Spain is added to that of the United States, the total area is approximately equal to the area of Canada.

Enrichment Activity 13-2: Population Density

Part 1.

State	Population	Area (sq mi)	Population Density
Alaska	606,276	656,424	1
California	31,430,697	163,707	192
Florida	13,952,714	65,756	212
Montana	856,047	147,046	6
New Jersey	7,903,925	8,722	906
New York	18,169,051	54,471	334
North Carolina	7,069,836	53,821	131
Texas	18,378,185	268,601	68

Part 2.
1. Student estimates will vary.
2. Population densities (people/sq mi) according to 1995 estimated figures are as follows:
   Canada: 7   China: 326   India: 766
   Japan: 861   Mexico: 124   Russia: 23

Enrichment Activity 13-4: Ratio and Inequalities

1. Proof: $\dfrac{a}{b} < \dfrac{c}{d}$

$$\frac{a}{\cancel{b}}(\cancel{b})(d) > \frac{c}{\cancel{d}}(b)(\cancel{d})$$

$$ad < cb$$
$$ad < bc$$

Alternative proof: $\dfrac{a}{b} < \dfrac{c}{d}$

$$\frac{a}{b}\left(\frac{d}{d}\right) > \left(\frac{b}{b}\right)\frac{c}{d}$$

$$\frac{ad}{bd} < \frac{bc}{bd}$$

$$ad < bc$$

273

2. **a.** $ad > bc$

  b. $ad \le bc$

  c. $d < b$

  d. $d > bc$

3. $\dfrac{1}{b} > \dfrac{1}{b+1}$ because $1(b + 1) > b\,(1)$ or $b + 1 > b$

4. $\dfrac{a}{b} > 1$ because $\dfrac{a}{b} > \dfrac{b}{a}$ leads to $a^2 > b^2$, and $\sqrt{a^2} >$ $\sqrt{b^2}$, or $a > b$. Therefore, $a\left(\dfrac{1}{b}\right) > b\left(\dfrac{1}{b}\right)$ or $\dfrac{a}{b} > 1$.

5. $a > b$. Since $\dfrac{a}{b} > \dfrac{a+c}{b+c}$ leads to $a(b + c) > b(a + c)$, or $ab + ac > ab + bc$, then, by subtraction, $ac > bc$, and, by division, $a > b$.

6. **a.** False **b.** Leads to contradiction ($x < 0$).

7. **a.** True **b.** Consistent with $x > 0$, $y > 0$.

8. **a.** False **b.** Leads to untruth ($y^2 < 0$).

9. **a.** False **b.** Leads to contradiction ($y < 0$).

10. $\dfrac{a}{b} < \dfrac{a+c}{b+d} < \dfrac{c}{d}$

Enrichment Activity 14-3: Probability and a Digital Clock

1. Answers will vary; student guesses.

2. **a.** $P(0) = \dfrac{450}{1,440} = \dfrac{5}{16} = .3125$

  b. $P(1) = \dfrac{720}{1,440} = \dfrac{1}{2} = .5$

  c. $P(2) = \dfrac{540}{1,440} = \dfrac{3}{8} = .375$

  d. $P(3) = \dfrac{450}{1,440} = \dfrac{5}{16} = .3125$

  e. $P(4) = \dfrac{450}{1,440} = \dfrac{5}{16} = .3125$

  f. $P(5) = \dfrac{450}{1,440} = \dfrac{5}{16} = .3125$

  g. $P(6) = \dfrac{252}{1,440} = \dfrac{7}{40} = .175$

  h. $P(7) = \dfrac{252}{1,440} = \dfrac{7}{40} = .175$

  i. $P(8) = \dfrac{252}{1,440} = \dfrac{7}{40} = .175$

  j. $P(9) = \dfrac{252}{1,440} = \dfrac{7}{40} = .175$

3. The digit appearing most often on a digital clock is 1, and the digit appearing the second most often is 2. The digits 0, 3, 4, and 5 appear the same number of times over a 24-hour period. The digits 6, 7, 8, and 9

also appear the same number of times over a 24-hour period, and these digits appear less than all others.

4. The answers will be exactly the same for *any* 12-hour period as for the 24-hour period discussed earlier because, in a 24-hour period, a 12-hour cycle is repeated twice.

Enrichment Activity 14-6: Probability and Area: *And, Or, Not*

1. **a.** $P(D) = \dfrac{7}{25} = .28$ **b.** $P(\text{not } D) = \dfrac{18}{25} = .72$

2. **a.** $P(D) = \dfrac{7}{25} = .28$ **b.** $P(\text{not } D) = \dfrac{18}{25} = .72$

3. **a.** $P(D) = \dfrac{7}{25} = .28$ **b.** $P(\text{not } D) = \dfrac{18}{25} = .72$

4. The areas of the three shaded regions in Exercises 1–3 are equal; each is 7 square units. The probability that a point from the 5 by 5 grid lies in the shaded region is $\dfrac{7}{25}$ for each region.

5. **a.**

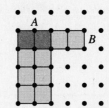

  A and *B* intersect in two squares.

  b. $P(A \text{ or } B) = \dfrac{10}{25} = \dfrac{2}{5} = .4$

6. **a.**

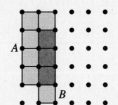

  A and *B* intersect in three squares.

  b. $P(A \text{ or } B) = \dfrac{9}{25} = .36$

7. **a.**

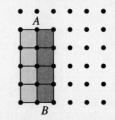

  B is a subset of *A*. *A* and *B* intersect in four squares.

b. $P(A \text{ or } B) = \dfrac{8}{25} = .32$

8. $P(A \text{ or } B)$ is found by either:

    (1) counting the number of square units in the 5 by 5 grid that are shaded by A, by B, or by both, and then dividing this area by 25, which is the area of the grid; or

    (2) using the formula

$$P(A \text{ or } B) = P(A) + P(B) - P(A \text{ and } B)$$

9. It is not possible for $P(A \text{ and } B) > .16$ or $P(A \text{ and } B) > \dfrac{4}{25}$. In Exercise 7, where B is a subset of A, it can be seen that $P(A \text{ and } B) = \dfrac{4}{25}$. No probability can exceed this using the given information, that is, $P(A \text{ and } B) = P(B)$, which serves as a maximum value.

Enrichment Activity 14-9: Probability on a Dart Board

1. a. π **b.** 3π (from $4\pi - \pi$)

  c. 5π (from $9\pi - 4\pi$)   **d.** 7π (from $16\pi - 9\pi$)

  e. 9π (from $25\pi - 16\pi$)

2. a. $\dfrac{1}{25} = .04$ **b.** $\dfrac{3}{25} = .12$

  c. $\dfrac{5}{25} = .2$ **d.** $\dfrac{7}{25} = .28$

  e. $\dfrac{9}{25} = .36$

3. a. $\dfrac{10}{25} = .4$ **b.** $\dfrac{14}{25} = .56$

  c. $\dfrac{15}{25} = .6$ **d.** $\dfrac{24}{25} = .96$

  e. $\dfrac{9}{25} = .36$

4. a. $\dfrac{4}{25} = .16$ **b.** $\dfrac{9}{25} = .36$

  c. $\dfrac{1}{625} = .0016$ **d.** $\dfrac{576}{625} = .9216$

  e. $\dfrac{81}{625} = .1296$ **f.** $\dfrac{256}{625} = .4096$

  g. $\dfrac{49}{625} = .0784$ **h.** $\dfrac{81}{625} = .1296$

Enrichment Activity 14-12: Expectation

1. a. Student answers will vary.

  b. Most should say "left" or "negative."

2. $E \text{ (game)} = \left(\dfrac{1}{6}\right)(+3) + \left(\dfrac{5}{6}\right)(-1)$

$$= \dfrac{3}{6} \qquad + \dfrac{-5}{6}$$

$$= \dfrac{-2}{6}$$

$$= \dfrac{-1}{3}$$

3. The expectation of $-\dfrac{1}{3}$ $\left(\text{or } -\dfrac{2}{6}\right)$ indicates that, on the average, a player expects to move 1 place in a negative direction for every 3 turns taken (or 2 places to the left for every 6 turns taken).

4. a. $E \text{ (game)} = \left(\dfrac{1}{6}\right)(+5) + \left(\dfrac{5}{6}\right)(-1) = 0$

  b. The expectation of 0 indicates that, on the average, a player does not expect to advance or fall behind over a long period of play. After many turns, the player should still be in the START box, although the marker may have moved to the right and to the left during different turns.

5. Answers can vary. To win on this board in an average of 24 turns, a player must advance 8 spaces to the right in that time. Therefore, $E \text{ (game)}$ should equal $\dfrac{+8}{24}$, or $+\dfrac{1}{3}$. Here is one possible set of rules to obtain $E \text{ (game)} = \dfrac{1}{3}$:

  (1) If a player guesses correctly, move 7 spaces in a positive direction (to the right).

  (2) If a player guesses incorrectly, move 1 space in a negative direction (to the left).

Thus:

$$E \text{ (game)} = \left(\dfrac{1}{6}\right)(+7) + \left(\dfrac{5}{6}\right)(-1) = \dfrac{7}{6} - \dfrac{5}{6} = \dfrac{2}{6} = \dfrac{1}{3}$$

Enrichment Activity 15-4: Locating the Median Value

a. 4th   **b.** 5th   **c.** 8th

d. 20.   **e.** 41st   **f.** 119th

g. $\dfrac{N+1}{2}$ **h.** 4th and 5th   **i.** 5th and 6th

j. 9th and 10th   **k.** 21st and 22nd   **l.** 44th and 45th

m. 115th and 116th   **n.** $\dfrac{N}{2}$ and $\dfrac{N}{2} + 1$

General rule: Arrange the data values in order. Let the number of data values be N.

If N is odd, the median is the value that is $\dfrac{N+1}{2}$ from either end.

If N is even, the median is the average of the values that are $\dfrac{N}{2}$ and $\dfrac{N}{2} + 1$ from either end.

Enrichment Activity 16-10: Graphing Step Functions

a.

Hours	Cost	Hours	Cost	Hours	Cost
$\frac{1}{4}$	$4.00	2	$6.00	$17\frac{3}{4}$	$38.00
$\frac{2}{3}$	$4.00	$2\frac{1}{4}$	$8.00	18	$38.00
1	$4.00	6	$14.00	19	$40.00
$1\frac{1}{2}$	$6.00	$12\frac{1}{5}$	$28.00	$20\frac{1}{3}$	$40.00

b.

In	Out	Cost	In	Out	Cost
9:15 A.M.	9:50 A.M.	$4.00	10:00 A.M.	2:30 P.M.	$12.00
9:30 A.M.	10:29 A.M.	$4.00	10:10 A.M.	10:00 P.M.	$26.00
9:30 A.M.	10:35 A.M.	$6.00	12:15 P.M.	8:00 A.M.	$40.00
10:00 A.M.	12:45 P.M.	$8.00	12:45 P.M.	11:00 A.M.	$40.00

c.

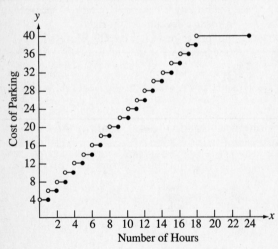

d. From 1 to 19 hours, the graph would be a straight line.

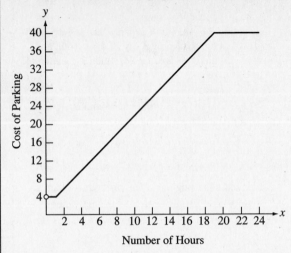

Enrichment Activity 17-2: Determinants and Cramer's Rule

1.
$$x = \frac{\begin{vmatrix} 5 & 1 \\ 1 & -3 \end{vmatrix}}{\begin{vmatrix} 2 & 1 \\ 2 & -3 \end{vmatrix}} = \frac{-16}{-8} = 2; \; y = \frac{\begin{vmatrix} 2 & 5 \\ 2 & 1 \end{vmatrix}}{\begin{vmatrix} 2 & 1 \\ 2 & -3 \end{vmatrix}} = \frac{-8}{-8} = 1$$

2.
$$x = \frac{\begin{vmatrix} 5 & 1 \\ -7 & -1 \end{vmatrix}}{\begin{vmatrix} 1 & 1 \\ 1 & -1 \end{vmatrix}} = \frac{2}{-2} = -1; \; y = \frac{\begin{vmatrix} 1 & 5 \\ 1 & -7 \end{vmatrix}}{\begin{vmatrix} 1 & 1 \\ 1 & -1 \end{vmatrix}} = \frac{-12}{-2} = 6$$

3.
$$x = \frac{\begin{vmatrix} 10 & 2 \\ 23 & -3 \end{vmatrix}}{\begin{vmatrix} 3 & 2 \\ 5 & -3 \end{vmatrix}} = \frac{-76}{-19} = 4; \; y = \frac{\begin{vmatrix} 3 & 10 \\ 5 & 23 \end{vmatrix}}{\begin{vmatrix} 3 & 2 \\ 5 & -3 \end{vmatrix}} = \frac{19}{-19} = -1$$

4.
$$x = \frac{\begin{vmatrix} -43 & -8 \\ -26 & -1 \end{vmatrix}}{\begin{vmatrix} 1 & -8 \\ 7 & -1 \end{vmatrix}} = \frac{-165}{55} = -3; \; y = \frac{\begin{vmatrix} 1 & -43 \\ 7 & -26 \end{vmatrix}}{\begin{vmatrix} 1 & -8 \\ 7 & -1 \end{vmatrix}} = \frac{275}{55} = 5$$

5. a. $\begin{vmatrix} 6 & 2 \\ 9 & 3 \end{vmatrix} = 0$; there is no solution.

b. The system is dependent.

Enrichment Activity 17-3: Systems with Three Variables

1. $(3, 5, 2)$ 2. $(1, -2, 2)$ 3. $(2, 1, -2)$
4. $(4, 3, \frac{1}{2})$ 5. $(10, 3, 7)$ 6. $(-6, 4, 2)$

Enrichment Activity 18-1: Finding Primes— The Sieves of Eratosthenes

1. 17
2. If a prime greater than 15 is a factor, there is another factor less than 15 that is either itself a prime or has a prime factor less than 15. Therefore any composite number between 15 and 200 that has a factor greater than 15 must also have a factor less than 15 and has already been crossed out.
3. 19, the largest prime less than 20
4. **a.** If x is replaced by any integer from 0 through 40, the expression $x^2 - x + 41$ yields a prime number. For example:

   $x = 1; \quad 1^2 - 1 + 41 = 41$
   $x = 2; \quad 2^2 - 2 + 41 = 43$
   $x = 3; \quad 3^2 - 3 + 41 = 47$
   $x = 4; \quad 4^2 - 4 + 41 = 53$
   $x = 5; \quad 5^2 - 5 + 41 = 61$
   $x = 6; \quad 6^2 - 6 + 41 = 71$
   $x = 7; \quad 7^2 - 7 + 41 = 83$
   $x = 8; \quad 8^2 - 8 + 41 = 97$
   $x = 9; \quad 9^2 - 9 + 41 = 113$
   $x = 10; \quad 10^2 - 10 + 41 = 131$

   b. $x = 41; \quad 41^2 - 41 + 41 = 1{,}681 = 41 \cdot 41$

Enrichment Activity 18-7: Factoring Trinomials

1. $(1)\ 4x^2(-10) = -40x^2$
   $(2)\ \begin{array}{rr} -1x & +40x \\ -2x & +20x \\ -4x & +10x \\ \boxed{-5x} & \boxed{+8x} \end{array}$
   $(3)\ 4x^2 + 8x - 5x - 10$
   $(4)\ 4x(x + 2) - 5(x + 2)$
   $(5)\ (x + 2)(4x - 5)$
2. **a.** $20x^2 = 4x \cdot 5x$
   $2x^2 + 4x + 5x + 10$
   $2x(x + 2) + 5(x + 2)$
   $(x + 2)(2x + 5)$
   b. $-36x^2 = -12x \cdot 2x$
   $4x^2 - 12x + 3x - 9$
   $4x(x - 3) + 3(x - 3)$
   $(x - 3)(4x + 3)$

c. $15x^2 = -15x \cdot -1x$
$3x^2 - 15x - 1x + 5$
$3x(x - 5) - 1(x - 5)$
$(x - 5)(3x - 1)$

d. $-24x^2 = -12x \cdot 2x$
$3x^2 - 12x + 2x - 8$
$3x(x - 4) + 2(x - 4)$
$(x - 4)(3x + 2)$

e. $36x^2 = -9x \cdot -4x$
$6x^2 - 9x - 4x + 6$
$3x(2x - 3) - 2(2x - 3)$
$(2x - 3)(3x - 2)$

f. $-48x^2 = 16x \cdot -3x$
$12x^2 + 16x - 3x - 4$
$4x(3x + 4) - 1(3x + 4)$
$(3x + 4)(4x - 1)$

g. $-120x^2 = -40x \cdot 3x$
$8x^2 - 40x + 3x - 15$
$8x(x - 5) + 3(x - 5)$
$(x - 5)(8x + 3)$

h. $50x^2 = 25x \cdot 2x$
$5x^2 + 25x + 2x + 10$
$5x(x + 5) + 2(x + 5)$
$(x + 5)(5x + 2)$

i. $-21x^2 = 21x \cdot -1x$
$7x^2 + 21x - 1x - 3$
$7x(x + 3) - 1(x + 3)$
$(x + 3)(7x - 1)$

Enrichment Activity 19-2: Is it Magic or Is It Math?

1. **a.** $\dfrac{3}{5} \to \dfrac{5}{8} \to \dfrac{8}{13} \to \dfrac{13}{21} \to \dfrac{21}{34} \to \dfrac{34}{55};$

   Yes, $\dfrac{34}{55} = 0.6$ to the nearest tenth.

   b. $\dfrac{12}{13} \to \dfrac{13}{15} \to \dfrac{15}{28} \to \dfrac{28}{43} \to \dfrac{43}{71} \to \dfrac{71}{114};$

   Yes, $\dfrac{71}{114} = 0.6$ to the nearest tenth.

2. Student-generated results. Each result should equal 0.6 when rounded to the nearest tenth.

3. $\dfrac{x}{y} \to \dfrac{y}{x + y} \to \dfrac{x + y}{x + 2y} \to \dfrac{x + 2y}{2x + 3y}$

   $\to \dfrac{2x + 3y}{3x + 5y}$

   $\to \dfrac{3x + 5y}{5x + 8y}$

4. $\dfrac{3x}{5x} < \dfrac{3x + 5y}{5x + 8y} < \dfrac{5y}{8y}$

becomes

$$\dfrac{3}{5} < \dfrac{3x + 5y}{5x + 8y} < \dfrac{5}{8}$$

or $0.6 < \dfrac{3x + 5y}{5x + 8y} < 0.625$

Therefore, $\dfrac{3x + 5y}{5x + 8y} = 0.6$ to the nearest tenth.

5. a. 0.62

b. The seventh term in the sequence beginning with $\dfrac{x}{y}$ ($x > 0$, $y > 0$) is $\dfrac{5x + 8y}{8x + 13y}$. Apply this algebraic fraction to the rule illustrated in Exercise 4, placing terms in a correct order, to discover:

$$\dfrac{8y}{13y} < \dfrac{5x + 8y}{8x + 13y} < \dfrac{5x}{8x}$$

which becomes

$$\dfrac{8}{13} < \dfrac{5x + 8y}{8x + 13y} < \dfrac{5}{8}$$

or $0.615384615 < \dfrac{5x + 8y}{8x + 13y} < 0.625$

Therefore, $\dfrac{5x + 8y}{8x + 13y} = 0.62$ to the nearest hundredth.

Enrichment Activity 19-6: Operations with Fractions

	$A + B$	$A - B$	$A \cdot B$	$A \div B$
1.	$\dfrac{x + w}{y}$	$\dfrac{x - w}{y}$	$\dfrac{xw}{y^2}$	$\dfrac{x}{w}$
2.	$\dfrac{x + wy}{y}$	$\dfrac{x - wy}{y}$	$\dfrac{xw}{y}$	$\dfrac{x}{wy}$

3. (2)   **4.** (4)   **5.** (4)

6. (2)   **7.** 1

8. If the sum and the difference in Exercise 1 are equal, then $w = 0$. This would contradict the given statement, $w > 0$.

9. No. If $x = 1$ and $y = 1$, then

$$\dfrac{x + w}{y} = \dfrac{xw}{y^2}$$

becomes $1 + w = w$ (an impossible statement), or $0 = 1$ (also impossible).

10. $w = 2$ **11.** $x = \dfrac{5}{4}$ **12.** $y = \dfrac{2}{3}$

Enrichment Activity 19-10: Fractions Between Fractions

1. a. $\dfrac{2}{3} < \dfrac{2 + 4}{3 + 5} < \dfrac{4}{5}$

$\dfrac{2}{3} < \dfrac{6}{8} < \dfrac{4}{5}$

$0.\overline{6} < 0.75 < 0.8$

b. $\dfrac{9}{4} < \dfrac{9 + 14}{4 + 5} < \dfrac{14}{5}$

$\dfrac{9}{4} < \dfrac{23}{9} < \dfrac{14}{5}$

$2.25 < 2.\overline{5} < 2.8$

c. $\dfrac{7}{8} < \dfrac{7 + 19}{8 + 20} < \dfrac{19}{20}$

$\dfrac{7}{8} < \dfrac{26}{28} < \dfrac{19}{20}$

$0.875 < 0.9285714\ldots < 0.95$

2. Student-generated examples.

3. No. Cite any one example to show that $\dfrac{a + c}{b + d}$ is not the average of $\dfrac{a}{b}$ and $\dfrac{c}{d}$.

4. a. $\dfrac{3}{4} < \dfrac{3 + 9}{4 + 4} < \dfrac{9}{4}$

$\dfrac{3}{4} < \dfrac{12}{8} < \dfrac{9}{4}$

$0.75 < 1.50 < 2.25$

b. $\dfrac{1}{6} < \dfrac{1 + 5}{6 + 6} < \dfrac{5}{6}$

$\dfrac{1}{6} < \dfrac{6}{12} < \dfrac{5}{6}$

$0.1\overline{6} < 0.5 < 0.8\overline{3}$

c. $\dfrac{9}{2} < \dfrac{9 + 10}{2 + 2} < \dfrac{10}{2}$

$\dfrac{9}{2} < \dfrac{9}{14} < \dfrac{10}{2}$

$4.5 < 4.75 < 5.0$

5. a. If $\dfrac{a}{b} < \dfrac{c}{b}$, then

$\dfrac{a}{b} < \dfrac{a + c}{2b} < \dfrac{c}{b}$ $(a > 0, b > 0, c > 0)$

b. Yes. To find the average of $\dfrac{a}{b}$ and $\dfrac{c}{b}$, add the terms and divide by 2. The average equals

$$\dfrac{a + c}{b} \div 2 = \dfrac{a + c}{b} \cdot \dfrac{1}{2} = \dfrac{a + c}{2b}$$

278

Enrichment Activity 20-2: Square Root: Divide and Average

1. 7.07 2. 6.32 3. 2.45
4. 9.38 5. 10.39 6. 17.03
7. 3.32 8. 23.00 9. 24.78
10. 0.77 11. 0.55 12. 50.25

13. $\sqrt{529}$ (Exercise 8) is rational because $23^2 = 529$, or because 529 is a perfect square, which can be expressed as a rational number, $\dfrac{23}{1}$.

14. 3.162 15. 10.100

Enrichment Activity 20-7: Operations with Radicals

1. a. $3\sqrt{2}$ b. $8\sqrt{11}$ c. $3\sqrt{2}$
   d. $6\sqrt{3} + 3\sqrt{5}$ e. $2\sqrt{10}$
   f. $5-2\sqrt{3}$ g. 0 h. $2\sqrt{5}$
   i. 0 j. $5 - 2\sqrt{3}$ k. $10\sqrt{6}$
   l. $4 + 2\sqrt{3}$ m. $11\sqrt{7}$ n. $6\sqrt{3} + 3\sqrt{5}$
   o. $11\sqrt{7}$ p. 3 q. $10\sqrt{6}$
   r. $2\sqrt{5}$ s. $\sqrt{5}$ t. $4 + 2\sqrt{3}$
   u. $8\sqrt{11}$ v. $-3\sqrt{5}$ w. 3
   x. $-3\sqrt{5}$ y. $5\sqrt{2}$

2.

Matches	Common Answers	Matches	Common Answers
a–c	$3\sqrt{2}$	k–g	$10\sqrt{6}$
b–u	$8\sqrt{11}$	l–t	$4 + 2\sqrt{3}$
d–n	$6\sqrt{3} + 3\sqrt{5}$	m–o	$11\sqrt{7}$
f–j	$5 - 2\sqrt{3}$	p–w	3
g–i	0	v–x	$-3\sqrt{5}$
h–r	$2\sqrt{5}$		

3. a. 100 b. Yes

Enrichment Activity 21-5: Pythagorean Triples

U	V	$U^2 - V^2$	$2UV$	$U^2 + V^2$
2	1	3	4	5
3	1	8	6	10
4	1	15	8	17
5	1	24	10	26
6	1	35	12	37
7	1	48	14	50
8	1	63	16	65
9	1	80	18	82

1. The difference between $U^2 + V^2$ and $U^2 - V^2$ is 2. The sum of $U^2 + V^2$ and $U^2 - V^2$ is U times $2UV$ [$5 + 3 = 2(4)$]. The sum of the three numbers is twice the product of U and the next consecutive integer [$3 + 4 + 5 = 2(2 \times 3)$]. Other relationships are possible.

U	V	$U^2 - V^2$	$2UV$	$U^2 + V^2$
3	2	5	12	13
4	3	7	24	25
5	4	9	40	41
6	5	11	60	61
7	6	13	84	85
8	7	15	112	113
9	8	17	144	145

2. The difference between the two largest numbers is 1 ($13 - 12 = 1$). The sum of the two largest numbers is the square of the smallest number, $U^2 - V^2$ ($12 + 13 = 5^2$). The sum of the three numbers is the product of the smallest number times 1 more than the smallest number [$5 + 12 + 13 = 5(5 + 1)$]. The smallest number is the sum of U and V ($5 = 3 + 2$). Other relationships are possible.

U	V	$U^2 - V^2$	$2UV$	$U^2 + V^2$
4	2	12	16	20
5	3	16	30	34
6	4	20	48	52
7	5	24	70	74
8	6	28	96	100
9	7	32	126	130
10	8	36	160	164

3. The difference between the two largest numbers is 4 ($20 - 16 = 4$). The sum of the largest number and the smallest number is twice U^2 ($20 + 12 = 2(4^2)$). The sum of the two largest numbers is the square of half the smallest [$16 + 20 = (\frac{1}{2} \times 12)^2$]. The smallest number is 4 times the average of U and V $\left[12 = 4\left(\dfrac{4 + 2}{2}\right)\right]$. Other relationships are possible.

4. 10 and 7

5. 33, 56, 65 or 42, 56, 70 (Many answers are possible.)

6. 69, 260, 269 or 69, 92, 115 (Many answers are possible.)

7. **a.** Yes. 6, 8, 10
   b. No. If a number is odd, its square is odd. The sum of the squares of two odd numbers is even. Therefore the third number must be even.
   c. Yes. 3, 4, 5
   d. No. If either a or b is odd and the other even, then c must be odd. If a and b are both even, then c must be even. Therefore it is not possible to have only one odd number in a Pythagorean triple.

ANSWERS FOR SUGGESTED TEST ITEMS

Chapter 1

1. **a.** 12 **b.** 108 **c.** 19 **d.** 112
2. **a.** infinite **b.** finite **c.** infinite **d.** empty
3. True **4.** False **5.** True **6.** True
7. False **8.** False
9. **a.** $\frac{3}{10}$ **b.** $\frac{16}{3}$ **c.** $\frac{0}{1}$ **d.** $\frac{73}{1}$ **e.** $\frac{-21}{100}$
10. 18.05
11. **a.** 0.05 **b.** $0.666\ldots = 0.\overline{6}$
    c. $0.4444\ldots = 0.\overline{4}$ **d.** $-3.1666\ldots = -3.1\overline{6}$
12. $\frac{7}{9}$
13. **a.** rational **b.** irrational **c.** irrational **d.** rational
14. **a.** 3.742 **b.** 1.183 **c.** 3.142 **d.** 0.142
15.

    $$A \quad B \quad C \quad D \quad E \quad F \quad G \quad H \quad I \quad J \quad K$$
    $$-1\tfrac{1}{2} \quad -1 \quad -\tfrac{1}{2} \quad 0 \quad \tfrac{1}{2} \quad 1 \quad 1\tfrac{1}{2} \quad 2 \quad 2\tfrac{1}{2} \quad 3 \quad 3\tfrac{1}{2}$$

16. **a.** A and B **b.** J and K **c.** H and I
    d. F and G **e.** D and E
17. **a.** Bar graph
    b. *One* conclusion is possible: Trails Ahead had highest cost, *or* Sundog and Homefront are closest in price, *or* the cost in 3 of the 5 catalogs was less than $100, and so on.
    c. No. A line graph is drawn when comparing changes in one item. A bar graph is used to compare many different items such as costs in 5 catalogs.

Chapter 2

1. (4) **2.** (2) **3.** 16
4. **a.** $\frac{1}{2}$ avg $\frac{1}{6}$ **b.** 0.5 **c.** 0.02 **d.** 1.25
5. **a.** 6 **b.** 4 **c.** 1 **d.** 0.36
6. **a.** True, distributive property
    b. True, commutative property of addition
    c. True, addition property of 0
    d. True, associative property of multiplication
    e. False
7. **a.** $>$ **b.** $<$ **c.** $>$
8. **a.** 5.5 **b.** 9 **c.** 3
9. **a.** $\overrightarrow{BA}, \overrightarrow{BD}, \overrightarrow{BC}$ **b.** $\angle ABC$ **c.** 108
10. **a.** $\{1, 2, 3, \ldots, 10, 12\}$ **b.** $\{3, 6, 9\}$
    c. $\{11, 12, 13, \ldots, 20\}$ **d.** U **e.** $\varnothing$

Bonus I: The commission

Bonus II: $(3 + 3 \div 3 - 3) \times 3 = 3$

Chapter 3

1. Sylvia, $15; Carlos, $9
2. 5 kisses and 2 peppermints
3. Monday, 3; Tuesday, 5; Wednesday, 12; Thursday, 24; Friday, 48
4. Ann is Mrs. Carroll's daughter and she works for Mrs. Adams.
    Beth is Mrs. Burke's daughter and she works for Mrs. Carroll.
    Chris is Mrs. Adams' daughter and she works for Mrs. Burke.
5. 29 **6.** 227 **7.** 59 oz. **8.** 9
9. The cashier made a mistake.

Chapter 4

1. **a.** $n + 12$ **b.** $n - 7$ **c.** $2n + 4$
    d. $\frac{1}{2}n - 6$ **e.** $\frac{n + 4}{3}$
2. **a.** $x + 5$ **b.** $10c$ **c.** $60h + m$
    d. $25q + 10d$ **e.** $35 + 0.15 (m - 100)$
3. $1, 17, a, b, 17a, 17b, ab, 17ab$
4. Base is x; exponent is 7.
5. **a.** $3a^2$ **b.** $5x^3y5$ **c.** $(5a)^3$
6. **a.** Coefficient = 6, base = h, exponent = 2
    b. Coefficient = 1, base = w, exponent = 5
    c. Coefficient = π, base = r, exponent = 3
    d. Coefficient = -1, base = m, exponent = 1
7. **a.** 1 **b.** 1 **c.** 64 **d.** 4 **e.** 3
    f. 37 **g.** 16 **h.** 0
8. 100.3275
9. **a.** 144π cm^2 **b.** 452.389 cm^2
10. **a.** 53π ft **b.** 166.504 ft
11. $c = 4n + p$ **12.** 77 cm^2
13. 56 mm **14.** $\{4,5\}$

BONUS: 13

Chapter 5

1. 4 **2.** 7 **3.** 6
4. -6 **5.** $+4$ **6.** $+30$
7. -22 **8.** -13 **9.** 0
10. -14.1 **11.** -4 **12.** 0
13. -3 **14.** $+17$ **15.** $+4$
16. $+3$ **17.** $+6$ **18.** $+12$
19. $-15\frac{1}{4}$ **20.** -5.7 **21.** $+15$

22. +56   **23.** −49   **24.** −42
25. 0   **26.** −1.6   **27.** −5
28. +9   **29.** +4   **30.** −17
31. +60   **32.** 0   **33.** 12
34. +42   **35.** −18   **36.** +14
37. 4
38. $A(-3, 1)$, $B(3, -3)$, $C(5, 4)$, $D(-3, -5)$, $E(-4, 0)$, $F(0, -2)$

39.

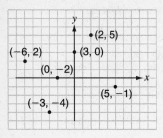

40. a.

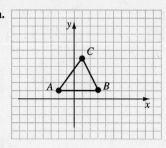

b. 10

BONUS:

$1(7) + 2(-3) = 1$	$1(11) = 11$	$1(3) + 1(7) + 1(11) = 21$
$1(11) + 3(-3) = 2$	$4(3) = 12$	$2(11) = 22$
$1(3) = 3$	$1(7) + 2(3) = 13$	$2(7) + 3(3) = 23$
$1(7) + 1(-3) = 4$	$1(11) + 1(3) = 14$	$8(3) = 24$
$1(11) + 2(-3) = 5$	$5(3) = 15$	$2(11) + 1(3) = 25$
$2(3) = 6$	$1(7) + 3(3) = 16$	$3(11) + 2(-3) = 26$
$1(7) = 7$	$1(11) + 2(3) = 17$	$9(3) = 27$
$(11) + 1(-3) = 8$	$1(11) + 1(7) = 18$	$4(7) = 28$
$3(3) = 9$	$1(7) + 4(3) = 19$	$2(11) + 1(7) = 29$
$1(3) + 1(7) = 10$	$2(7) + 2(3) = 20$	$3(7) + 3(3) = 30$

Chapter 6

1. a. Conditional {3}   **b.** Identity
   c. Conditional {−4}   **d.** Conditional {−3, 2}
2. a. 5   **b.** −6   **c.** 5   **d.** 14
   e. 4   **f.** −36   **g.** 7   **h.** −1

   i. 24   **j.** 5   **k.** $\frac{2}{3}$ **l.** −27

3. 4   **4.** 15 cm   **5.** −280 ft
6. $5.20   **7.** $74

Bonus I: 8 dimes or 2 quarters and 3 dimes

Bonus II: **a.** 23   **b.** 9 cm

Chapter 7

1. a. Yes   **b.** No   **c.** No   **d.** Yes
   e. No   **f.** No
2. a. True   **b.** False   **c.** True   **d.** Open
   e. True   **f.** Open
3. a. $\sim r$ **b.** True
4. a. $\sim p \wedge q$ **b.** False
5. a. $\sim q \vee r$ **b.** False
6. a. $\sim p \rightarrow \sim q$ **b.** True
7. a. $q \rightarrow \sim p$ **b.** False

8. a. I do not study French.   **b.** True
9. a. I study French and do not study biology.
   b. False
10. a. If biology is a science, then I do not study
   biology.
   b. False
11. a. I study biology or biology is not a science.
   b. True
12. a. {1,2,3,4}   **b.** {5,6,7,8,9,10}   **c.** {7,8,9,10}
   d. ∅   **e.** {7,8,9,10}
13. a. Today is Monday.
   b. Tomorrow is not Wednesday.
14. a. It does not rain.   **b.** I will walk home.
15. is false   **16.** is true
17. is true   **18.** is true
19. is false   **20.** may be true or false

Bonus: Ben, Andy, Donna, Carlos, and Elsie

Chapter 8

1. a. $\sim p \rightarrow \sim q$ **b.** True
2. a. $\sim(p \wedge q) \rightarrow r$ **b.** True
3. a. $(r \vee \sim r) \rightarrow p$ **b.** True
4. a. $p \leftrightarrow r$ **b.** False
5. a. If today is not Wednesday, then tomorrow
   is not Thursday.

b. If tomorrow is Thursday, then today is not Wednesday.
c. If tomorrow is not Thursday, then today is not Wednesday.
6. a. If a carrot is not a vegetable, then vegetables grow on trees.
   b. If vegetables do not grow on trees, then a carrot is a vegetable.
   c. If vegetables grow on trees, then a carrot is not a vegetable.

7. a. (1)

p	q	$\sim q$	$p \rightarrow \sim q$
T	T	F	F
T	F	T	T
F	T	F	T
F	F	T	T

(2)

p	q	$\sim p$	$\sim q$	$\sim p \vee \sim q$
T	T	F	F	F
T	F	F	T	T
F	T	T	F	T
F	F	T	T	T

(3)

p	q	$\sim q$	$p \wedge \sim q$
T	T	F	F
T	F	T	T
F	T	F	F
F	F	T	F

b. (1) and (2)

8. a.

p	q	$\sim p$	$\sim q$	$p \wedge q$	$\sim(p \wedge q)$	$\sim p \vee \sim q$	$\sim(p \wedge q) \leftrightarrow (\sim p \vee \sim q)$
T	T	F	F	T	F	F	T
T	F	F	T	F	T	T	T
F	T	T	F	F	T	T	T
F	F	T	T	F	T	T	T

b. Yes
c. It is true for all possible truth values of p and q.
9. True   **10.** False   **11.** Cannot be determined
12. True

BONUS: **a.** 5   **b.** Yes

Chapter 9

1. $-3a^3$ **2.** $3x - 2$ **3.** $-27x - 63$
4. $4x^4 - 5$ **5.** $-4a^3b^3$ **6.** $2x^2 - 2x - 2$
7. $-3x + 22$ **8.** $-27x^2y^3$ **9.** $14y - x$
10. $2x^2 + 7x - 4$ **11.** $4x^2 - 4x + 1$
12. $4x^2 - 1$ **13.** $48r^3s^4$ **14.** $a^3 - 2a^2 + a$
15. $13x^2 - 3$ **16.** $7a$ **17.** 5
18. $5y^2 - 4$ **19.** $x + 9$ **20.** 3.2×10^3
21. 9.3×10^7 **22.** 5.4×10^{-2} **23.** 2×10^{-6}
24. 80,000   **25.** 1,700,000,000
26. 0.073   **27.** 0.0000005
28. a. $8x - 6$ **b.** $3x^2 + 5x - 28$ **c.** 2 $\left(x \leq \dfrac{7}{3}\right)$
29. $4a^2 - 12a + 9$ **30.** $4(x - 5) + 3 = 4x - 17$
31. (1)   **32.** (4)   **33.** (1)

Bonus: **a.** 17 and 18
b. No. The squares of consecutive counting numbers always differ by an odd number since one square will be odd and the other square even.

Chapter 10

1. $x < x + 1$ **2.** $a = 5$
3. $b = 22$ **4.** $y = 42.5$
5. $x = 5$ **6.** $n = -10$
7. $a = 7.2$ **8.** $x = -5.5$
9. $c = 9$ **10.** $y = \dfrac{1}{3}$
11. $x = 87$

12. Length is 10 cm, width is 7.5 cm

13. $h = \dfrac{3V}{A}$

14. **a.** $C = \dfrac{5F-160}{9}$ or $C = \dfrac{5}{9}(F-32)$

    b. $C = -5$

15. 7   **16.** $x < 3$

17. $x \geq 3$ **18.** $x > -2$

19. $(x > 2) \vee (x < -2)$ **20.** $1 \leq x \leq 6$

21. (2)   **22.** (1)

23. 3 hr

Bonus: 72

Chapter 11

1. **a.** $\overrightarrow{EB}$
    b. $\angle AEC, \angle BEC, \angle AED, \angle BED$
    c. $\angle A, \angle B, \angle ACE, \angle BCE$
    d. $\angle ACF, \angle BCF$
    e. $\overline{AE}$
    f. $\angle CAE$
    g. $\angle BCE$

2. **a.** 95   **b.** 85   **c.** 85   **d.** 95

3. $m\angle A = 76, m\angle B = 56, m\angle C = 48$

4. **a.** 118   **b.** 118   **c.** 62   **d.** 62

5. 76°

6. 80°, 100°

Bonus: $m\angle ECD = 70$

Chapter 12

1. **a.** $\overline{EA}$ **b.** $\overleftrightarrow{FD}$ **c.** B **d.** B **e.** (3)

2. 20

3. **a.** 5   **b.** $m\angle A = 20, \ m\angle B = 160, \ m\angle C = 20$
            $m\angle D = 160$

4.

5. H, point and line
   E, line
   A, line
   R, neither
   T, line
   S, point

6. **a.** $(5, 4)$ **b.** $(-5, -4)$ **c.** $(-5, 4)$ **d.** $(2, 2)$

7. **a.**

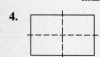

    b. $A'\ (-1, 1); \ B'\ (-7, 1); \ C'\ (-4, 5)$
    c. 12

8. $(2, 3), (2, -3), (-2, -3)$

BONUS: Draw the image of the campfire, using the river as a line of reflection. The shortest distance between the hiker and the image is a straight line. The point of intersection of this line with the river determines the shortest path, first to the river and then to the campfire.

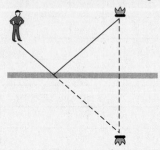

Chapter 13

1. 1:3   **2.** 6:1   **3.** 4:5   **4.** 1 to 400

5. 1.2 boxes per second   **6.** 384 miles

7. $x = 8$ **8.** $a = 6$ **9.** $y = 18$ **10.** $x = 9$

11. 3   **12.** 40°, 40°, 100°   **13.** 25%

14. 21   **15.** 25   **16.** 14

17. 32 cm, 40 cm, 56 cm

Bonus I: 20:5

Bonus II:

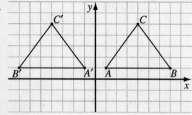

Chapter 14

1. **a.** 24   **b.** 5,040   **c.** 120   **d.** 60   **e.** 9

2. 70%

3. **a.** $\dfrac{12}{20} \cdot \dfrac{11}{19} = \dfrac{132}{380}$ or $\dfrac{33}{95}$

    b. $\dfrac{8}{20} \cdot \dfrac{7}{19} = \dfrac{56}{380}$ or $\dfrac{14}{95}$

    c. $\dfrac{12}{20} \cdot \dfrac{8}{19} + \dfrac{8}{20} \cdot \dfrac{12}{19} = \dfrac{192}{380}$ or $\dfrac{48}{95}$

4. 6! or 720   **5.** $_{12}P_3$ or 1,320   **6.** 60

7. $\dfrac{4}{52} \cdot \dfrac{3}{51} = \dfrac{12}{2,652}$ or $\dfrac{1}{221}$

8. 8! or 40,320   **9.** 9   **10.** $\dfrac{4}{36}$ or $\dfrac{1}{9}$

11. **a.** (H, H, H, H), (H, T, H, H), (T, H, H, H), (T, T, H, H)
       (H, H, H, T), (H, T, H, T), (T, H, H, T) (T, T, H, T)
       (H, H, T, H), (H, T, T, H), (T, H, T, H) (T, T, T, H)

(H, H, T, T), (H, T, T, T), (T, H, T, T) (T, T, T, T)

b. 16   **c.** $\frac{6}{16}$ or $\frac{3}{8}$ **d.** $\frac{15}{16}$

12. Let x = number of red marbles.

$$\frac{x - 10}{4x - 10} = \frac{1}{6}$$

25 red, 75 green

13. a. (A, B), (B, A), (C, A), (D, A), (E, A), (F, A),
(A, C), (B, C), (C, B), (D, B), (E, B), (F, B),
(A, D), (B, D), (C, D), (D, C), (E, C), (F, C)
(A, E), (B, E), (C, E), (D, E), (E, D), (F, D)
(A, F), (B, F), (C, F), (D, F), (E, F), (F, E)

b. $\frac{2}{30}$ or $\frac{1}{15}$ **c.** $\frac{16}{30}$ or $\frac{8}{15}$ **d.** $\frac{20}{30}$ or $\frac{2}{3}$

14. a. 5! or 120   **b.** $2 \cdot 4 \cdot 3 \cdot 2 \cdot 1 = 48$

c. $\frac{48}{120}$ or $\frac{2}{5}$

BONUS: 10 possible 15's:
(6, 6, 3),
(6, 5, 4),
(6, 4, 5),
(6, 3, 6),
(5, 6, 4),
(5, 5, 5),
(5, 4, 6),
(4, 6, 5),
(4, 5, 6),
(3, 6, 6)

Total number in sample space:

$6 \cdot 6 \cdot 6 = 216$

$$P(E) = \frac{n(E)}{n(S)} = \frac{10}{216} = \frac{5}{108}$$

Chapter 15

1. a. 129 **b.** 128 **c.** 127
2. 51, 53, 55, 57, 59
3. 83   **4.** 14.4 lb   **5.** 5   **6.** 18   **7.** $3a - 2$

8. a.

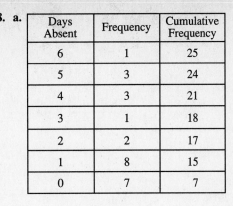

Days Absent	Frequency	Cumulative Frequency
6	1	25
5	3	24
4	3	21
3	1	18
2	2	17
1	8	15
0	7	7

b.

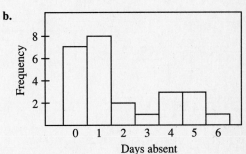

c.

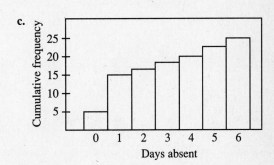

d. 1 **e.** 0 **f.** 1.92 **g.** 4 **h.** $\frac{3}{25}$ **i.** $\frac{1}{25}$ **j.** 1

9. a.

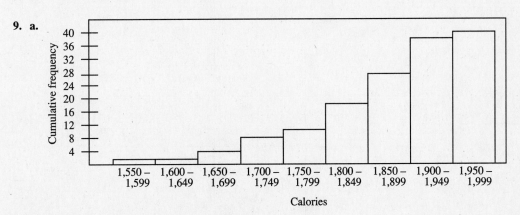

b. 1,850 – 1,899 **c.** 1,750 – 1,799 **d.** 1,900 – 1,949

Chapter 16

1. No   **2.** −5

3. a.   **b.**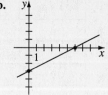

c. 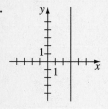   **d.**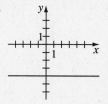

4. $y = 3x − 1$

5. a. 5   **b.** $y = 5x$

    c. 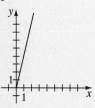   **d.** 5

6. a. $m = 2, b = 1$ **b.** $m = −1, b = 7$

    c. $m = \dfrac{1}{2}, b = −3$ **d.** $m = 0, b = 3$

7. $y = 3x + 2$ **8.** $x = −2$

9. a. $y + 2x \geq 2$ **b.**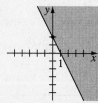

10. −3

11. a. 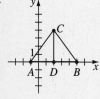   **b.** (2, 0)
                       c. 6
                       d. 4
                       e. 12
                       f. $x = 2$

12. a. $y = 5x + 220$

b.

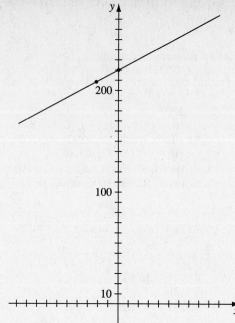

c. (*1*) 195
    (*2*) 9 years ago ($x = −9$)

d. (*1*) 260
    (*2*) in 11 years

13.

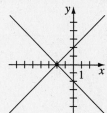

BONUS: (9, 2), (9, 6), (1, 6)

Chapter 17

1. 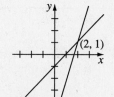   (2, 1)

2. a. 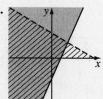   **b.** (1, 1)

3. a. $(3, -2)$ **b.** $(-6, 8)$

4. a. $\left(\dfrac{5}{2}, 3\right)$

b.

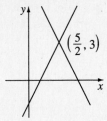

5. 1; any value except $\dfrac{7}{2}$

6. $-\dfrac{1}{2}$

7. Last year's garden was 3 ft by 14 ft
This year's garden is 6 ft by 7 ft

8. First meeting: 7 girls and 5 boys;
Second meeting: 14 girls and 15 boys

BONUS: a. 94 spectators,
b. 24 parents, 12 faculty, 58 students

Chapter 18

1. $3^2 \cdot 5 \cdot 11$

2. 1, 2, 3, 5, 6, 9, 10, 15, 18, 30, 45, 90

3. $6ab$ **4.** $25a^2b^4$ **5.** $4x^2 - 4x + 1$

6. $2x^2 + 3x - 9$ **7.** $y^2 - 49$ **8.** $6a(2a - b)$

9. $(a - 3)(a - 2)$ **10.** $(s + 5)(s - 5)$

12. $(x + 10)(x - 2)$ **13.** $(y + 3)^2$

14. $(2x + 3)(x - 2)$ **15.** $(4b + 3)(b + 3)$

16. $4(x^2 + 4)$ **17.** $(3b + 4)(3b - 4)$

18. $5(y + 2)(y - 2)$ **19.** $5(x - 1)^2$

20. $6x^2 + x - 1$ **21.** $2s - 3$

BONUS I: a. $n(n + 2) = n^2 + 2n$

$$\frac{n + (n + 2)}{2} = \frac{2n + 2}{2} = n + 1$$

$$n^2 + 2n \stackrel{?}{=} (n + 1)^2 - 1$$

$$\stackrel{?}{=} n^2 + 2n + 1 - 1$$

$$= n^2 + 2n$$

b. The integers n and $n + 2$ can be even or odd.

BONUS II: $n^2 - 1 = (n - 1)(n + 1)$
$n - 1$ and $n + 1$ are consecutive even integers if n is odd.
$n - 1$ and $n + 1$ are consecutive odd integers if n is even.

Chapter 19

1. -4 **2.** $\dfrac{x}{3y}$ **3.** $\dfrac{a + b}{2}$

4. $\dfrac{3c - 1}{3c^2}$ **5.** $\dfrac{2x + 1}{10x}$ **6.** $\dfrac{2x}{5}$

7. $\dfrac{y - 2}{y}$ **8.** $9x$ **9.** $\dfrac{3}{5}$

10. $\dfrac{15x^2 + 1}{5x}$ **11.** $\dfrac{11x - 16}{15}$ **12.** $\dfrac{4}{9}$

13. $-\dfrac{3a + 21}{10a}$ **14.** $\dfrac{2}{7}$ **15.** $\dfrac{23b}{10}$

16. $x = 4$ **17.** $a = 5$ **18.** $y = 54$

19. $x = 19$ **20.** $b = 4$ **21.** $d = 25$

22. 18   **23.** 10

BONUS: a. $\dfrac{31}{60}$ **b.** 60

Chapter 20

1. a. Rational   **b.** Irrational   **c.** Irrational
d. Rational   **e.** Rational   **f.** Rational
g. Irrational

2. a. $4\sqrt{3}$ **b.** $3\sqrt{2}$ **c.** $12\sqrt{6}$ **d.** 75
e. 4   **f.** 5   **g.** $2\sqrt{2}$

3. a. $11a^2$ **b.** $0.6x$ **c.** $3y^3$ **d.** $3a$

4. 4.5   **5. a.** $x = \pm 1.2$ **b.** $x = \pm 7$

6. a. 37   **b.** -6.08 **c.** 2.4

7. 15 and 16

8. a. 9.591663047 or 9.591663
b. 9.592

9. a. -46.9041576 or -46.904157 or -46.904158
b. -46.90

10. (3)   **11.** (1)

12. a. The length, $5\sqrt{10}$, is greater.
b. (1) $10\sqrt{10} + 8\sqrt{15}$ in.
(2) 62.61 in.
c. (1) $100\sqrt{6}$ sq in.
(2) 244.95 sq in.

Chapter 21

1. $x = 3$ or $x = 4$ **2.** $x = -1$ or $x = 6$

3. $a = 5$ or $a = -5$ **4.** $y = 0$ or $y = 5$

5. $b = -\dfrac{9}{2}$ or $b = 4$ **6.** $x = -5$ or $x = 7$

7. $-9, -8$ or $8, 9$ **8.** 25 in.

9. 40 cm
10. **a.** $\sqrt{41}$ in.   **b.** 6.4 in.
11. Base = 10 cm, Altitude = 6 cm
12. $10\sqrt{130}$ ft or 114.0 ft
13. **a.** $2 \pm \sqrt{3}$ **b.** 3.73, 0.27

14.

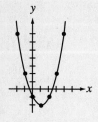

Bonus I: **a.** Area of rectangle = 60
b. Area of circle = 169π

Bonus II:

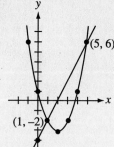

$x = 1$ and $y = -2$;
or $x = 5$ and $y = 6$

288

ANSWERS FOR SAT PREPARATION EXERCISES

Chapter 1

1. C	2. D	3. C
4. B	5. C	6. B
7. B	8. E	9. B
10. A	11. A	12. C
13. B	14. B	15. C
16. A	17. A	18. B
19. A	20. A	21. 8
22. 198	23. 0	24. 76
25. $\frac{1}{2}$ or 0.5		

Chapter 2

1. C	2. A	3. D
4. B	5. C	6. E
7. A	8. B	9. D
10. B	11. B	12. A
13. A	14. D	15. B
16. A	17. C	18. B
19. B	20. C	21. 7
22. 4	23. 72	24. 2
25. {1, 2, 3, 6}		

Chapter 3

1. B	2. D	3. C
4. B	5. A	6. C
7. E	8. D	9. A
10. C	11. C	12. B
13. A	14. C	15. B
16. A	17. B	18. A
19. D	20. C	21. 7
22. 10	23. 6	24. 6
25. 2		

Chapter 4

1. D	2. D	3. B
4. B	5. B	6. C
7. E	8. C	9. C
10. A	11. D	12. B
13. A	14. C	15. A
16. B	17. 15.8 or 15.9	18. 8
19. 5.83	20. 12	

Chapter 5

1. A	2. C	3. B
4. C	5. D	6. D
7. D	8. B	9. A
10. C	11. A	12. C
13. B	14. D	15. A
16. B	17. B	18. A
19. D	20. 29	21. 56
22. 39.1	23. 17	24. 4, 6, 8
25. 4, 6, 12	26. 9	

Chapter 6

1. B	2. D	3. D
4. A	5. E	6. A
7. A	8. C	9. C
10. A	11. D	12. A
13. D	14. C	15. B
16. B	17. C	18. A
19. A	20. 8	21. 6
22. 66	23. 4	24. 25

Chapter 7

1. A	2. C	3. E
4. C	5. D	6. C
7. E	8. B	9. A
10. D	11. C	12. C
13. D	14. 700	15. 6, 8, or 10

Chapter 8

1. A	2. B	3. C
4. D	5. E	6. E
7. C	8. C	9. D
10. C	11. C	12. D
13. B	14. D	15. B

Chapter 9

1. A	2. D	3. B
4. C	5. C	6. B
7. D	8. C	9. A
10. D	11. E	12. C
13. B	14. C	15. B
16. D	17. C	18. A

19. C   20. B   21. 14.64
22. 705   23. 24   24. 6.7

Chapter 10

1. E	2. A	3. D
4. B	5. D	6. C
7. D	8. B	9. A
10. A	11. A	12. D
13. B	14. B	15. A
16. B	17. B	18. B
19. C	20. B	21. $\{-3, 3\}$
22. 131	23. 27	24. 4

Chapter 11

1. A	2. D	3. E
4. B	5. A	6. B
7. D	8. A	9. C
10. C	11. A	12. B
13. B	14. A	15. C
16. A	17. D	18. 24
19. 65	20. 139.5	21. 10:04
22. 90		

Chapter 12

1. A	2. C	3. A
4. C	5. A	6. C
7. D	8. D	9. A
10. B	11. A	12. C
13. C	14. D	15. A
16. C	17. C	18. A
19. B	20. B	21. 24
22. 24	23. 36	24. 55
25. 14		

Chapter 13

1. A	2. E	3. B
4. B	5. A	6. A
7. A	8. C	9. B
10. A	11. B	12. D
13. A	14. C	15. A
16. B	17. C	18. A
19. D	20. B	21. B
22. B	23. A	24. A

25. $\frac{35}{3}$ or 11.6 or 11.67   26. $\frac{2}{15}$ or .133

27. 48   28. 80   29. $\frac{1}{3}$ or .333

30. 50   31. 640   32. $\frac{4}{9}$ or .444

33. $\frac{1}{720}$ or .0013

Chapter 14

1. C	2. D	3. C
4. D	5. A	6. A
7. D	8. D	9. C
10. C	11. C	12. D
13. B	14. A	15. A
16. D	17. C	18. A
19. B	20. B	

21. $\frac{1}{16}$ or .062 or .063   22. 0

23. $\frac{1}{8}$ or .125   24. $\frac{1}{4}$ or .25

25. $\frac{2}{3}$ or .666 or .667

Chapter 15

1. C	2. B	3. B
4. D	5. C	6. B
7. A	8. B	9. C
10. B	11. A	12. D
13. B	14. B	15. B
16. B	17. A	18. B
19. A	20. 1991	21. 10

Chapter 16

1. E	2. B	3. B
4. D	5. B	6. A
7. E	8. E	9. E
10. A	11. A	12. B
13. C	14. B	15. A
16. C	17. D	18. 10
19. 60	20. $0 < x < 2$	21. 20

22. $\frac{39}{2}$ or 19.5   23. 4

Chapter 17

1. A	2. E	3. D
4. A	5. C	6. B
7. E	8. E	9. C
10. B	11. C	12. B
13. A	14. C	15. A
16. D	17. B	18. 5
19. 65	20. 13	21. 14
22. 123	23. 2000	24. 1
25. 10		

Chapter 18

1. A	**2.** C	**3.** C
4. B	**5.** A	**6.** B
7. C	**8.** A	**9.** D
10. E	**11.** E	**12.** C
13. C	**14.** C	**15.** D
16. C	**17.** A	**18.** B
19. C	**20.** 16	**21.** 8
22. 144	**23.** 5	**24.** 20
25. 0	**26.** 64	

Chapter 19

1. E	**2.** C	**3.** D
4. A	**5.** B	**6.** E
7. B	**8.** B	**9.** E
10. D	**11.** A	**12.** B
13. B	**14.** A	**15.** D
16. C	**17.** A	

18. $\frac{4}{15}$ or .266 or .267   **19.** 120

20. $\frac{3}{7}$ or .428 or .429

21. 4   **22.** 20

Chapter 20

1. E	**2.** C	**3.** C
4. B	**5.** D	**6.** C
7. C	**8.** D	**9.** D
10. A	**11.** A	**12.** E
13. A	**14.** B	**15.** A
16. C	**17.** A	**18.** A
19. 2	**20.** 2	**21.** 14
22. 8	**23.** 9	**24.** 15

Chapter 21

1. A	**2.** C	**3.** B
4. A	**5.** B	**6.** D
7. D	**8.** A	**9.** C
10. A	**11.** B	**12.** A
13. C	**14.** D	**15.** D
16. C	**17.** C	**18.** B

19. B   **20.** 126   **21.** $\frac{10}{3}$ or 3.33

22. $\frac{27}{2}$ or 13.5   **23.** 196   **24.** 16

25. 98

ANSWERS FOR TEXTBOOK EXERCISES

Chapter 1. The Real Numbers

1-1 The Whole Numbers *(pages 5–6)*

1. 12	**2.** None	**3.** 32
4. None	**5.** 40	**6.** 0
7. 400	**8.** 1	**9.** 6
10. 6	**11.** 0	**12.** None
13. 175	**14.** 74	**15.** 1,026
16. 54	**17.** 16	**18.** 9
19. 24	**20.** 5	**21.** 3
22. 12	**23.** 88	**24.** 32
25. 29	**26.** 9	**27.** $3-12$
28. 10×0	**29.** $14 \div 14$	**30.** 75×80
31. $522 \div 29$	**32.** 1	**33.** 0
34. 76	**35.** 1,000	**36.** 1,910
37. 0		

38. No answer; every counting number is a whole number.

39. No answer; every whole number has a successor that is larger, so there is no largest whole number.

40. 0	**41.** 9	**42.** Infinite
43. Finite	**44.** Finite	**45.** Infinite
46. Empty	**47.** Finite	**48.** Finite
49. Empty		

1-2 The Integers *(page 9)*

1. True; on the horizontal number line, $+5$ is further to the right of 0 than is $+2$.
2. True; on the horizontal number line, -3 is to the left of 0.
3. False; on the horizontal number line, -7 is to the left of -1 and therefore is less than -1.
4. True; on the horizontal number line, -2 is to the right of -10 and therefore is greater than -10.

5. $+8 > +6$	**6.** $-8 < 0$	**7.** $-5 < -2$
8. $-5 > -25$	**9.** $16 + 3 > 9 \times 2$	

10. $6 \times 7 < 100 \div 2$

11. $+7$ is greater than -7.　**12.** -20 is less than -3.

13. -4 is less than 0.

14. -9 is greater than or equal to -90.

15. True	**16.** False	**17.** False
18. True	**19.** True	**20.** True
21. False	**22.** True	**23.** True
24. False	**25.** True	**26.** $-4 < +8$

27. $-6 < -3$　**28.** $-4 < -2 < +3$

29. $-2 < 0 < +8$

30. $8 < 14, 8 \not> 14, 8 \neq 14, 8 \leq 14$

31. $9 > 3, 9 \geq 3, 9 \not< 3, 9 \neq 3$

32. $15 = 15, 15 \leq 15, 15 \geq 15, 15 \not> 15, 15 \not< 15$

33. $6 > -2, 6 \geq -2, 6 \not< -2, 6 \neq -2$

34. 1	**35.** -1

36. a. No

　b. Every integer has a successor that is greater.

37. a. No

　b. For every integer, there is always a number that is 1 less. This process continues forever, without end.

38.　1-b, 2-f, 3-c, 4-h, 5-j, 6-ℓ, 7-e, 8-a, 9-g, 10-i, 11-d, 12-k

39.　Distance below sea level; decline in a stock price; loss of yardage in a football game; going "in the hole" in a card game; etc.

1-3 The Rational Numbers *(pages 15–16)*

1. $\dfrac{7}{10}$	**2.** $\dfrac{18}{100}$ or $\dfrac{9}{50}$	**3.** $-\dfrac{21}{100}$
4. $\dfrac{9}{1}$	**5.** $-\dfrac{3}{1}$	**6.** $\dfrac{0}{1}$
7. $\dfrac{11}{2}$	**8.** $-\dfrac{10}{3}$	**9.** $\dfrac{7}{1,000}$
10. $-\dfrac{23}{10}$	**11.** $\dfrac{7}{2}$	**12.** $-\dfrac{9}{3}$
13. $\dfrac{5}{6}$	**14.** $-\dfrac{1}{5}$	**15.** $\dfrac{5}{2}$
16. $-\dfrac{13}{6}$	**17.** $\dfrac{13}{6}$	**18.** $-\dfrac{5}{12}$
19. $1\dfrac{3}{5}$	**20.** $-3\dfrac{1}{3}$	**21.** $\dfrac{1}{6}$
22. $-\dfrac{11}{15}$	**23.** 5.5	**24.** -3.5
25. $-\dfrac{1}{2}$	**26.** $\dfrac{3}{8}$	**27.** $\dfrac{11}{16}$
28. $-\dfrac{17}{24}$	**29.** -2.15	**30.** $2\dfrac{9}{16}$
31. $-1\dfrac{7}{24}$	**32.** 3.075	**33.** $0.625\overline{0}$
34. $2.25\overline{0}$	**35.** $-5.5\overline{0}$	**36.** $1.625\overline{0}$
37. $-0.58\overline{3}$	**38.** $1.\overline{6}$	**39.** $0.\overline{7}$
40. $0.\overline{18}$	**41.** $0.0\overline{5}$	**42.** $-0.8\overline{3}$
43. $\dfrac{1}{2}$	**44.** $\dfrac{5}{9}$	**45.** $-\dfrac{2}{9}$

46. $\dfrac{125}{1,000}$ or $\dfrac{1}{8}$ **47.** $\dfrac{25}{99}$ **48.** $\dfrac{7}{90}$

49. True; integers are a subset of the rational numbers.
50. False; whole numbers are the counting numbers and 0. The negative integers, such as -1, -2, and -3, are the *opposites* of the positive whole numbers. These negatives are not whole numbers.
51. False; the statement given is true only when numbers are positive. Note that -40 is further from 0 than -2, but -40 is less than -2.
52. True; a rational number terminates (repeating 0) or repeats.
53. True; between any two rational numbers, another rational can be found by taking the mean (or average) of the numbers. Since this process has no end, there is an infinite number of fractions (which are rational numbers).
54. True; same reason as for Exercise 53.
55. False. Imagine any positive number. Half of that number is a smaller value. Halve it again and again and again. The process never ends, so there is no smallest positive rational number.

1-4 The Irrational Numbers *(page 22)*

1. Rational **2.** Rational **3.** Rational
4. Irrational **5.** Irrational **6.** Irrational
7. Irrational **8.** Rational **9.** Irrational
10. Rational **11.** Rational **12.** Irrational
13. Rational **14.** Rational **15.** Irrational
16. Irrational **17.** Irrational **18.** Rational
19. Rational **20.** Irrational

In 21–30, part **a**, answers will vary depending on the number of digits in the calculator display.

21. a. 2.236068 **b.** 2.236 **c.** 2.24
22. a. 2.6457513 **b.** 2.646 **c.** 2.65
23. a. 4.3588989 **b.** 4.359 **c.** 4.36
24. a. 8.660254 **b.** 8.660 **c.** 8.66
25. a. 7.9372539 **b.** 7.937 **c.** 7.94
26. a. 9.486833 **b.** 9.487 **c.** 9.49
27. a. -3.7416574 **b.** -3.742 **c.** -3.74
28. a. -4.6904158 **b.** -4.690 **c.** -4.69
29. a. 0.4472136 **b.** 0.447 **c.** 0.45
30. a. 0.5477225 **b.** 0.548 **c.** 0.55

31. a. 2.999824 **b.** 0.000176
32. a. 9.998244 **b.** 10.004569
c. The better approximation for $\sqrt{10}$ is 3.162 because the value obtained in part **a** is 0.001756 from 10, which is closer than the value in part **b**, which is 0.004569 from 10.

33. $\dfrac{22}{7}$ is closer to π than 3.14:

$$\dfrac{22}{7} - \pi \approx 3.1428571 - 3.1415927,\ \text{or } 0.0012644$$

$$\pi - 3.14 \approx 3.1415927 - 3.14,\ \text{or } 0.0015927$$

34. a. 7π **b.** 21.99 **35. a.** 15π **b.** 47.12

36. a. 72π **b.** 226.19 **37. a.** $\dfrac{1}{2}\pi$ **b.** 1.57
38. a. $3\dfrac{1}{3}\pi$ or $\dfrac{10}{3}\pi$ **b.** 10.47

39. There is an infinite number of answers to each part, including these:
a. 0.113111311113... (same as the given number)
b. 7.113111311113... **c.** 0.15113111311113...
d. 2.0113111311113...
40. False. Since $\sqrt{4} = 2$, we know that
$\sqrt{4} + \sqrt{4} = 2 + 2 = 4$.
But $4 < 8 < 9 \Rightarrow \sqrt{4} < \sqrt{8} < \sqrt{9} \Rightarrow 2 < \sqrt{8} < 3$
Therefore, $\sqrt{4} + \sqrt{4} = 4$, but $\sqrt{8} < 3$.
41. False.
$16 < 18 < 25 \Rightarrow \sqrt{16} < \sqrt{18} < \sqrt{25} \Rightarrow$
$4 < \sqrt{18} < 5$
On the left of the given equation,
$\sqrt{18} + \sqrt{18} > 4 + 4$, or $\sqrt{18} + \sqrt{18} > 8$.
On the right, $\sqrt{36} = 6$. Some value greater than 8 cannot equal 6.
42. Irrational. There is no number that, when multiplied by itself, equals 0.35 exactly. (A rational approximation for $\sqrt{0.35}$ is 0.5916079....)

1-5 The Real Numbers *(pages 24–25)*

1. a. 1, 2 **b.** 0, 1, 2 **c.** $-2, -1, 0, 1, 2$
d. $-2.\overline{7}, -2, -1, -0.63, 0, \dfrac{1}{3}, 1, 2$
e. $-\sqrt{3}, \sqrt{0.5}, \dfrac{\pi}{2}, \sqrt{6}$
f. *All* numbers shown.
2. a. $\sqrt{0}, \sqrt{1}, \sqrt{4}, \sqrt{9}$ **b.** $\sqrt{2}, \sqrt{3}, \sqrt{5}, \sqrt{6}, \sqrt{7}, \sqrt{8}$
c. All
3. a. None **b.** All **c.** All
4. 2.5 **5.** 8 **6.** $0.\overline{2}$
7. 0.23 **8.** $0.\overline{7}$ **9.** -5.6
10. -0.43 **11.** $\sqrt{2}$ **12.** $0.\overline{2}$
13. π **14.** $-\sqrt{5}$ **15.** $\sqrt{0.5}$
16. 0.41414141... **17.** 0.57577577757777...
18. $0.202 < 0.2022 < 0.\overline{2}$
19. $0.\overline{4} < 0.4499 < 0.45$
20. $0.\overline{6} < 0.667 < 0.67$
21. $-\sqrt{3} < -1.5 < -\sqrt{2}$
22. $0.5 < \sqrt{0.3} < 0.\overline{5}$
23. $-\sqrt{5} < -2 < -\sqrt{3}$
24. $\pi < \sqrt{10} < 3.5$
25. $\sqrt{16} < \dfrac{13}{3} < 4.\overline{4}$
26. $4 < \sqrt{17} < \dfrac{17}{4}$

27. False **28.** True **29.** True
30. False **31.** True **32.** False
33. True **34.** False **35.** False
36. True

1-6 Number Lines and Rulers *(pages 28–29)*

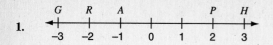

1. Number line with points G at -2, R at -2, A at -1, P at 2, H at 3; scale $-3, -2, -1, 0, 1, 2, 3$

2. Number line with points U, N, I, T, S; scale $-\frac{1}{2}, 0, \frac{1}{2}, 1, 1\frac{1}{2}, 2, 3$

3. Number line with points L, O, C, A, T, E, D; scale $-2, -1, -\frac{1}{3}, 0, \frac{1}{3}, \frac{2}{3}, 1, \frac{5}{3}, 2$

4. Number line with points P, O, I, N, T, S; scale $-1, -\frac{1}{2}, 0, \frac{1}{4}, \frac{3}{4}, 1, 1\frac{1}{4}, 2$

5. a. 0 **b.** $\frac{1}{4}$ **c.** 3 **d.** $\frac{3}{4}$ **e.** $\frac{9}{4}$ **f.** $\frac{6}{4}$

6. a. E **b.** I **c.** H **d.** K **e.** C **f.** F **g.** L

7. a. Number line A through H; scale $-3, -2, -1, 0, 1, 2, 3, 4$

b. Number line A through H; scale $-1, -\frac{1}{2}, 0, \frac{1}{2}, 1, \frac{3}{2}, 2, \frac{5}{2}$

c. Number line A through H; scale $0, \frac{1}{5}, \frac{2}{5}, \frac{3}{5}, \frac{4}{5}, 1, \frac{6}{5}, \frac{7}{5}$

d. Number line A through H; scale $-5, -4, -3, -2, -1, 0, 1, 2$

e. Number line A through H; scale $-\frac{2}{4}, -\frac{1}{4}, 0, \frac{1}{4}, \frac{2}{4}, \frac{3}{4}, 1, \frac{5}{4}$

f. Number line A through H; scale $-1, -\frac{2}{3}, -\frac{1}{3}, 0, \frac{1}{3}, \frac{2}{3}, 1, \frac{4}{3}$

8. a. L and M **b.** Q and R **c.** M and N **d.** P and Q
e. J and K **f.** O and P **g.** L and M **h.** N and O
i. R and S **j.** K and L

9. a. Number line with points at $2, 3, 4$; scale $0, 1, 2, 3, 4$

b. $2 < 3 < 4$

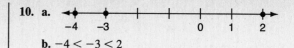

10. a. Number line with points at $-4, -3, 2$; scale $-4, -3, 0, 1, 2$

b. $-4 < -3 < 2$

11. a. Number line with points at $-4, -2, 3$; scale $-4, -2, 0, 1, 3$

b. $-4 < -2 < 3$

12. a. Number line with points at $0.\overline{3}, 2, 3$; scale $0, 0.\overline{3}, 1, 2, 3$

b. $0.\overline{3} < 2 < 3$

13. a. Number line with points at $0.02, 0.2, 2$; scale $0, 0.2, 1, 2$ and 0.02

b. $0.02 < 0.2 < 2$

14. a. Number line with points at $0.15, 0.5, 1.5$; scale $0, 0.15, 0.5, 1, 1.5, 2$

b. $0.15 < 0.5 < 1.5$

15. a. Number line with points at $\sqrt{8}, \sqrt{20}, 5$; scale $0, 1, \sqrt{8}, \sqrt{20}, 5$

b. $\sqrt{8} < \sqrt{20} < 5$

16. a. 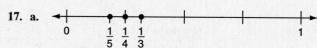 Number line with points at $-3, 0.3, \sqrt{3}$; scale $-3, 0, 1$ and $0.3, \sqrt{3}$

b. $-3 < 0.3 < \sqrt{3}$

17. a. Number line with points at $\frac{1}{5}, \frac{1}{4}, \frac{1}{3}$; scale $0, \frac{1}{5}, \frac{1}{4}, \frac{1}{3}, 1$

b. $\frac{1}{5} < \frac{1}{4} < \frac{1}{3}$

$\left(\text{Note: } \frac{1}{5} = \frac{12}{60}, \frac{1}{4} = \frac{15}{60}, \frac{1}{3} = \frac{20}{60}\right)$

18. a. Number line with points at $-\frac{3}{2}, -\frac{3}{4}, -\frac{2}{3}$; scale $-2, -\frac{3}{2}, -1, \frac{3}{4}, -\frac{2}{3}, 0, 1$

b. $-\frac{3}{2} < -\frac{3}{4} < -\frac{2}{3}$

19. a. Number line with points at $\frac{\pi}{2}, 2, \pi$; scale $0, 1, \frac{\pi}{2}, 2, 3, \pi$

b. $\frac{\pi}{2} < 2 < \pi$

20. a. Number line with points at $-1, \pi-1, \pi$; scale $-1, 0, 1, \pi-1, \pi$

b. $-1 < \pi - 1 < \pi$

21. a. 1 ft **b.** 1 cm **c.** 1 mi **d.** 1 in.
e. 1 m **f.** 1 km **g.** 1 m **h.** 1 mi

22. a. and **b.** Answers may vary.
   c. Approximations. No device, such as a ruler, can measure exact lengths.

1-7 Number Lines and Graphs *(pages 31–34)*

1. a. Amoco: 1,150; John Hancock: 1,100; Sears Tower: 1,450; Empire State: 1,250; World Trade: 1,400; Chrysler: 1,050.
   b. Sears Tower   **c.** 100 ft   **d.** John Hancock
   e. 350 ft   **f.** None

2. a. Calcot: 55,000; Parr City: 25,000; Sampler: 25,000; Tyne: 5,000
   b. Parr City and Sampler   **c.** 5
   d. Equal in number

3. a. 20   **b.** Lettuce   **c.** 80

4. a. 2 cm   **b.** 10 cm   **c.** 0.5 cm or 5 mm
   d. 2.5 cm or 25 mm

5. a. $\frac{2}{4}$ or $\frac{1}{2}$ in.   **b.** $\frac{4}{4}$ or 1 in.   **c.** $\frac{20}{4}$ or 5 in.

   d. $\frac{5}{4}$ or $1\frac{1}{4}$ in.   **e.** $\frac{15}{4}$ or $3\frac{3}{4}$ in.   **f.** $\frac{1}{8}$ in.

6. a. \$0.75 or $\frac{3}{4}$ dollar   **b.** Day 2

   c. 9 and 10   **d.** 5 and 6   **e.** 8 and 11

7. a. 1940–1950   **b.** 1960–1970   **c.** 61
   d. 65   **e.** 2

8. a.

LIFE EXPECTANCY AT BIRTH
FOR U.S. FEMALES

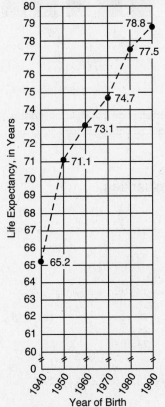

LIFE EXPECTANCY
FOR U.S. MALES AND FEMALES

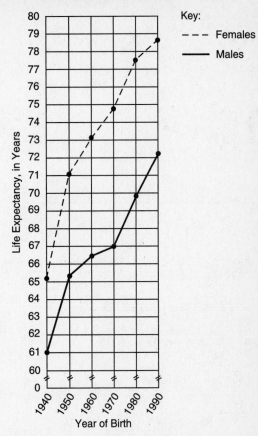

b. Females have a greater life expectancy than males. Females gained greater increases in life expectancy than males over this time period.

9. a. A graph, where the bars compare different items (years).

U.S. UNEMPLOYMENT RATE
(per 100 workers)

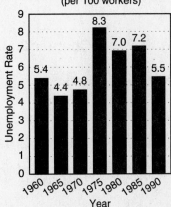

b. A line graph shows changes in one item, and the rate of unemployment may be considered as that single item.

U.S. UNEMPLOYMENT RATE
(per 100 workers)

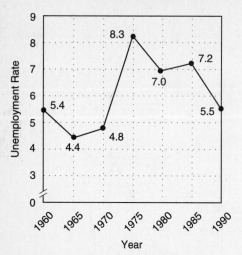

c. A graph, where the line shows change in one item (rate of unemployment).

Review Exercises *(pages 35–36)*

1. 0   **2.** 9   **3.** 36   **4.** 324
5. a. 45 **b.** 25   **c.** 45   **d.** 13
6. $3 > -1 > -5$ **7.** True   **8.** False

9. False   **10.** True   **11.** $\frac{9}{10}$

12. $\frac{45}{100}$ or $\frac{9}{20}$ **13.** $\frac{17}{2}$ **14.** $\frac{14}{1}$

15. $\frac{1}{3}$ **16.** $-\frac{63}{1}$ **17.** 19.95

18. Rational   **19.** Irrational   **20.** Rational
21. Irrational   **22.** Irrational
23. a. 3.3166248   **b.** 3.32
24. a. 0.83666   **b.** 0.84
25. a. 30.083218   **b.** 30.08

26. a. 39.987498   **b.** 39.99
27. a. 3.1415927   **b.** 3.14
28. 5   **29.** -5 **30.** 3.2
31. $0.\overline{4}$ **32.** $0.\overline{12}$ **33.** True
34. False   **35.** False   **36.** True
37. True   **38.** False

39.

40.

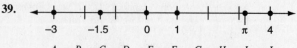

41. a. *F* and *G*   **b.** *A* and *B*   **c.** *E* and *F*   **d.** *I* and *J*
    e. *G* and *H*

42. a.

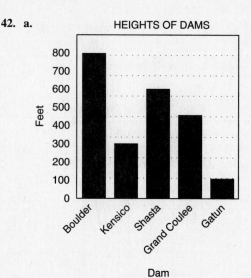

b. A line graph is used to show how one particular item changes, not to compare different items.

Chapter 2. Operations and Properties

Introductory Page *(page 37)*

Jesse added numbers using clock arithmetic, mod 12.

2-1 Operations in Arithmetic *(pages 42–43)*

1. True   **2.** False ($3 - 5$ is not a whole number)
3. True   **4.** False (cannot divide by 0)
5. True
6. a. 1   **b.** $0, 1, \frac{0}{1}$ **c.** $0, 1, \frac{0}{1}$ **d.** $\frac{1}{0}$

7. $\frac{10}{5}$ or 2   **8.** 2.00 or 2   **9.** $\frac{8}{8}$ or 1

10. $\frac{13}{4}$ or $3\frac{1}{4}$ **11.** $\frac{7}{7}$ or 1   **12.** 2.40 or 2.4

13. $\frac{5}{8}$ **14.** $\frac{27}{6}$ or $\frac{9}{2}$ or $4\frac{1}{2}$

15. 4   **16.** $\frac{21}{14}$ or $\frac{3}{2}$ or $1\frac{1}{2}$

17. 1   **18.** 1.6   **19.** 6.15
20. 5   **21.** 1.57   **22.** 48
23. 8   **24.** 0.05   **25.** 2
26. 10

27. $\frac{11}{10}$ or $1\frac{1}{10}$ **28.** $\frac{17}{10}$ or $1\frac{7}{10}$ **29.** $\frac{73}{18}$ or $4\frac{1}{18}$

30. $\frac{13}{8}$ or $1\frac{5}{8}$ **31.** $\frac{47}{15}$ or $3\frac{2}{15}$ **32.** $\frac{41}{6}$ or $6\frac{5}{6}$

33. $\frac{33}{10}$ or $3\frac{3}{10}$ **34.** $\frac{19}{8}$ or $2\frac{3}{8}$ **35.** $\frac{3}{2}$ or $1\frac{1}{2}$

36. $\frac{4}{5}$ **37.** 6 **38.** 16

39. $\frac{2}{3}$ **40.** $\frac{5}{2}$ or $2\frac{1}{2}$ **41.** $\frac{1}{3}$

42. 3 **43.** 4.07 **44.** 1.99

45. 1.81 **46.** 2.89 **47.** 0.40 or 0.4

48. 0.3000 or 0.3 **49.** 0.025

50. 0.02 **51.** $1\frac{4}{5}$ or $\frac{9}{5}$ **52.** 1.8

53. $\frac{19}{4}$ or $4\frac{3}{4}$ **54.** 4.75 **55.** $\frac{9}{10}$ or 0.9

56. $\frac{4}{9}$ **57.** 0.35 or $\frac{7}{20}$

58. 2.05 or $\frac{41}{20}$ or $2\frac{1}{20}$ **59.** 14

60. 0.1875 **61.** 0.625 **62.** 3

63. 5 **64.** 1 **65.** 5.5 or $5\frac{1}{2}$

66. 82.5 or $82\frac{1}{2}$ **67.** 3.5

68. $\frac{5}{8}$ **69.** $\frac{4}{6}$ or $\frac{2}{3}$ **70.** $\frac{5}{8}$

71. 0.35 **72.** 1.35 **73.** 1.32

74. 20.54 **75.** 9.99 **76.** 0.249225

77. 23 **78.** 11 **79.** 18.625

80. 8 **81.** 11 **82.** 8

83. 1.2 **84.** 0.2 **85.** 0.8

86. 0.4 or 0.40 **87.** $\frac{2}{5}$ **88.** $\frac{1}{5}$

89. $\frac{8}{5}$ **90.** $\frac{8}{5}$ or 1.6 **91.** $\frac{5}{8}$

92. 5 **93.** −4 **94.** π

95. −12 **96.** $\sqrt{2.89}$ or 1.7

97. 7.21 **98.** 7

99. Any number equal to or less than 4

100. Not possible; false statement

101. a. Mary Rose **b.** Max

102. a. 2.25 mi **b.** Avg, or addition and division

103. a. 2 **b.** 4 **c.** 1

d. The smallest whole number less than or equal to $\frac{b}{24}$

104. a. 2 **b.** 2 **c.** None

d. The largest whole number less than or equal to $\frac{c}{19}$

2-2 Bases, Exponents, and Powers
(page 46)

1. 81 **2.** 1,000 **3.** 125

4. 225 **5.** 100,000 **6.** 243

7. $\frac{1}{9}$ **8.** $\frac{1}{4}$ **9.** $\frac{1}{1,000}$

10. $\frac{9}{16}$ **11.** $\frac{1}{10,000}$ **12.** $\frac{8}{9}$

13. 0.64 **14.** 0.125 **15.** 0.09

16. 0.0016 **17.** 0.00001 **18.** 0.0625

19. 1.331 **20.** 9.61 **21.** 6.25

22. 6.25 or $6\frac{1}{4}$ **23.** 9.61 or $9\frac{61}{100}$ **24.** $\frac{64}{27}$ or $2\frac{10}{27}$

25. a. 25, 125, 625 **b.** $(5)^4$

26. a. 0.25, 0.36, 0.49 **b.** $(0.7)^2$

27. a. 1.21, 1.331, 1.4641 **b.** $(1.1)^4$

28. a. 1, 1.44, 1.96 **b.** $(1.4)^2$

29. a. $\frac{1}{25}, \frac{1}{36}, \frac{1}{49}$ **b.** $\left(\frac{1}{5}\right)^2$

30. a. 0.001, 0.04, 0.3 **b.** $(0.3)^1$

31. a. 0.125, 0.16, 0.0016 **b.** $(0.4)^2$

32. a. 3.375, 1.96, 2.0736 **b.** $(1.5)^3$

33. 8836 **34.** 5639.752 **35.** 0.238328

36. 5220.0625 **37.** 1211.7361 **38.** 0.5927

39. 0.4305 **40.** 6.2749 **41.** 481.7173

42. 201.5994

43. a. $\frac{4}{49}$ **b.** 0.0816326

44. a. $\frac{16}{81}$ **b.** 0.1975308

45. a. $\frac{1}{216}$ **b.** 0.0046296

46. a. $\frac{25}{144}$ **b.** 0.1736111

47. a. $\frac{169}{36} = 4\frac{25}{36}$ **b.** 4.6944444

48. a. $\frac{625}{81} = 7\frac{58}{81}$ **b.** 7.7160494

49. $3.21

50. a. 9 years $(1.08^9 \approx 1.9990046)$
b. 9 years (same as part **a**)

2-3 Order of Operations *(pages 50–52)*

1. a. The sum of 6 and 1 is to be added to 20; 27
b. Add 6 to 20, then add 1 to that result; 27

2. a. The sum of 4 and 3 is to be subtracted from 18; 11
b. Subtract 4 from 18, then add 3 to that result; 17

3. a. The difference of 3 and $\frac{1}{2}$ is to be subtracted from 12; $9\frac{1}{2}$

b. Subtract 3 from 12, then subtract $\frac{1}{2}$ from that result; $8\frac{1}{2}$

4. a. Multiply 15 by the sum of 2 and 1; 45
  b. Multiply 15 by 2, then add 1 to that result; 31
5. a. The sum of 12 and 8 is to be divided by 4; 5
  b. The quotient of 8 and 4 is to be added to 12; 14
6. a. Divide 48 by the difference of 8 and 4; 12
  b. Subtract 4 from the quotient of 48 and 8; 2
7. a. Add the square of 5 to 7; 32
  b. The sum of 7 and 5 is to be squared; 144
8. a. Multiply the square of 3 by 4; 36
  b. The product of 4 and 3 is to be squared; 144
9. $(10 + 8) - 5$ **10.** $(25 - 15) + 7$
11. $8 \times (6 - 2)$ **12.** $(10 \times 5) - 12$
13. $(12 - 2) \times (3 + 4)$ **14.** $(16 \times 3) - (20 \div 5)$
15. 14   **16.** 29   **17.** 32
18. 41   **19.** 16   **20.** 26
21. 18   **22.** 100   **23.** 3
24. 16   **25.** 8   **26.** 2,700
27. 81   **28.** 4   **29.** 169
30. 337   **31.** 144   **32.** 388
33. 106   **34.** 18   **35.** 24
36. 15   **37.** 3   **38.** 34
39. 49   **40.** 50   **41.** 2
42. 4   **43.** 8   **44.** 2
45. 12   **46.** 23   **47.** 43
48. 18   **49.** 8   **50.** 60
51. 3,525   **52.** 100   **53.** 12
54. 25   **55.** 8   **56.** 190
57. 8   **58.** 108   **59.** 65
60. a. $2(8) + 3(8)$ **b.** 40¢

61. a. $30(\frac{3}{4}) + 55(\frac{3}{2})$ **b.** 105 mi

62. a. $2(0.38) + 3(0.69)$ **b.** $2.83
63. a. $5(0.29) + 3(0.75) + 1.75$ **b.** $5.45
64. In each case, one answer is shown. Others are possible.
  a. $3 + 2 - 1 = 4$
  b. $1 \times 3 + 1 = 4$
  c. $(1 + 2) \div 3 + 4 = 5$
  d. $(4 + 3 - 2) \times 1 = 5$
  e. $(6 \times 6 - 6) \div 6 = 5$
  f. $6 + 6 \times (6 - 6) = 6$

2-4 Properties of Operations *(pages 57–59)*

1. 0   **2.** 1

3. a. 9 **b.** 0 **c.** 9 **d.** 0 **e.** $\frac{2}{3}$ **f.** $\frac{2}{3}$

4. a. 8   **b.** Commutative property of addition
5. a. 5   **b.** Commutative property of multiplication
6. a. 15   **b.** Associative property of multiplication
7. a. 6   **b.** Distributive property of multiplication over addition
8. a. $\frac{1}{3}$ **b.** Associative property of addition

9. a. 4   **b.** Addition property of zero, or additive identity
10. a. 5   **b.** Distributive property of multiplication over addition
11. a. 7   **b.** Commutative property of multiplication
12. a. 50   **b.** Commutative property of multiplication
13. a. 1   **b.** Multiplication property of one, or multiplicative identity
14. a. 8   **b.** Commutative property of multiplication
15. a. 6   **b.** Associative property of addition
16. a. 6   **b.** Commutative property of average (avg)
17. a. $\frac{1}{2}$ **b.** Commutative property of multiplication
18. a. 0   **b.** Addition property of zero, or additive identity
19. a. 1   **b.** Multiplication property of one, or multiplicative identity
20. a. 9   **b.** Associative property of Maximum (max)
21. a. 4   **b.** Commutative property of addition
22. -7 **23.** -1 **24.** 10
25. -2.5 **26.** 1.8   **27.** $-\frac{1}{9}$
28. $\frac{1}{7}$ **29.** 1   **30.** $-\frac{1}{10}$ or -0.1
31. $\frac{2}{5}$ or 0.4   **32.** $-\frac{5}{9}$ or -0.5 **33.** 9
34. -4 **35.** 0.25   **36.** 1.25
37. -0.8 **38.** 1   **39.** 0
40. a. (1) -12 (2) -12
  b. The displays are equal because the additive inverse of the sum of 3 and 9 is equal to the additive inverse of 3 added to the additive inverse of 9.

41. a. $\frac{8}{5}$ or $1\frac{3}{5}$ **b.** 1.6

  c. The answers to parts **a** and **b** are equal because $\frac{5}{8} = -0.625$, and both parts **a** and **b** state the reciprocal of this number.

42. Yes   **43.** No; $10\left(\frac{1}{2} + \frac{1}{5}\right) = 10 \times \frac{1}{2} + 10 \times \frac{1}{5}$
44. No; $(7 + 9)5 = 7 \times 5 + 9 \times 5$
45. Yes
46. No; $2(y + 6) = 2y + 2 \times 6$
47. Yes   **48.** Yes
49. No; $4b(c - 2) = 4bc - 4b \times 2$
50. Yes   **51.** Yes
52. True; yes   **53.** False; no   **54.** False; no
55. True; yes   **56.** True; yes   **57.** False; no
58. True; yes   **59.** False; no   **60.** False; no
61. True; yes   **62.** False; no   **63.** False; no
64. a. 0 **b.** 0 **65.** 1   **66.** 0
67. $4p + 4q$ **68.** $2(x - y)$ **69.** $(8 + 13)t = 21t$
70. $15m - 7m$ **71. a.** 7 **b.** 9 **c.** Different **d.** No

72. (1) Multiplication property of 1
(2) Distributive property
(3) Substitution principle
73. (1) Distributive property
(2) Substitution principle
(3) Distributive property
(4) Substitution principle
(5) Multiplication property of 1
74. **a.** $3 \times (2 + 1) \div 3 = 3$
b. $4 \times 3 \div (2 + 2) = 3$
c. $(8 + 8 \div 8 - 8) \times 8 = 8$
d. $3 \div 3 + 3 \times (3 - 3) = 1$
e. $3 \div (3 + 3) \times (3 - 3) = 0$
f. $0 \times (12 \times 3 - 16 \div 8) = 0$

2-5 Properties of a Field *(pages 60–61)*

1. (3)   **2.** (4)   **3.** (2)

4. $-n$ **5.** $\dfrac{1}{n}$ **6.** 0

7. 1   **8.** **a.** (1) -8 (2) -50 (3) -999
    b. No   **c.** True

9. **a.** (1) $\dfrac{1}{8}$ (2) $\dfrac{1}{50}$ (3) $\dfrac{1}{999}$

b. No **c.** True
10. Integers (except 1 and -1) do not have multiplicative inverses that are integers.

2-6 Operations in Geometry *(pages 65–66)*

1. **a.** 4 **b.** 6 **c.** 2 **d.** 2 **e.** 9 **f.** 2
2. **a.** M **b.** E **c.** I **d.** E **e.** L **f.** M
3. $\overline{PE}, \overline{MW}, \overline{IO}, \overline{SR}$ **4.** 12
5. 18   **6.** 23
7. **a.** 3 **b.** 3 **c.** 6 **d.** 15 **e.** 15 **f.** 6
8. **a.** 1.5 **b.** 1.5 **c.** 3 **d.** 7.5 **e.** 7.5 **f.** 3
9. 4   **10.** 5   **11.** 16.5
12. 28.5   **13.** 10.4   **14.** 5.4

15. $\dfrac{3}{6}$ or $\dfrac{1}{2}$ **16.** $\dfrac{25}{8}$ or $3\dfrac{1}{8}$ **17.** 16

18. 20   **19.** 10   **20.** $19\dfrac{2}{3}$

21. 13 or 11   **22.** 15 or 9   **23.** 22 or 2

24. 24 or 0   **25.** $12\dfrac{1}{2}$ or $11\dfrac{1}{2}$ **26.** 13.5 or 10.5

27. 12.8 or 11.2 **28.** $12\dfrac{2}{3}$ or $11\dfrac{1}{3}$

29. **a.** $\overrightarrow{BA}, \overrightarrow{BD}, \overrightarrow{BC}$ **b.** $\angle ABC, \angle DBC, \angle ABD$
   c. $\angle ABC$ **d.** 180 or 180°
30. **a.** 20 **b.** 90   **c.** 70 **d.** 95 **e.** 180 **f.** 160
31. $\angle ABQ, \angle QBC$

2-7 Operations with Sets *(page 69)*

1. $\{3\}$ **2.** $\{1, 3\}$ **3.** $\{1, 2, 3, 4, 5, 6\}$
4. $\{1, 2, 3, 4, 6\}$ **5.** $\{3, 4, 6\}$
6. $\{\ \}$ or $\varnothing$ **7.** $\{1, 3, 4, 5, 6\}$ **8.** $\{3, 4, 5, 6\}$

9. $\{1, 2, 3, 4, 5, 6\}$ **10.** $\{2, 3, 4\}$
11. $\{1, 3, 4\}$ **12.** $\{1, 3, 4, 5\}$ **13.** $\{1, 2, 5\}$
14. $\{5\}$ **15.** $\{1, 3, 4, 5\}$ **16.** $\{3, 4\}$
17. $\{1, 2, 3, 4\}$ **18.** B **19.** B
20. D **21.** A **22.** $\varnothing$
23. C **24.** C **25.** A
26. C **27.** D **28.** D
29. B **30.** U **31.** U
32. B **33.** U
34. **a.** 5   **b.** 3   **c.** 2   **d.** 0

Review Exercises *(pages 71–72)*

1. 9.14   **2.** 7.86   **3.** 5.44

4. 30   **5.** $\dfrac{5}{6}$ **6.** $3\dfrac{1}{18}$

7. 24   **8.** 4   **9.** 19
10. 1.6   **11.** 18   **12.** 0.3

13. $\dfrac{2}{5}$ **14.** $1\dfrac{1}{3}$ **15.** 2

16. 0   **17.** 8   **18.** 68
19. 10   **20.** 0.0256   **21.** 100
22. 56   **23.** 3.24   **24.** -23.00826
25. 1.728   **26.** 1.875
27. 8   **28.** 0.2083333
29. **a.** 2 **b.** Commutative property of addition
30. **a.** 2 **b.** Associative property of addition
31. **a.** 1 **b.** Multiplication property of one
32. **a.** 0 **b.** Multiplication property of zero
33. **a.** 5 **b.** Distributive property
34. **a.** 5 **b.** Commutative property of multiplication
35. **a.** 3 **b.** 9 **c.** 18 **d.** 6
36. **a.** T **b.** R
37. **a.** 90 or 90° **b.** 180 or 180° **c.** $\angle ACB$
   d. 90 or 90°
38. 12 or 22   **39.** $\{2, 4\}$ **40.** $\{1, 2, 4, 5, 6\}$
41. $\{3, 6\}$ **42.** $\{6\}$ **43.** $\varnothing$
44. (4)   **45.** g   **46.** h
47. a   **48.** e   **49.** b
50. d   **51.** f   **52.** c

Cumulative Review *(page 72)*

1. 24.5   **2.** 7   **3.** 2
4. 5.25
5. Any one of the four numbers can be a correct answer.
-30 is negative. The others are positive.
10 is not a multiple of 3. The others are multiples of 3. 15 is odd. The others are even. 18 is not a multiple of 5. The others are multiples of 5.

Exploration

Student responses will vary.

Chapter 3. Problem Solving

In this chapter, hints suggest how to apply appropriate strategies. In every case, however, other approaches are possible, and students should be encouraged to propose alternative solutions.

Introductory Page *(page 73)*

Use $125 + 48 = 2.604\overline{16}$ or $2\frac{29}{48}$ for each problem.

Three buses: 48 students on each of 2 buses and 29 on the third.

2.6 hours or 2 hours and 36 minutes.

Two cases of empties can be returned. There are 29 extra cans.

Each problem uses 125 and 48 to find the answer, but the way in which the quotient is used to determine the answer is different.

3-2 Guessing and Checking *(page 77)*

1. 36 and 24   30 and 30 No
                  34 and 26 No
                  36 and 24 ✓
2. Cynthia, 9; Sylvia, 4 6 and 7 No
                        5 and 8 No
                        4 and 9 ✓
3. 4 nickels, 20 dimes
   $\left.\begin{array}{l}\text{12 nickels + 12 dimes} = \$1.80 \\ \text{6 nickels + 18 dimes} = \$2.10\end{array}\right\}$ Need more dimes
   4 nickels + 20 dimes = $2.20 ✓
4. 2 with 3 legs, 16 with 4 legs

Number of Stools		Total Number
With 3 Legs	With 4 Legs	of Legs
8	10	24 + 40 = 64
4	14	12 + 56 = 68
2	16	6 + 64 = 70 ✓

$\left.\begin{array}{l} \\ \\ \end{array}\right\}$ Need more 4-legged stools

5. 20 gardenias, 30 roses

Number of Corsages		Total Number
Gardenia	Rose	of Flowers
30	20	60 + 60 = 120
20	30	40 + 90 = 130 ✓

$\left.\begin{array}{l} \\ \\ \end{array}\right\}$ Need more rose corsages

6. 25 and 52 $\begin{array}{r}43 \\ -34 \\ \hline 9\end{array}$ No $\begin{array}{r}52 \\ -25 \\ \hline 27\end{array}$ ✓   7. 25 $\begin{array}{r}25 \\ -5 \\ \hline 20\end{array}$ $\begin{array}{r}15 \\ +5 \\ \hline 20\end{array}$ ✓

8. Shelly, $35; John, $2

Shelly	John	
25	15	25 − 5 = 15 + 5, but 25 + 5 ≠ 2(15 − 5)
30	20	30 − 5 = 20 + 5, but 30 + 5 ≠ 2(20 − 5)
35	25	35 − 5 = 25 + 5, and 35 + 5 = 2(25 − 5) ✓

9. **a.** 37 tickets **b.** $41 each
   The cost of a ticket must be a factor of 1,517.
   Therefore, it cannot end in 5 or an even number.

	Bill			
$20	$10	$5	$1	
	1	1	1	1,517 ÷ 16 = 94.8125
	2		1	1,517 ÷ 21 = 72.238095
1	1		1	1,517 ÷ 31 = 48.935484
2			1	1,517 ÷ 41 = 37 ✓

10. **a.** 37 rows **b.** 29 seats
    The number of rows must be a factor of 1,073.
    Therefore, it cannot end in 5 or an even number.
    Try 31, 33, 37. 1,073 ÷ 37 = 29 ✓

3-3 Using a Simpler Related Problem *(pages 79–80)*

1. 10 dimes, 40 quarters
   1 dime + 4 quarters = $1.10
   Use 10 times as many, for $11.
2. $6,000 Trip   1
                Repairs   3
                Savings 2(3) $\underline{6}$ 10,000 ÷ 10 = 1,000
                Total   10 Use 6 × 1,000
3. 3, 6, 12, 24, and 3 sold
   Try small numbers: 1 + 2 + 4 + 8 = 15
   48 ÷ 15 = 3, remainder 3
   $\quad\quad\quad\quad\quad\hookrightarrow$ Use 3 as a multiplier:
   $\quad\quad\quad\quad$ 1 × 3, 2 × 3, 4 × 3, 8 × 3
4. 495 $\begin{array}{r}1 + 2 + 3 + \ldots + 9 = 45 \\ 50(9) = \underline{450} \\ 495\end{array}$
5. 24 oz
   2 oz con.
   $\underline{\text{30 oz water}}$
   32 oz cleaning sol.
   384 ÷ 32 = 12
   Use 12 × 2 oz = 24 oz
6. 5 lb apricots
   1 lb nuts
   0.5 lb apricots
   $\underline{2\ \ \text{lb apples}}$
   3.5 lb mixture
   35 ÷ 3.5 = 10
   Use 10 × 0.5 = 5 lb apricots
7. $4.80   Choose any convenient cost of meat.
               For each $1.20 spent on meat:
               $2 \times \frac{1}{3}\ (1.20) = \$0.80$ spent on bread
               $12 ÷ $2 = 6
               6 × $1.20 = $7.20 spent on meat
               6 × $0.80 = $4.80 spent on bread

8. 5,285

Number of Families	1 Child	2 Children	0 Child	Total Number of Children
13	7 × 1 +	3 × 2 +	3 × 0 =	13
21	13 × 1 +	4 × 2 +	4 × 0 =	21
30	20 × 1 +	5 × 2 +	5 × 0 =	30

The table shows that the number of children is the same as the number of families.

9. 961   The factors of 961 are 1, 31, and 961. Notice that only numbers that are the squares of primes have exactly 3 factors.

10.

$$\frac{1}{2} + \frac{1}{4} = \frac{3}{4} \text{ or } \frac{1}{4} \text{ less than 1}$$

$$\frac{1}{2} + \frac{1}{4} + \frac{1}{8} = \frac{7}{8} \text{ or } \frac{1}{8} \text{ less than 1}$$

$$\frac{1}{2} + \frac{1}{4} + \frac{1}{8} + \frac{1}{16} = \frac{15}{16} \text{ or } \frac{1}{16} \text{ less than 1}$$

Since this pattern continues,

$$\frac{1}{2} + \frac{1}{4} + \cdots + \frac{1}{1,024} = 1 - \frac{1}{1,024} = \frac{1,023}{1,024}$$

3-4 Working Backward (pages 81–82)

1. a. 8th (1 + 6 + 5 − 4)
   b. 15 (7 below + middle + 7 above)
2. 3   0 + 6 = 6
   6 + 5 − 4 = 7
   7 − 2 = 5
   5 + 3 − 5 = 3
3. 4   19 − (5 + 2) = 12
   Of the 12 points scored in the first half:

   $\frac{1}{3}$ of 12 or 4 in the first quarter

   $\frac{2}{3}$ of 12 or 8 in the second quarter

4. $133.27
   287.15 + 2.50 + 54.25 + 114.37 − 325
5. 40   5 + 5 + 10 + 20
6. 8   2 + 1 + 1 = 4; 4 × 2 = 8
7. $175   Given: amount won − $25; $\frac{1}{5}$ loan ($\frac{4}{5}$ kept);

   $\frac{2}{3}$ deposited ($\frac{1}{3}$ kept) to arrive at $40

   Using inverses: $40 \times \frac{3}{1} = 120$;

   $$120 \times \frac{5}{4} = 150;$$

   $$150 + 25 = 175$$

8.   18   Given: $\frac{1}{2}$ done ($\frac{1}{2}$ remain);

   $\frac{2}{3}$ done ($\frac{1}{3}$ remain) to get 3

   Using inverses: $3 \times \frac{3}{1} = 9$; $9 \times \frac{2}{1} = 18$

3-5 Discovering Patterns (pages 83–84)

1. 5,050   1 + 2 + 3 + ⋯ + 100 $\dfrac{100(101)}{2}$
   100 + 99 + 98 + ⋯ + 1

2. 2,550   2 + 4 + 6 + ⋯ + 100 $\dfrac{50(102)}{2}$
   100 + 98 + 96 + ⋯ + 2

3. 100   1 + 3 + 5 + ⋯ + 19 $\dfrac{10(20)}{2}$
   19 + 17 + 15 + ⋯ + 1

4. 90   1 + 2 + 3 + ⋯ + 12 $\dfrac{12(13)}{2}$
   12 + 11 + 10 + ⋯ + 1
   78 on the hour + 12 half-hour strikes

5. 57   1   3   7   13   21   31   43
   +2 +4 +6 +8 +10 +12 +14

6. 1,458   2   6   18   54   162   486
   ×3   ×3   ×3   ×3   ×3   ×3

7. 255   1   3   7   15   31   63   127
   +2 +4 +8 +16 +32 +64 +128

8. 84   4(3) = 12   8(2) = 16   1(5) = 5   6(7) = 42
   × 2   × 2   × 2   × 2
   24   32   10   84

9. 36   2(3) = 6   3(5) = 15   4(5) = 20   3(4) = 12
   ↳× 2   ↳ × 3   ↳ × 4   ↳ × 3
   12   45   80   36

3-6 Drawing Pictures and Diagrams (page 86)

1. 8

2. 6

3. 13

The 8-ft and 10-ft intervals first meet at 40 ft. One post less in 40 ft results in 3 less in 120 ft.
In 120 ft, 12 posts at 10-ft intervals, plus 1 post at the start, are needed.

4. 21

$\dfrac{60}{3} + 1$

5. 6 dogs, 4 pens

301

6. 15 dolls, 7 shelves

| II | II | II | II | II | II | II | I |

| III | III | III | III | III |

In Exercises 7 and 8, many arrangements are possible. Interchanging rows or columns gives other arrangements.

7.

O	O		O	O
	O	O	O	O
O		O	O	O
		O	O	

8.

	O	O		O
			O	
	O	O		O
	O			
O		O		O

3-7 Making Lists and Charts *(pages 89–90)*

1.

Color	White	Blue	Assorted
Label	Assorted	White	Blue

2.

	Mark	Jay	Fred
Sister	Joan	Marion	Sally
Date	Marion	Sally	Joan

3.

Carnations	30	21	12	3
Roses	0	2	4	6

4. 9 ways

Ones	20	15	10	10	5	5	0	0	0
Fives	0	1	2	0	1	3	4	2	0
Tens	0	0	0	1	1	0	0	1	2

5.

Ones	8	7	7	7	6	6	6	5	5	4	4	3
Fives	0	1	0	0	2	0	1	3	2	4	3	5
Tens	0	0	1	0	0	2	1	0	1	0	1	0
Twenties	0	0	0	1	0	0	0	0	0	0	0	0

    ↑ ↑   ↑ ↑ ↑ ↑ ↑ ↑ ↑

6. There are 10 possibilities, as shown by the arrows pointing to these solutions for Exercise 5.

7. 19   Consider multiples of 5, plus 4.
         14 No   19 ✓

8. 59   Consider odd multiples of 5, plus 4.
         19 No   29 No   39 No   49 No   59 ✓

9. 58

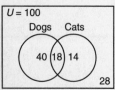

$U = 100$

Dogs   Cats

40 (18) 14

28

10. 178

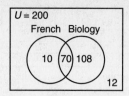

$U = 200$

French   Biology

10 (70) 108

12

3-8 Choosing and Combining Strategies *(pages 92–93)*

1. 41 red, 40 black. Below each red square in Row 1 there is a black square in row 2 and below each black square in Row 1 there is a red square in Row 2. Therefore, there is an equal number of red and black squares in the first two rows. This pattern continues for each pair of rows. The last row, Row 9, starts and ends with a red square. It has one more red square than black squares. Therefore, the complete diagram has one more red square than black squares. Draw a 3×3 diagram.

R		R
	R	
R		R

There is one more red square than black. (Using a simpler problem to draw a diagram)

2. 1 kg

Bucket	Kitten	Rabbit	
2	1	3	$1 + 3 \neq 6$
1	2	4	$2 + 4 = 6$ ✓

(guessing; making a chart)

3. 10 people, 6 benches

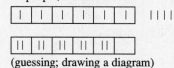

| I | I | I | I | I | I | I | I |

    I I I I

| II | II | II | II | II |

(guessing; drawing a diagram)

4. 35 adults, 64 children

Adults	Children	Total for Tickets	
39	60	$156 + 150 = 306$	No
35	64	$140 + 160 = 300$	✓

(guessing; making a chart)

5. \$8,000 $\frac{1}{2}(\text{car} + 10{,}000) = \text{car} + 1{,}000$

    Try car values.

        $4{,}000: \frac{1}{2}(14{,}000) \neq 5{,}000$

        $6{,}000: \frac{1}{2}(16{,}000) \neq 7{,}000$

        $8{,}000: \frac{1}{2}(18{,}000) = 9{,}000$ ✓

    (guessing and checking)

6. 48 $\frac{1}{3} + \frac{1}{2} + \frac{1}{8} = \frac{23}{24}$ $2 = \frac{1}{24} \times ?$
   (working backwards)

7. Sample solutions are shown. Many are possible.
   (drawing a diagram)

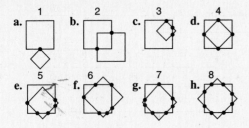

8. **a.** See chart.

Number of Weekdays in Month	20	21	22	23
Rosa's Monthly Earnings	$640	$672	$704	$736
Who Earns More?	Tony	Tony	Rosa	Rosa

b. Rosa

Yearly Earnings	
Tony	$680 × 12 = $8,160
Rosa	Estimate 260 weekdays × 32 = $8,320

(making charts)

9. 16 gumdrops, 4 chocolate drops

Gumdrops	Chocolate Drops	Total Cost
12	8	3¢ + 32¢ = 20¢
16	4	4¢ + 16¢ = 20¢ ✓

(guessing; making a chart)

10. 35 Five of each type of triangle shown
    (drawing diagrams)

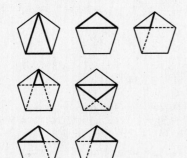

11. 12 minutes

   In 1 minute, Mary and Eddy completed $\frac{1}{20}$ and $\frac{1}{30}$ respectively, of the chore.
   Together, they completed $\frac{1}{20} + \frac{1}{30} = \frac{6}{60} = \frac{1}{12}$
   of the chore every minute.

12. 30 minutes   Eddy still needs this much time to read the paper.

13. No definite answer; it could take them more than 30 minutes.

14. All three problems, on the surface, appear to be the same: same people, same times, and the element of working together. Actual conditions, however, dictate that the solutions are very different.

Review Exercises (pages 93–94)

1. In all three problems, $125 \div 48 = 2.60416\overline{6}$.
   a. 3 buses (a whole number greater than 2.6)
   b. 2.6 hr or 2 hr 36 min (a rational number rounded to the nearest tenth of an hour or the nearest minute)
   c. 2 cases (a whole number less than 2.6)

2. A mistake was made, perhaps in counting the money or in giving change. The largest amount of money that could have been collected for 155 tickets would be $930 if all tickets sold were adult tickets. One child's ticket would bring total to $934.50.

3. Edith   B   E   L   J   P
   Place Bernie and Pierre, then Edith and Joel, and finally Lester.

4. 13   Two numbers such that one is twice the other and their difference is 4 are 8 and 4. These were the ages 5 yr ago.

5. 95¢

Number of Charities	25¢ for All but One	20¢ Each	Amount Left	
3	25 25 20	20 20 20	10¢	No
4	25 25 25 20	20 20 20 20	15¢	✓

6. Ernestine, 15; Lucy, 5
   Guess at Lucy's age now.

Lucy	Ernestine		
2	6	ages now	
7	11	ages in 5 yr	7 × 2 ≠ 11
4	12	ages now	
9	17	ages in 5 yr	9 × 2 ≠ 17
5	15	ages now	
10	20	ages in 5 yr	10 × 2 = 20 ✓

7. 220 400 − 40 = 360 voted for one or both
225 + 355 = 580 votes cast in favor
580 − 360 = 220 voted for both

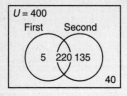

8. 10 (2 + 4) × 2 = 12
(3 + 5) × 2 = 16
(1 + 2) × 2 = 6

9. 20 In general, $a * b = (a + b) × 2$ if all are aligned the same way in the closed carton.

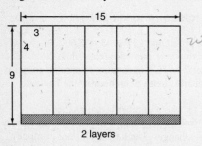

2 layers

22 if placed any way in the closed carton

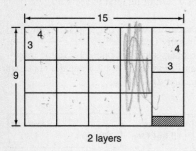

2 layers

10. 39

	Males		Females	
	Boys	Men	Girls	Women
Americans	2	1	3	4
Canadians	6	8	15	

11. Saturday (Friday in leap year)
July 4 is the 185th day of a year that is not a leap year.
185 ÷ 7 = 26 with a remainder of 3
Twenty six full weeks before Monday would be a Tuesday. Three days before that would be Saturday.

12. $870 Using 4 large trucks and 2 small trucks
Large truck costs $40 + 3($50) = $190 per trip.
Small truck costs $5 + 2($25) = $55 per trip.

Large Trucks	Small Trucks	Cost
5	0	$950
4	2	$870
3	6	$900
2	10	$930
1	14	$960
0	18	$990

13.

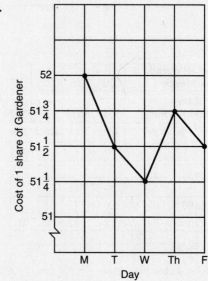

Cumulative Review *(pages 95–96)*

1. a. $A(-4)$, $B(-2.7)$, $C(-2)$, $D(-\sqrt{3})$, $E\left(-\dfrac{\sqrt{5}}{3}\right)$, $F(0)$, $G(0.5)$, $H\left(\dfrac{2}{3}\right)$, $I(1)$, $J(\pi)$

b. 1 **c.** 0, 1 **d.** $-4, -2.7, -2, 0, 0.5, \dfrac{2}{3}, 1$

e. $-\sqrt{3}, -\dfrac{\sqrt{5}}{3}, \pi$ **f.** $-4, -2.7, -2, -\sqrt{3}, -\dfrac{\sqrt{5}}{3},$ $0, 0.5, \dfrac{2}{3}, 1, \pi$ **g.** 0 **h.** 1 **i.** -2 **j.** $\dfrac{2}{3}$

2. $-8.1 < 0 < 8.1$ **3.** $1.7 < \sqrt{3} < 1.\overline{7}$

4. $-\pi < -3.\overline{14} < -3.14$

5. 113.4 **6.** 12.5 **7.** 147

8. 1,035 **9.** 26 **10.** 269

11. $3 + 3 × (3 − 3) = 3$ **12.** $(1 + 2) × 3 − 4 = 5$

13. a. (2) **b.** (4) **c.** (1) **d.** (3)

Exploration

(1) Place a 0 at the end of the number.
(2) Place a 0 at the end of the number and divide the result by 2.
(3) Move the decimal point one place to the left.
(4) Move the decimal point one place to the left and multiply the result by 2.
(5) Multiply by the tens digit of the two-digit number and place a 0 at the end, multiply by the units digit of the two-digit number, and then add the two results.

(6) A number divisible by 2 ends in 0, 2, 4, 6, or 8.
The sum of the digits of a number divisible by 3 is divisible by 3.
A number divisible by 4 ends in 0, 4, or 8 if the tens digit is even, or ends in 2 or 6 if the tens digit is odd. Or a number is divisible by 4 if the last two digits of the number are divisible by 4.
A number divisible by 5 ends in 0 or 5.
A number divisible by 6 is divisible by 2 and by 3.
The sum of the digits of a number divisible by 9 is divisible by 9.
A number divisible by 10 ends in 0.

Chapter 4. Algebraic Expressions, Geometric Formulas, and Open Sentences

Introductory page *(page 97)*

Count the number of seconds elapsed. Take one-fifth of the number of seconds to find the approximate number of miles that you are from the storm.

4-1 Translating Verbal Phrases Into Algebraic Language *(page 100)*

1. $y + 8$
2. $8 + y$ or $y + 8$
3. $r - 4$
4. $4 - r$
5. $7x$
6. $7x$ or $x \cdot 7$
7. $\dfrac{x}{10}$ or $x \div 10$
8. $\dfrac{10}{x}$ or $10 \div x$
9. $6d$
10. $c - 6$
11. $b + 15$
12. $\dfrac{1}{10}w$ or $\dfrac{w}{10}$
13. $b + 8$
14. $x - y$
15. xy
16. $\dfrac{s}{t}$ or $s \div t$
17. $12 + a$
18. $d - 5$
19. $\dfrac{8}{y}$ or $8 \div y$
20. $10y$ or $y \cdot 10$
21. $2c(3d)$ or $2c \cdot 3d$
22. $t + w$ or $w + t$
23. $\dfrac{1}{3}z$ or $\dfrac{z}{3}$
24. $2(p - q)$
25. $m + 4$
26. $\dfrac{1}{2}(L + W)$ or $\dfrac{L + W}{2}$
27. $5x + 2$
28. $10 - 2a$
29. $n + 2$
30. $n + 20$ or $20 + n$
31. $8 + n$
32. $n - 6$
33. $n - 2$
34. $3n$
35. $\dfrac{3}{4}n$
36. $4n + 3$
37. $2n - 3$
38. $10n - 2$
39. $4(5 + n)$ or $(n + 5) \cdot 4$
40. $L + W$
41. LW
42. $L - W$
43. $\dfrac{W}{L}$ or $W \div L$
44. $2L + 2W$
45. $10W - 6L$
46. **a.** 40, 41, 42, 44   **b.** 40, 41, 42, 44, 45
   c. 40, 41, 42, 43, 44   **d.** All, 40–45

4-2 Using Letters to Represent Variables *(pages 102–103)*

1. $x + 200$
2. $1,000 - d$
3. $5x$
4. $\dfrac{1}{2}\ell$ or $\dfrac{\ell}{2}$
5. $c + 12$
6. $100 - x$
7. $s - x$
8. $150n$
9. $39x$
10. tg
11. $45 - x$
12. $c - d$
13. $250 - y$
14. $c + 25$
15. $w + 8$
16. $2x + 3$
17. $550h$
18. $5r$
19. **a.** $100m$ **b.** $0.01i$ or $\dfrac{1}{100}i$ **c.** $7w$ **d.** $\dfrac{1}{7}d$ or $\dfrac{d}{7}$
   e. $24d$ **f.** $\dfrac{1}{24}h$ or $\dfrac{h}{24}$ **g.** $\dfrac{1}{12}c$ or $\dfrac{c}{12}$
   h. $1,000k$
20. $7w + d$
21. $\dfrac{c}{m}$ or $c \div m$
22. $15x + 18y$
23. $0.45 + 0.09(m-3)$
24. $0.50 + 0.06(c - 8)$
25. $5 + 0.75(6) + 0.55(g-9)$ or $9.50 + 0.55(g-9)$
26. **a.** $\dfrac{d}{b}$
   b. No. If d is not a multiple of b, then $\dfrac{d}{b}$ is not a whole number. For example, $\dfrac{76}{10} = 7.6$.
27. **a.** The smallest integer greater than or equal to $\dfrac{c}{x}$
   b. The smallest integer greater than or equal to $n \cdot \dfrac{c}{x}$, or the smallest integer greater than or equal to $\dfrac{nc}{x}$
   c. If c is not a multiple of x, then $\dfrac{c}{x}$ is not a whole number. Also, if nc is not a multiple of x, then $\dfrac{nc}{x}$ is not a whole number. The cost is the smallest integer greater than either of these values when they are not integers.

4-3 Algebraic Terms and Vocabulary
(page 105)

1. x, y, xy 2. $3, a, 3a$ 3. $5, n, 5n$
4. $7, m, n, 7m, 7n, mn, 7mn$
5. $13, x, y, 13x, 13y, xy, 13xy$
6. $11, s, t, 11s, 11t, st, 11st$
7. 8   8. $(5 + 2)$ or 7   9. $\frac{1}{2}$
10. 1   11. -1.4 12. 7
13. Base m; exponent 2
14. Base s; exponent 3
15. Base t; exponent 1
16. Base 10; exponent 6
17. Base $5y$; exponent 4
18. Base $(x + y)$; exponent 5
19. m^3 20. b^5 21. $4x^5$
22. πr^2 23. $a^4 b^2$ 24. $7r^3 s^2$
25. $9c^3 d$ 26. $(6a)^3$ 27. $(x + y)^2$
28. $(a - b)^3$ 29. $(b - 5)^2$ 30. $(m + 2n)^4$
31. $r \cdot r \cdot r \cdot r \cdot r \cdot r$
32. $5 \cdot x \cdot x \cdot x \cdot x$
33. $x \cdot x \cdot x \cdot y \cdot y \cdot y \cdot y \cdot y$
34. $4 \cdot a \cdot a \cdot a \cdot a \cdot b \cdot b$
35. $3 \cdot c \cdot c \cdot d \cdot d \cdot d \cdot e$
36. $(3y)(3y)(3y)(3y)(3y)$
37. Coefficient $= -3$, base $= k$, exponent $= 1$
38. Coefficient $= -1$, base $= k$, exponent $= 3$
39. Coefficient $= \pi$, base $= r$, exponent $= 2$
40. Coefficient $= 1$, base $= (ax)$, exponent $= 5$
41. Coefficient $= \sqrt{2}$, base $= y$, exponent $= 1$
42. Coefficient $= 0.0004$, base $= t$, exponent $= 12$

4-4 Evaluating Algebraic Expressions
(pages 108–109)

1. 40   2. 54   3. 2   4. 1.5
5. 11   6. 12   7. 6   8. 0
9. 2   10. 32   11. 60   12. 4
13. 6   14. 17   15. 9   16. 16
17. 30   18. 36   19. 35   20. 78
21. 25   22. 0   23. 64   24. 16
25. 216   26. 125   27. 81   28. 1
29. 32   30. 108   31. 108   32. 6
33. 4   34. 32   35. 48   36. 192
37. 100   38. 24   39. 27,648   40. 100
41. 36   42. 100   43. 11   44. 91
45. 20   46. 48   47. 5   48. 78
49. 8   50. 33   51. 28   52. 26
53. 24   54. 54   55. 4   56. 28
57. 28   58. 9   59. 36   60. 15
61. 192   62. 576   63. 29   64. 49
65. 488   66. 8   67. 172   68. 196
69. 644   70. 1,600   71. 6,400   72. 21
73. 11
74. **a.** 10   **b.** 25   **c.** 30   **d.** 0   **e.** 100
75. 0.945   76. 30.6656   77. 107.3296
78. 0.0108   79. 0.492075   80. 3.77
81. 0.41   82. 23.5066   83. 23.2106

84. 69.8116   85. 219.04   86. 5,476
87. 1,850   88. 9   89. 0.041664
90. Smallest is (1). Values are (1) 0.00378, (2) 0.5292, (3) 0.015876, (4) 588, (5) 140.
91. Greatest is (4). Values are (1) 14.765625, (2) 4.134375, (3) $\approx$ 15.503906, (4) 23.04, (5) 19.683.

4-5 Translating Verbal Sentences Into Formulas *(pages 110–111)*

1. $\ell = 10\,m$ 2. $S = c + m$
3. $p = 2\ell + 2w$ 4. $M = \dfrac{a + b + c}{3}$
5. $A = \dfrac{1}{2}bh$ 6. $A = s^2$
7. $V = e^3$ 8. $S = 6e^2$
9. $S = 4\pi r^2$ 10. $r = \dfrac{D}{t}$
11. $F = \dfrac{9}{5}C + 32$ 12. $C = \dfrac{5}{9}(F - 32)$
13. $D = dq + r$ 14. $T = 0.08v$
15. $E = s + 0.02v$ 16. $N = rt$
17. $N = 2rs$ or $N = rs + rs$
18. $C = 20 + d(n - 1)$
19. $C = x + 6y$ 20. $D = a + 17b$
21. $D = 0.12n + 0.03(n - 25{,}000)$ or $D = 3{,}000 + 0.15(n - 25{,}000)$

4-6 Formulas for Perimeter and Area of Polygons *(pages 114–116)*

1. **a.** 32 in.   **b.** 10 m   **c.** $18\frac{1}{2}$ ft or 222 in.
   d. $19\frac{3}{4}$ ft   **e.** 4.25 m or 425 cm
2. **a.** 36 cm   **b.** 14.4 m   **c.** 28 ft
   d. 8 ft or 96 in.   **e.** 218.94 m
3. **a.** 16 m   **b.** 20.4 m   **c.** 12 ft
   d. 19.32 m or 1,932 cm
4. **a.** 16 cm   **b.** 14 m   **c.** 35 in.
   d. 356 in. or 29 ft 8 in.   **e.** 323.6 cm
5. **a.** 58 cm   **b.** 28.4 m   **c.** $21\frac{1}{2}$ in.
   d. 10.1 m or 1,010 cm
6. **a.** 195 sq ft   **b.** 25.5 m^2 **c.** 51 sq ft
   d. 4,000 cm^2 or 0.4 m^2 **e.** 3 sq ft or 432 sq in.
   f. 2.262 m^2 or 22,620 cm^2
7. **a.** 96 sq ft   **b.** 22.4 m^2 **c.** 60 sq in.
   d. 1,000 cm^2 or 0.1 m^2 **e.** 51 mm^2 or 0.51 cm^2
   f. 13.5 sq ft or 1,944 sq in.
8. **a.** 15 m^2 **b.** 31.5 sq in.   **c.** 85 sq ft
   d. 165.3 cm^2 **e.** 30 sq ft or 4,320 sq in.
   f. 1.0738 m^2 or 10,738 cm^2
9. **a.** 625 sq in.   **b.** 81 cm^2
   c. $6\frac{1}{4}$ sq ft or 900 sq in.
   d. 37.21 m^2 **e.** 203.6329 km^2

10. a. 30 cm² **b.** 39.9 m² **c.** 14 sq in. **d.** 33 sq in.
e. 1.8125 m² or 18.125 cm²
f. 432 sq ft or 48 sq yd
11. a. 99 sq ft **b.** 10 sq in. **c.** 2.9 m²

d. 336 sq in. or $2\frac{1}{3}$ sq ft

e. 7,950 cm² or 0.795 m²

4-7 Formulas for Circumference and Area of a Circle *(pages 119–121)*

1. a. 4 in.   **b.** 26 ft   **c.** $4\frac{1}{4}$ in.   **d.** 73 mm

e. 992.74 cm   **f.** 40.1 m

2. a. 2 ft   **b.** $3\frac{1}{2}$ in.   **c.** $1\frac{3}{4}$ in.   **d.** 6.95 cm

e. 147.5 mm   **f.** 97.725 m

3. a. 10π cm **b.** 9π ft   **c.** 4.8π mm **d.** $\frac{1}{3}\pi$ in.

e. 25π yd **f.** 8.75π m **g.** 9π mm **h.** 195π cm
4. a. 50.24 cm   **b.** 25.12 in.
c. 15.7 mm   **d.** 10.99 in.
5. a. 88 cm   **b.** 22 ft   **c.** 22 mm   **d.** 33 in.
6. a. 62.832 mm   **b.** 23.876 cm
c. 100.531 in.   **d.** 53.407 ft
e. 4.712 yd   **f.** 1.885 km
g. 27.458 m   **h.** 109.956 mi
7. 88 in.
8. a. 16π **b.** 81π **c.** 0.64π **d.** 0.09π

e. $\frac{1}{9}\pi$ **f.** $\frac{9}{4}\pi$ or $2\frac{1}{4}\pi$

9. a. 64π sq in.   **b.** 81π cm²

c. $\frac{1}{16}\pi$ sq in.   **d.** 0.09π mm²

e. 2.25π m²   **f.** $\frac{4}{9}\pi$ sq ft

10. a. 314 cm²   **b.** 314 sq ft   **c.** 0.5024 mm²
d. 7.065 sq in.   **e.** 0.0314 m²   **f.** 1.76625 cm²
11. a. 154 sq ft   **b.** 15,400 mm²   **c.** 1,386 cm²

d. 38.5 sq in.   **e.** $\frac{11}{14}$ sq in.

f. $1\frac{43}{56}$ mm² (approx. 1.7678571 mm²)

12. a. 113.097 cm²   **b.** 3.142 sq ft   **c.** 4.524 mm²
d. 3,216.991 sq in.   **e.** 2.011 km²   **f.** 4.909 sq yd
g. 33.388 m²   **h.** 0.126 sq mi
13. a. 12.25π m²   **b.** 38.5 m²
14. 254.47 sq in.   **15.** 13.2 m
16. (3)   **17.** (3)   **18.** (3)
19. 140 yd
20. Circumference = 4π *units*, while area = 4π *square units*. Length and area use different units of measure.

4-8 Reasoning with Perimeter, Area and Shaded Regions *(pages 122–125)*

1. a. 22   **b.** 24   **2. a.** 0.16   **b.** 0.0016
3. a. 18   **b.** 12   **4. a.** 16   **b.** 12
5. a. 90   **b.** 330   **6. a.** 16   **b.** 12
7. a. 30   **b.** 30   **8. a.** 27   **b.** 31.5
9. 200 cm²   **10.** 280 sq in.

11. 23.375 cm² or $23\frac{3}{8}$ cm²

12. a. 5 cm   **b.** 25 cm²
13. a. 25 mm   **b.** 625 mm²
14. a. 1 ft   **b.** 1 sq ft
15. a. 0.5 in.   **b.** 0.25 sq in.
16. a. 0.7 m   **b.** 0.49 m²
17. a. $x = 5, x + y = 9$ **b.** 45
18. a. $2x = 10, y = 4$ **b.** 40
19. a. $x + 1 = 6$ **b.** 36
20. a. $x = 5, x + y = 9, y = 4$ **b.** 28
21. a. $2x = 10, y = 4$ **b.** 20
22. a. $3x + 2 = 17, y + 1 = 5$ **b.** 85
23. a. $x + 3 = 8, 2x + 1 = 11$ **b.** 44
24. a. $y + 1 = 5, y - 1 = 3$ **b.** 15
25. a. $3x + 1 = 16, 2x = 10$ **b.** 80
26. a. $2x = 10, y + 2 = 6$ **b.** 60
27. a. $2x = 10$ **b.** 100

28. a. $\frac{y}{2} = 2, x + 7 = 12$ **b.** 24

29. a. $x + 3 = 8, y + 3 = 7, x + y = 9$
b. 64
30. 30,000 sq ft
31. 18 ft (Draw a picture.)
32. a. 12   **b.** 6   **c.** 144   **d.** 36π **e.** $144 - 36\pi$
33. a. 5   **b.** 10π **c.** 28   **d.** 25π **e.** 48
f. $25\pi - 48$

34. a. Girl; each boy's share was $\frac{16\pi}{2} = 8\pi$, while each

girl's share was $\frac{36\pi}{4} = 9\pi$

b. $1.60
c. $1.35
d. 12-inch pizza, since it is more pie for less money per person.
35. 64 sq in.
36. a. 214 sq ft **b.** 66 ft **c.** The amount of carpet would be the same; the amount of stripping would increase to 82 ft. **d.** The amount of carpet would be the same; the amount of stripping would increase to 96 ft.

37. 248   **38.** 588   **39.** 648
40. 28.5   **41.** 21
42. a. 12 ft by 7 ft; 84 sq ft
b. 10 ft by 8 ft Since the area is now 80 sq ft, there is less room.

c. 13 ft by $6\frac{1}{2}$ ft

4-9 Formulas for Volume of Solid
(pages 127–130)

1. 140 cu ft   2. 280 cm³   3. 214.2 m³
4. 105 cu in.   5. 167.04 cm³   6. 8 cu yd

7. 27 m³   8. 512 cm³   9. $\dfrac{1}{27}$ cu ft

10. 3.375 cu in.   11. 21.024576 m³
12. a. (1) 24 cm²   (2) 232.8 cm³
     b. 3,370.25 cu in.
13. a. (1) 32 sq ft   (2) 384 cu ft
     b. 16,707.6 cm³
14. 208 mm³   15. 28 cu in.
16. a. 2,592; 100m³
     b. 91,826; 784 cu ft
17. 27   18. 125   19. 1

20. 64   21. $\dfrac{27}{8}$ or $3\dfrac{3}{8}$ 22. 144

23. 72   24. 368.48
25. a. 4,410π cu in.   b. 13,854 cu in.
26. a. 588π cu ft   b. 1,847 cu ft
27. a. 420π cm³   b. 1,319 cm³
28. a. 11.76π m³   b. 37 m³
29. a. 400π cu in.   b. 1,257 cu in.
30. a. 4π cu ft   b. 13 cu ft
31. a. π mm³   b. 3 mm³
32. a. 3.2π cm³   b. 10 cm³

33. a. $\dfrac{4,000}{3}\pi$ cu ft   or $1,333\dfrac{1}{3}\pi$ cu ft

     b. 4,189 cu ft

34. a. $\dfrac{1}{6}\pi$ mm³ or 0.1666666π mm³

     b. 1 mm³

35. a. 972π cu in.   b. 3,054 cu in.
36. a. ≈ 23.434667π cm³   b. 74 cm³
37. a. 463 cm³   b. 28 cu in.
38. 11,880 gal
39. a. (1) Volume of cone = 18π
        (2) Volume of sphere = 36π
        (3) Volume of cylinder = 54π
     b. In all three solids, radii are equal, and height
     h = diameter d, or twice radius r. Then:

Volume of cone = $\dfrac{1}{3}$ volume of cylinder

Volume of sphere = $\dfrac{2}{3}$ volume of cylinder

Volume of cone + volume of sphere = volume of cylinder
Volume of sphere = 2 (volume of cone)

4-10 Open Sentences and Solution Sets
(pages 131–132)

1. Not open   2. Open   3. Open
4. Not open   5. Open   6. Open
7. x 8. y 9. r
10. 4   11. 3   12. 0

13. None   14. 0, 1, 2, 3, 4, 5
15. 3, 4, 5   16. None   17. 0, 1, 2, 3
18. 3   19. None   20. 5
21. None   22. {3}   23. {3}
24. ∅   25. {2}   26. {10}
27. {5, 6, 7, 8, 9, 10}   28. {9, 10}

29. ∅   30. $\{2\dfrac{1}{2}\}$ 31. $\{3\dfrac{1}{2}\}$

32. $\{4\dfrac{1}{2}\}$ 33. $\{4\dfrac{1}{2}\}$ 34. $\{4\dfrac{1}{2}\}$

35. $\{2, 2\dfrac{1}{2}\}$ 36. $\{4\dfrac{1}{2}\}$ 37. ∅

38. {2.3}   39. {2.1}   40. ∅
41. ∅   42. {16}   43. {5}
44. {24}   45. {0, 1, 2, 3}
46. {0, 1, 2, 3, 4, 5}   47. {∅}
48. {0, 1, 2, 3}   49. {26}
50. a. ∅   b. {2.5}   c. ∅   d. {2.5}   e. {2.5}

Review Exercises (pages 134–135)

1. $\dfrac{x}{b}$ 2. $r - 4$ 3. $q - d$

4. $2g + 3$ 5. $30 - x$ 6. 26
7. 100   8. 29   9. 21
10. 4   11. 180   12. 380
13. 30   14. 64   15. $g = 1,000\,k$

16. $\dfrac{P}{3}$ 17. 48 cm²   18. 29 in.

19. 168 m²   20. {1, 3}   21. {9}
22. {1, 3, 5, 7, 9}   23. {1, 3, 5}
24. ∅   25. ∅   26. {5}
27. {5, 7, 9}
28. a. $\overline{OF}, \overline{OG}, \overline{OH}$ b. $\overline{FG}$ c. $\overline{FG}, \overline{GH}$
29. 14
30. a. 225π mm²   b. 707 mm²
31. a. 2,500π cu in.   b. 7,854 cu in.
32. a. 40π   b. 400π   c. 1,600 − 400π
33. (3)   34. (2)   35. (1)
36. (3)   37. (2)

Cumulative Review (page 135)

1. The commutative property of addition
2. The addition property of zero (Zero is the additive identity)
3. The distributive property of multiplication over addition
4. The multiplication property of zero
5. The associative property of multiplication
6. The closure property of addition
7. a. 14
    b. Add three to the last number to find the next number or nth term in the list is equal to $3n - 1$
    c. 74
8. Any one of the four numbers can be a correct number.
    6 is even. The other numbers are odd.
    3 is a prime. The other numbers are composite.

35 is a two digit number, divisible by 5, not divisible by 3.
The other numbers are single digit numbers, not divisible by 5, divisible by 3.
9 is a perfect square. The other numbers are not perfect squares.

9. 2 apples

Exploration

Let r be the radius of the circle. Then the length of a side of the square is the diameter of the circle, $2r$. Since the circle is contained within the square, the area of the circle, πr^2 is less than the area of the square, $(2r)^2$.

Chapter 5. Signed Numbers

5-1 The Opposite of a Directed Number
(page 138)

1. -8 **2.** 8 or $+8$ **3.** $-3\frac{1}{2}$

4. 6.5 or $+6.5$ **5.** -19 **6.** -14 ?

7. 0   **8.** 0   **9.** -7

10. $-\frac{3}{4}$ **11.** -5 **12.** -14

13. 10   **14.** 7   **15.** -4

16. 0   **17.** False   **18.** True

19. False (The opposite of 0 is 0.)   **20.** True

21. False   **22.** True   **23.** True

24. True   **25.** True

5-2 The Absolute Value of a Number
(pages 139–140)

1. a. 3   **b.** -3 **2. a.** 5   **b.** 5

3. a. 18   **b.** -18 **4. a.** 13   **b.** 13

5. a. 20   **b.** 20   **6. a.** $1\frac{1}{2}$ **b.** $-1\frac{1}{2}$

7. a. $3\frac{3}{4}$ **b.** $3\frac{3}{4}$ **8. a.** $1\frac{1}{2}$ **b.** $1\frac{1}{2}$

9. a. 2.7   **b.** -2.7 **10. a.** 1.4   **b.** 1.4

11. True   **12.** True   **13.** False

14. True   **15.** False   **16.** True

17. True   **18.** False   **19.** 12

20. 6   **21.** 10   **22.** 5

23. 0   **24.** 10   **25.** 14

26. 5   **27.** 0   **28.** 8

29. 9   **30.** 0   **31.** 7

32. -2 **33.** -6 **34.** True

35. False   **36.** False   **37.** True

38. False   **39.** True   **40.** True

41. False   **42.** True

5-3 Addition of Signed Numbers
(pages 145–147)

1. $+10$ **2.** $+13$ **3.** -37

4. -45 **5.** $+2$ **6.** -2

7. $+4$ **8.** -7 **9.** -12

10. $+6$ **11.** -5 **12.** $+4$

13. -9 **14.** 0   **15.** 0

16. $+24$ **17.** -66 **18.** -30

19. $+8$ **20.** -9 **21.** $+18\frac{1}{4}$

22. $-8\frac{1}{2}$ **23.** $-13\frac{2}{3}$ **24.** $+2\frac{3}{4}$

25. -7.8 **26.** 8.3   **27.** -16.3

28. 2.3   **29.** 2.5   **30.** $-1\frac{3}{4}$

31. -6 **32.** $+25$ **33.** $+23$

34. -18 **35.** -28 **36.** 0

37. 54   **38.** -17 **39.** 0

40. 16   **41.** 0   **42.** 0

43. $+6$ **44.** -20 **45.** 0

46. 0   **47.** -6.1 **48.** 12

49. 12   **50.** 0   **51.** -26

52. 4   **53.** -6 **54.** 0

55. -3 **56.** -2 **57.** -1

58. 1

59. Negative   The sum of the difference of the absolute value of the numbers.

60. Positive   The sum of the two negative numbers is negative, so one number must be positive.

61. Positive   A positive must be added in order for this sum to be larger than the negative number.

62. Negative   The sum of the two positive numbers is positive, so one number must be negative.

63. Yes $-2 + (-1) = -3$

64. $+7°$ **65.** 18th   **66.** Lost 3

67. $270   **68.** $-\frac{3}{4}$ (loss of $\frac{3}{4}$)

5-4 Subtraction of Signed Numbers
(pages 150–151)

1. $+6$ **2.** $+7$ **3.** -2

4. -8 **5.** -4 **6.** -14

7. $+4$ **8.** $+16$ **9.** $+6$

10. $+45$ **11.** $+13$ **12.** $+140$

13. -8 **14.** -92 **15.** -12

16. -86 **17.** $+10$ **18.** -7

19. $+20$ **20.** 0   **21.** -11

22. 0   **23.** $+51$ **24.** -54

25. -62 **26.** -12 **27.** 0

28. $+15$ **29.** $+2.2$ **30.** $+14.5$

31. -10.6 **32.** -1.3 **33.** $+3$

34. $4\frac{1}{2}$ **35.** $+10$ **36.** $-10\frac{1}{6}$

37. -11 38. $+13$ 39. $+30$
40. -1.7 41. $+1.5$ 42. -17.5
43. 25   44. 27   45. 3
46. 9   47. -12 48. 19
49. -26 50. 3   51. -5
52. $+3$ 53. -8.5 54. $+3.7$

55. $-1\frac{7}{8}$ 56. $+\frac{9}{2}$ 57. $+20$

58. -41 59. -28 60. 0

61. $7\frac{1}{2}$ 62. 0

63. **a.** $+3°$ **b.** $+28°$ **c.** $-12°$ **d.** $-16°$
64. $+110$ m   65. 185   66. $114°$
67. 0.25 km   68. **a.** False   **b.** False
69. **a.** No   **b.** Yes; if $x = y$ **c.** They are opposites.
    d. No
70. **a.** False   **b.** False   71. No
72. 4   73. 3   74. 6
75. 10   76. 2   77. 5

5-5 Multiplication of Signed Numbers
(pages 154–155)

1. $+24$ 2. $+7$ 3. $+105$
4. -32 5. -120 6. -144
7. 0   8. $+100$ 9. -192
10. 0   11. $+225$ 12. -135
13. -3.6 14. -20 15. $+4$

16. -9 17. $+\frac{1}{6}$ 18. -36 *error*

19. $+2$ 20. $+12$ 21. -1
22. $+24$ 23. -56 24. -60
25. 0   26. -120 27. 0
28. $+16$ 29. $+9$ 30. $+125$
31. -64 32. -125 33. $+1$

34. $+\frac{1}{4}$ 35. $+\frac{1}{4}$ 36. $+\frac{8}{27}$

37. $-\frac{27}{125}$ 38. $-\frac{1}{64}$ 39. $+\frac{1}{625}$

40. $5(9) +5(7)$ 41. $-4x + (-4y)$
42. $6[-3+(-5)]$ 43. $7(a+b)$
44. $8[5 + (-3)] = 8 \cdot 5 + 8 \cdot (-3)$
45. $2(-3 +3) = 2(-3) +2(3)$
46. Commutative property of multiplication
47. Associative property of multiplication
48. Distributive property
49. Distributive property
50. **a.** Distributive property of multiplication over
    addition
    b. Communicative property of addition
    c. Associative property of addition
    d. Addition property of zero
    e. Communicative property of multiplication
51. **a.** True   **b.** True   52. Yes

5-6 Division of Signed Numbers
(pages 158–159)

1. $\frac{1}{6}$ 2. $-\frac{1}{5}$ 3. $\frac{1}{9}$

4. $-\frac{1}{7}$ 5. 1   6. -1

7. 5   8. -10 9. $\frac{4}{3}$

10. $-\frac{3}{2}$ 11. $\frac{1}{x}$ 12. $-\frac{1}{x}$

13. $+5$ 14. $+7$ 15. -2

16. -3 17. -25 18. -6

19. $+1$ 20. -1 21. 0

22. -13 23. -7 24. $+5$

25. -4 26. Undefined   27. -13

28. 0   29. $-\frac{1}{2}$ 30. $+\frac{2}{3}$

31. $+\frac{5}{4}$ or $+1\frac{1}{4}$ 32. $-\frac{9}{2}$ or $-4\frac{1}{2}$

33. $-\frac{8}{3}$ or $-2\frac{2}{3}$ 34. $-\frac{17}{2}$ or $-8\frac{1}{2}$

35. $-\frac{25}{2}$ or $-12\frac{1}{2}$ 36. $+\frac{9}{2}$ or $+ 4\frac{1}{2}$

37. 0   38. $+\frac{5}{9}$ 39. $-\frac{3}{7}$

40. -2.1 41. $+32$ 42. -3

43. -8 44. $+5$ 45. Undefined

46. -36 47. $-\frac{1}{8}$ 48. $+\frac{9}{8}$ or $+1\frac{1}{8}$

49. **a.** 2   **b.** 2

50. $\frac{1}{x - 5}$; 5   51. $\frac{1}{x + 3}$; -3

52. $\frac{1}{2x - 1}$, $\frac{1}{2}$ 53. $\frac{1}{3x + 1}$, $-\frac{1}{3}$

54. **a.** False   **b.** False

55. **a.** No
    b. Yes; $(+2) \div (-2) = (-2) \div (+2)$;
    $x \div y = y \div x$ whenever $|y| = |x|$
    c. Reciprocals
    d. No
56. **a.** False   **b.** False   57. No
58. **a.** True   **b.** True   59. Yes

5-7 Evaluating Algebraic Expressions Using Signed Numbers *(page 161)*

1. −48	**2.** −30	**3.** −48
4. −40	**5.** +24	**6.** −1
7. −4	**8.** −3	**9.** −10
10. +36	**11.** +64	**12.** −27
13. −25	**14.** −9	**15.** +1
16. +32	**17.** −75	**18.** −108
19. +36	**20.** +2	**21.** −100
22. 384 or +384		**23.** 450 or +450
24. −54	**25.** +54	**26.** −2
27. −4	**28.** −9	**29.** 9 or +9
30. −2	**31.** 18 or +18	**32.** −10
33. 62 or +62	**34.** 12 or +12	
35. 78 or +78	**36.** 20 or +20	**37.** 21 or +21
38. −43	**39.** 88 or +88	**40.** 65 or +65
41. 9 or +9	**42.** − 8	**43.** 98 or +98
44. 27 or +27	**45.** 49 or +49	**46.** 9 or +9
47. − 4	**48.** −21	**49.** 34 or +34
50. 10 or +10	**51.** 28 or +28	**52.** 0
53. 13	**54.** 0	**55. a.** 32 **b.** 64
56. a. 12 **b.** 36		

57. a. 1   **b.** 4   **58.** $-\dfrac{2}{3}$ **59.** +3

60. −2   **61.** +24   **62.** $-\dfrac{3}{5}$ or 0.6

5-8 Number Lines and Graphs Using Signed Numbers *(page 166)*

1. $A(1, 2)$ $B(-2, 1)$ $C(-2, -1)$ $D(2, -2)$ $E(2, 0)$
$F(0, 1)$ $G(-1, 0)$ $H(0, -2)$ $O(0, 0)$

2–21.

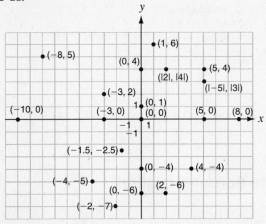

22. I	**23.** III	**24.** II
25. IV	**26.** I	**27.** 0
28. 0	**29.** (0, 0)	

30. a.

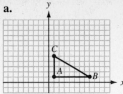

b. Triangle
c. 14

31. a.

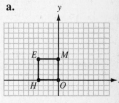

b. Rectangle
c. 20

32. a.

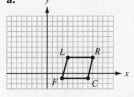

b. Parallelogram
c. 10

33. a.

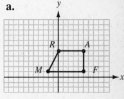

b. Square
c. 16

34. a.

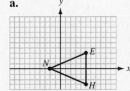

b. Triangle
c. 21

35. a.

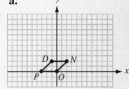

b. Trapezoid
c. 24

36. a.

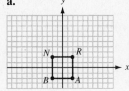

b. Square
c. 16

37. a.

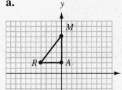

b. Parallelogram
c. 6

38. a.

b. Triangle
c. 10

39. a.

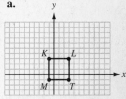

b. Square
c. 16

40. (1, 4)

41. (2, 0) and (−2, 0), or
(2, −8) and (−2, −8)

42. a.

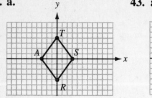

b. 24

43. a.

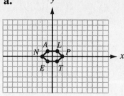

b. 6

45–49.

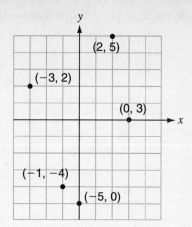

Review Exercises *(pages 167–169)*

1. +7	**2.** −13	**3.** −54
4. −14	**5.** +62	**6.** + 1.3
7. −42	**8.** −104	**9.** +0.9
10. −3	**11.** +7	**12.** $-\dfrac{1}{4}$
13. False	**14.** True	**15.** False
16. False	**17.** True	**18.** False
19. 22	**20.** −1	**21.** +1
22. −16	**23.** −51	**24.** +15
25. −32	**26.** +0.6	**27.** −240
28. +6	**29.** 0	**30.** $+\dfrac{1}{9}$
31. 2	**32.** −3	**33.** 36
34. 144	**35.** −4	**36.** 20
37. −6	**38.** −24	**39.** −9
40. 5	**41.** −36	**42.** 3
43. −2		

44. a. $A(-4, -4)$, $B(6, -4)$, $C(5, 3)$, $D(0, 3)$

   b. $\dfrac{105}{2} = 52.5$

50. a. −15   **b.** 8   **c.** No, if all questions are answered.

Cumulative Review *(page 169)*

1. Yes. Two boys and two girls

2. $2m + 4$ **3.** $\dfrac{12}{3x}$ **4.** $2b + m$

5. $10 + 2w$

6. a. $0.60S - (4.50 D + 2.10)$ **b.** \$30.30

   c. −\$4.50   Tom lost \$4.50 on Tuesday

Exploration

(1) below par
(2) in the hole
(3) loss
(4) loss, decline, down
(5) deficit, in the red
(6) below sea level

Chapter 6. Introduction to Solving Equations

6-1 Preparing to Solve an Equation
   (page 173)

1. No	**2.** Yes	**3.** No
4. Yes	**5.** Yes	**6.** No
7. No	**8.** Yes	**9.** No
10. {2}	**11.** {4}	**12.** {−1}
13. ∅ or { }	**14.** {−2}	**15.** {−3}
16. {−2, 2}	**17.** {−3, 3}	**18.** ∅ or { }
19. {−1, 1}	**20.** {0, 4}	**21.** {−2, 2}

22. Identity   **23.** Conditional   **24.** Identity
25. Identity   **26.** Conditional   **27.** Identity
28. Reflexive   **29.** Transitive   **30.** Symmetric
31. Reflexive   **32.** Symmetric   **33.** Transitive
34. a. No; the sum of a positive integer and 10 is greater than 10.
   b. Yes; −7 + 10 = 3. Therefore, −7 is a solution
35. a. No;   the sum of $x + 1$ is greater than 4.
   b. No;   the sum of $x + 1$ is greater than 4.
   c. No;   the sum of $x + 1$ is greater than 4.

6-2 Solving Equations Using Addition
(page 176)

1. 5	**2.** 5	**3.** 12
4. −2	**5.** 25	**6.** −6
7. −9	**8.** −15	**9.** 4.7
10. −1.6	**11.** −0.39	**12.** 4.8

13. $\frac{2}{3}$ **14.** $\frac{7}{8}$ **15.** $\frac{1}{9}$

16. $5\frac{1}{3}$ **17.** 5 **18.** $4\frac{3}{4}$

19. $-5\frac{1}{4}$ **20.** $-4\frac{2}{5}$ **21.** $-2\frac{3}{5}$

22. 0 **23.** −52 **24.** 0

25. $-7\frac{3}{4}$ **26.** $-\frac{1}{8}$ **27.** $-12\frac{3}{5}$

28. $1\frac{7}{8}$ **29.** $-10\frac{1}{2}$ **30.** $2\frac{2}{7}$

31. −4.5 **32.** −0.009 **33.** −2.7

34. −7.5 **35.** 1 **36.** −102

37. 9.8 **38.** 10.1 **39.** 1.2

40. 14 **41.** 10 **42.** 56

43. 28 **44.** 0 **45.** 24

6-3 Solving Equations Using Multiplication
(pages 179–180)

1. 5	**2.** 9	**3.** 4
4. 12	**5.** 1	**6.** 0

7. −9 **8.** −4 **9.** $\frac{1}{8}$

10. $\frac{1}{6}$ **11.** −0.2 **12.** −0.06

13. 36 **14.** 200 **15.** 27
16. −6 **17.** 1 **18.** 0

19. −81 **20.** $\frac{15}{2} = 7.5$ **21.** $7\frac{1}{3}$

22. $\frac{1}{9}$ **23.** −200 **24.** −0.3

25. 8 **26.** −4 **27.** 3

28. 20 **29.** 2 **30.** $\frac{4}{3}$

31. 12 **32.** −27 **33.** 8
34. 1.5 **35.** 7 **36.** 12
37. 7.1 **38.** 2.0 **39.** 4.7
40. 6.7 **41.** 8 **42.** −0.14
43. 93 **44.** −3

6-4 Solving Equations Using More Than One Operation *(page 182)*

1. 10	**2.** −3	**3.** 4
4. 7	**5.** 8	**6.** 3

7. −4 **8.** 2 **9.** $-\frac{1}{3}$

10. 12 **11.** −2 **12.** 7
13. 32 **14.** −12 **15.** 16
16. 18 **17.** −50 **18.** 9
19. 27 **20.** −16 **21.** 161
22. −25 **23.** 30 **24.** 2
25. 1.2 **26.** 1.4 **27.** −24
28. 81 **29.** −12 **30.** 50
31. −3 **32.** 50 **33.** −40

34. $\frac{1}{3}$ **35.** $\frac{1}{2}$ **36.** $\frac{1}{2}$

6-5 Writing Verbal Sentences as Equations
(pages 184–185)

1. (2)	**2.** (1)	**3.** (2)
4. (4)	**5.** (2)	**6.** (1)
7. (2)	**8.** (2)	**9.** (4)

10. $n + 8 = 15$ **11.** $n - 4 = 24$
12. $n + 12 = 26$ **13.** $n - 5 = 25$

14. $3n = 39$ **15.** $\frac{n}{4} = 16$

16. $7n = 70$ **17.** $2n + 7 = 27$

18. $\frac{1}{2}n - 7 = 11$ **19.** $2n - 5 = 25$

20. $3n + 7 = 22$ **21.** $5n - 9 = 31$
22. $100 + n = 3n$ **23.** $3n + 12 = 2n + 24$
24. $8n - 20 = 3n + 80$ **25.** $n + 2n = 45$

26. $3n - \frac{1}{2}n = 40$

For **27–30**, answers will vary.
27. After Jane had earned $12, she had $18.   Let $x =$ the amount Jane had before she earned $12.
28. The cost of five tickets to a concert is $50.   Let $x =$ the cost of one ticket.
29. The perimeter of a rectangle is 80, and the width is 5. Let $x =$ the length of the rectangle.
30. After Liam had solved six problems, he had 14 left to do. Let $y =$ the number of problems Liam was assigned.

6-6 Using Equations to Solve Problems
(pages 186–188)

1. 56	**2.** 9	**3.** 53
4. 10	**5.** 15	**6.** 18
7. 14	**8.** 85	**9.** 52

10. 14	**11.** 24	**12.** 50
13. 54	**14.** 20	**15.** 400
16. $1.10	**17.** 103 kg	**18.** 12 ft
19. 52 km/hr	**20.** $4.50	**21.** 17.5 ft
22. 1,203	**23.** 24	**24.** $250
25. $27.48	**26.** $15.75	**27.** 8
28. 30 m	**29.** $12	**30.** 78
31. $1,823	**32.** 96	**33.** 11 hr
34. 5	**35.** 4	**36.** 12
37. 7	**38.** 14	**39.** 12
40. 40	**41.** 90	**42.** 162
43. 20.5	**44.** 12	**45.** 11
46. 9 cm	**47.** $.79	**48.** 12
49. 21 min		

6-7 Solving Percent Problems
(pages 189–190)

1. 200	**2.** 48	**3.** 45
4. 30	**5.** 10	**6.** $10
7. 40	**8.** $120	**9.** 50
10. $25	**11.** $8	**12.** 700
13. 1,150	**14.** $24,850	**15.** $80
16. $16	**17.** $30	**18.** 7,000

6-8 More Practice in Solving Equations
(page 190)

1. 12	**2.** 0	**3.** 9
4. 0.4	**5.** 17	**6.** −3
7. −2	**8.** 19.6	**9.** 49
10. 7.8	**11.** 10	**12.** −7
13. 9	**14.** −20	**15.** 2
16. −37	**17.** 400	**18.** $10\frac{3}{8}$
19. −25	**20.** 112	**21.** 9.5
22. −0.2	**23.** −32	**24.** 9
25. 500	**26.** 0.2	**27.** −5
28. 11	**29.** 26	**30.** 40
31. −5	**32.** 51	**33.** 10.5
34. −30	**35.** 50	**36.** 10
37. 10	**38.** $\frac{3}{4}$	**39.** −39
40. 5	**41.** −4	**42.** −1.5
43. −10	**44.** $\frac{1}{8}$ or 0.125	

Review Exercises *(page 192)*

1. {3}	**2.** {5}	**3.** ∅ or { }
4. 30	**5.** 13	**6.** 21
7. (3)	**8.** (2)	**9.** 23
10. 8	**11.** 0.5	**12.** 9.5
13. 32	**14.** 9	**15.** 7
16. 8	**17.** 10	**18.** 25

19. $\frac{1}{4}$ **20.** 0

21. a. $2n - 5 = 27$ **b.** 16

22. a. $\frac{1}{6}n = 1\frac{1}{3}$ **b.** 8

23. a. $5n + 4 = 40$ **b.** 7.2
24. a. $0.05n = 16$ **b.** 320
25. $270 **26.** $250,000

Cumulative Review *(pages 192–193)*

1. 44 cm
2. a.

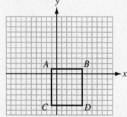

b. 56
3. a. $17.6 = 2(3.5) + 2w$ **b.** 5.3
4. a. $0.60S - (4.50D + 2.10)$ or $0.60S - 4.50D - 2.10$
 b. $30.30
 c. −$4.50 His expenses were greater than his
  income so he lost money on Tuesday.

5. a. $5n = \left(\frac{1}{2} \cdot 10\right)n = \frac{1}{2}(10n)$

 Associative property of multiplication

 b. $15n = 10n + 5n = (10 + 5)n$
 Distributive property of multiplication over
 addition.

Exploration

Student answers will vary.

Chapter 7. Introducing Logic

Introductory Page *(page 194)*

There are various ways to solve the problem presented on this page. Here is one solution:

The following cannot be the first runner, that is, run leg 1: Jones (by clue 2); McCormack (by clue 3); Cavallaro (by clue 4). Therefore, Dunn is the runner for leg 1, and (by clue 4) Cavallaro is the runner for leg 2.

Clue 3 gives the order of Al to McCormack to Gary, which means McCormack must run leg 3, Al runs leg 2, and Gary runs leg 4.

Jones is left to run leg 4, so he must be Gary. By clue 5, Joe does not run leg 1; he runs leg 3. Sal is left to run leg 1. The answer is:

Leg 1   Sal Dunn
Leg 2   Al Cavallaro
Leg 3   Joe McCormack
Leg 4   Gary Jones

7-1 Sentences, Statements, and Truth Values
(page 198)

1. Yes	**2.** No	**3.** No	**4.** No
5. Yes	**6.** Yes	**7.** No	**8.** No
9. She	**10.** We	**11.** It	**12.** *y*
13. This	**14.** It	**15.** He	**16.** *x*

17. True   **18. a.** Open   **b.** They
19. a. False   **20. a.** True
21. a. Open   **b.** *x*   **22. a.** False
23. a. True   **24. a.** False
25. {Hawaii}   **26.** {Kansas}
27. {New York, Florida}   **28.** {California}
29. {New York, Florida, California, Hawaii, Kansas}
30. {12}   **31.** {22}   **32.** {18}   **33.** {20}
34. {2}   **35.** {1}   **36.** {1,2}   **37.** {1,2,3,4}
38. {4}   **39.** {4}   **40.** {15}   **41.** { }
42. {triangle}
43. {square, rectangle, parallelogram, rhombus}
44. {square, rhombus}   **45.** {square, rectangle}
46. { }   **47.** {triangle}
48. {trapezoid}   **49.** {square}

7-2 Negations and Symbols
(pages 202–203)

1. The school does not have a cafeteria.
2. It is not true that Georgia is not a city. (Georgia is a city.)
3. A school bus is not painted yellow.
4. $18 + 20 \div 2 \neq 28$
5. The measure of a right angle is not 90°.
6. $1 + 2 + 3 = 4$
   (It is not true that $1 + 2 + 3 \neq 4$.)
7. There are not 100 centimeters in a meter.
8. It is not true that today is not Saturday. (Today is Saturday.)

9. a. *p*   **b.** True   **10. a.** *q*   **b.** False
11. a. $\sim q$ **b.** True   **12. a.** $\sim p$ **b.** False
13. a. *r*   **b.** Open   **14. a.** $\sim r$ **b.** Open
15. a. $\sim q$ **b.** True   **16. a.** $\sim p$ **b.** False
17. a. $\sim(\sim p)$ **b.** True   **18. a.** $\sim(\sim q)$ **b.** False

19.

p	$\sim p$
T	F
F	T

20.

q	$\sim q$
T	F
F	T

21.

r	$\sim r$
T	F
F	T

22.

k	$\sim k$
T	F
F	T

23.

q	$\sim q$	$\sim(\sim q)$	$\sim(\sim(\sim q))$
T	F	T	F
F	T	F	T

24. a. Row 2   **b.** Row 1   **c.** Row 2
 d. Row 2   **e.** Row 1   **f.** Row 1
 g. Row 2   **h.** Row 1   **i.** Row 2

25. a. Summer does not follow spring.   **b.** False
26. a. Baseball is not a sport.   **b.** False
27. a. Baseball is not a summer sport.   **b.** False
28. a. He does not like baseball   **b.** Open
29. a. It is not true that baseball is not a sport.   **b.** True
30. a. It is not true that summer does not follow spring.   **b.** True
31. a. It is not true that baseball is not a summer sport.   **b.** True
32. a. It is not true that he does not like baseball.   **b.** Open
33. false   **34.** true   **35.** *p*   **36.** $\sim p$

7-3 Conjunctions *(pages 210–213)*

1. $p \wedge q$ **2.** $p \wedge r$ **3.** $\sim p$
4. $\sim p \wedge r$ **5.** $q \wedge \sim r$ **6.** $\sim p \wedge \sim q$
7. $\sim r \wedge \sim p$ **8.** $\sim r \wedge p$ **9.** $\sim(p \wedge q)$
10. $\sim(q \wedge \sim p)$
11. a. $t \wedge b$ **b.**

t	*b*	$t \wedge b$
T	T	T

12. a. $t \wedge r$ **b.**

t	*r*	$t \wedge r$
T	F	F

315

13. **a.** $f \wedge b$ **b.**

f	b	$f \wedge b$
T	T	T

14. **a.** $f \wedge r$ **b.**

f	r	$f \wedge r$
T	F	F

15. **a.** $\sim b \wedge \sim f$ **b.**

b	f	$\sim b$	$\sim f$	$\sim b \wedge \sim f$
T	T	F	F	F

16. **a.** $\sim r \wedge b$ **b.**

r	b	$\sim r$	$\sim r \wedge b$
F	T	T	T

17. **a.** $\sim t \wedge r$ **b.**

t	r	$\sim t$	$\sim t \wedge r$
T	F	F	F

18. **a.** $\sim(\sim b)$ **b.**

b	$\sim b$	$\sim(\sim b)$
T	F	T

19. **a.** $\sim(b \wedge f)$ **b.**

b	f	$b \wedge f$	$\sim(b \wedge f)$
T	T	T	F

20. **a.** $\sim(b \wedge r)$ **b.**

b	r	$b \wedge r$	$\sim(b \wedge r)$
T	F	F	T

21. Open   **22.** False   **23.** True   **24.** Open
25. True   **26.** False   **27.** True

28.

p	q	$p \wedge q$
T	T	T
T	F	F
F	T	F
F	F	F

29.

m	r	$m \wedge r$
T	T	T
T	F	F
F	T	F
F	F	F

30.

f	g	$f \wedge g$
T	T	T
T	F	F
F	T	F
F	F	F

31. **a.**

p	q	$\sim q$	$\sim q$	$\sim p \wedge \sim q$
T	T	F	F	F
T	F	F	T	F
F	T	T	F	F
F	F	T	T	T

b.

p	q	$\sim p$	$\sim p \wedge q$
T	T	F	F
T	F	F	F
F	T	T	T
F	F	T	F

32.

p	q	$p \wedge q$	$\sim(p \wedge q)$
T	T	T	F
T	F	F	T
F	T	F	T
F	F	F	T

33.

p	q	$\sim q$	$p \wedge \sim q$
T	T	F	F
T	F	T	T
F	T	F	F
F	F	T	F

34.

p	q	$\sim p$	$\sim p \wedge q$
T	T	F	F
T	F	F	F
F	T	T	T
F	F	T	F

35.

p	q	$\sim q$	$q \wedge \sim q$	$\sim(q \wedge \sim q)$
T	T	F	F	T
T	F	T	F	T
F	T	F	F	T
F	F	T	F	T

36.

p	q	$\sim q$	$p \wedge \sim q$	$\sim(p \wedge \sim q)$
T	T	F	F	T
T	F	T	T	F
F	T	F	F	T
F	F	T	F	T

37. a. $\{6, 7\}$ **b.** $\{5, 6\}$ **c.** $\{3, 4, 5, 6\}$ **d.** $\{0, 1\}$
e. $\{0, 1, 2, 3\}$ **f.** $\{9, 10, 11, 12, \ldots\}$ or $\{x | x > 8\}$
g. $\{\ \}$ or $\varnothing$ **h.** $\{9, 10\}$

38. a. A banjo is a stringed instrument and a guitar is a stringed instrument.
b. True

39. a. A banjo is a stringed instrument and a drum is a stringed instrument.
b. False

40. a. A guitar is a stringed instrument and she plays a guitar.
b. Open

41. a. A banjo is a stringed instrument and a drum is not a stringed instrument.
b. True

42. a. A banjo is a stringed instrument and a guitar is not a stringed instrument.
b. False

43. a. A banjo is a stringed instrument and she does not play a guitar.
b. Open

44. a. A guitar is a stringed instrument and a drum is not a stringed instrument.
b. True

45. a. She does not play a guitar and a drum is a stringed instrument.
b. Open

46. a. A drum is not a stringed instrument and a banjo is not a stringed instrument.
b. False

47. a. It is not true that a drum is a stringed instrument and a banjo is a stringed instrument.
b. True

48. a. It is not true that a banjo is a stringed instrument and a guitar is a stringed instrument.
b. False

49. a. It is not true that a guitar is a stringed instrument and she plays a guitar.
b. Open

50. true **51.** false **52.** false
53. true, true **54.** true, false **55.** false, true
56. true **57.** true **58.** True
59. False **60.** Uncertain **61.** False
62. True **63.** False **64.** Uncertain
65. a. True **b.** True **c.** False
66. a. True **b.** True **c.** False

7-4 Disjunctions (pages 217–219)

1. $s \vee f$ **2.** $s \vee \sim p$ **3.** $s \wedge p$
4. $p \vee f$ **5.** $\sim f \wedge p$ **6.** $\sim s \vee f$
7. $s \vee \sim s$ **8.** $\sim(s \vee f)$ **9.** $(s \wedge p) \vee f$
10. $\sim(\sim s \vee \sim f)$ **11. a.** $m \vee k$ **b.** True
12. a. $c \vee \ell$ **b.** True
13. a. $c \vee m$ **b.** True
14. a. $\sim k \vee \sim c$ **b.** False
15. a. $\ell \vee k$ **b.** True
16. a. $\ell \wedge c$ **b.** False
17. a. $\sim(c \vee m)$ **b.** False
18. a. $\sim(\sim k \vee \ell)$ **b.** True
19. a. $(c \wedge m) \vee \ell$ **b.** True
20. a. $\sim(c \vee t)$ **b.** False

21.

p	q	$p \vee q$
T	T	T
T	F	T
F	T	T
F	F	F

22.

k	t	$k \vee t$
T	T	T
T	F	T
F	T	T
F	F	F

23.

p	r	$p \vee r$
T	T	T
T	F	T
F	T	T
F	F	F

24.

p	q	$p \vee q$	$\sim(p \vee q)$
T	T	T	F
T	F	T	F
F	T	T	F
F	F	F	T

25.

p	q	$\sim p$	$\sim p \vee q$	$\sim(\sim p \vee q)$
T	T	F	T	F
T	F	F	F	T
F	T	T	T	F
F	F	T	T	F

26.

p	q	$\sim p$	$\sim q$	$\sim p \vee \sim q$
T	T	F	F	F
T	F	F	T	T
F	T	T	F	T
F	F	T	T	T

27.

p	q	$\sim q$	$p \vee \sim q$	$q \vee (p \vee \sim q)$
T	T	F	T	T
T	F	T	T	T
F	T	F	F	T
F	F	T	T	T

28.

p	q	$\sim q$	$q \vee \sim q$	$p \vee (q \vee \sim q)$
T	T	F	T	T
T	F	T	T	T
F	T	F	T	T
F	F	T	T	T

29.

p	q	$p \vee q$	$p \wedge q$	$(p \vee q) \vee (p \wedge q)$
T	T	T	T	T
T	F	T	F	T
F	T	T	F	T
F	F	F	F	F

30. a. {0, 1, 2} **b.** {0, 8, 9} **c.** {0, 1, 2, 3}
  d. {3, 4, 5, 6} **e.** {0, 1, 2, 3, 4} **f.** ∅
31. a. Spanish is a language or homemaking is a language.
  b. True
32. a. Biology is a science or Spanish is a language.
  b. True
33. a. It's a difficult course.
  b. Open
34. a. Spanish is not a language or homemaking is a language.
  b. False
35. a. It's not a difficult course.
  b. Open
36. a. Biology is a science or homemaking is not a language.
  b. True
37. a. Biology is not a science or Spanish is not a language.
  b. False
38. a. It is not true that Spanish is a language or homemaking is a language.
  b. False
39. a. Spanish is a language and homemaking is a language.
  b. False
40. a. Spanish is a language and biology is a science.
  b. True
41. a. It is false that biology is not a science or Spanish is a language.
  b. False
42. a. It is not the case that either Spanish is not a language or homemaking is a language.
  b. True
43. true **44.** true **45.** false
46. false, true **47.** true, false **48.** false
49. true **50.** True **51.** True
52. Uncertain **53.** Uncertain **54.** Uncertain

7-5 Conditionals (pages 224–226)

1. a. it rains
  b. the game is canceled
2. a. it is 9:05 A.M.
  b. I'm late to class
3. a. it rains
  b. I do not have to water the lawn
4. a. you take the Third Avenue bus
  b. you can get to the stadium
5. a. one side of the square is $x + 2$
  b. the perimeter of the square is $4x + 8$

6. a. the shoe fits
  b. wear it
7. a. a polygon has exactly three sides
  b. it is a triangle
8. a. you have a headache
  b. you should take time out and get some rest
9. a. $p \rightarrow r$ **10.** $q \rightarrow r$ **11.** $\sim p \rightarrow \sim r$
12. $\sim q \rightarrow \sim r$ **13.** $q \rightarrow p$ **14.** $p \rightarrow r$
15. a. $p \rightarrow w$ **b.** True
16. a. $w \rightarrow p$ **b.** False
17. a. $w \rightarrow r$ **b.** True
18. a. $\sim r \rightarrow w$ **b.** True
19. a. $\sim p \rightarrow \sim w$ **b.** False
20. a. $r \rightarrow p$ **b.** False
21. a. $(\sim r \wedge p) \rightarrow w$ **b.** True
22. a. $(r \wedge \sim p) \rightarrow \sim w$ **b.** False

23.

r	t	$r \rightarrow t$
T	T	T
T	F	F
F	T	T
F	F	T

24.

k	m	$k \rightarrow m$
T	T	T
T	F	F
F	T	T
F	F	T

25.

q	r	$q \rightarrow r$
T	T	T
T	F	F
F	T	T
F	F	T

26. True **27.** True **28.** True
29. True **30.** True **31.** False
32. False **33.** False
34. a. If I jog, then I feel well. **b.** True
35. a. If I diet, then I get hungry. **b.** True
36. a. If I get hungry, then I diet. **b.** False
37. a. If I do not feel well, then I jog. **b.** True
38. a. If I do not feel well, then I do not jog.
  b. True
39. a. If I feel well then I do not get hungry.
  b. False
40. a. If I get hungry, then I do not diet.
  b. True
41. a. If I do not diet, then I do not get hungry.
  b. False
42. a. If I do not jog then I do not feel well.
  b. True
43. a. If I jog then I diet.
  b. False
44. a. If I jog and get hungry then I feel well.
  b. True
45. a. If I jog then I get hungry and feel well.
  b. True
46. a. If I jog or diet then I get hungry.
  b. True
47. a. If I diet then I get hungry and do not feel well.
  b. True

48. a. If I do not jog then I diet and get hungry.
    b. True
49. a. If I jog and get hungry then I diet.
    b. False
50. $p \rightarrow q$ **51.** $q \rightarrow p$ **52.** true, false
53. true   **54.** true   **55.** true
56. True   **57.** False   **58.** Uncertain
59. Uncertain   **60.** True

Review Exercises *(pages 228–229)*

1. a. $j \rightarrow a$ **b.** True   **2. a.** $j \wedge w$ **b.** False
3. a. $w \vee j$ **b.** True
4. a. $a \rightarrow \sim j$ **b.** False
5. a. $\sim a \wedge \sim w$ **b.** False
6. a. at first you don't succeed
    b. you should try again
7. a. you are late one more time
    b. you will get a detention
8. $\sim p \rightarrow q$ **9.** $q \rightarrow p$ **10.** 6
11. p **12.** true   **13.** false; true
14. true   **15.** False   **16.** False
17. False   **18.** True   **19.** True
20. a. {6, 7, 8, 9, 10}   **b.** {1, 2, 3, 4, 5}
    c. {2, 3, 5, 7}   **d.** {1, 4, 6, 8, 9, 10}
    e. {2, 3, 5, 6, 7, 8, 9, 10}   **f.** {7}   **g.** {2, 3, 5}

21.

	Peter	Carl	Ralph
Instrument	Violin	Cello	Flute
Sport	Tennis	Soccer	Baseball

  1. Ralph plays baseball (clue 4).
  2. The violinist who plays tennis (clue 1) is either
      Peter or Carl.

  3. (a) If Carl is the violinist, then Peter must play
         the flute (clue 3) and Ralph the cello.
     (b) But then, if Ralph plays baseball and Carl
         plays tennis, Peter must play soccer.
         This contradicts clue 2.
  4. Therefore, Peter plays the violin, and the other
      instruments and sports fall into place.

Cumulative Review *(page 229)*

1. $x = 4$
2. a. $13.7 + 12.6 + x = 32.1$ or $26.3 + x = 32.1$
    b. 5.8 in.
3. a. $-\dfrac{5}{6}$ in.
    b. $\sqrt{5}$ irrational (any calculator result, such as
       2.2360679, is a rational approximation of the
       irrational number).
    c. 5 rational
4. a. $36 \, cm^2$
    b. the areas are equal

Exploration

    Any number divisible by 4, such as 4, 8, 12 etc.,
will make both the hypothesis and the conclusion
true.
    Any odd number, such as 1, 3, 5 etc., will make
both the hypothesis and the conclusion false.
    Any even number that is not divisible by 4, such
as 2, 6, 10 etc., will make the hypothesis false and the
conclusion true.
    There is no number that will make the hypothesis
true and the conclusion false. This would make the
statement false.

Chapter 8. Using Logic

8-1 Compound Statements and Truth Values *(pages 232–234)*

1. $p \wedge q$ **2.** $p \rightarrow q$ **3.** $p \vee q$
4. $\sim q$ **5.** (3)   **6.** (1)
7. (2)   **8.** (3)   **9.** (2)
10. (3)   **11.** (2)   **12.** (3)
13. a. 28 is a multiple of 7 and 28 is not the square of an
      integer.
    b. True
14. a. 7 is a factor of 28 or 28 is not a multiple of 7.
    b. True
15. a. If 28 is not a multiple of 7 then 28 is the square of
      an integer.
    b. True
16. a. It is not true that 7 is a factor of 28 and 28 is
      the square of an integer.
    b. True
17. a. 28 is the square of an integer or 7 is not a factor
      of 28.
    b. False

18. a. At is false that 28 is a multiple of 7 or 28 is the
      square of an integer.
    b. False
19. a. If 7 is not a factor of 28 then 28 is not a multiple of 7.
    b. True
20. a. If 28 is the square of an integer then 28 is not a
      multiple of 7.
    b. True
21. a. If 28 is a multiple of 7 and 7 is a factor of 28, then
      28 is the square of an integer.
    b. False
22. a. If 28 is a multiple of 7 then 28 is the square of an
      integer or 7 is a factor of 28.
    b. True
23. a. If 28 is a multiple of 7 or the square of an integer
      then 7 is a factor of 28.
    b. True
24. a. If 7 is a factor of 28 then 28 is the square of an
      integer or a multiple of 7.
    b. True
25. True   **26.** False   **27.** True

28. False   **29.** True   **30.** True
31. True   **32.** True   **33.** False
34. False   **35.** True   **36.** False
37. False   **38.** True   **39.** True
40. True   **41.** False   **42.** True
43. True   **44.** True

In 45 and 46, consider the conditions:
        p: She is over 21.
        q: She is unmarried.
        r: She smokes.

45. $(p \vee q) \wedge \sim r$: Any niece who smokes will not inherit, since the conjunct $\sim r$ is false. Also, Diane is eliminated because she does not satisfy $p \vee q$. Janice, Sarah, and Laurie will inherit.

46. $p \vee (q \wedge \sim r)$: Any niece over 21 will inherit, since the disjunct p is true. In addition, Sarah satisfies $q \wedge r$. Judy, Janice, Sue, Sarah, and Laurie will inherit.

47. a. (1) 6 or any multiple of 6   (2) No values
    (3) 4 or any even number not divisible by 3
    (4) 3 or any add number
b. No value of x will give a true antecedent and a false consequent. Thus, $p \rightarrow q$ is true for all values of x.

8-2 Compound Sentences and Truth Tables
(page 236)

1.

p	q	$p \vee q$	$\sim q$	$(p \vee q) \rightarrow \sim q$
T	T	T	F	F
T	F	T	T	T
F	T	T	F	F
F	F	F	T	T

2.

p	q	$p \wedge q$	$p \vee q$	$(p \wedge q) \rightarrow (p \vee q)$
T	T	T	T	T
T	F	F	T	T
F	T	F	T	T
F	F	F	F	T

3.

p	q	$\sim p$	$q \rightarrow \sim p$	$(q \rightarrow \sim p) \wedge p$
T	T	F	F	F
T	F	F	T	T
F	T	T	T	F
F	F	T	T	F

4.

p	q	$\sim p$	$\sim p \wedge q$	$p \vee (\sim p \wedge q)$
T	T	F	F	T
T	F	F	F	T
F	T	T	T	T
F	F	T	F	F

5.

p	q	$\sim p$	$p \vee \sim p$	$q \rightarrow (p \vee \sim p)$
T	T	F	T	T
T	F	F	T	T
F	T	T	T	T
F	F	T	T	T

6.

p	q	$p \rightarrow q$	$\sim q$	$(p \rightarrow q) \rightarrow \sim q$
T	T	T	F	F
T	F	F	T	T
F	T	T	F	F
F	F	T	T	T

7.

p	q	$p \wedge q$	$p \wedge (p \wedge q)$
T	T	T	T
T	F	F	F
F	T	F	F
F	F	F	F

8.

p	q	$\sim p$	$\sim p \vee q$	$p \wedge q$	$(\sim p \vee q) \rightarrow (p \wedge q)$
T	T	F	T	T	T
T	F	F	F	F	T
F	T	T	T	F	F
F	F	T	T	F	F

9.

p	q	$p \wedge q$	$\sim(p \wedge q)$	$\sim p$	$\sim q$	$\sim p \wedge \sim q$	$\sim(p \wedge q) \to (\sim p \wedge \sim q)$
T	T	T	F	F	F	F	T
T	F	F	T	F	T	F	F
F	T	F	T	T	F	F	F
F	F	F	T	T	T	T	T

10.

p	q	$\sim q$	$\sim q \wedge p$	$\sim q \to (\sim q \wedge p)$
T	T	F	T	T
T	F	T	T	T
F	T	F	F	T
F	F	T	F	F

11.

p	q	$p \vee q$	$\sim(p \vee q)$	$p \to \sim(p \vee q)$
T	T	T	F	F
T	F	T	F	F
F	T	T	F	T
F	F	F	T	T

12.

p	q	$p \wedge q$	$\sim(p \wedge q)$	$\sim(p \wedge q) \vee p$
T	T	T	F	T
T	F	F	T	T
F	T	F	T	T
F	F	F	T	T

13.

p	q	$\sim p$	$\sim p \wedge q$	$(\sim p \wedge q) \vee p$
T	T	F	F	T
T	F	F	F	T
F	T	T	T	T
F	F	T	F	F

14.

p	q	$\sim q$	$p \to \sim q$	$(p \to \sim q) \wedge q$
T	T	F	F	F
T	F	T	T	F
F	T	F	T	T
F	F	T	T	F

15.

p	q	$\sim p$	$\sim q$	$\sim p \wedge \sim q$	$p \wedge q$	$(\sim p \wedge \sim q) \vee (p \wedge q)$
T	T	F	F	F	T	T
T	F	F	T	F	F	F
F	T	T	F	F	F	F
F	F	T	T	T	F	T

16. a. $\sim e \to (e \vee p)$

b.

e	p	$\sim e$	$e \vee p$	$\sim e \to (e \vee p)$
T	T	F	T	T
T	F	F	T	T
F	T	T	T	T
F	F	T	F	F

c. e is false and p is false

d. 9 or 15 or 21 or any product of odd numbers greater than 1

8-3 Biconditionals *(pages 240–242)*

1. $t \leftrightarrow r$ **2.** $n \leftrightarrow t$ **3.** $n \leftrightarrow r$
4. $t \leftrightarrow n$ **5.** $\sim t \leftrightarrow \sim n$

6.

p	q	$p \leftrightarrow q$
T	T	T
T	F	F
F	T	F
F	F	T

7.

r	s	$r \leftrightarrow s$
T	T	T
T	F	F
F	T	F
F	F	T

8.

d	k	$d \leftrightarrow k$
T	T	T
T	F	F
F	T	F
F	F	T

9. a.

p	q	$p \rightarrow q$
T	T	T
T	F	F
F	T	T
F	F	T

9. b.

p	q	$\sim q$	$p \rightarrow \sim q$
T	T	F	F
T	F	T	T
F	T	F	T
F	F	T	T

10.

p	r	$\sim r$	$\sim r \rightarrow p$
T	T	F	T
T	F	T	T
F	T	F	T
F	F	T	F

11.

t	v	$t \wedge v$	$(t \wedge v) \rightarrow t$
T	T	T	T
T	F	F	T
F	T	F	T
F	F	F	T

12.

b	c	$b \vee c$	$(b \vee c) \leftrightarrow c$
T	T	T	T
T	F	T	F
F	T	T	T
F	F	F	T

13.

p	t	$t \rightarrow p$	$p \rightarrow t$	$(t \rightarrow p) \wedge (p \rightarrow t)$
T	T	T	T	T
T	F	T	F	F
F	T	F	T	F
F	F	T	T	T

14.

p	q	$q \rightarrow p$	$(q \rightarrow p) \rightarrow q$
T	T	T	T
T	F	T	F
F	T	F	T
F	F	T	F

15.

r	s	$\sim r$	$\sim r \rightarrow s$	$(\sim r \rightarrow s) \leftrightarrow r$
T	T	F	T	T
T	F	F	T	T
F	T	T	T	F
F	F	T	F	T

16. True **17.** False **18.** True
19. True **20.** False **21.** True
22. True **23.** True **24.** False
25. True
26. a. $p \leftrightarrow q$
   b. $(p \rightarrow q) \wedge (q \rightarrow p)$ *or* $p \leftrightarrow q$
   c. $(p \rightarrow q) \wedge (q \rightarrow p)$ *or* $p \leftrightarrow q$
   d. $q \leftrightarrow p$
   e. $(p \rightarrow q) \vee (q \rightarrow p)$
27. Sentence **e**

8-4 Tautologies *(pages 246–248)*

1. a.

p	$\sim p$	$\sim(\sim p)$	$p \leftrightarrow \sim(\sim p)$
T	F	T	T
F	T	F	T

   b. Tautology

2. a.

p	$\sim p$	$\sim p \wedge p$	$\sim(\sim p \wedge p)$
T	F	F	T
F	T	F	T

   b. Tautology

3. a.

p	$\sim p$	$p \rightarrow \sim p$	$(p \rightarrow \sim p) \leftrightarrow \sim p$
T	F	F	T
F	T	T	T

   b. Tautology

4. a.

q	$\sim q$	$\sim q \rightarrow q$
T	F	T
F	T	F

   b. Not a tautology

322

5. a.

p	q	$\sim p$	$\sim p \vee q$	$p \vee (\sim p \vee q)$
T	T	F	T	T
T	F	F	F	T
F	T	T	T	T
F	F	T	T	T

b. Tautology

6. a.

p	q	$\sim p$	$\sim p \wedge q$	$p \wedge \sim p \wedge q$
T	T	F	F	F
T	F	F	F	F
F	T	T	T	F
F	F	T	F	F

b. Not a tautology

7. a.

p	q	$p \wedge q$	$p \vee q$	$(p \wedge q) \to (p \vee q)$
T	T	T	T	T
T	F	F	T	T
F	T	F	T	T
F	F	F	F	T

b. Tautology

8. a.

p	q	$p \vee q$	$p \wedge q$	$(p \vee q) \to (p \wedge q)$
T	T	T	T	T
T	F	T	F	F
F	T	T	F	F
F	F	F	F	T

b. Not a tautology

9. a.

p	q	$p \vee q$	$p \to (p \vee q)$
T	T	T	T
T	F	T	T
F	T	T	T
F	F	F	T

b. Tautology

10. a.

p	q	$\sim p$	$\sim p \wedge q$	$p \wedge (\sim p \wedge q)$	$\sim[p \wedge (\sim p \vee q)]$
T	T	F	F	F	T
T	F	F	F	F	T
F	T	T	T	F	T
F	F	T	F	F	T

b. Tautology

11. a.

p	q	$\sim q$	$p \to \sim q$	$\sim(p \to \sim q)$	$p \wedge q$	$\sim(p \to \sim q) \leftrightarrow (p \wedge q)$
T	T	F	F	T	T	T
T	F	T	T	F	F	T
F	T	F	T	F	F	T
F	F	T	T	F	F	T

b. Tautology

12.

p	q	$p \vee q$	$p \to (p \vee q)$
T	T	T	T
T	F	T	T
F	T	T	T
F	F	F	T

13.

p	q	$p \wedge q$	$q \wedge p$	$(p \wedge q) \leftrightarrow (q \wedge p)$
T	T	T	T	T
T	F	F	F	T
F	T	F	F	T
F	F	F	F	T

14.

p	$p \vee p$	$(p \vee p) \to p$
T	T	T
F	F	T

15.

p	q	$p \wedge q$	$(p \wedge q) \rightarrow q$
T	T	T	T
T	F	F	T
F	T	F	T
F	F	F	T

16.

p	q	$p \wedge q$	$p \vee (p \wedge q)$	$[p \vee (p \wedge q)] \leftrightarrow p$
T	T	T	T	T
T	F	F	T	T
F	T	F	F	T
F	F	F	F	T

17.

p	q	$\sim p$	$\sim p \vee q$	$p \rightarrow q$	$(\sim p \vee q) \rightarrow (p \rightarrow q)$
T	T	F	T	T	T
T	F	F	F	F	T
F	T	T	T	T	T
F	F	T	T	T	T

18.

p	q	$p \rightarrow q$	$\sim q$	$(p \rightarrow q) \wedge \sim q$	$\sim p$	$[(p \rightarrow q) \wedge \sim q] \rightarrow \sim p$
T	T	T	F	F	F	T
T	F	F	T	F	F	T
F	T	T	F	F	T	T
F	F	T	T	T	T	T

19.

p	q	$\sim p$	$\sim p \vee q$	$\sim q$	$(\sim p \vee q) \vee \sim q$	$\sim[(\sim p \vee q) \vee \sim q]$	$p \wedge q$	$\sim[(\sim p \vee q) \vee \sim q] \rightarrow (p \wedge q)$
T	T	F	T	F	T	F	T	T
T	F	F	F	T	T	F	F	T
F	T	T	T	F	T	F	F	T
F	F	T	T	T	T	F	F	T

20.

p	q	$p \vee q$	$\sim(p \vee q)$	$\sim p$	$\sim q$	$\sim p \wedge \sim q$	$\sim(p \vee q) \leftrightarrow \sim p \wedge \sim q$
T	T	T	F	F	F	F	T
T	F	T	F	F	T	F	T
F	T	T	F	T	F	F	T
F	F	F	T	T	T	T	T

21.

p	q	$\sim p$	$\sim p \vee q$	$p \wedge (\sim p \vee q)$	$p \wedge q$	$[p \wedge (\sim p \vee q)] \leftrightarrow (p \wedge q)$
T	T	F	T	T	T	T
T	F	F	F	F	F	T
F	T	T	T	F	F	T
F	F	T	T	F	F	T

22. a.

p	q	$\sim p$	$\sim q$	$q \to \sim p$	$\sim p \vee \sim q$	$\sim q \to \sim p$
T	T	F	F	F	F	T
T	F	F	T	T	T	F
F	T	T	F	T	T	T
F	F	T	T	T	T	T

b. $(q \to \sim p) \leftrightarrow \sim p \vee \sim q$

23. a.

p	q	$\sim p$	$\sim q$	$q \vee \sim p$	$p \vee \sim q$	$p \to q$
T	T	F	F	T	T	T
T	F	F	T	F	T	F
F	T	T	F	T	F	T
F	F	T	T	T	T	T

b. $(q \vee \sim p) \leftrightarrow (p \to q)$

24. a.

p	q	$\sim p$	$\sim q$	$\sim p \to q$	$q \wedge \sim p$	$\sim q \to p$
T	T	F	F	T	F	T
T	F	F	T	T	F	T
F	T	T	F	T	T	T
F	F	T	T	F	F	F

b. $(\sim p \to q) \leftrightarrow (\sim q \to p)$

25. a.

p	q	$\sim p$	$\sim q$	$p \wedge q$	$p \leftrightarrow q$	$\sim p \leftrightarrow \sim q$
T	T	F	F	T	T	T
T	F	F	T	F	F	F
F	T	T	F	F	F	F
F	F	T	T	F	T	T

b. $(p \leftrightarrow q) \leftrightarrow (\sim p \leftrightarrow \sim q)$

26. a.

p	q	$\sim q$	$p \to \sim q$	$p \wedge q$	$\sim(p \wedge q)$	$p \leftrightarrow \sim q$
T	T	F	F	T	F	F
T	F	T	T	F	T	T
F	T	F	T	F	T	T
F	F	T	T	F	T	F

b. $(p \to \sim q) \leftrightarrow \sim(p \wedge q)$

27. a.

p	q	$\sim p$	$p \to q$	$\sim p \vee q$	$(p \to q) \to (\sim p \vee q)$
T	T	F	T	T	T
T	F	F	F	F	T
F	T	T	T	T	T
F	F	T	T	T	T

b. (2)

28. a.

p	q	$\sim p$	$\sim q$	$p \vee \sim q$	$\sim(p \vee \sim q)$	$\sim p \wedge q$	$\sim(p \vee \sim q) \leftrightarrow (\sim p \wedge q)$
T	T	F	F	T	F	F	T
T	F	F	T	T	F	F	T
F	T	T	F	F	T	T	T
F	F	T	T	T	F	F	T

b. (1)

29. a.

p	q	$\sim p$	$\sim p \rightarrow q$	$p \vee q$	$(\sim p \rightarrow q) \leftrightarrow (p \vee q)$
T	T	F	T	T	T
T	F	F	T	T	T
F	T	T	T	T	T
F	F	T	F	F	T

b. (4)

30. a.

p	q	$\sim p$	$q \wedge \sim p$	$p \vee (q \wedge \sim p)$	$p \vee q$	$[p \vee (q \wedge \sim p)] \leftrightarrow (p \vee q)$
T	T	F	F	T	T	T
T	F	F	F	T	T	T
F	T	T	T	T	T	T
F	F	T	F	F	F	T

b. (2)

31. a. $l \rightarrow t$
   b. $\sim t \rightarrow \sim l$
   c.

l	t	$l \rightarrow t$	$\sim l$	$\sim t$	$\sim t \rightarrow \sim l$	$(l \rightarrow t) \leftrightarrow (\sim t \rightarrow \sim l)$
T	T	T	F	F	T	T
T	F	F	F	T	F	T
F	T	T	T	F	T	T
F	F	T	T	T	T	T

The sentences are equivalences.

32.

f	s	$f \vee s$	$\sim f$	$(f \vee s) \wedge \sim f$	$[(f \vee s) \wedge \sim f] \rightarrow s$
T	T	T	F	F	T
T	F	T	F	F	T
F	T	T	T	T	T
F	F	F	T	F	T

8-5 Inverses, Converses, and Contrapositives *(pages 254–257)*

1. $\sim p \rightarrow \sim q$ **2.** $\sim t \rightarrow w$ **3.** $m \rightarrow \sim p$
4. $p \rightarrow q$ **5.** $q \rightarrow p$ **6.** $\sim w \rightarrow t$
7. $p \rightarrow \sim m$ **8.** $p \rightarrow q$ **9.** $\sim q \rightarrow \sim p$
10. $w \rightarrow \sim t$ **11.** $\sim p \rightarrow m$ **12.** $p \rightarrow q$
13. If you do not use Charm face powder, then you will not be beautiful.
14. If you do not buy Goal toothpaste, then your children will not brush longer.
15. When you do not serve imported sparkling water, then you do not show good taste.
16. The man who does not wear Cutrite clothes is not well
17. a. If a polygon is not a triangle then it does not have exactly three sides.
   b. True   **c.** False
18. a. If a polygon is not a trapezoid, then the polygon does not have exactly four sides.
   b. True   **c.** True
19. a. If $2 \cdot 2 \neq 4$ then $2 \cdot 3 \neq 6$.   **b.** True   **c.** True
20. a. If $2^2 \neq 4$ then $3^2 \neq 6$.   **b.** False   **c.** True
21. If you eat Nano yogurt then you live to an old age.
22. If you care about your family, then you take pictures of your family with a Blinko camera.
23. If you get good mileage, then you drive a Superb car.

24. If you make a better chicken dinner, then you use Dust and Roast.

25. **a.** If a number is exactly divisible by 2, then the number is even.
   b. True   **c.** True

26. **a.** If two segments are equal in measure, then the two segments are each 5 cm in length.
   b. True   **c.** False

27. **a.** If $5^2 = 1^2 + 4^2$ then $5 = 1 + 4$
   b. False   **c.** True

28. **a.** $2(5) + 3 = 13$ then $2(5) + 3 = 10 + 3$.
   b. True   **c.** True

29. If you do not send Trademark cards, then you do not care enough to send the best.

30. If you have body odor, then you do not use Trickle deodorant.

31. If your teeth are not pearly white, then you do not brush with Brite.

32. If you do not get a high school diploma, then you do not want a good job.

33. **a.** If a quadrilateral is not a parallelogram, then the opposite sides of the quadrilateral are not parallel.
   b. True   **c.** True

34. **a.** If two segments are not equal in measure, then the segments are not 8 cm each.
   b. True   **c.** True

35. **a.** If $2 + 3 \neq 4$, then $1 + 2 \neq 3$.
   b. False   **c.** False

36. **a.** If a quadrilateral is not a rectangle, then the angles of the quadrilateral are not all equal in measure.
   b. True   **c.** True

37. **a.** If a number is an even number, then it is not prime.
   b. False   **c.** False

38. (4)   **39.** (4)   **40.** (2)

41. (3)   **42.** (2)

43. **a.** $\sim p \rightarrow \sim q$ **b.** $\sim q \rightarrow \sim p$
   c. They are contrapositives.
   d. The contrapositive is the converse of the inverse of the conditional (or the inverse of the converse of the conditional).

44. **a.** If today is not Friday, then tomorrow is not Saturday.
   b. If tomorrow is Saturday, then today is Friday.
   c. If tomorrow is not Saturday, then today is not Friday.

45. **a.** If Douglas does not do well in college, then he will not apply to medical school.
   b. If Douglas applies to medical school, then he did well in college.
   c. If Douglas does not apply to medical school, then he did not do well in college.

46. **a.** Arlette will not get a role in the play if she does not audition.
   b. If Arlette gets a role in the play, then she auditioned.
   c. If Arlette does not get a role in the play, then she did not audition.

47. **a.** Dorothea will not graduate from law school in January if she does not take courses this summer.
   b. If Dorothea will graduate from law school in January, then she took courses this summer.

   c. If Dorothea will not graduate from law school in January then she did not take courses this summer.

48. **a.** If John is not accepted at the Culinary Institute, then he does not have a chance of earning a high salary as a chef.
   b. If John has a chance of earning a high salary as a chef, then he is accepted at the Culinary Institute.
   c. If John does not have a chance of earning a high salary as a chef, then he is not accepted at the Culinary Institute.

49. **a.** If a man is not honest, he steals.
   b. If a man does not steal, he is honest.
   c. If a man steals, he is not honest.

50. **a.** If Julia waters the plants, then the plants will not die.
   b. If the plants die, then Julia didn't water them.
   c. If the plants do not die, Julia watered them.

51. **a.** Rachel will get her allowance, if she does not forget to do her chores.
   b. If Rachel does not get her allowance then she forgot to do her chores.
   c. If Rachel gets her allowance, then she did not forget to do her chores.

52. (3)   **53.** (3)   **54.** (2)

55. **a.** (*1*) If he lives in California then Eddie lives in San Francisco.
   (2) Uncertain
   b. (*1*) If Eddie does not live in San Francisco, then he does not live in California.
   (2) Uncertain
   c. (*1*) If he does not live in California, then Eddie does not live in San Francisco
   (2) True

56. **a.** (*1*) If a number is divisible by 3, then it is divisible by 12.
   (2) False
   b. (*1*) If a number is not divisible by 12, then it is not divisible by 3.
   (2) False
   c. (*1*) If a number is not divisible by 3, then it is not divisible by 12.
   (2) True

57. **a.** (*1*) If I am ill, then I have the flu.
   (2) Uncertain
   b. (*1*) If I do not have the flu, then I am not ill.
   (2) Uncertain
   c. (*1*) If I am not ill, then I do not have the flu.
   (2) True

58. **a.** (*1*) If three pens cost 87 cents, then one pen costs 29 cents.
   (2) True
   b. (*1*) If one pen does not cost 29 cents, then three pens do not cost 87 cents.
   (2) True
   c. (*1*) If three pens do not cost 87 cents, then one pen does not cost 29 cents.
   (2) True

59. **a.** (*1*) If a polygon has four sides, then it is a rhombus.
   (2) False

b. (*1*) If a polygon is not a rhombus, then it does not have four sides.
(*2*) False
c. (*1*) If a polygon does not have four sides, then it is not a rhombus.
(*2*) True
60. a. (*1*) Alex loves computers if he will learn how to write programs.
(*2*) Uncertain
b. (*1*) If Alex does not love computers, then he will not learn how to write programs.
(*2*) Uncertain
c. (*1*) Alex does not love computers if he will not learn how to write programs.
(*2*) True

8-6 Drawing Conclusions (pages 260–261)

1. True
2. True
3. Cannot be determined
4. True
5. Cannot be determined
6. True
7. True
8. Cannot be determined
9. False
10. Cannot be determined
11. I pass the course.
12. x is not prime

13. We played Hockey
14. Parallelogram *ABCD* does not contain a right angle.
15. $x \geq 10$
16. $2x = 2$; $x = 1$
17. x is even and a prime
18. 3 has exactly two factors.
19. No conclusion
20. No conclusion
21. It is not July.
22. $\sqrt{7}$ is irrational.
23. $\sqrt{5} \neq 2.236068$
24. I study Spanish
25. It is October.

Review Exercises (pages 262–263)

1. **a.** If there is one even prime, then 2 is not a prime.
   b. False
2. **a.** If 4 is a prime, then 2 is a prime and there is one even prime. **b.** True
3. **a.** 2 is not a prime or 4 is not a prime. **b.** True
4. **a.** If there is one even prime, then 2 is a prime or 4 is a prime. **b.** True
5. **a.** $q \to p$ **b.** $\sim p \to \sim q$ **c.** $\sim q \to \sim p$
6. (4)   7. (2)
8. (2)   9. (1)
10. (2)   11. (2)
12. (4)   13. (2)

14. **a.**

p	q	$\sim q$	$p \to \sim q$	$(p \to \sim q) \wedge p$	$[(p \to \sim q) \wedge p] \to \sim q$
T	T	F	F	F	T
T	F	T	T	T	T
F	T	F	T	F	T
F	F	T	T	F	T

b. Yes
c. The statement is always true, shown by the last column of *T*'s in the truth table.

15. **a.**

p	q	$p \wedge q$	$\sim(p \wedge q)$	$\sim p$	$\sim q$	$\sim p \vee \sim q$	$\sim(p \wedge q) \leftrightarrow (\sim p \vee \sim q)$
T	T	T	F	F	F	F	T
T	F	F	T	F	T	T	T
F	T	F	T	T	F	T	T
F	F	F	T	T	T	T	T

b. Yes
c. The statement is always true (all *T*'s in the last column).

16. a.

p	q	$p \rightarrow q$	$\sim(p \rightarrow q)$	$\sim(p \rightarrow q) \vee q$	$p \leftrightarrow [\sim(p \rightarrow q) \vee q]$
T	T	T	F	T	T
T	F	F	T	T	T
F	T	T	F	T	F
F	F	T	F	F	T

   b. No.   **c.** The truth values vary for the statement, as seen in the last column of the truth table.

17. (3)   **18.** $\triangle ABC$ is not isosceles.   **19.** Virginia, Kay, Janice

Chapter 9. Operations with Algebraic Expressions

Introductory Page *(page 265)*

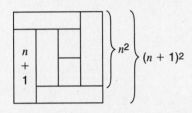

$$n \quad \left.\begin{array}{c} \\ \\ \end{array}\right\} n^2 \left.\begin{array}{c} \\ \\ \end{array}\right\} (n+1)^2$$
$$+$$
$$1$$

9-1 Adding Algebraic Expressions
(pages 270–272)

1. $+15c$ **2.** $+7t$ **3.** $-10a$

4. $-15r$ **5.** $0w = 0$ **6.** $-4ab$

7. $+15c$ **8.** $-61r$ **9.** $-13t$

10. $+13c$ **11.** $-0.3m$ **12.** $0e = 0$

13. $+11x^2$ **14.** $-61y^2$ **15.** $+6d^2$

16. $1.3y^3$ **17.** $-\dfrac{2}{3}c^4$ **18.** $0r^3 = 0$

19. $14rs$ **20.** $-7mn$ **21.** $+1xyz = xyz$

22. $-0.4cd$ **23.** $0xy = 0$ **24.** $+12(x + y)$

25. $+13a^2b$ **26.** $-4xy^2$ **27.** $11x + 12y$

28. $13a - 3b$ **29.** $-10m - 4n$

30. $-6ab$ **31.** $18x - 40y + 5z$

32. $-3x^2 - 15x - 21$ **33.** $2a^2 - 7b^2$

34. $-2x^2 + x + 8$ **35.** c^2

36. $1.2 + 0.4z + 0.8z^2$ **37.** $+7x$

38. $-4y$ **39.** $+6c$ **40.** $0m = 0$

41. $-3x^2$ **42.** $5y^2$ **43.** $13a + 3$

44. $11b - 6$ **45.** $7 - c$ **46.** -4

47. $3r + s$ **48.** $14d^2 - 4d$ **49.** $11x - 2$

50. 0 **51.** $-15y + 7$ **52.** $3a + 7b$

53. $2x^2$ **54.** $9y^2 + 3y - 4$ **55.** $x^3 + x^2 - 9$

56. $-5d^2 + 9d + 2$ **57.** $x - 15$

58. $x^3 - 4x^2 - 3x$

59. a. $15x$ **b.** $24m$ **c.** $13a$ **d.** $23\dfrac{3}{4}y$

60. a. $4x - 20$ **b.** 5 $(x \le 5)$

61. a. $6x - 6$ **b.** 4 $(x \le 4)$

62. a. $6x - 12$ **b.** 2 $(x \le 2.5)$

63. a. $5x - 2$ **b.** $\dfrac{1}{2}$ $\left(x \le \dfrac{1}{2}\right)$

64. $6s$ **65.** $\dfrac{7}{2}x = 3.5x$ **66.** $6p$

67. $14x - 30$ **68.** $12x - 3$ **69.** $4x + 8$

70. $2h - 40$ **71.** $3b + 11$ **72.** $5x - 3$

73. Binomial   **74.** Monomial   **75.** Trinomial

76. None of these

77. (answers to parts **a–d** will vary)

  a. $(x + 2) + (2x - 3) = 3x - 1$

  b. $(x + 2) + (2x - 2) = 3x$

  c. $(x + 2) + (2y - 3) = x + 2y - 1$

  d. $(x + 2) + (x^3 - x^2) = x^3 - x^2 + x + 2$

  e. No

9-2 Subtracting Algebraic Expressions
(pages 274–275)

1. $-9x$ **2.** $5x$ **3.** $6x + 6y$

4. $-2x^2 + 3x - 2$ **5.** $y^2 - 5y + 4$

6. $-7ab + 3bc$ **7.** $6a$

8. b **9.** $-3d + 14e$ **10.** $12x - 11y$

11. $-r$ **12.** $-8a + 6b$ **13.** $-3rs$

14. $8xy - cd$ **15.** $-2x^2 - 4x + 7$

16. $8y^2 - 7$ **17.** $4a^2 + 3ab$ **18.** $4a + 6b - 3c$

19. $3x^2 - 5x - 6$ **20.** $5 - 2d$

21. $7r$ **22.** $20s$ **23.** 0

24. $-28n$ **25.** $+8x$ **26.** $-8x$

27. $3x - 5$ **28.** $-2y + 4$ **29.** $-2z + 2$

30. $3m - 6$ **31.** n **32.** $-5c$

33. $c + 6c^2$ **34.** $16r + 6s$ **35.** $-7x - 8$

36. $-5d + 2c$ **37.** 0 **38.** $a - b$

39. $-4x^2 - 12x + 12$ **40.** $-6c + 6$

41. $24 - 6x$ **42.** $8x + 4$

43. $x^2 + 10x - 4$

44. $2x^2 - 3x - 3$ **45.** $-7a^2 + 18a + 7$

46. $-2x^2 + 2x$
47. $y^2 + 2y - 4$
48. $3x + 6y$
49. $-2a - 2b$
50. $4x^2 + 8x - 9$
51. $3r^2 - 6r + 1$
52. $8m - 3$
53. $13x - 12y + 12z$
54. $-x^2 + 9x - 19$
55. $2x^2 + 2x + 9$
56. $8x$ 57. $7y$
58. $17k$
59. $\frac{1}{3}x$ 60. $4p$
61. $8d$
62. a. 3 b. $3x + 8$
63. $2c$
64. $6x^2 - 9x - 12$
65. $-4x^2 + 8$
66. $3x^2 - 7x + 5$
67. $6y + 6$
68. $5c^2 - 9c + 12$

9-3 Multiplying Powers That Have the Same Base (pages 277–278)

1. a^5 2. b^7 3. c^7
4. d^{10} 5. r^{11} 6. t^4
7. r^6 8. s^8 9. e^{10}
10. z^{11} 11. x^5 12. a^7
13. s^9 14. y^6 15. t^{14}
16. x^2 17. a^3 18. b^5
19. c^6 20. e^{10} 21. 2^5 or 32
22. 3^7 or 2,187 23. 5^6 or 15,625 24. 4^4 or 256
25. 2^{10} or 1,024 26. x^6 27. a^8
28. y^8 29. y^{10} 30. z^{14}
31. x^4y^6 32. a^4b^8 33. r^3s^3
34. $2^6 \cdot 3^6$ or 6^6 35. $5^4 \cdot 2^{12}$
36. x^{3a} 37. y^{c+2}
38. c^{r-2} 39. x^{m-1}
40. $(3y)^{a+b}$ 41. True 42. False
43. False 44. False 45. True
46. True 47. False 48. True
49. False

9-4 Multiplying by a Monomial (pages 281–283)

1. By writing the product with no sign between the constant and the variable or between the different variables
2. Multiplication 3. Addition
4. Multiplication 5. No
6. Yes
7. $-12a$ 8. $24b^2$ 9. $30y^2$
10. $20ab$ 11. $16rs$ 12. $-42xyz$
13. $-3xy$ 14. $-6ab$ 15. xyz
16. $-15abc$ 17. $-35rst$ 18. $12cde$
19. $-18cdxy$
20. $-60cdms$ 21. $-20a^4$ 22. $18x^7$
23. $-140y^5$ 24. $-90r^7$ 25. $12z^3$
26. $-40y^6$ 27. $-72z^8$ 28. $-24x^6y^5$
29. $-35a^5b^3$ 30. $-8a^3b^5$ 31. $18c + 9d$

32. $-20m + 30n$ 33. $-16a - 12b$
34. $20x - 2y$ 35. $8m - 48n$
36. $-32r + 2s$ 37. $-12c + 10$
38. $20x^2 + 24x$ 39. $5d^3 - 15d^2$
40. $-75c^3 + 20c^4$ 41. $m^2n + mn^2$
42. $-a^2b + ab^2$ 43. $15a^3b - 21ab^3$
44. $-6r^7s^4 + 3r^3s^7$ 45. $20ad - 30cd + 40bd$
46. $-16x^2 + 24x + 40$ 47. $3x^3y + 3x^2y^2 + 3xy^3$
48. $-10r^4s^2 + 15r^3s^3 - 20r^2s^4$
49. $15y^2$ 50. $15xy$ 51. $24c^2 - 6c$
52. a. $12x^2 - 24x$ b. $2x^2 + 4x$ c. $10x^2 - 28x$
53. $5d + 5$ 54. $6 - 4c$ 55. $14x - 3$
56. $-2x + 8$ 57. $17a - 12$ 58. $25 - 12e$
59. $6 + 4e$ 60. b 61. $4b + 4$
62. $3 - 5t$ 63. $2 + 8s$ 64. $21 - 6x$
65. $10x^2 - 6x$ 66. $-6y^2 + 24y$ 67. $13x - 11$
68. $-c + 2d$ 69. $-7a^2 + 3a$ 70. $6b$
71. $29x + 14$ 72. $5x - 3y$ 73. $-18x^2 + 11x$
74. $-2y$ 75. $175x$ 76. $40z$
77. $10n$ 78. $10x - 15$ 79. $15y^2 - 21y$
80. $6b^2 + 4b$ 81. $9x - 21$ 82. $3xy - 6y$
83. $3w^2 - 2w$ 84. $12x - 18$ 85. $5x - 35$
86. $5x - 35$ 87. $8x - 19$

9-5 Multiplying Polynomials (pages 285–286)

1. $a^2 + 5a + 6$ 2. $c^2 + 7c + 6$
3. $x^2 - 8x + 15$ 4. $d^2 - 11d + 30$
5. $d^2 + 6d - 27$ 6. $x^2 - 5x - 14$
7. $m^2 - 4m - 21$ 8. $z^2 + 3z - 40$
9. $f^2 + 2f - 80$ 10. $t^2 + 9t - 90$
11. $b^2 - 18b + 80$ 12. $w^2 - 6w - 91$
13. $30 + 11y + y^2$ 14. $48 - 14e + e^2$
15. $72 + 6r - r^2$ 16. $x^2 - 25$
17. $y^2 - 49$ 18. $a^2 - 81$
19. $2x^2 - 11x - 6$ 20. $2c^2 - 14c + 20$
21. $6a^2 + 29a + 9$ 22. $15y^2 - 11y + 2$
23. $4x^2 - 9$ 24. $9d^2 - 64$ 25. $x^2 + 2xy + y^2$
26. $a^2 - 2ab + b^2$ 27. $a^2 - b^2$
28. $a^2 + 5ab + 6b^2$ 29. $6c^2 - cd - d^2$
30. $x^2 - 16y^2$ 31. $6z^2 + 7wz - 20w^2$
32. $18x^2 + 17xy - 15y^2$
33. $15kr + 20ks + 6mr + 8ms$
34. $9x^2 - 16y^2$ 35. $r^4 + 3r^2 - 10$
36. $x^4 - y^4$ 37. $x^3 + 5x^2 + 11x + 10$
38. $4c^3 - 4c^2 - 5c - 1$ 39. $15 - 16d - d^2 + 2d^3$
40. $c^3 + 8$ 41. $6x^3 - 13x^2 + 9x - 2$
42. $12x^3 - 7x^2y - 8xy^2 + 3y^3$
43. $3x^4 - 10x^3 + 9x^2 - 14x + 4$
44. $6x^3 + 13x^2 - 19x - 12$
45. $x^4 + x^3 - 21x^2 + 13x - 2$ 46. $x^3 + 12x + 48x + 64$

47. $a^3 + 15a^2 + 75a + 125$ **48.** $x^3 - 3x^2y + 3xy^2 - y^3$
49. $2x^3 - 7x^2 + 16x - 15$ **50.** $8x^3 + 26x^2 - x - 12$
51. $x^3 + 3x^2y + 3xy^2 + y^3$
52. $a^3 - ab^2$ **53.** $5x - 14$ **54.** $12x^2 - 6$
55. $-2x + 3$ **56.** $14x + 2$ **57.** $y^2 - 33y - 8$
58. $14y + 7$ **59.** $r^2 - 2rs - r + s$
60. $a^3 - 8a$ **61.** $(2x-5)(x+7) = 2x^2 + 9x - 35$
62. $(11x-8)(3x+5) = 33x^2 + 31x - 40$
63. $(x+100)(2x+3) = 2x^2 + 203x + 300$

64. a. $x^2 + 5x + 6$

b.

$3x$	x^2	x
6	$2x$	2
3	x	

65. a. $x^2 + 11x + 30$

b.

$6x$	x^2	x
30	$5x$	5
6	x	

66. a. $10x^2 + 31x + 15$

b.

$25x$	15	5
$10x^2$	$6x$	$2x$
$5x$	3	

67. a. $9x^2 + 6x + 1$

b.

$9x^2$	$3x$	$3x$
$3x$	1	1
$3x$	1	

68. a. $2x^2 + 5xy + 3y^2$

b.

$2x^2$	$3xy$	x
$2xy$	$3y^2$	y
$2x$	$3y$	

69. a. $6x^2 + 23xy + 20y^2$

b.

$6x^2$	$8xy$	$2x$
$15xy$	$20y^2$	$5y$
$3x$	$4y$	

70. a. The product of two binomials has four terms when at least three of the terms in the binomials are unlike terms. After multiplying, all four terms are unlike terms.

b. The product of two binomials is a trinomial when each term of the first binomial is a like term of one of the terms in the second binomial, but the binomials are not the sum and difference of the same terms.

c. The product of two binomials is a binomial when the binomials are the sum and difference of the same terms. After multiplying, two terms are opposites.

9-6 Dividing Powers That Have the Same Base (pages 288–289)

1. x^6 **2.** a^5 **3.** b^4
4. c **5.** 1   **6.** d^2
7. e^6 **8.** m^8 **9.** n
10. 1   **11.** x^7 **12.** y^6

13. z^9 **14.** t^4 **15.** 1
16. 2^3 or 8   **17.** 10^2 or 100   **18.** 3^2 or 9
19. 5^2 or 25   **20.** 10^3 or 1,000   **21.** x^{3a}
22. y^{8b} **23.** r^{c-d} **24.** s^{x-2}
25. 1   **26.** 2^{a-b} **27.** 2^5 or 32
28. 5^3 or 125   **29.** 10   **30.** 1
31. 1   **32.** 6^8 or 1,679,616
33. False   **34.** True   **35.** False

9-7 Powers with Zero and Negative Exponents (pages 291–292)

1. $\dfrac{1}{10^4}$ **2.** $\dfrac{1}{2}$ or $\dfrac{1}{2^1}$ **3.** $\dfrac{1}{\left(\frac{2}{3}\right)^2}$ or $\left(\dfrac{3}{2}\right)^2$

4. $\dfrac{1}{m^6}$ **5.** $\dfrac{1}{r^3}$ **6.** 1

7. 1   **8.** 1   **9.** 1

10. $\dfrac{1}{9}$ **11.** $\dfrac{1}{16}$ **12.** $-\dfrac{1}{6}$

13. -1 **14.** $\dfrac{1}{10}$ **15.** $\dfrac{1}{100}$

16. $\dfrac{1}{1,000}$ **17.** $\dfrac{1}{10,000}$ **18.** $\dfrac{4}{100}$ or $\dfrac{1}{25}$

19. $\dfrac{1.5}{1,000}$ or $\dfrac{3}{2,000}$ or 0.0015   **20.** $1\dfrac{1}{36}$

21. $1\dfrac{1}{27}$ **22.** 10^3 or 1,000   **23.** 3^{-6} or $\dfrac{1}{3^6}$

24. 10^2 or 100   **25.** 3^4 or 81

26. 4^{-2} or $\dfrac{1}{4^2}$ or $\dfrac{1}{16}$ **27.** 3^6

28. a^4 **29.** x^{-4} or $\dfrac{1}{x^4}$ **30.** m^{-5} or $\dfrac{1}{m^5}$

31. t^{-8} or $\dfrac{1}{t^8}$ **32.** a^{-12} or $\dfrac{1}{a^{12}}$ **33.** x^0 or 1

34. 6   **35.** $5\dfrac{1}{2}$

9-8 Using Scientific Notation (pages 295–296)

1. 10^5 **2.** 10^9 **3.** 10^{12}
4. 10,000,000
5. 10,000,000,000
6. 10,000,000,000,000
7. 1,000,000,000,000,000
8. 300,000   **9.** 400,000,000
10. 600,000,000,000,000   **11.** 9,000,000,000
12. 13,000   **13.** 8,300,000,000,000

14. 1,270　　　　　　　　**15.** 61,400,000,000

16. 2　　　**17.** 2　　　**18.** 3

19. 4　　　**20.** 3　　　**21.** 5

22. 6　　　**23.** 8　　　**24.** 10^{-2}

25. 10^{-5}　　**26.** 10^{-8}　　**27.** 10^{-10}

28. 0.000001　　**29.** 0.00000001

30. 0.000000000000001

31. 0.000000000000000001

32. 0.004　　　　　　　**33.** 0.000000007

34. 0.0000000008　　　**35.** 0.0000000000009

36. 0.00012　　　　　　**37.** 0.000036

38. 0.000000000074

39. 0.0000000000000314

40. -2　　**41.** -5　　**42.** -8

43. -11　　**44.** -3　　**45.** -7

46. 8.4×10^3　**47.** 2.7×10^4　**48.** 5.4×10^7

49. 3.2×10^8　**50.** 6.75×10^3　**51.** 8.16×10^4

52. 4.53×10^5　**53.** 3.75×10^8　**54.** 5.2×10^{-3}

55. 6.1×10^{-4}　**56.** 3.9×10^{-6}　**57.** 1.4×10^{-8}

58. 1.56×10^{-1}　**59.** 3.81×10^{-3}　**60.** 7.63×10^{-5}

61. 9.17×10^{-7}

mistake **62.** **a.** 8.7×10^2　**b.** 870

63. **a.** 7.5×10^{-5}　**b.** 0.000075

64. **a.** 3×10^{-7}　**b.** 0.0000003

65. **a.** 2×10^3　**b.** 2,000　　**66.** 9.5×10^{12}

67. 1.2×10^{22}　**68.** 1×10^{-6}　**69.** 5×10^{-13}

70. 8×10^{-4}　**71.** 2,000,000,000

72. 240,000　　**73.** 0.06　　**74.** 0.00000002

75. 5,900,000,000,000,000,000,000,000

9-9 Dividing by a Monomial *(page 299)*

1. $9x$　　　　**2.** $-2x^2y^2$　　**3.** $-6y^8$

4. $9x^4$　　　**5.** $-x^2$　　　**6.** $-7c^2b$

7. $8x$　　　　**8.** -7　　　　**9.** $-3y$

10. $2x + 4y$　**11.** $2r - 3s$　**12.** $2x + 1$

13. $m + n$　　**14.** $t - 1$　　**15.** $-6a + 3b$

16. $-2c^2 + 3d^2$　　　　　　**17.** $m + 8$

18. $1 + rt$　　**19.** $-y + 5$　**20.** $3d^2 + 2d$

21. $4x + 3$　　**22.** $3r^3 + 2r$　**23.** $4t^3 - 2t^2$

24. $-3y^6 + 2y^3$　**25.** $-2a + 1$　**26.** $3b - 4a$

27. $c - 3d$　　**28.** $-2a^2 + 1$　**29.** $y^5 - 3y + 5$

30. $2a^2 + 3a - 1$　**31.** $-4y^2 - 2y + 1$

32. $3y$ cents　　**33.** $4b$　　**34.** $6r$ mi

35. $8b$

9-10 Dividing by a Polynomial *(page 301)*

1. $b + 2$　　**2.** $y + 1$　　**3.** $m - 7$

4. $w - 3$　　**5.** $y + 3 + \dfrac{10}{y + 17}$

6. $m + 12 + \dfrac{33}{m - 5}$　　**7.** $x - 2$

8. $3t - 8$　　**9.** $5r - 8$　　**10.** $3c - 4$

11. $11 + x$　　**12.** $6 + m$　　**13.** $x + 8$

14. $2y - 7$　　**15.** $x + 3$　　**16.** $x - 9$

17. $y + 2$

Review Exercises *(pages 302–303)*

1. $5r^2$　　　　**2.** $4bc$　　　　**3.** $4y^2 - 10y - 2$

4. $13t - 4$　　　　　　　　　　**5.** $-24mg^2$

6. $12x^4 + 6x^3 - 3x^2$　　　**7.** $8x^2 + 2x - 3$

8. $36a^2b^6$　　**9.** $36a^2 - 12ab + b^2$

10. $4a^2 - 25$　**11.** $4a^2 - 20a + 25$

12. $7x - 2x^2$　**13.** $-5bx^5$　　**14.** $2y$

15. $3w^2 - 4w + 1$　　　**16.** $\dfrac{1}{8^2} = \dfrac{1}{64}$

17. $\dfrac{1}{k^6}$　　**18.** $\dfrac{1}{10^3} = \dfrac{1}{1,000} = 0.001$

19. $\left(\dfrac{5}{2}\right)^2 = \dfrac{25}{4} = 6.25$　　**20.** $\dfrac{2}{x^4}$

21. $3^{-1} = \dfrac{1}{3}$　**22.** 1　　**23.** $10^2 = 100$

24. $12^{-2} = \dfrac{1}{12^2} = \dfrac{1}{144}$　　**25.** **a.** $2h$　**b.** $\dfrac{1}{4}h^2$

26. $16px$　　**27.** **a.** $4x + 20$　**b.** $x^2 + 10x + 25$

28. $x - 12$　　**29.** $3y + 5$　　**30.** 10

31. $24x - 40$　**32.** 5.8×10^3　**33.** 1.42×10^7

34. 6×10^{-5}　**35.** 2.77×10^{-6}　**36.** 40,000

37. 0.003　　**38.** 390,000,000　　**39.** 0.000103

Cumulative Review *(page 303)*

1. (2)

2. 24.5

Exploration

$15^2 = 225$	$65^2 = 4225$
$25^2 = 625$	$75^2 = 5625$
$35^2 = 1225$	$85^2 = 7225$
$45^2 = 2025$	$95^2 = 9025$
$55^2 = 3025$	

Multiply the tens digit of the number by the next consecutive integer and write 25 after this product. This method can also be used for a three digit number.

$115^2 = 13225$ Write 25 after 132, the product of $11(12)$.

$(10a + 5)^2 = 100a^2 + 100a + 25 = 100a(a + 1) + 25$

Chapter 10. First-Degree Equations and Inequalities in One Variable

10-1 Simplifying Each Side of an Equation Before Solving *(pages 308–309)*

1. $x = 13$ 2. $x = 25$

3. $x = \dfrac{3}{5}$ or $x = 0.6$ 4. $c = 20$

5. $x = -4$ 6. $x = -13$ 7. $x = 2$
8. $y = 19$ 9. $c = 4$ 10. $c = -2$
11. $y = -5$ 12. $c = 7$ 13. $t = 3$
14. $x = 3$ 15. $m = 15$ 16. $x = 11$
17. $x = 3$ 18. $a = -17$ 19. $b = 9$
20. $c = 3$ 21. $r = 2$ 22. $y = 6$

23. $x = 10$ 24. $z = \dfrac{6}{7}$ 25. $b = 4$

26. $m = \dfrac{7}{3}$ or $m = 2\dfrac{1}{3}$ 27. $v = 12$

28. $r = 1$ 29. $a = 2$ 30. $r = 5$
31. $x = 7$ 32. $x = 4$ 33. $2x + 8$
34. $3x - 12$ 35. $4(x + 3)$ 36. $3(x + 5)$
37. $2(x + 5)$ 38. $10(2x - 10)$
39. a. $10 - x$ b. $25 - x$ c. $36 - x$
    d. $50 - x$ e. $100 - x$ f. $3,000 - x$
40. $S - x$ 41. $S - \ell$ 42. 2.25 yd, 3.75 yd
43. 35   44. $25, $45
45. 32 on 2 buses, 36 on 1 bus
46. a. $25 - x$ b. $0.10x$ dollars or $10x$ cents
    c. $0.25(25 - x)$ dollars or $25(25 - x)$ cents
    d. 9 dimes, 16 quarters
47. a. $38 - x$ b. $8.50x$ c. $12.75(38 - x)$
    d. 4 hr

10-2 Solving Equations That Have the Variable in Both Numbers *(pages 313–314)*

1. $x = 2$ 2. $x = 4$ 3. $c = 7$
4. $y = -10$ 5. $d = -12$ 6. $y = -8$
7. $m = 40$ 8. $y = 9$ 9. $x = -18$
10. $x = 96$ 11. $a = 20$ 12. $c = -27$
13. $x = 9$ 14. $m = -50$ 15. $c = -8$
16. $r = 10$ 17. $y = 11$ 18. $x = -7$
19. $x = 0$ 20. $x = 7$ 21. $y = 4$
22. $c = 7$ 23. $d = -18$ 24. $y = -17$

25. $m = \dfrac{1}{2}$ or -0.5 26. $x = 10$

27. $b = 2$ 28. $t = 15$ 29. $n = -1$
30. $y = -3$ 31. $x = 13$ 32. $x = 3$
33. $a = 20$ 34. $c = -5$ 35. $x = 11$
36. $d = -13$ 37. $m = 9$ 38. $z = -1$
39. 5   40. 8   41. 9
42. 7, 15   43. 5, 11, 10   44. 12, 11, 6
45. 500 mi on the first day, 425 mi on the second day
46. $660 first 6 months, $790 last 6 months

47. 14 five-dollar bills, 7 ten-dollar bills
48. $40 first month, $60 second month
49. 348 mi

10-3 Consecutive-Integer Problems *(pages 316–317)*

1. 3, 4, 5, 6   2. $-3, -2, -1, 0$
3. 8, 10, 12, 14   4. $-5, -3, -1, 1$
5. a. 15, 16, 17, 18   b. $-6, -5, -4, -3$
   c. $-1, 0, 1, 2$ d. $y, y + 1, y + 2, y + 3$
   e. $y - 1, y, y + 1, y + 2$
6. a. 12, 14, 16, 18   b. $-10, -8, -6, -4$
   c. $-2, 0, 2, 4$ d. $y, y + 2, y + 4, y + 6$
   e. $y - 2, y, y + 2, y + 4$
7. a. 17, 19, 21, 23   b. $-7, -5, -3, -1$
   c. $-15, -13, -11, -9$ d. $y, y + 2, y + 4, y + 6$
   e. $y + 4, y + 6, y + 8, y + 10$
8. 1, 2, 3, 4 (or any set of 4 consecutive integers)
9. a. No.   b. Every set of 4 consecutive integers consists of 2 even and 2 odd integers whose sum is even.
10. 45, 46   11. $-9, -8$
12. 30, 31, 32   13. $-7, -6, -5$
14. 26, 27, 28, 29   15. 42, 44
16. $-6, -4, -2$ 17. No solution
18. 13, 15   19. 83, 85, 87
20. 111, 113, 115, 117   21. 19, 20, 21
22. 64, 65, 66, 67   23. 21, 23
24. 20, 22   25. 14, 15, 16
26. 25, 26, 27   27. 10, 12, 14
28. 19, 20   29. 9, 11, 13, 15
30. 15, 17, 19
31. a. Yes   b. 1, 2, 3 (any set of 3 with the first and last odd)
    c. Yes   d. 2, 3, 4 (any set of 3 with the first and last even)
    e. The sum is odd when the smallest number is even, so that there are two even and one odd integer. It is even when the smallest number is odd, so that there are one even and two odd integers.
32. $n + (n + 1) + (n + 2) = 3n + 3$, and $3(n + 1) = 3n + 3$.

10-4 Solving for a Variable in a Formula *(pages 318–319)*

1. $c = 35$
2. a. $s = 5$ b. $s = 8$ c. $s = 1.6$
3. a. $w = 20$ b. $w = 4$
4. a. $h = 6$ b. $h = 8$
5. $w = 8$
6. a. $w = 3$ b. $w = 8\dfrac{1}{2}$

7. a. $\ell = 11$ b. $\ell = 7.7$
8. $b = 20$ cm   9. $a = 6.4$ cm

10. $h = 6$ **11.** $b = 14$ cm

12. a. 40   **b.** 80   **13.** \$750

14. a. $C = 35°$ **b.** $C = 20°$ **c.** $C = 15°$
   d. $C = 0°$ **e.** $C = 100°$ **f.** $C = -25°$

15. 11.6 cm   **16. a.** 9 cm   **b.** 6 cm

17. a. 7 cm   **b.** 49 cm²

18. a. $\dfrac{3}{4}$ in.   **b.** $\dfrac{9}{16}$ sq. in.

19. a. 4.2 cm   **b.** 17.64 cm²

20. a. $\dfrac{1}{2}$ ft.   **b.** $\dfrac{1}{4}$ sq. ft.

10-5 Perimeter Problems (pages 320–321)

1. a. $7x + 2$ **b.** $8x - 10$
   c. $7x + 2$ **d.** $12x - 8$

2. a. $2x, 6x$ **b.** $x + 4, 4x + 8$
   c. $2x - 5, 6x - 10$ **d.** $2x + 3, 6x + 6$

3. $3x + 15$ **4.** $8x - 4$

5. $10x + 15$ **6.** $12x - 18$

7. a. $4x - 8$ **b.** $3x - 6$ **c.** $2x - 4$

8. 9 cm, 27 cm   **9.** 12 cm, 30 cm

10. 21 in., 19 in., 33 in.   **11.** 30 cm

12. 14 m, 19 m   **13.** 34 yd, 31 yd

14. 16 m, 57 m   **15.** 36 ft, 78 ft

16. 20 m   **17.** 6, 7, 7

18. 32 in., 64 in.   **19.** 6 ft, 10 ft

20. 8 m

21. Hexagon: 8 in.; square: 12 in.

10-6 Solving for a Variable in Terms of Another Variable (page 323)

1. $x = \dfrac{b}{5}$ **2.** $x = \dfrac{8}{s}$ **3.** $y = \dfrac{s}{r}$

4. $y = \dfrac{t}{3}$ **5.** $y = \dfrac{5}{c}$ **6.** $y = \dfrac{m}{h}$

7. $x = r - 5$ **8.** $x = 7 - a$ **9.** $y = d - c$

10. $x = k - 4$ **11.** $y = 9 - d$ **12.** $x = \dfrac{p + q}{3}$

13. $x = r + 2$ **14.** $y = 7 + a$ **15.** $x = d + c$

16. $x = \dfrac{r + e}{3}$ **17.** $y = \dfrac{4 + d}{c}$ **18.** $x = \dfrac{c - b}{a}$

19. $x = \dfrac{s}{r}$ **20.** $y = \dfrac{t - r}{s}$

21. $x = \dfrac{m - 2n}{2}$ or $x = \dfrac{m}{2} - n$

22. $x = 2c$ **23.** $x = 9b$ **24.** $x = c$

25. $x = \dfrac{c + 5}{b}$ **26.** $y = \dfrac{a - 6}{b}$ **27.** $y = \dfrac{t - s}{r}$

28. $x = \dfrac{6d}{ab}$ **29.** $x = s$ **30.** $x = 15$

31. $x = 6a$ **32.** $x = 2a$

10-7 Transforming Formulas (pages 324–325)

1. $h = \dfrac{A}{6}$ **2.** $h = \dfrac{36}{b}$ **3.** $s = \dfrac{P}{4}$

4. $t = \dfrac{D}{r}$ **5.** $\ell = \dfrac{V}{wh}$ **6.** $r = \dfrac{p}{b}$

7. $b = \dfrac{A}{h}$ **8.** $\ell = \dfrac{A}{w}$ **9.** $h = \dfrac{V}{lw}$

10. $h = \dfrac{V}{4b}$ **11.** $p = \dfrac{I}{rt}$ **12.** $b = \dfrac{400}{h}$

13. $h = \dfrac{2A}{b}$ **14.** $h = \dfrac{3V}{B}$ **15.** $g = \dfrac{2S}{t^2}$

16. $c = \ell + s$ **17.** $\ell = \dfrac{P - 2w}{2}$ or $\ell = \dfrac{P}{2} - w$

18. $C = \dfrac{5}{9}(F - 32)$ or $C = \dfrac{5F - 160}{9}$

19. $a = \dfrac{2S}{n} - \ell$ or $a = \dfrac{2S - n\ell}{n}$

20. $h = \dfrac{A}{b}$ **21.** $b = P - 2a$

22. $a = \dfrac{P - b - c}{2}$ or $a = \dfrac{P - (b + c)}{2}$

23. a. $h = \dfrac{V}{\pi r^2}$

   b. (*1*) 27.9 cm   (*2*) 17.8 cm   (*3*) 7.0 cm

   c. (*2*) It would be easier to hold then (*3*), and the bottom could be reached more easily than that of (*1*).

24.

Leave Buffalo	9:00 A.M.
Arrive Rochester	10:30 A.M.
Leave Rochester	11:00 A.M.
Arrive Syracuse	12:42 P.M.
Leave Syracuse	1:12 P.M.
Arrive Albany	4:06 P.M.

25. a. Student estimates

   b. (*1*) 50   (*2*) 32   (*3*) 5
     (*4*) -10 (*5*) $-17.\overline{7}$

10-8 Properties of Inequalities (pages 329–330)

1. $>$ **2.** $<$ **3.** $>$

4. $>$ **5.** $>$ **6.** $>$

7. $<$ **8.** $<$ **9.** $>$

10. $<$ **11.** $>$ **12.** $<$

13. $<$ **14.** $>$ **15.** $>, >$

16. $<, <$ **17.** $<, <$ **18.** $>, >$

19. $<, <$ **20.** $>, >$ **21.** $<, <$

22. $<$ **23.** $>$ **24.** $>$

25. $<$ **26.** $<$ **27.** $>$

28. It is not possible to determine the correct symbol.

29. $>$

10-9 Finding and Graphing the Solution of an Inequality (pages 334–336)

1–51. require graphs.

1. $x > 6$

2. $z < 10$

3. $y > 2\frac{1}{2}$

4. $x < 5$

5. $x > 3$

6. $y > 2$

7. $d > 2\frac{3}{4}$

8. $c < -4$

9. $y \geq 8$

10. $d \geq 3$

11. $t > 2$

12. $x \leq 6$

13. $y \geq 5$

14. $h \geq -2\frac{1}{2}$

15. $y > -4$

16. $y > -3$

17. $x < 2$

18. $r \leq -10$

19. $x > 6$

20. $z \leq -9$

21. $x > 2$

22. $y \leq -3$

23. $z \geq 2$

24. $y \geq -10$

25. $z \leq -4$

26. $x > 3$

27. $y \geq 6$

28. $x > -6$

29. $y \geq -1$

30. $x > 2$

31. $y \geq 2$

32. $c > -2$

33. $d \leq 3.5$

34. $x > 1$

35. $y \leq 6$

36. $x > -6$

37. $x > 6$

38. $y < 2$

39. $x \leq -3$

40. $x > 2$

41. $c \leq -27$

42. $x \geq -24$

43. $x > 5$

44. $x > -10$

45. $x > 3$

46. $m \geq 1.5$

47. $r > -2$

48. $-3 < x < 3$

49. $-7 \leq x < 5$

50. $x > 4$

51. $(x < 1) \lor (x \geq 5)$

52. (2)

53. (4)

54. (3)

55. (2)

56. $x > 1$

57. $x < -1$

58. $x \leq 2$

59. $x \geq -3$

60. $-3 < x \leq 2$

61. $(x < -2) \lor (x > 3)$

62. a.

b. $x \geq 2$

63. a. No b. Write $\dfrac{-7x}{-7} > \dfrac{-21}{-7}$ or $x > 3$. The symbol $\not<$ means $\geq$.

64. a. (1) $x < 3$ (2) $x = 3$ (3) $x > 3$

b. The solution of the equation and two inequalities together include all real numbers. The solution of the equation is the boundary between the solution sets of the two inequalities.

c. (1) No. (2) There is no largest real number less than 3.

10-10 Using Inequalities to Solve Problems (pages 338–339)

1. $x \leq 15$

2. $y \geq 4$

3. $x \leq 50$

4. $x > 50$

5. $3y \leq 30$

6. $5x + 2x \geq 70$

7. $4x - 6 \leq 54$

8. $2x + 1 \geq 13$

9. $3x (x + 1) < 35$

10. $x - 6 > 4; x > 10$

11. $x - 6 < 4; x < 10$

12. $6x < 72; x < 12$

13. $x + 10 > 50; x > 40$

14. $x - 15 < 35; x < 50$

15. $2x + 6 < 48; x < 21$

16. $5x - 24 > 3x; x > 12$

17. $s + 100 \geq 550; \$450$

18. $b + b - 80 \geq 250; 165$

19. $s + 3s + 20 \leq 120; \$25$

20. $3n + 8 \leq n + 40; 16$

21. $2w + 2 (5w - 8) \leq 104; 10$ m

22. $2w + 2 (3w - 10) \leq 180; 65$ m

23. $300 + 8x \geq 1,500; \$150$

24. $x + x + 2 > 98 - 2 (x + 2); 24, 26$

25. $x + 6x \geq 29; 4$ hr

26. $3x \geq 20 - 2; \$6.01$ Since Fred got less than \$2 in change from a \$20 bill, the shirts cost more than \$18. Therefore, each shirt cost more than \$6, and the minimum cost of a shirt is \$6.01.

27. $2 \leq 4x \leq 3$; a. $\dfrac{1}{2}$ hr b. $\dfrac{3}{4}$ hr c. $1\dfrac{1}{2}$ hr

Review Exercises (pages 340–342)

1. $x = 23$

2. $m = -6$

3. $c = \dfrac{1}{2}$ or $c = 0.5$

4. $x = 7$

5. $d = 20$

6. $b = -64$

7. $p = 50$

8. $z = 13$

9. $w = 5$

10. $w = 15$

11. $h = 4$

12. $y = -1$

13. $z = -2$

14. $b = -2$

15. $x = -3$

16. $x = \dfrac{1}{3}$

17. $x = b + c - a$

18. $x = \dfrac{b - a}{c}$

19. $x = \dfrac{6a + c}{b}$

20. $x = \dfrac{2b}{a + c}$

21. a. $h = \dfrac{2A}{b}$ b. $h = 12$ 22. $w = \dfrac{7}{2}$ or $w = 3.5$

23. $C = 2c$

24. $x < 3$

25. $x \leq -4$

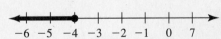

26. $x > -3$

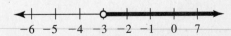

27. $x \geq -1$

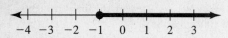

28. $-3 < x \leq 2$

29. $3 \leq x < 7$

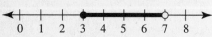

30. $(x \leq -2) \vee (x > 0)$

31. $5 \leq x < 9$

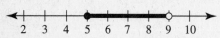

32. Always   **33.** Sometimes
34. Always   **35.** Never
36. (1)   **37.** (1)
38. (3)
39. Width is 6.5 ft, length is 24.5 ft
40. 4, 5, 6   **41.** 18,310 lb
42. a. More than 150 lb   **b.** Someone who weighs
                                  less than 150 lb. can
                                  take this part to the roof
                                  in the elevator.

43. a. Fewer than 6   **b.** 6 or more

Cumulative Review *(page 342)*

1. $3s^2$
2. 1.5×10^{-6}
3. $2x^2 - 12x + 9$
4. a.

p	q	$\sim p$	$\sim q$	$p \rightarrow q$	$\sim p \vee q$	$(p \rightarrow q) \leftrightarrow (\sim p \vee q)$
T	T	F	F	T	T	T
T	F	F	T	F	F	T
F	T	T	F	T	T	T
F	F	T	T	T	T	T

b. Yes   The statement is always true.

Exploration

a. The program prints the squares of integers from 1 to 24.
b. The statement X = X + 1 replaces the number currently stored as the value of X by 1 more than that number. In the algebraic equation, the value of X must be a number equal to 1 more than itself. The equation has no root.
c. In BASIC, the THEN statement is performed when the IF statement is true and not performed when the IF statement is false. An IF, THEN statement in

Chapter 11. Angle Measure in Geometry

11-1 Points, Lines, and Planes
(page 346)

1. a. Line *PR* (no endpoints)
   b. The distance between *P* and *R* (a number)
   c. Segment *PR* (two endpoints *P*, *R* and all the points between *P* and *R*)
2. $\overline{PQ}$, $\overline{PR}$, $\overline{PS}$, $\overline{PT}$, $\overline{QR}$, $\overline{QS}$, $\overline{QT}$, $\overline{RS}$, $\overline{RT}$, $\overline{ST}$
3. *R*
4. Yes
5. No
6. a. 8   **b.** 2   **c.** 5   **d.** 4
7. a. $\overline{QS}$ **b.** *R* **c.** $\overline{PT}$ **d.** $\overline{RS}$ **e.** $\varnothing$

11-2 Angles, Angle Measures, and Perpendicularity *(pages 349–350)*

1. a. 60   **b.** Acute   **2. a.** 120   **b.** Obtuse
3. a. 40   **b.** Acute   **4. a.** 60   **b.** Acute
5. a. 120 **b.** Obtuse

6–11. Student drawings
12. a. $\angle BOA$ or $\angle AOB$ **b.** $\angle y$
    c. $\angle x$ or $\angle y$ ($\angle BOA$ or $\angle COB$)   **d.** $\angle COA$
13. a. 180   **b.** 270   **c.** 30   **d.** 150
14. 30   **15.** 120   **16.** 180   **17.** 15
18. 12 o'clock; any time when the two hands are together

11-3 Pairs of Angles *(pages 354–357)*

1. $50°$ **2.** $65°$ **3.** $45°$
4. $20.5°$ **5.** $2\frac{2}{3}°$ **6.** $(90 - m)°$
7. $(90 - d)°$ **8.** $y°$ **9.** $(80 - x)°$
10. $(110 - x)°$ **11.** $15°, 75°$ **12.** $20°, 70°$
13. $65°, 25°$ **14.** $20°, 70°$ **15.** $30°, 60°$
16. $80°$ **17.** $72°$ **18.** $35°$
19. $41°$ **20.** $140°$ **21.** $111°$
22. $90°$ **23.** $70°$ **24.** $12\frac{1}{2}°$
25. $(180 - m)°$ **26.** $(180 - c)°$ **27.** $(180 - 2y)°$

28. $t°$ **29.** $(140 - x)°$ **30.** 45°, 135°

31. 144°, 36°   **32.** 150°, 75°   **33.** 50°, 130°

34. 60°, 120°   **35.** 110°   **36.** 140°

37. 130°   **38.** (3)   **39.** 30°

40. 65°   **41.** 90°   **42.** 128.4°

43. $175\frac{1}{2}°$ **44.** 25   **45.** 60

46. 72

47. m∠FGH = 90; m∠HGI = 28

48. m∠JLN = 42; m∠MLK = 90; m∠KLO = 42; m∠JLO = 138

49. m∠HKI = 56; m∠HKG = 124; m∠GKJ = 146

50. m∠PMO = 90; m∠OML = 50

51. m∠RSQ = 90; m∠QST = 90; m∠TSU = 91

52. m∠VWY = 91; m∠YWX = 89; m∠XWZ = 91

53. m∠ABD = 70; m∠DBE = 70

54. m∠FKJ = 40; m∠FKG = 40; m∠GKH = 100; m∠JKI = 140

55. m∠CEB = 20; m∠BED = 160; m∠CEA = 160

56. m∠RQS = 60; m∠SQT = 120; m∠PQT = 150

57. m∠LRP = 50; m∠LRQ = 130; m∠PRM = 130

58. m∠FEB = 10; m∠CEF = 80; m∠AEF = 170

59. $\overleftrightarrow{AC} \perp \overleftrightarrow{BD}$

11-4 Angles and Parallel Lines
(page 360)

1. m∠1 = m∠5 = m∠7 = 80; m∠2 = m∠4 = m∠6 = m∠8 = 100

2. m∠6 = m∠8 = m∠4 = m∠2 = 150; m∠7 = m∠5 = m∠3 = m∠1 = 30

3. m∠5 = m∠7 = m∠3 = m∠1 = 60; m∠6 = m∠8 = m∠4 = m∠2 = 120

4. m∠1 = m∠3 = m∠5 = m∠7 = 75; m∠2 = m∠4 = m∠6 = m∠8 = 105

5. m∠1 = 150; m∠2 = 30; m∠3 = 150; m∠6 = 140; m∠7 = 40; m∠8 = 140; m∠9 = 40; m∠10 = 110; m∠11 = 30

6. m∠1 = m∠3 = m∠5 = m∠7 = 66; m∠2 = m∠4 = m∠6 = m∠8 = 114

7. m∠2 = m∠4 = m∠6 = m∠8 = 110; m∠1 = m∠3 = m∠5 = m∠7 = 70

8. m∠2 = m∠4 = m∠6 = m∠8 = 124; m∠1 = m∠3 = m∠5 = m∠7 = 56

9. m∠2 = m∠4 = m∠6 = m∠8 = 130; m∠1 = m∠3 = m∠5 = m∠7 = 50

10. Measure of each angle is 90°

11. Never

12. Sometimes (if they lie in the same plane)

13. Always   **14.** Always

15. Sometimes   **16.** Sometimes

17. (1) ∠1 ≅ ∠3 because they are corresponding angles

    (2) ∠3 ≅ ∠2 because they are vertical angles

    (3) ∠1 ≅ ∠2 by substitution

    (4) m∠1 ≅ m∠2 because congruent angles have equal measures

11-5 Triangles and Angles
(pages 363–364)

The Sum of the Measures of the Angles of a Triangle:

1. Yes   **2.** No   **3.** Yes   **4.** 80°

5. 60°   **6.** 43.2°   **7.** 74°   **8.** 60°

9. a. No   **b.** No

    c. No; the sum of the measures would be greater than 180°

10. 90°

11. Congruent; the sum of the measures of the three angles must be 180°

12. 20°, 60°, 100°   **13.** 18°, 72°, 90°

14. 35°, 65°, 80°   **15.** 35°, 75°, 70°

16. a. m∠x = 50, m∠y = 40, m∠z = 90   **b.** Right

17. a. m∠R = 60, m∠S = 90, m∠T = 30   **b.** Right

18. a. m∠K = 60, m∠L = 60, m∠M = 60

    b. Equiangular

The Exterior Angle of a Triangle:

1. a. ∠BCD   **b.** ∠A and ∠B

2. a. ∠ACE   **b.** ∠A and ∠B

3. a. ∠CBF   **b.** ∠A and ∠C

4. a. ∠BAG   **b.** ∠B and ∠C

5. a. ∠ABH   **b.** ∠A and ∠C

6. 110°   **7.** 65°   **8.** 70°   **9.** 27°

10. 60°   **11.** x = 30   **12.** x = 30   **13.** x = 12

14. The measure of ∠F is 40°.

15. The measure of an exterior angle at M is 130°.

16. 120°   **17.** 90°   **18.** (3)

19. a. 360°   **b.** Yes

20. (1) m∠1 = m∠2; alternate interior angles

    (2) m∠3 = m∠4; corresponding angles

    (3) m∠1 + m∠3 = m∠2 + m∠4; addition property

    (4) m∠A + m∠B = m∠ACD; substitution

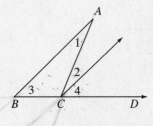

Triangles with Congruent Angles
(pages 369–371)

1. **a.** Legs, $\overline{LN}$ and $\overline{MN}$; base, $\overline{LM}$;
vertex angle, $\angle N$; base angles, $\angle L$ and $\angle M$
   b. Legs, $\overline{OP}$ and $\overline{OQ}$; base, $\overline{PQ}$;
vertex angle, $\angle O$; base angles, $\angle P$ and $\angle Q$
   c. Legs, $\overline{RT}$ and $\overline{RS}$; base, $\overline{ST}$;
vertex angle, $\angle R$; base angles, $\angle T$ and $\angle S$
   d. Legs, $\overline{XY}$ and $\overline{XZ}$; base, $\overline{YZ}$;
vertex angle, $\angle X$; base angles, $\angle Y$ and $\angle Z$

2. **a.** Isosceles   **b.** $\angle A$ and $\angle C$
   c. Angles A and C are opposite sides of equal
measure (base angles of an isosceles triangle
are congruent).

3. **a.** $70°$ **b.** $\overline{RT} \cong \overline{ST}$
   c. Sides $\overline{RT}$ and $\overline{ST}$ are opposite angles of equal
measure.
   d. Isosceles

4.
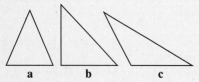
    a   **b**   **c**

5. **a.** No   **b.** No
   c. The second base angle would be equal in measure,
and a triangle cannot have two right or obtuse
angles (the sum of the measures of the angles of
the triangle would be greater than $180°$).

6. **a.** $20°$ **b.** $70°$ **c.** $96°$ **d.** $135°$ **e.** $77°$

7. **a.** $70°$ **b.** $65°$ **c.** $52°$ **d.** $40°$ **e.** $57\frac{1}{2}°$

8. $45°$

9. $12°, 84°, 84°$ 10. $90°, 45°, 45°$
11. $36°, 36°, 108°$ 12. $55°, 55°, 70°$
13. $64°, 58°, 58°$ 14. $22°, 79°, 79°$

15. **a.** $m\angle A = 40, m\angle B = 70, m\angle C = 70$
   b. Isosceles

16. $60°$

17. **a.** $60°, 60°, 60°$ **b.** Equilateral

18. **a.**
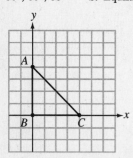

b. Isosceles right triangle
c. $m\angle A = 45, m\angle C = 45, m\angle B = 90$
d. 8

19. $130°$ 20. $50°$ 21. $30°$

22. **a.** $60°, 60°, 60°$
   b. Equilateral

23. $120°$

24. **a.** True
   b. If the angles opposite two sides of a triangle are
equal in measure, then these sides are equal in
measure.
   c. True
   d. Two sides of a triangle are equal in measure if and
only if the angles opposite these sides are equal in
measure.
   e. True

Review Exercises *(pages 372–373)*

1. 135 2. $50°$ 3. $90°$ 4. 55
5. $70°$ 6. $m\angle GHD = 73$ 7. 24
8. $m\angle GHD = 70$
9. **a.** $m\angle A = 50; m\angle R = 80; m\angle T = 50$ **b.** (2)
10. $m\angle BCD = 119$ 11. $m\angle B = 64$
12. 52 13. $m\angle A = 65$
14. **a.** x **b.** 30 **c.** *(1)* 30 *(2)* 120 *(3)* 150
15. $50°, 65°, 65°$ 16. $130°, 50°$
17. (3) 18. (3) 19. (4)

Cumulative Review *(pages 373–374)*

1.
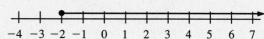

2. True
3. (4)
4. 16
5. $x = 4$
6. $x = 10$
7. **a.** $x = \dfrac{7 - 3b}{a}$ **b.** $x = 0.17$
8. -5.25
9. $12x^3y - 7xy^2$
10. $58°, 60°, 62°$
11. 10 lb. and 7 lb.

Exploration

Student responses will vary.

Chapter 12. Congruence and Transformations

12-1 Geometric Figures *(pages 379–380)*

1. **a.** (2), (3), (4), (6), (7), (8)   **b.** (4), (7), (8)
2. **a.** *C, S*   **b.** *A, R*   **c.** *B, T*
3. **a.** (6)   **b.** (4)   **c.** (3)   **d.** (8)   **e.** (5)
4. **a.** (1), (3), (5), (8), (10)   **b.** (3)   **c.** (1)
   d. (5)   **e.** (8)   **f.** (10)
5. **a.** Rectangle, quadrilateral
   b. Square, quadrilateral
   c. Triangle
   d. Octagon

6. **a.**
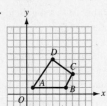
   b. Quadrilateral

7. **a.**
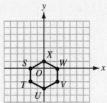
   b. Hexagon

8. **a.**
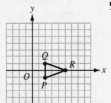
   b. Triangle

9. **a.**
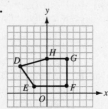
   b. Pentagon

10. **a.**
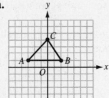
   b. $\frac{15}{2} = 7.5$

11. **a.**
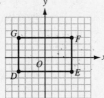
   b. 40

12. **a.**
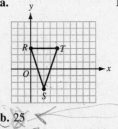
   b. 25

13. **a.**
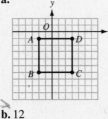
   b. 12

14. **a.**
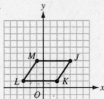
   b. 15

15. **a.** (4, −2)   **b.** 35

16. **a.**
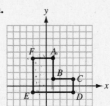
   b. 21

12-2 Congruent Triangles *(pages 385–387)*

1. **a.** (2), (4)   **b.** (3), (5)   **c.** (1), (3)
2. **a.** Yes
   b. Figures in the copies have the same size and shape as their originals (corresponding sides and angles will be congruent).
3. **a.** They will be similar.
   b. Lengths should be in proportion and angles congruent.
4.a–6.a Student drawings
4. **b.** $\triangle ABC \cong \triangle FED$; s.a.s. $\cong$ s.a.s.
   (Note that $\triangle ABC \ncong \triangle DEF$ because $\overline{AB} \ncong \overline{DE}$ and $\overline{BC} \ncong \overline{EF}$.)
5. **b.** $\triangle ABC \cong \triangle FED$; a.s.a. $\cong$ a.s.a.
   (Note that $\triangle ABC \ncong \triangle DEF$ because $\overline{AB} \ncong \overline{DE}$ and $\angle A \ncong \angle D$.)
6. **b.** $\triangle ABC \cong \triangle DEF$; a.s.a. $\cong$ a.s.a.
7. The congruent angle may not have been the included angle in both triangles.
8. **a.** $\triangle ABC \cong \triangle VTS$ by a.s.a. $\cong$ a.s.a.
   $\triangle DEF \cong \triangle QPR$ by s.a.s. $\cong$ s.a.s.
   $\triangle JKL \cong \triangle YXZ$ by a.s.a. $\cong$ a.s.a.
   b. For $\triangle ABC$ and $\triangle VTS$:
   $$\angle A \cong \angle V, \angle B \cong \angle T, \angle C \cong \angle S$$
   $$\overline{AB} \cong \overline{VT}, \overline{BC} \cong \overline{TS}, \overline{AC} \cong \overline{VS}$$
   or
   $$\angle A \cong \angle T, \angle B \cong \angle V, \angle C \cong \angle S$$
   $$\overline{AB} \cong \overline{VT}, \overline{BC} \cong \overline{TS}, \overline{AC} \cong \overline{TS}$$

For $\triangle DEF$ and $\triangle QPR$:

$\angle D \cong \angle Q, \angle E \cong \angle P, \angle F \cong \angle R$

$\overline{DE} \cong \overline{QP}, \overline{EF} \cong \overline{PR}, \overline{DF} \cong \overline{QR}$

For $\triangle JKL$ and $\triangle YXZ$:

$\angle J \cong \angle Y, \angle K \cong \angle X, \angle L \cong \angle Z$

$\overline{JK} \cong \overline{YX}, \overline{KL} \cong \overline{XZ}, \overline{JL} \cong \overline{YZ}$

9. a. s.a.s. $\cong$ s.a.s.
  b. $m\angle RTS = m\angle R'T'S' = 60$

10. a. a.s.a. $\cong$ a.s.a.   **b.** $BC = B'C' = 3.4$ m

11. a. They are equal.   **b.** a.s.a. $\cong$ a.s.a.
  c. They are equal.

12. a. $\triangle ABE \cong \triangle CBE$; s.a.s. $\cong$ s.a.s.
  b. $AE = CE = 25$ ft

13. a. s.s.s. $\cong$ s.s.s.   **b.** $x = 20$

14.

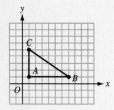
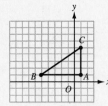
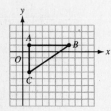
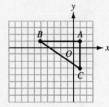

  a. Four   **b.** $(7, 1)$ or $(-5, 1)$
  c. $(1, 5)$ or $(1, -3)$ **d.** Yes; s.a.s. $\cong$ s.a.s.

15.

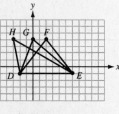
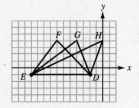
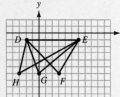
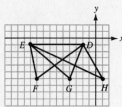

  a. Any point with y-coordinate 4 or -6
  b. H is any point on a line parallel to the x-axis
  and 4 units above, or 6 units below, the axis.

12-3 Quadrilaterals *(pages 390–392)*

1. a. If a polygon is a trapezoid, it is a quadrilateral; true.
  b. If a polygon is a quadrilateral, it is a trapezoid; false (not always true).
  c. If a polygon is not a trapezoid, it is not a quadrilateral; false (not always true).
  d. If a polygon is not a quadrilateral, it is not a trapezoid; true.

2. a. If a polygon is a rectangle, it is a parallelogram; true.
  b. If a polygon is a parallelogram, it is a rectangle; false (not always true).
  c. If a polygon is not a rectangle, it is not a parallelogram; false (not always true).
  d. If a polygon is not a parallelogram, it is not a rectangle; true.

3. a. If a polygon is a rhombus, it is a parallelogram; true.
  b. If a polygon is a parallelogram, it is a rhombus; false (not always true).
  c. If a polygon is not a rhombus, it is not a parallelogram; false (not always true).
  d. If a polygon is not a parallelogram, it is not a rhombus; true.

4. a. If a polygon is a rhombus, it is a square; false (not always true).
  b. If a polygon is a square, it is a rhombus; true.
  c. If a polygon is not a rhombus, it is not a square; true.
  d. If a polygon is not a square, it is not a rhombus; false (not always true).

5. a. If a polygon is a parallelogram, it is a square; false (not always true).
  b. If a polygon is a square, it is a parallelogram; true.
  c. If a polygon is not a parallelogram, it is not a square; true.
  d. If a polygon is not a square, it is not a parallelogram; false (not always true).

6. a. If two angles are opposite angles of a parallelogram, they are congruent; true.
  b. If two angles are congruent, they are opposite angles of a parallelogram; false (not always true).
  c. If two angles are not opposite angles of a parallelogram, they are not congruent; false (not always true).
  d. If two angles are not congruent, they are not opposite angles of a parallelogram; true.

7. a. $x = 50$
  b. $m\angle A = 110, m\angle B = 50, m\angle C = 120,$
  $m\angle D = 80$

8. a. $x = 90$
  b. $m\angle E = 90, m\angle F = 90, m\angle G = 70,$
  $m\angle H = 110$

9. a. $x = 60$
  b. $m\angle K = 60, m\angle L = 50, m\angle M = 130,$
  $m\angle N = 120$

10. a. $x = 45$
 b. $m\angle Q = 55$, $m\angle R = 105$, $m\angle S = 110$,
   $m\angle T = 90$
11. $AB = DC = 14$
12. $m\angle A = 110$, $m\angle B = 70$, $m\angle C = 110$, $m\angle D = 70$
13. $BC = AD = 11$
14. 20 　　　**15.** 42 　　　**16.** 18
17. a. $PR = TS = 4$, $RS = 7$, $PT = 11$
 b. $m\angle P = m\angle T = 60$, $m\angle TSR = m\angle SRP = 120$
18. a. 360° 　　**b.** 360° 　　　**c.** Yes

19. a.
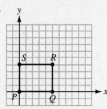
 b. Rectangle
 c. 20

20. a.
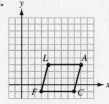
 b. Parallelogram
 c. 20

21. a.
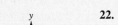
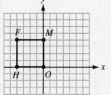
 b. Square
 c. 16

22. a.
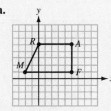
 b. Trapezoid
 c. 24

23. a.
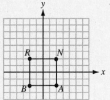
 b. Square
 c. 16

24. a.
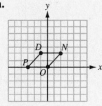
 b. Parallelogram
 c. 6

25. a.
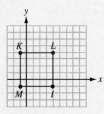
 b. Square
 c. 25

26. a.
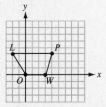
 b. Trapezoid
 c. $\dfrac{27}{2}$ or 13.5

27.
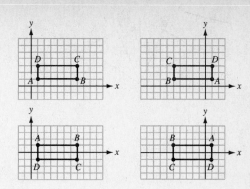
 a. Four
 b. (7, 1) or (−5, 1)
 c. (7, 3) or (7, −1) if B is (7, 1);
   (−5, 3) or (−5, −1) if B is (−5, 1)
 d. (1, 3) if C is (7, 3) or (−5, 3);
   (1, −1) if C is (7, −1) or (−5, −1)

28.
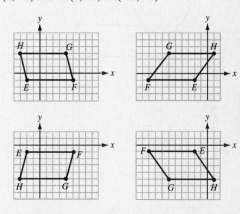
 a. (5, −1) or (−9, −1)
 b. Infinitely many (Four possible parallelograms are
   shown.)
 c. Any point whose y-coordinate is 3 or − 5
 d. If F is (5, −1), any point whose x-coordinate is 7
   less than that of G and whose y-coordinate is
   equal to that of G
   If F is (−9, −1), any point whose x-coordinate is
   more than that of G and whose y-coordinate is
   equal to that of G

12-4 Line Reflections *(page 397)*

1. a, b.
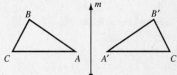

341

2. a, b.

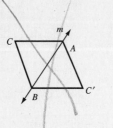

3. a, b.

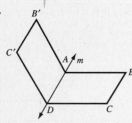

4. a, b.

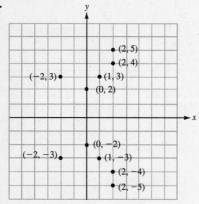

5. a–d.

6–10. a.

(2, 5)
(2, 4)
(−2, 3) (1, 3)
(0, 2)
(0, −2)
(−2, −3) (1, −3)
(2, −4)
(2, −5)

6. b. (2, −5)   **7. b.** (1, −3)
8. b. (−2, −3)   **9. b.** (2, 4)
10. b. (0, −2)

11–15. a.

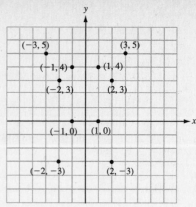

(−3, 5)   (3, 5)
(−1, 4) (1, 4)
(−2, 3) (2, 3)
(−1, 0) (1, 0)
(−2, −3) (2, −3)

11. b. (−3, 5)   **12. b.** (−1, 4)
13. b. (−2, −3)   **14. b.** (2, 3)
15. b. (1, 0)

Line Symmetry *(page 399)*

1. a, b.

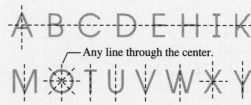

A B C D E H I K

— Any line through the center.

M O T U V W X Y

2. a, b. *(1)*

M O M

(2) D A D   None

(3) S I S   None

(4) O T T O

(5) B O O K

(6) R A D A R   None

(7) U N   None

(8) N O O N   None

(9) H I K E

(10)  S W I M S   None

(11)  O H H O

(12)  C H O K E D

3. a.   **b.** Two

4. a. 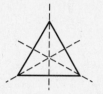   **b.** Three

5. a. 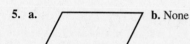   **b.** None

6. a.   **b.** One

7. a.   **b.** Two

8. a.   **b.** Six

9. a.   **b.** None (unless the trapezoid is isosceles)

10. a.   **b.** None

11. a.   **b.** Infinitely many (any line through the center)

12. a.   **b.** Eight

13. a. 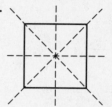   **b.** Four

14. a. 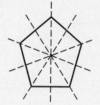   **b.** Five

15. a.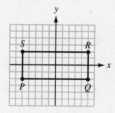

    b. The *x*-axis and *y*-axis

8759

16. a, b.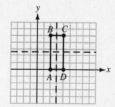

343

Point Reflections *(page 402)*

1.

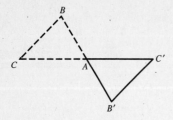

2.

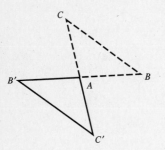

3.

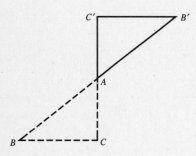

4.

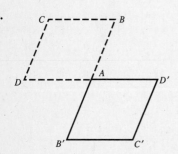

5. **a.** D **b.** B **c.** E **d.** A
   e. C **f.** $\overline{DE}$ **g.** $\overline{DB}$ **h.** $\overline{AC}$

6–9. **a.**

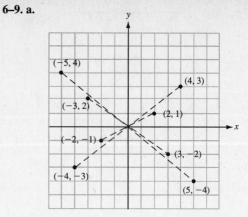

6. **b.** $(-4, -3)$
7. **b.** $(3, -2)$
8. **b.** $(2, 1)$
9. **b.** $(5, -4)$

Point Symmetry *(page 403)*

1. **a, b.**   H I N O S X Z

2. Yes   3. No   4. Yes
5. No   6. No   7. Yes
8. (2), (3), (6), (7), (8), (10), (11), (12)
9. Student drawings
10. Student drawings
11. (4)

12-6 Translations *(pages 404–405)*

1. **a.** P **b.** H **c.** O **d.** L **e.** K
2. **a.** I **b.** A **c.** N **d.** K **e.** F
3. **a.** No   **b.** Yes, F **c.** Yes, E **d.** No

4. **a, c.**

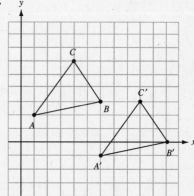

b. B' $(11, 0)$; C' $(9, 3)$

5. a, b.

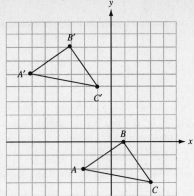

c. $A'(-6, 5); B'(-2, 7); C'(-1, 4)$

6. a. (2)

7. $(x, y) \rightarrow (x, y-4)$

8. a, d.

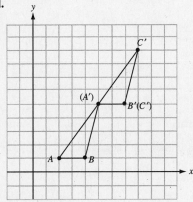

b. $(x, y) \rightarrow (x + 3, y + 4)$

c. $B'(7, 5); C'(8, 9)$

9. a, c.

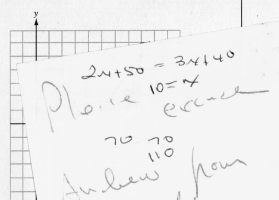

b. $A'(1, -3)$

d. 0

12-7 Rotations *(page 407)*

1. a. D **b.** E **c.** F **d.** J **e.** K **f.** A **g.** B
2. a. J **b.** K **c.** L **d.** D **e.** E **f.** G **g.** H
3. a, b.   **c.** 180°

4. a, b.   **c.** 180°

5. a, b.   **c.** 180°

6. a, b. **c.** No symmetry

7. a, b. **c.** 60°

8. a, b. **c.** 72°

Review Exercises *(pages 408–409)*

1. a. s.a.s. $\cong$ s.a.s. **b.** 4
   c. C **d.** $\overrightarrow{BD}$
2. 9
3. 70
4. a.   **b.** (1, 4)

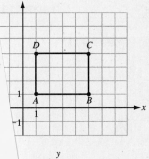

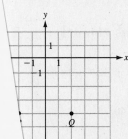

$\ldots, 0), S(-2, 0)$ or $R(2, -8), S(-2, -8)$

345

6. a.

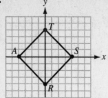

b. 24

7. a.

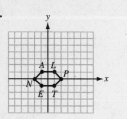

b. 6

8. (3, −4) and (−3, 5)

9. (3)

10. a. B **b.** E **c.** $\overline{BO}$ **d.** $\angle FCO$

11. a. C **b.** G **c.** $\overline{CO}$ **d.** $\angle FBO$

12. a. D **b.** H **c.** $\overline{DO}$ **d.** $\angle GCO$

13. a. G **b.** C **c.** $\overline{OG}$ **d.** $\angle COG$

14. (3)

15. Yes; point symmetry or rotational symmetry (180°)

16. a–d. Student responses **17.** N, S, Z

Cumulative Review *(pages 409–410)*

1. $2x^2 + 13$ **2.** $2x^2 − 11x + 15$

3. 15   **4.** $2x^2 − 3x − 1$

5.

6. (4)

7. −5

8. −4

9. a. 8π irrational (Any calculator result, such as 25.132741, is a rational approximation of the irrational number.)

b. 1 rational

c. $\dfrac{\sqrt{2}}{2}$ irrational (Any calculator result, such as 0.7071068, is a rational approximation of the irrational number.)

10. $−2x^2 − 2x + 4$

11. a. 74°

b. 106°

c. 74°

d. 106°

e. 106°

f. 106°

g. 74°

h. 74°

12. $247.00

Exploration

Student responses will vary.

Chapter 13. Ratio and Proportion

Introductory page *(page 411)*

$$\frac{1 + \sqrt{5}}{2} \approx 1.618033989 \qquad \frac{13}{8} = 1.625$$

$$\frac{89}{55} \approx 1.618181818 \qquad \frac{233}{144} \approx 1.618055556$$

13-1 Ratio *(pages 414–415)*

1. a. $\dfrac{36}{12}$ **b.** 36:12 **2. a.** $\dfrac{48}{24}$ **b.** 48:24

3. a. $\dfrac{40}{25}$ **b.** 40:25 **4. a.** $\dfrac{2}{3}$ **b.** 2:3

5. a. $\dfrac{5}{4}$ **b.** 5:4

6. a. $\dfrac{1}{4}$ or 1:4 **b.** $\dfrac{8}{1}$ or 8:1 **c.** $\dfrac{3}{7}$ or 3:7

d. $\dfrac{4}{3}$ or 4:3 **e.** $\dfrac{3}{2}$ or 3:2 **f.** $\dfrac{2}{1}$ or 2:1

g. 1:3 **h.** 1:1 **i.** 12:5

j. 3:5 **k.** 3:2 **l.** 1:4

m. 3:5 **n.** $x:y$ **o.** 3:1

7. a. 2 **b.** 3 **c.** 1.5 **d.** 2.5 **e.** $\dfrac{5}{3}$

8. 10 **9.** $\dfrac{1}{8}$

10. a. Yes **b.** No **c.** No

d. Yes **e.** Yes **f.** No

11. a. $\dfrac{2}{3} = \dfrac{6}{9} = \dfrac{50}{75}$ **b.** 10:8 = 20:16 = 50:40

12. a. $2:4 = 3:6 = 4:8$ **b.** $2:10 = 3:15 = 4:20$
  c. $6:2 = 9:3 = 12:4$ **d.** $8:2 = 12:3 = 16:4$
  e. $6:8 = 9:12 = 12:16$ **f.** $4:6 = 6:9 = 8:12$
13. a. $1:1$ **b.** $1:1$
14. a. $3:1$ **b.** $3:1$ **c.** $1:2$
  d. $3:1$ **e.** $24:1$
15. a. $5:1$ **b.** $3:4$ **c.** $1:2$
  d. $3:5$ **e.** $150:7$ **f.** $4:1$
  g. $3:250$ **h.** $3:100$ **i.** $1:4$
16. a. $3:1$ **b.** $6:1$ **c.** $12:1$
  d. $3:1$ **e.** $2:1$ **f.** $1:4$
  g. $4:1$ **h.** $12:1$ **i.** $4:1$
17. a. $90:162$ or $5:9$ **b.** 5
18. a. $6:4$ or $3:2$ **b.** 3
19. a. $1\frac{1}{4}:1\frac{3}{4}$ or $5:7$ **20.** $10:5$ or $2:1$
21. $b:(b + g)$ **22.** $2x:10x$ or $1:5$
23. a. $3x$ and $4x$ **b.** $5x$ and $3x$
  c. x and $4x$ **d.** x and $2x$
  e. $3x$ and $5x$
24. a. $x, 2x, 3x$ **b.** $3x, 4x, 5x$
  c. $x, 3x, 4x$ **d.** $2x, 3x, 5x$
25. a. $12:7:6$
26. a. $6:5:2$ **b.** $3:1:2$
  c. $6:3:8$ **d.** $2:1:1$
  e. $36:12:1$ **f.** $4:2:1$
27. a. 45 or 80

13-2 Using a Ratio to Express a Rate
(page 417)

1. $2:1$ (2 apples per person)
2. $8:1$ (8 patients per nurse)
3. $0.5:1$ ($0.50/L)
4. $6:1$ (6¢/gr)
5. $3:1$ (3 oz/dollar)
6. $0.62:1$ (0.62 mi/km)
7. 3
8. 8 cents
9. a. 57.5 mi/hr **b.** 4.5 mi/hr
  c. 32 mi/hr **d.** 124 mi/hr
10. a. 3.5 **b.** 3.3 **c.** Giant size
11. Johanna is faster.
  (Johanna: 46 words/min; Al: 43 words/min)
12. Ronald is faster.
  (Ronald: 7.5 m/s; Carlos: $6.\overline{6}$ m/s)

13-3 Verbal Problems Involving Ratio
(page 419)

1. 40, 30 **2.** 100, 60 **3.** 42, 30
4. 48, 12 **5.** 12 cm, 20 cm
6. 12 cm, 12 cm, 10 cm **7.** 275 boys
8. 12 cm, 16 cm, 20 cm **9.** 132 cm, 48 cm
10. 36°, 54° **11.** 80°, 100°

12. $m\angle 1 = m\angle 3 = m\angle 5 = m\angle 7 = 60$;
  $m\angle 2 = m\angle 4 = m\angle 6 = m\angle 8 = 120$;
13. a. 40°, 40°, 100° **b.** Isosceles
14. 84°, 48°, 48° **15.** 25 in., 25 in., 15 in.
16. Carl $70; Donald $30 **17.** 9, 21
18. 12, 20 **19.** Sam 21; Wilbur 27
20. $7\frac{1}{2}$ L of water, 5 L of acid
21. 20°, 80°, 80°

13-4 Proportion (pages 423–424)

1. Yes **2.** No **3.** No **4.** No
5. Yes **6.** Yes **7.** 4 **8.** 30
9. 24 **10.** 28 **11.** 20 **12.** 5
13. 36 **14.** 12 **15.** 9 **16.** 15
17. 18 **18.** 4 **19.** 3 **20.** 7
21. 36 **22.** 8 **23.** 3 **24.** $\dfrac{bc}{a}$
25. $6r$ **26.** $\dfrac{2mr}{s}$ **27.** $\dfrac{12}{20}$ **28.** $\dfrac{25}{60}$
29. $\dfrac{20}{50}$ **30.** $\dfrac{36}{12}$ **31.** 29 **32.** $\dfrac{12}{9}$
33. $\dfrac{12}{19}$ **34.** 24

13-5 Direct Variation (pages 427–429)

1. 4 **2.** 40 **3.** $\dfrac{1}{9}$ **4.** 4
5. $\dfrac{3}{2}$ **6.** $\dfrac{17}{2}$ **7.** $\dfrac{4}{5}$ **8.** $\dfrac{53}{50}$
9. $\dfrac{3}{2}$ **10.** Yes; $p = 3s$ **11.** Yes; $c = 2n$
12. No **13.** Yes; $d = 20t$ **14.** Yes; $y = -3x$
15. No **16.** $A = 10, h = 5, A = 5h$
17. $S = 12, h = 10, S = \dfrac{3}{2}h$
18. $W = 4, L = 14, L = 2W$
19. No; the ratio $\dfrac{R}{T}$ is not constant.
20. Yes; the ratio $\dfrac{t}{D}$ is constant.
21. Yes; the ratio $\dfrac{e}{i}$ is constant.
22. No; the ratio $\dfrac{b}{h}$ is not constant.
23. a. Directly
  b. The cost of 9 articles will be 3 times as much.
  c. C is doubled.

24. a. Directly
  b. The rectangle having an 8-in. length will have 2 times the area.
  c. A is tripled.

25. $D = 360$	**26.** $Y = 140$	**27.** $h = 3$
28. $N = 15$	**29.** \$4.45	**30.** \$30.80

31. $1\frac{1}{4}$ lb   **32.** 140 shots

33. 420 calories   **34.** 1,620 calories

35. 170 calories   **36.** $5\frac{1}{2}$ hr   **37.** 7.65 kg

38. $2\frac{1}{2}$ cups   **39.** 25 bags   **40.** \$1,320

41. 5.6 km   **42.** \$21.00   **43.** $4\frac{1}{4}$ in.

44. a. \$12.82   **b.** \$15.58   **c.** \$0.89   **d.** 22.5 lb

45. $\dfrac{dn}{p}$ **46.** $\dfrac{qh}{d}$

13-6 Percent and Percentage Problems
(pages 433–435)

1. 0.72	**2.** 9	**3.** 7.2	**4.** 10
5. 33.6	**6.** 7.5	**7.** 16	**8.** 24
9. 27	**10.** 200	**11.** 80	**12.** 200
13. 72	**14.** 36	**15.** 160	**16.** 81
17. 62	**18.** 50%	**19.** 30%	**20.** 60%

21. 80%   **22.** $33\frac{1}{3}$%   **23.** 100%   **24.** 150%

25. $\frac{1}{2}$% or 0.5%   **26.** 25%

27. 30 students   **28. a.** \$1.92   **b.** \$25.92
29. 90 planes   **30.** \$8,000,000
31. \$814.50   **32.** 6 kg
33. 52,464   **34.** 16 games
35. \$120 (before the 20% discount)
36. \$3,500   **37.** \$120   **38.** 25%   **39.** 5%
40. \$78   **41.** \$3,000   **42.** 8%   **43.** \$60
44. a. Coat \$111.99; blouse \$35.19; shoes \$71.99; jeans \$26.39

  b. *Method 1*: Amount of discount = regular price times 0.2; subtract amount of discount from regular price to find sale price; round sale price to the nearest cent.
  Method 2: Sale price = regular price times 0.8; round sale price to the nearest cent.

45. Both plans save the same amount of money.
  Explanation: Let P = regular price. Then:
  Plan 1: Deduct 30%; sale price = $P - 0.3P = 0.7P$. Find 8% tax on sale price; $0.08\,(0.7P) = 0.056P$. Sale price + tax = $0.7P + 0.056P = 0.756P$.
  Plan 2: Find 8% tax on regular price; $0.08P$. Regular price + 8% tax = $P + 0.08P = 1.08P$. Deduct 30% of this amount, or find 70% of $1.08P$; $1.08P - 0.3\,(1.08P) = 1.08P - 0.324P = 0.756P$. Or $0.7\,(1.08P) = 0.756P$.

Under each plan, the customer pays 75.6% of the regular price, including payment of taxes.

46. Stock ABC: Original value = x
  March, rose 10%; $x + 0.1x = 1.1x$
  April, fell 10%; $1.1x - 0.1(1.1x) = 0.99x$
  Stock XYZ: Original value = x
  March, fell 10%; $x - 0.1x = 0.9x$
  April, rose 10%; $0.9x - 0.1(0.9x) = 0.99x$
  Each stock is now worth 99% of its original price.

13-7 Similar Polygons *(pages 436–438)*

1. No; corresponding sides are not in proportion.
2. No; corresponding angles are not congruent.
3. Yes; corresponding sides are in proportion, and corresponding angles are congruent.
4. Yes; corresponding sides are in proportion, and corresponding angles are congruent.
5. No; corresponding sides may not be in proportion.
6. No; corresponding angles may not be congruent, and corresponding sides may not be in proportion.
7. No; corresponding angles may not be congruent.

8. 9 cm   **9.** 12 cm   **10.** $5\frac{1}{2}$ in.

11. $BC = 6$, $A'B' = 8$, $B'C' = 12$, $C'D' = 8$

12. $XY = 15$, $YZ = 20$, $X'Y' = 7\frac{1}{2}$, $Y'Z' = 10$, $W'Z' = 7\frac{1}{2}$

13. $B'C' = 5$, $A'C' = 6$
14. $RT = 8$, $ST = 10$, $R'T' = 16$, $S'T' = 20$
15. a. None

  b. *(1)* 12″   *(2)* $7\frac{1}{2}$″   *(3)* $4\frac{1}{2}$″   *(4)* $6\frac{2}{3}$″

  (5) $4\frac{2}{3}$″   *(6)* $3\frac{1}{3}$″

13-8 Similar Triangles *(pages 441–444)*

1. a. $\angle A$ and $\angle E$, $\angle B$ and $\angle F$, $\angle C$ and $\angle D$
  b. $\overline{AB}$ and $\overline{EF}$, $\overline{BC}$ and $\overline{FD}$, $\overline{CA}$ and $\overline{DE}$
2. a. $\angle L$ and $\angle Q$, $\angle M$ and $\angle P$, $\angle N$ and $\angle R$
  b. $\overline{LM}$ and $\overline{QP}$, $\overline{MN}$ and $\overline{PR}$, $\overline{NL}$ and $\overline{RQ}$
3. a. $\angle R$ and $\angle Y$, $\angle S$ and $\angle Z$, $\angle T$ and $\angle X$
  b. $\overline{RS}$ and $\overline{YZ}$, $\overline{ST}$ and $\overline{ZX}$, $\overline{TR}$ and $\overline{XY}$
4. a. $\angle J$ and $\angle R$, $\angle K$ and $\angle Q$, $\angle L$ and $\angle P$
  b. $\overline{JK}$ and $\overline{RQ}$, $\overline{KL}$ and $\overline{QP}$, $\overline{LJ}$ and $\overline{PR}$
5–6. Student drawings
7. a. Yes   **b.** Corresponding angles are congruent.
8. $\triangle ABC \sim \triangle STR$ and $\triangle DEF \sim \triangle ZXY$; corresponding angles are congruent.
9. $\triangle ACB \sim \triangle MNL$; corresponding angles are congruent.
10. 2 cm
11. a. Yes   **b.** Corresponding angles are congruent.
  c. 4.5 cm

12. $DF = 8$, $EF = 10$
13. a. Corresponding angles are congruent.
  b. 8
14. 12   **15.** 4.5
16. a. Yes   **b.** Corresponding angles are congruent.
  c. 16 ft
17. 3 m   **18.** 30 ft
19. a. Yes; corresponding angles are congruent.
  b. 8 m
20. 75 ft
21. a. Corresponding angles are congruent.
  b. (*1*) 150 m   (2) 90 m
22. a. 27′6″ **b.** 11′11″ **c.** 58′8″
  d. 4′11″ (rounded from $58\frac{2}{3}''$ or $4'10\frac{2}{3}''$

13-9 Dilations *(pages 446–447)*

1. a. $OA' = 48$, $OB' = 72$ **b.** $OA' = 18$, $OB' = 27$
  c. $OA' = 16$, $OB' = 24$
2. a. 3   **b.** $\dfrac{6}{5}$ **c.** $\dfrac{5}{2}$
3. 16
4. Here, m$\angle ACB$ = m$\angle AC'B'$ because the angles are
  right angles. $\angle A$ is an angle in both triangles, and so
  the second pair of corresponding angles are equal in
  measure. $\triangle ABC \sim \triangle AB'C'$ because two triangles
  are similar if two angles of one are equal in measure
  to two corresponding angles of the other.
5. 6 in.   **6.** 20 m   **7.** 5:4
8. a. 24 m **b.** 864 m² **c.** 384 m² **d.** 480 m²
9. a. C' **b.** $B'C' = 12$, $AC' = 16$, $AB' = 20$
10. a. 16   **b.** 8   **c.** 12   **d.** 6
11. a. 24   **b.** 16   **c.** 18   **d.** 12
12. a. 10   **b.** 2   **c.** 7.5   **d.** 1.5
13. a. (*1*) 12 (2) 18   **b.** (*1*) 8 (2) 12
  c. $\dfrac{1}{2}$ or 0.5
14. a. $\angle L \cong \angle L$ Reflexive property of equality
   $\angle LAB \cong \angle LCD$ All right angles equal 90°.
   $\triangle LAG \sim \triangle LCD$ Two triangles are similar if
   two angles of one triangle are equal in measure to
   two corresponding angles of the other triangle.
  b. 50   **c.** 1.6 m or 1,600 mm   **d.** 12 m

13-10 Ratio of Perimeters and Ratio of Areas of Similar Polygons
(pages 453–454)

1. a. $\dfrac{3}{1}$ **b.** $\dfrac{9}{1}$ **2. a.** $\dfrac{4}{1}$ **b.** $\dfrac{16}{1}$
3. a. $\dfrac{1}{2}$ **b.** $\dfrac{1}{4}$ **4. a.** $\dfrac{1}{4}$ **b.** $\dfrac{1}{16}$
5. a. $\dfrac{6}{5}$ **b.** $\dfrac{36}{25}$ **6. a.** $\dfrac{10}{3}$ **b.** $\dfrac{100}{9}$

7. a. 5:2   **b.** $BC = 12.5$ in., $CA = 15$ in.
  c. 5:2
8. 9   **9.** 81   **10.** 90   **11.** (4)
12. (3)   **13.** (3)
14. a. 1:3
  b. $A'B' = 24$ in., $B'C' = 36$ in., $C'D' = 12$ in.
  c. 1:3   **d.** 1:9
15. 25:81   **16.** 242 cm² **17.** $\dfrac{5}{1}$ **18.** $\dfrac{4}{3}$
19. $\dfrac{1}{2}$ **20.** $\dfrac{15}{7}$ **21.** $\dfrac{2}{5}$ **22.** $\dfrac{5}{6}$
23. 13.5 sq ft   **24. a.** 2:1   **b.** 4:1
25. a. 4:5   **b.** 16:25
26. 24 mm   **27.** 25 in.; 40 in.
28. a. 81:16 **b.** 9:4   **29.** 12:5
30. a. 2:1   **b.** 3:1
  c. No; corresponding sides are not in the same ratio
   (or not in proportion).
  d. 6:1

Review Exercises *(pages 456–458)*

1. 6:7   **2.** 2 to 3   **3.** 3 to 5   **4.** 1 to 2
5. 165 g   **6.** 500 words   **7.** 3:4
8. 3   **9.** 5   **10.** 6   **11.** 8 and 32
12. (3)   **13.** (3)   **14.** (1)   **15.** 300
16. 125%   **17.** 0.07
18. a. $HJ = 11\frac{1}{4}$ in.; $GJ = 7\frac{1}{2}$ in.
  b. $\dfrac{4}{3}$ **c.** $\dfrac{4}{3}$ **d.** $\dfrac{16}{9}$
19. 1,700 students   **20.** 21 in.
21. a. $\angle A$ and $\angle T$, $\angle B$ and $\angle R$, $\angle C$ and $\angle S$
  b. $\overline{AB}$ and $\overline{TR}$, $\overline{BC}$ and $\overline{RS}$, $\overline{CA}$ and $\overline{ST}$
  c. 6
22. 16
23. a. 8   **b.** 5   **c.** 8   **d.** 16   **e.** 10   **f.** 20
24. 25 ft
25. a. Yes, by a.a. $\cong$ a.a. (m$\angle C$ = 65° and m$\angle F$ = 45°)
  b. 3
26. a. a.a. $\cong$ a.a.   **b.** 5 in.
  c. (*1*) 9 sq in.   (2) 25 sq in.   (3) 16 sq in.
  d. $\dfrac{10}{6}$ or $\dfrac{5}{3}$
27. 7:2   **28.** 4 days   **29.** 50

Cumulative Review *(page 458)*

1. 12 and 13
2. 3
3. a. 30 cm
  b. 2:3

Exploration

Student responses will vary

Chapter 14. Probability

14-1 Empirical Probability *(pages 464–466)*

1. a. $P(2) = \dfrac{1}{4}$

b.

Barbara	29	100	$\dfrac{29}{100} = 0.290$
Tom	60	200	$\dfrac{60}{200} = 0.300$
Ann	79	300	$\dfrac{79}{300} = 0.263$
Eddie	102	400	$\dfrac{102}{400} = 0.255$
Cathy	126	500	$\dfrac{126}{500} = 0.252$

c. Yes: cumulative relative frequency is approaching 0.250 or $\dfrac{1}{4}$.

2. $P(5) = \dfrac{1}{6}$ **3.** $P(\text{any heart}) = \dfrac{1}{4}$

4. $P(7) = \dfrac{1}{10}$ **5.** $P(\text{black}) = \dfrac{2}{5}$

6. $\dfrac{4}{26}$ or $\dfrac{2}{13}$ **7.** $P(4) = \dfrac{1}{4}$

8–13. Answers will vary.

14. a. 1 **b.** 1 **c.** 0 **d.** 0

14-2 Theoretical Probability
(pages 470–472)

1. a. {H, T} **b.** $P(\text{head}) = \dfrac{1}{2}$ **c.** $P(\text{tail}) = \dfrac{1}{2}$

2. a. 3 **b.** $\dfrac{1}{6}$

3. a. 2, 4, 6, **b.** $\dfrac{3}{6} = \dfrac{1}{2}$

4. a. 1, 2 **b.** $\dfrac{2}{6} = \dfrac{1}{3}$

5. a. 1, 3, 5 **b.** $\dfrac{3}{6} = \dfrac{1}{2}$

6. a. 4, 5, 6 **b.** $\dfrac{3}{6} = \dfrac{1}{2}$

7. a. 3, 4, 5, 6 **b.** $\dfrac{4}{6} = \dfrac{2}{3}$

8. a. 3 **b.** $\dfrac{1}{5}$

9. a. 2, 4 **b.** $\dfrac{2}{5}$

10. a. 1, 2 **b.** $\dfrac{2}{5}$

11. a. 1, 3, 5 **b.** $\dfrac{3}{5}$

12. a. 4, 5 **b.** $\dfrac{2}{5}$

13. a. 3, 4, 5 **b.** $\dfrac{3}{5}$

14. a. $\dfrac{1}{52}$ **b.** $\dfrac{4}{52} = \dfrac{1}{13}$ **c.** $\dfrac{13}{52} = \dfrac{1}{4}$

d. $\dfrac{26}{52} = \dfrac{1}{2}$ **e.** $\dfrac{1}{52}$ **f.** $\dfrac{13}{52} = \dfrac{1}{4}$

g. $\dfrac{4}{52} = \dfrac{1}{13}$ **h.** $\dfrac{2}{52} = \dfrac{1}{26}$ **i.** $\dfrac{2}{52} = \dfrac{1}{26}$

j. $\dfrac{12}{52} = \dfrac{3}{13}$

15. a. $\dfrac{1}{4}$ **b.** $\dfrac{1}{2}$ **c.** $\dfrac{1}{3}$

16. a. $\dfrac{2}{5}$ **b.** $\dfrac{1}{5}$ **c.** $\dfrac{2}{10} = \dfrac{1}{5}$ **d.** $\dfrac{4}{10} = \dfrac{2}{5}$

e. $\dfrac{3}{12} = \dfrac{1}{4}$ **f.** $\dfrac{2}{100} = \dfrac{1}{50}$

17. $\dfrac{2}{4} = \dfrac{1}{2}$

18. a. $\dfrac{16}{30} = \dfrac{8}{15}$ **b.** $\dfrac{14}{30} = \dfrac{7}{15}$

19. a. $\dfrac{1}{168}$ **b.** $\dfrac{1}{210}$

20. a. $\dfrac{2}{5}$ **b.** $\dfrac{3}{6} = \dfrac{1}{2}$ **c.** $\dfrac{3}{8}$ **d.** $\dfrac{4}{11}$

21. a. It is not equally likely that a person will be born in each state. (State populations are not the same.)
b. It is not equally likely that a person will be born in each month. (If it were equally likely, the *exact* same number of people would be born in each of the 12 months of the year.)
c. Point up and point down are not equally likely.
d. It is not equally likely that a person will attend a religious service each day. (Many people worship on Saturday or Sunday.)

22. a. $\dfrac{3}{8}$ **b.** $\dfrac{4}{8} = \dfrac{1}{2}$ **c.** $\dfrac{3}{8}$ **d.** $\dfrac{5}{8}$

e. $\dfrac{3}{8}$ **f.** $\dfrac{6}{8} = \dfrac{3}{4}$ **g.** $\dfrac{7}{8}$ **h.** $\dfrac{3}{8}$

i. $\dfrac{5}{8}$ **j.** $\dfrac{3}{8}$

14-3 Evaluating Simple Probabilities
(pages 476–478)

1. **a.** { }, {H}, {T}, {H, T}
   b. P(neither H nor T) = 0
   $$P(H) = \frac{1}{2}$$
   $$P(T) = \frac{1}{2}$$

2. **a.** {5}   **b.** $\frac{1}{7}$

3. **a.** {2, 4, 6}   **b.** $\frac{3}{7}$

4. **a.** {1, 2, 3, 4}   **b.** $\frac{4}{7}$

5. **a.** {1, 3, 5, 7}   **b.** $\frac{4}{7}$

6. **a.** {6, 7}   **b.** $\frac{2}{7}$

7. **a.** {2, 3, 4, 5, 6, 7}   **b.** $\frac{6}{7}$

8. **a.** { }   **b.** 0

9. **a.** {1, 2, 3, 4, 5, 6, 7}   **b.** 1

10. **a.** $\frac{5}{7}$ **b.** $\frac{2}{3}$ **c.** $\frac{3}{8}$
    d. 1   **e.** 0   **f.** 1

11. **a.** $\frac{1}{6}$ **b.** $\frac{3}{6} = \frac{1}{2}$ **c.** $\frac{2}{6} = \frac{1}{3}$
    d. 0   **e.** $\frac{4}{6} = \frac{2}{3}$ **f.** 1
    g. 0   **h.** 1   **i.** 0

12. **a.** 0   **b.** 1   **c.** $\frac{4}{6} = \frac{2}{3}$
    d. 0   **e.** 1   **f.** 0

13. **a.** $\frac{4}{52} = \frac{1}{13}$ **b.** $\frac{13}{52} = \frac{1}{4}$ **c.** 0
    d. 0   **e.** 1   **f.** $\frac{13}{52} = \frac{1}{4}$
    g. 0   **h.** 0   **i.** 0

14. **a.** .6   **b.** .4   **c.** 1   **d.** 0

15. **a.** 10%   **b.** 50%   **c.** 40%   **d.** 100%
    e. 0%

16. **a.** $\frac{3}{5}$ **b.** $\frac{2}{5}$ **c.** $\frac{1}{5}$ **d.** 0
    e. $\frac{2}{5}$ **f.** 0   **g.** 0   **h.** $\frac{1}{5}$
    i. $\frac{3}{5}$ **j.** 1   **k.** 0   **l.** 1

17. **a.** $\frac{3}{6} = \frac{1}{2}$ **b.** 0   **c.** 0   **d.** $\frac{3}{6} = \frac{1}{2}$
    e. $\frac{1}{6}$ **f.** 0   **g.** 1

18. 8 marbles   19. 12 boys, 9 girls
20. 18 caramels, 12 nut clusters
21. 28 rides
22. Answers will vary for both *a* and *b*.
23. Probability is never greater than 1, which represents certainty.
24. Probability is never less than 0, which represents impossibility.
25. This is a certainty with probability 1 or 100%.

26. **a.** {E_1, E_2}   **b.** $\frac{2}{5}$

27. **a.** {S_1, S_2, S_3, S_4}   **b.** $\frac{4}{11}$

28. **a.** {I, A, E}   **b.** $\frac{3}{8}$

29. **a.** {E_1, E_2, E_3, I}   **b.** $\frac{4}{7}$

30. **a.** {S, P, R, Y}   **b.** 1

14-4 The Probability of (*A* and *B*)
(pages 480–481)

1. **a.** $\frac{2}{6} = \frac{1}{3}$ **b.** $\frac{1}{6}$ **c.** $\frac{1}{6}$
   d. 0   **e.** $\frac{3}{6} = \frac{1}{2}$ **f.** 0

2. **a.** $\frac{1}{52}$ **b.** $\frac{2}{52} = \frac{1}{26}$ **c.** $\frac{1}{52}$
   d. $\frac{2}{52} = \frac{1}{26}$ **e.** $\frac{1}{52}$ **f.** 0
   g. $\frac{1}{52}$ **h.** $\frac{2}{52} = \frac{1}{26}$ **i.** $\frac{6}{52} = \frac{3}{26}$

3. **a.** $\frac{2}{4} = \frac{1}{2}$ **b.** $\frac{1}{4}$ **c.** $\frac{1}{4}$
   d. 1   **e.** $\frac{3}{4}$

4. **a.** $\frac{7}{12}$ **b.** $\frac{5}{12}$ **c.** $\frac{4}{12} = \frac{1}{3}$
   d. $\frac{8}{12} = \frac{2}{3}$ **e.** $\frac{3}{12} = \frac{1}{4}$ **f.** $\frac{2}{12} = \frac{1}{6}$
   g. $\frac{2}{12} = \frac{1}{6}$ **h.** $\frac{5}{12}$ **i.** 0
   j. $\frac{2}{12} = \frac{1}{6}$

5. **a.** 21   **b.** *(1)* $\frac{23}{30}$ *(2)* $\frac{28}{30}$ *(3)* $\frac{21}{30}$

14-5 The Probability of (*A* or *B*)
(pages 485–486)

1. a. $\frac{1}{5}$ **b.** $\frac{2}{5}$ **c.** $\frac{3}{5}$

d. $\frac{4}{5}$ **e.** $\frac{3}{5}$ **f.** $\frac{4}{5}$

g. $\frac{3}{5}$ **h.** $\frac{3}{5}$

2. a. $\frac{1}{6}$ **b.** $\frac{2}{6}=\frac{1}{3}$ **c.** $\frac{3}{6}=\frac{1}{2}$

d. $\frac{4}{6}=\frac{2}{3}$ **e.** $\frac{3}{6}=\frac{1}{2}$ **f.** $\frac{4}{6}=\frac{2}{3}$

g. $\frac{3}{6}=\frac{1}{2}$ **h.** $\frac{3}{6}=\frac{1}{2}$ **i.** $\frac{2}{6}=\frac{1}{3}$

j. 1

3. a. $\frac{8}{52}=\frac{2}{13}$ **b.** $\frac{8}{52}=\frac{2}{13}$ **c.** $\frac{26}{52}=\frac{1}{2}$

d. $\frac{16}{52}=\frac{4}{13}$ **e.** $\frac{28}{52}=\frac{7}{13}$ **f.** $\frac{12}{52}=\frac{3}{13}$

g. $\frac{16}{52}=\frac{4}{13}$ **h.** $\frac{39}{52}=\frac{3}{4}$ **i.** $\frac{16}{52}=\frac{4}{13}$

4. a. $\frac{2}{16}=\frac{1}{8}$ **b.** $\frac{8}{16}=\frac{1}{2}$ **c.** $\frac{9}{16}$

d. $\frac{6}{16}=\frac{3}{8}$ **e.** $\frac{2}{16}=\frac{1}{8}$ **f.** $\frac{14}{16}=\frac{7}{6}$

g. 1   **h.** $\frac{11}{16}$ **i.** $\frac{10}{16}=\frac{5}{8}$

5. (2)   **6.** (2)   **7.** (1)

8. (2)   **9.** (2)   **10.** (3)

11. a. .85   **b.** 289 students

12. a. 2   **b.** 10   **c.** 4   **d.** 16

14-6 The Probability of (Not *A*); Probability as a Sum *(pages 489–490)*

1. a. $\frac{1}{6}$ **b.** $\frac{5}{6}$ **c.** $\frac{3}{6}=\frac{1}{2}$

d. $\frac{3}{6}=\frac{1}{2}$ **e.** $\frac{2}{6}=\frac{1}{3}$ **f.** $\frac{4}{6}=\frac{2}{3}$

g. 1   **h.** 0

2. a. $\frac{3}{10}$ **b.** $\frac{7}{10}$

3. a. $\frac{13}{52}=\frac{1}{4}$ **b.** $\frac{39}{52}=\frac{3}{4}$ **c.** $\frac{12}{52}=\frac{3}{13}$

d. $\frac{40}{52}=\frac{10}{13}$ **e.** $\frac{48}{52}=\frac{12}{13}$

f. $\frac{50}{52}=\frac{25}{26}$ **g.** $\frac{51}{52}$

4. a. (*1*) $\frac{3}{12}=\frac{1}{4}$ (*2*) $\frac{4}{12}=\frac{1}{3}$ (*3*) $\frac{5}{12}$

b. $\frac{3}{12}+\frac{4}{12}+\frac{5}{12}=\frac{12}{12}=1$

5. a. $P(\text{P})=\frac{1}{10}$

$P(\text{I})=\frac{3}{10}$

$P(\text{C})=\frac{2}{10}=\frac{1}{5}$

$P(\text{N})=\frac{2}{10}=\frac{1}{5}$

$P(\text{K})=\frac{1}{10}$

$P(\text{G})=\frac{1}{10}$

b. $\frac{1}{10}+\frac{3}{10}+\frac{2}{10}+\frac{2}{10}+\frac{1}{10}+\frac{1}{10}=\frac{10}{10}=1$

6. $\frac{6}{7}$ **7.** .907   **8.** $\frac{8}{9}$

9. a. $\frac{3}{7}$ **b.** $\frac{4}{7}$ **c.** $\frac{4}{7}$

d. 1   **e.** 0

10. a. $\frac{3}{4}$ **b.** $\frac{1}{4}$ **c.** $\frac{1}{4}$

d. 1   **e.** $\frac{3}{4}$

11. a. .2   **b.** .3   **c.** .5   **d.** .7

e. .8   **f.** .7   **g.** .5   **h.** 0

12. a. $\frac{1}{11}$ **b.** $\frac{2}{11}$ **c.** 0   **d.** $\frac{3}{11}$

e. $\frac{3}{11}$ **f.** $\frac{4}{11}$ **g.** $\frac{7}{11}$ **h.** $\frac{4}{11}$

i. 1

13. a. $\frac{4}{52}=\frac{1}{13}$ **b.** $\frac{13}{52}=\frac{1}{4}$ **c.** $\frac{1}{52}$

d. $\frac{16}{52}=\frac{4}{13}$ **e.** $\frac{39}{52}=\frac{3}{4}$ **f.** $\frac{48}{52}=\frac{12}{13}$

g. $\frac{8}{52} = \frac{2}{13}$ **h.** $\frac{51}{52}$ **i.** 0

j. $\frac{2}{52} = \frac{1}{26}$ **k.** $\frac{28}{52} = \frac{7}{13}$

14. a. $\frac{1}{10}$ **b.** $\frac{4}{10} = \frac{2}{5}$ **c.** $\frac{6}{10} = \frac{3}{5}$

d. $\frac{6}{10} = \frac{3}{5}$ **e.** $\frac{7}{10}$ **f.** $\frac{9}{10}$

g. 0   **h.** $\frac{7}{10}$ **i.** 0

j. $\frac{5}{10} = \frac{1}{2}$ **k.** $\frac{3}{10}$ **l.** 1

14-7 The Counting Principle and Sample Spaces (pages 493–494)

1. a. 10   **b.** 40   **c.** 36
2. 80   **3.** 56   **4.** 42   **5.** 12
6. a. 40   **b.** 24   **c.** 12
7. a. {(T, H), (T, T), (H, H), (H,T)}   **b.** $2 \cdot 2 = 4$
c. 1   **b.** 2
8. a.

b. {(T, T), (T, F), (F, T), (F, F)}
c. This set is the same as the set of all possible truth values for two statements
9. a. 8   **b.**

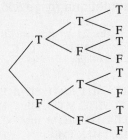

c. {(T, T, T), (T, T, F), (T, F, T), (T, F, F), (F, T, T), (F, T, F), (F, F, T), (F, F, F)}
10. a.

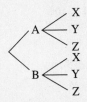

b. {(A, X), (A, Y), (A, Z), (B, X), (B, Y), (B, Z)}
11. a. 4   **b.** 64   **c.** 4^n
12. 180

13. a. 36
b.

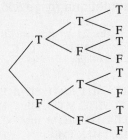

14. a. $26^2 \cdot 10^3 = 676,000$
b. $10^3 \cdot 26^3 = 17,576,000$
c. $10^4 \cdot 26^2 = 6,760,000$
15. a. $31 \cdot 30 = 930$ **b.** 31   **c.** $31 \cdot 31 = 961$

14-8 Probabilities and the Counting Principle; Predicting Outcomes (pages 496–497)

1. a. $\frac{1}{2}$ **b.** $\frac{1}{6}$ **c.** $\frac{1}{12}$

2. a. $\frac{1}{12}$ **b.** $\frac{1}{4}$ **c.** $\frac{1}{3}$ **d.** $\frac{1}{6}$

3. $\frac{1}{4}$ **4.** $\frac{1}{4}$ **5.** $\frac{2}{15}$

6. a. $\frac{1}{2}$ **b.** $\frac{1}{16}$ **c.** $\left(\frac{1}{2}\right)^n$ or $\frac{1}{2^n}$

7. a. $\frac{1}{6}$ **b.** $\frac{1}{4}$ **8. a.** $\frac{1}{8}$ **b.** $\frac{1}{8}$

9. a. $\frac{1}{64}$ **b.** $\frac{49}{64}$

10. a. .49   **b.** .21   **c.** .09
d. .21   **e.** .42   **f.** .58
11. 25 radios   **12.** 4 days
13. On the next toss, $P(\text{H}) = \frac{1}{2}$. Every toss of a coin is independent of all other tosses of that same coin.

14. 175 patients   **15.** 50   **16.** 17
17. a. (*1*) $\frac{1}{2,000,000}$ (*2*) $\frac{2}{2,000,000} = \frac{1}{1,000,000}$

(*3*) $\frac{100}{2,000,000} = \frac{1}{20,000}$

b. 5,000
c. 994,897

14-9 Probabilities with Two or More Activities (pages 501–502)

1. a. {(H, H), (H, T), (T, H), (T, T)}

b. $\frac{1}{4}$ **c.** $\frac{1}{4}$ **d.** $\frac{3}{4}$

2. a. $\frac{1}{4}$ **b.** $\frac{1}{4}$ **c.** $\frac{2}{4} = \frac{1}{2}$ **d.** $\frac{2}{4} = \frac{1}{2}$

e. $\frac{3}{4}$ **f.** $\frac{1}{2}$ **g.** $\frac{1}{4}$

3. a. $\frac{1}{8}$ **b.** $\frac{1}{8}$ **c.** $\frac{2}{8} = \frac{1}{4}$ **d.** $\frac{3}{8}$

e. $\frac{1}{2}$ **f.** $\frac{7}{8}$ **g.** $\frac{1}{4}$

4. {(B, B, B, B), (B, B, B, G), (B, B, G, B),
(B, B, G, G), (B, G, B, B), (B, G, B, G),
(B, G, G, B), (B, G, G, G), (G, B, B, B),
(G, B, B, G), (G, B, G, B), (G, B, G, G),
(G, G, B, B), G, G, B, G), (G, G, G, B),
(G, G, G, G)}

a. $\frac{1}{16}$ **b.** $\frac{1}{16}$ **c.** $\frac{2}{16} = \frac{1}{8}$ **d.** $\frac{6}{16} = \frac{3}{8}$

e. $\frac{1}{2}$ **f.** $\frac{15}{16}$ **g.** $\frac{1}{4}$

5. a. {(H, H, H), (H, H, T), (H, T, H), (H, T, T)
(T, H, H), (T, H, T), (T, T, H), (T, T, T)}
(B, B, G, G), (B, G, B, B), (B, G, B, G),

b. $\frac{1}{8}$ **c.** $\frac{3}{8}$ **d.** $\frac{4}{8} = \frac{1}{2}$

6. a.

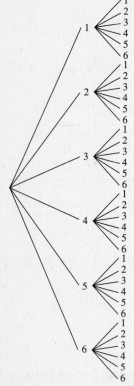

b. (1, 1) (2, 1) (3, 1) (4, 1) (5, 1) (6, 1)
(1, 2) (2, 2) (3, 2) (4, 2) (5, 2) (6, 2)
(1, 3) (2, 3) (3, 3) (4, 3) (5, 3) (6, 3)
(1, 4) (2, 4) (3, 4) (4, 4) (5, 4) (6, 4)

(1, 5) (2, 5) (3, 5) (4, 5) (5, 5) (6, 5)
(1, 6) (2, 6) (3, 6) (4, 6) (5, 6) (6, 6)

7. a. $\frac{1}{36}$ **b.** $\frac{2}{36} = \frac{1}{18}$ **c.** $\frac{3}{36} = \frac{1}{12}$

d. $\frac{4}{36} = \frac{1}{9}$ **e.** $\frac{5}{36}$ **f.** $\frac{6}{36} = \frac{1}{6}$

g. $\frac{5}{36}$ **h.** $\frac{4}{36} = \frac{1}{9}$ **i.** $\frac{3}{36} = \frac{1}{12}$

j. $\frac{2}{36} = \frac{1}{18}$ **k.** $\frac{1}{36}$

8. $\frac{36}{36}$ or 1

9. a. {(1, M), (1, A), (1, T), (1, H), (2, M), (2, A),
(2, T), (2, H), (3, M), (3, A), (3, T), (3,H)}

b. $\frac{1}{12}$ **c.** $\frac{1}{12}$ **d.** $\frac{2}{12} = \frac{1}{6}$

e. $\frac{1}{12}$ **f.** 0 **g.** $\frac{6}{12} = \frac{1}{2}$

10. The result will be the same as in Exercise 6.

11. a. $\frac{1}{36}$

b. $\frac{1}{36}$ (the 5 must appear first, then the 2)

c. 0 **d.** $\frac{3}{36} = \frac{1}{12}$ **e.** $\frac{3}{36} = \frac{1}{12}$

f. $\frac{18}{36} = \frac{1}{2}$ **g.** $\frac{18}{36} = \frac{1}{2}$ **h.** $\frac{6}{36} = \frac{1}{6}$

i. 1

12. (3) **13.** (4) **14.** (2)

14-10 Permutations *(page 506)*

1. a. 2 **b.** 24 **c.** 720 **d.** 5,040
e. 8 **f.** 120 **g.** 6 **h.** 40,320
i. 120 **j.** 336 **k.** 1 **l.** 144

2. a. 24
b. EMIT, EMTI, EIMT, EITM, ETIM, ETMI, MITE,
MIET, MTIE, MTEI, MEIT, METI, ITEM, ITME,
IMET, IMTE, IETM, IEMT, TEIM, TEMI, TIEM,
TIME, TMEI, TMIE

3. 120 **4.** 6 **5.** 24 **6.** 24

7. 40,320

8. a. 60! **b.** $8.320987112 \times 10^{81}$

9. a. 26! **b.** $4.032914611 \times 10^{26}$

10. a. 35! **b.** $1.033314797 \times 10^{40}$

14-11 More About Permutations
(pages 510–511)

1. a. 120 **b.** 90 **c.** 600 **d.** 24
e. 380 **f.** 7,920 **g.** 9,240 **h.** 5,040
i. 5,040 **j.** 999,900 **k.** 6,720 **l.** 720

2. a. 24   **b.** 60   **c.** 120   **d.** 210
e. 6
3. a. 30   **b.** 870   **c.** 24,360
4. a. 210   **b.** 504   **c.** 990
    d. $n(n-1)(n-2)$
5. a. 6   **b.** 15,600
6. 755,160   **7. a.** 650   **b.** 676
8. 421,200   **9.** 86,694,720
10. 10,077,480   **11.** 3,628,800
12. 45,239,040
13. Both expressions equal 362,880.

$_9P_8 = 9 \cdot 8 \cdot 7 \cdot 6 \cdot 5 \cdot 4 \cdot 3 \cdot 2;$

$_9P_9 = 9 \cdot 8 \cdot 7 \cdot 6 \cdot 5 \cdot 4 \cdot 3 \cdot 2 \cdot 1.$

Therefore $_9P_9 = \,_9P_8$ multiplied by 1, the identity element for multiplication.

14. (2)

14-12   Probability Without Replacement; Probability With Replacement
(pages 516–517)

1. a. $\dfrac{2}{7}$ **b.** $\dfrac{5}{7}$

2. a. $\dfrac{4}{49}$ **b.** $\dfrac{25}{49}$ **c.** $\dfrac{29}{49}$ **d.** $\dfrac{20}{49}$

3. a. $\dfrac{2}{42} = \dfrac{1}{21}$ **b.** $\dfrac{20}{42} = \dfrac{10}{21}$

   c. $\dfrac{22}{42} = \dfrac{11}{21}$ **d.** $\dfrac{20}{42} = \dfrac{10}{21}$

4. a. {(1, 1), (1, 2), (1, 3), (1, 4), (2, 1), (2, 2), (2, 3), (2, 4), (3, 1), (3, 2), (3, 3), (3, 4), (4, 1), (4, 2), (4, 3), (4, 4)}

   b. $\dfrac{1}{16}$ **c.** $\dfrac{4}{16} = \dfrac{1}{4}$ **d.** $\dfrac{6}{16} = \dfrac{3}{8}$

5. a. {(l_1, l_2), (l_1, l_3), (l_1, g_1) (l_1, g_2), (l_2, l_1), (l_2, l_3), (l_2, g_1), (l_2, g_2), (l_3, l_1) (l_3, l_2), (l_3, g_1), (l_3, g_2) (g_1, l_1), (g_1, l_2), (g_1, l_3) (g_1, g_2), (g_2, l_1), (g_2, l_2) (g_2, l_3), (g_2, g_1)}

   b. (1) $\dfrac{6}{20} = \dfrac{3}{10}$ (2) $\dfrac{2}{20} = \dfrac{1}{10}$

     (3) $\dfrac{8}{20} = \dfrac{2}{5}$ (4) $\dfrac{18}{20} = \dfrac{9}{10}$

6. a. {(g_1, g_1), (g_1, g_2), (g_1, g_3) (g_1, b_1), (g_1, b_2), (g_2, g_1), (g_2, g_2), (g_2, g_3) (g_2, b_1), (g_2, b_2), (g_3, g_1), (g_3, g_2), (g_3, g_3) (g_3, b_1), (g_3, b_2), (b_1, g_1), (b_1, g_2), (b_1, g_3) (b_1, b_1), (b_1, b_2), (b_2, g_1), (b_2, g_2), (b_2, g_3) (b_2, b_1), (b_2, b_2)}

   b. (1) $\dfrac{9}{25}$ (2) $\dfrac{4}{25}$

---

     (3) $\dfrac{5}{25} = \dfrac{1}{5}$ (4) $\dfrac{16}{25}$

7. a. $\dfrac{12}{2{,}652} = \dfrac{1}{221}$ **b.** $\dfrac{156}{2{,}652} = \dfrac{1}{17}$

   c. $\dfrac{650}{2{,}652} = \dfrac{25}{102}$ **d.** $\dfrac{132}{2{,}652} = \dfrac{11}{221}$

   e. $\dfrac{2{,}496}{2{,}652} = \dfrac{16}{17}$ **f.** $\dfrac{2}{2{,}652} = \dfrac{1}{1{,}326}$

   g. $\dfrac{16}{2{,}652} = \dfrac{4}{663}$ **h.** $\dfrac{169}{2{,}652} = \dfrac{13}{204}$

8. a. {(H, Q), (H, D), (H, N), (Q, H), (Q, D), (Q, N), (D, H), (D, Q), (D, N), (N, H), (N, Q), (N, D)}

   b. (1) $\dfrac{2}{12} = \dfrac{1}{6}$ (2) $\dfrac{4}{12} = \dfrac{1}{3}$

     (3) $\dfrac{6}{12} = \dfrac{1}{2}$ (4) $\dfrac{2}{12} = \dfrac{1}{6}$

9. a. (1) $\dfrac{56}{182} = \dfrac{4}{13}$ (2) $\dfrac{30}{182} = \dfrac{15}{91}$

     (3) $\dfrac{86}{182} = \dfrac{43}{91}$

   b. 3

10. a. $\dfrac{9}{49}$ **b.** $\dfrac{16}{49}$ **c.** $\dfrac{24}{49}$ **d.** $\dfrac{7}{49} = \dfrac{1}{7}$

   e. $\dfrac{40}{49}$ **f.** 0   **g.** $\dfrac{33}{49}$

11. a. (1) $\dfrac{72}{132} = \dfrac{6}{11}$ (2) $\dfrac{27}{132} = \dfrac{9}{44}$

     (3) $\dfrac{27}{132} = \dfrac{9}{44}$ (4) $\dfrac{6}{132} = \dfrac{1}{22}$

   b. (1) $\dfrac{6}{132} = \dfrac{1}{22}$ (2) $\dfrac{54}{132} = \dfrac{9}{22}$

     (3) $\dfrac{126}{132} = \dfrac{21}{22}$ (4) $\dfrac{78}{132} = \dfrac{13}{22}$

     (5) $\dfrac{60}{132} = \dfrac{5}{11}$ (6) 0

Review Exercises (pages 519–521)

1. 8   **2.** 25   **3.** 65%

4. a. $\dfrac{2}{3}$ **b.** $\dfrac{1}{3}$ **c.** 0   **d.** 0

5. a. $\dfrac{2}{9}$ **b.** $\dfrac{7}{9}$ **c.** $\dfrac{6}{9}$ **d.** 0

6. a. $\dfrac{26}{52}$ **b.** $\dfrac{4}{52}$ **c.** $\dfrac{2}{52}$ **d.** $\dfrac{13}{52}$

   e. $\dfrac{16}{52}$ **f.** $\dfrac{28}{52}$ **g.** $\dfrac{39}{52}$

7. 12

8. a. $\dfrac{5}{36}$ **b.** $\dfrac{6}{36}$ **c.** $\dfrac{18}{36}$ **d.** 1

9. $\frac{2}{8}$

10. a. 120   **b.** 90   **c.** 24   **d.** 870
    e. 210   **f.** 96,909,120

11. (3)   **12.** (3)   **13.** (4)

14. a.   (1, 1)   (1, 2)   (1, 3)   (1, 4)   (1, 5)
       (2, 1)   (2, 2)   (2, 3)   (2, 4)   (2, 5)
       (3, 1)   (3, 2)   (3, 3)   (3, 4)   (3, 5)
       (4, 1)   (4, 2)   (4, 3)   (4, 4)   (4, 5)
       (5, 1)   (5, 2)   (5, 3)   (5, 4)   (5, 5)

   b. $\frac{5}{25}$ **c.** $\frac{9}{25}$ **d.** $\frac{9}{25}$ **e.** $\frac{12}{25}$

15. a.

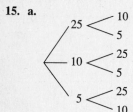

   b. (1) $\frac{2}{6}$ (2) 0   (3) $\frac{4}{6}$ (4) 1   (5) $\frac{4}{6}$

   c. $\frac{2}{6}$ **d.** $\frac{2}{6}$

16. 25   **17.** 10   **18.** 8 girls, 16 boys

Cumulative Review *(page 521)*

1. a. 20 cm, $\frac{100}{3}$ cm, 40 cm or
      12 cm, 20 cm, 24 cm or
      10 cm, $\frac{50}{3}$ cm, 20 cm

Exploration

   a. About 59 or 60
   b. Student answers will vary.
   c. (*1*) Catch and tag a number of fish. Note the number tagged.

      (*2*) Return the fish to the pond.

      (*3*) Catch some fish from the pond. Record the number caught and the number of these that are tagged.

      (*4*) Return the fish to the pond.

      (*5*) Repeat steps (3) and (4) at least 10 times.

Let x = the number of fish in the pond
    n = the number of fish that were tagged
    c = the total number of fish caught and recorded
    t = the total number of tagged fish recorded

Use the proportion $\dfrac{t}{c} = \dfrac{n}{x}$

Chapter 15. Statistics

15-1 Collecting Data *(page 525)*

   1. a. Unfair
      b. Basketball players are taller than average.
   2. a. Unfair
      b. Seniors would be taller than underclassmen.
   3. a. Unfair
      b. Fourteen-year-old students would be shorter than older students.
   4. a. Unfair
      b. Girls are usually shorter than boys.
   5. a. Fair
   6. a. Unfair
      b. Boys are usually taller than girls.
   7. a. Unfair
      b. Three is too small a sample.
   8. a. The sample is fair, consisting of 3 times the number of homerooms.
   9. No   **10.** No   **11.** Yes   **12.** No
   13. No   **14.** Yes   **15.** *b, c, e*
   16. Collecting data, organizing data, drawing conclusions.

15-2 Organizing Data *(pages 530–531)*

   1. a.

Interval	Tally	Frequency
180–189	⊞ I	6
170–179	⊞ ⊞	10
160–169	⊞ ⊞ II	12
150–159	⊞ I	6
140–149	II	2

   b. (*1*) 8   (*2*) 28   (*3*) 160–169   (*4*) 140–149

2. a.

Interval	Tally	Frequency
50–59	THL	5
60–69	|||	3
70–79	THL THL ||	12
80–89	THL THL ||||	14
90–99	THL ||	7
100–109	THL ||||	9

b. (*1*) 30   (*2*) 20   (*3*) 80–89   (*4*) 60–69

3. a.

Interval	Frequency
35–39	1
30–34	2
25–29	5
20–24	5
15–19	10
10–14	4
5–9	6
0–4	5

b.

Interval	Frequency
32–39	2
24–31	6
16–23	14
8–15	7
0–7	9

4. a.

Interval	Frequency
91–100	7
81–90	10
71–80	7
61–70	2
51–60	2
41–50	2

b.

Interval	Frequency
89–100	8
77–88	9
65–76	8
53–64	3
41–52	2

c. 81–90   **d.** 77–88

e. Yes. The scores from 81 to 88 are common to both intervals.

5. a. There are too few intervals.
  b. The intervals are not equal in size.
  c. Some scores fall in two intervals.
  d. 0 is not included in an interval.

6. 3 | 1 2 6
    2 | 0 0 0 1 2 5 5 5 7 8
    1 | 0 1 2 3 5 6 7 7 7 8 8 9 9 9
    0 | 0 3 3 4 4 5 6 6 7 8 9

7. 18 | 0 0 0 1 3 3
    17 | 0 1 1 1 3 4 5 5 7 8
    16 | 0 2 2 2 3 3 4 4 6 8 8 9
    15 | 0 5 7 8 8 8
    14 | 7 9

15-3 The Histogram (*pages 534–535*)

1.

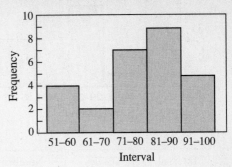

2.

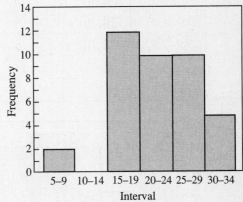

3.

(histogram with x-axis intervals 1–3, 4–8, 7–9, 10–12, 13–15, 16–18)

4. a. 150   **b.** 10–12   **c.** 20%   **d.** 68

5. a.

Interval	Tallies	Number
35–37	||||	4
32–34	THL		6
29–31	THL ||	7
26–28			1
23–25	||	2

b.

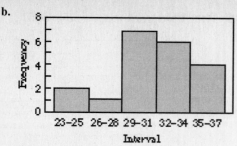

c. 29–31   **d.** 10   **e.** 10%

6. a.

Interval	Tallies	Number
37.0–40.9	⅏ III	8
33.0–36.9	⅏ IIII	9
29.0–32.9	⅏ III	8
25.0–28.9	IIII	4
21.0–24.9	I	1

b.

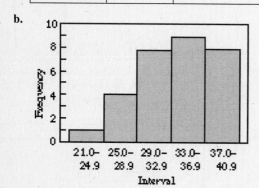

c. 5   **d.** $\dfrac{5}{30}$

15-4 The Mean, the Median, and the Mode
(pages 540–542)

1. 82   **2.** 86   **3.** $\dfrac{2x + 3y}{5}$
4. 95   **5.** 100
6. a. 82   **b.** 100   **c.** 63
  d. Not possible; Al would need a test score of 115.
7. a. 165 kg   **b.** 56.25 kg   **8.** 1.3 in.
9. 33   **10.** 18, 20, 22   **11.** 16, 33, 44
12. 174 cm
13. a. 7 **b.** 10 **c.** 4.1 **d.** 7.5 **e.** 9.5 **f.** 4.05
14. a. 3 **b.** 7 **c.** 4 **d.** 80 **e.** 3.2 **f.** 2
  g. 22.5   **h.** 6.5
15. 13.5 yr   **16.** 15 yr   **17.** $1
18. 70   **19.** 5   **20.** 50.5
21. a. 2 **b.** 2, 8 **c.** 8 **d.** No mode **e.** 2, 8, 9
  f. 1 **g.** 2 **h.** No mode **i.** 2, 7 **j.** 19
22. a. 9 **b.** 8 **c.** No mode **d.** 8, 9

23. a. 2 **b.** 4 or 5 **c.** 3 (or any number except 2, 4, and 5)
24. a. (*1*) mean is 7   (*2*) median is 7
    (*3*) no mode
  b. (*1*) mean is 24   (*2*) median is 22
    (*3*) mode is 22
  c. (*1*) mean is 5   (*2*) median is $5\dfrac{1}{2}$
    (*3*) no mode
  d. (*1*) mean is 0.71   (*2*) median is 1
    (*3*) mode is 1
25. (3)   **26.** (2)   **27.** (4)
28. (3)   **29.** (3)   **30.** (3)
31. (2)
32. a. (*1*) $375   (*2*) $347.50
    (*3*) $345, $350
  b. Mean; it makes "average" salary appear higher.
  c. Median or mode; it makes "average" salary appear lower.
33. a. (*1*) 2   (*2*) 1   (*3*) 1
  b. 2
  c. The mean is higher than all but two of the distances.
34. a. (*1*) 1   (*2*) $\dfrac{3}{4}$ (*3*) $\dfrac{3}{4}$
  b. The mode $\dfrac{3''}{4}$ is the best average; it describes the nail the carpenter uses most often.

15-5 Measures of Central Tendency and Grouped Data *(pages 549–551)*

1. a. 15   **b.** 7   **c.** 7   **d.** 6
2. a. 21   **b.** 18   **c.** 19   **d.** 20
3. a. 20   **b.** 21.75 **c.** 21   **d.** 20
4. a.

Grade	Frequency
20	0
19	1
18	2
17	4
16	3
15	2
14	1
13	1

  b. 16 12   **č.** 17   **d.** 16
5. a. (*1*) 4   (*2*) 4   (*3*) 4
  b. Median, mean, and mode are equal.
6. a. (*1*) 25 (*2*) 40 (*3*) 40 (*4*) 38
  b. Median or mean best describes the "average" suit.

7. a. 26   **b.** 35–44   **c.** 45–54
8. a. 71   **b.** 22–27   **c.** 28–33
9. a. 28   **b.** 76–100   **c.** 26–50

10. a.

Test Scores	Frequency
91–100	9
81–90	6
71–80	3
61–70	0
51–60	2

b. 91–100   **c.** 81–90

11. a.

Interval	Frequency
180–199	4
160–179	10
140–159	7
120–139	9
100–119	5

b.

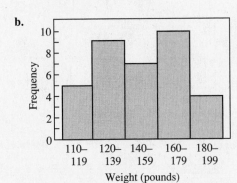

c. 140–159   **d.** 160–179

15-6 Quartiles, Percentiles, and Cumulative Frequency *(pages 559–562)*

1. a. 30   **b.** 21   **c.** 37
2. a. 79   **b.** 74.5   **c.** 87
3. a. 2   **b.** 1   **c.** 3
4. a. 4.4   **b.** 4.1   **c.** 4.85

5. a.

Height	Frequency	Cumulative Frequency
77	2	22
76	2	20
75	7	18
74	5	11
73	3	6
72	2	3
71	1	1

b.

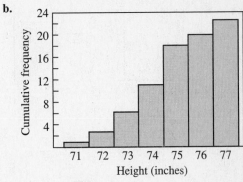

c. 73 in.   **d.** 75 in.

6. a.

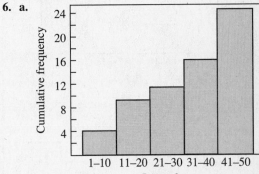

b. 11–20   **c.** 31–40   **d.** 41–50

7. a.

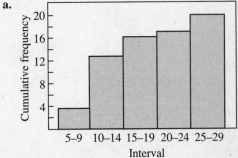

b. 10–14   **c.** 10–14   **d.** 15–19

8. a.

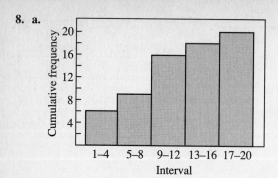

b. 1–4 **c.** 9–12 **d.** 9–12

9. a.

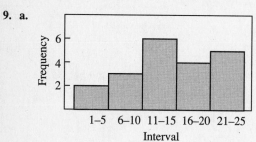

b.

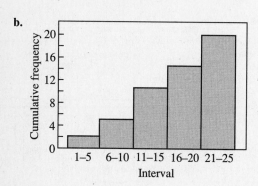

c. 11–15 **d.** 20.7 percentile

10. a.

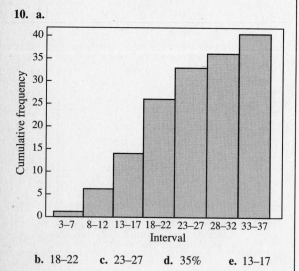

b. 18–22 **c.** 23–27 **d.** 35% **e.** 13–17

11. a. 70% **b.** 280 **c.** 91–120
  d. 1–30 **e.** 35% or $\frac{7}{20}$

12. 188 **13.** 510 **14.** (4) **15.** (1)

Review Exercises *(pages 563–564)*

1. a. 67 **b.** 70 **c.** 72 **2.** 93
3. $5y + 8$ **4. a.** 80° **b.** 81° **c.** 83°
5. (4) **6.** (3) **7.** (2)

8. a.

Interval	Frequency
24–29	2
18–23	0
12–17	6
6–11	9
0–5	3

b.

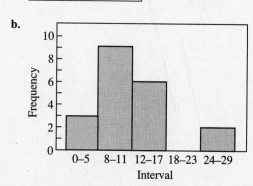

c. 6–11 **d.** 6–11

9. a. 80.4 **b.** 80 **c.** 70

d.

Scores	Frequency	Cumulative Frequency
60	1	1
70	9	10
80	8	18
90	2	20
100	5	25

e.

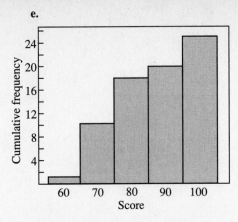

f. 76 percentile   **g.** $\dfrac{8}{25}$

10. a.

```
5 | 20  23  25
4 | 04  26  32  35  42  44  49  57  72  86  89
3 | 01  03  03  21  36  70  82
2 | 77  92  97
```

    b. 429

    c. 312, 464.5

d.

```
   ├──┼──┼──┼──┼──┼──┼──┼──┼──┼──┤
  275 300 325 350 375 400 425 450 475 500 525
```

11. a. 15   **b.** 50 percentile   **c.** 7

Cumulative Review *(page 564)*

1. 5

2. $-4x^2 + x + 7$

3. 15

4. 50°, 50°, 80°

5. **a.** 2 hr, 1 hr, 0.5 hr, 0.25 hr

   b. 0.9375 hr or $\dfrac{15}{16}$ hr

Exploration

Student answers will vary.

Chapter 16. Graphing Linear Functions and Relations

16-1 Solutions of Open Sentences in Two Variables *(pages 568–569)*

1. 6	**2.** 0	**3.** −4	**4.** 5.5
5. −4	**6.** 9	**7.** $4\dfrac{1}{2}$	**8.** 4
9. $5\dfrac{1}{4}$	**10.** −12	**11.** Yes	**12.** No
13. Yes	**14.** No	**15.** Yes	**16.** Yes
17. No	**18.** Yes	**19.** No	**20.** Yes
21. No	**22.** Yes	**23.** Yes	**24.** No

25. Yes   **26.** (8, −2)   **27.** $\left(-2, -\dfrac{1}{4}\right)$

28. (1, 8)

29. a. $y = 5 + 2.5x$

   b. (1, 7.50), (2, 10), or any other pair with a positive value of x.

30. a. $x + 2y = 54$

   b. (4, 25), (14, 20), or any other pair with $0 < x < 27$

31. a. $y = 265 - 8.50x$

   b. (1, 246.5), (2, 248), or any other pair where x is an integer from 0 to 31, that is, $0 \le x \le 31$.

32. a. $y = 2 + 0.4x$

   b. (1, 2.4), (1.5, 2.6), or any other pair where x is a nonnegative number less than or equal to 24, that is, $0 \le x \le 24$.

33. a. $2x + y = 10$

   b. (0 , 10), (1, 8), (2, 6), (3, 4), (4, 2), (5, 0)

   c. (0, 10) and (5, 0)

   d. (1.5, 7), (2.25, 5.5), or any other pair with $0 < x < 5$, x not an integer

   e. In problem (1), x and y must be integers. In problem (2), x and y can be values that are not integers $(0 < x < 5; 0 < y < 10$.

16-2 Graphing Linear Functions Using Their Solutions *(pages 572–574)*

1. a. Yes	**b.** No	**c.** No	**2.** Yes
3. Yes	**4.** No	**5.** Yes	**6.** 1
7. 4	**8.** −1	**9.** Any number	
10. 7	**11.** 8	**12.** −1	**13.** 0

14. $y = -3x - 1$ **15.** $y = 4x - 6$

16. $y = 3x$ **17.** $y = 8x$

18. $y = -2x + 4$ **19.** $y = 2x - \dfrac{5}{3}$

20. a.

x	y
0	0
1	4
2	8

   b.

21. a.

x	y
−1	−2
0	1
1	4

b.

31.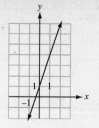

32.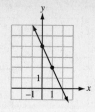

22. a.

x	y
−1	−2
2	$\frac{1}{2}$
5	−1

b.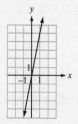

33.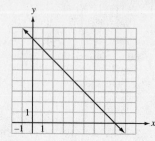

23.

24.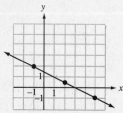

34.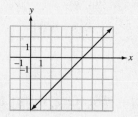

25.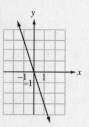

26.

35.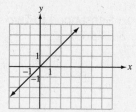

27.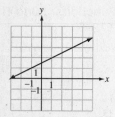

28.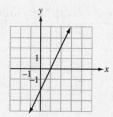

36.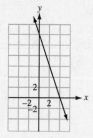

37.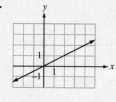

29.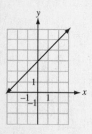

30.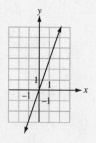

38.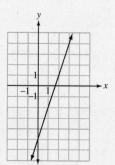

39.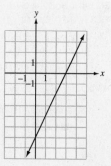

40.

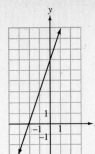

41.

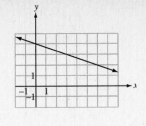

42.

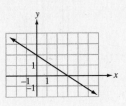

43.

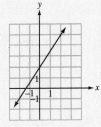

44.

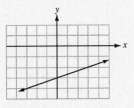

45.

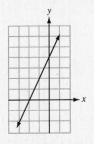

46.

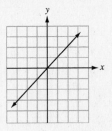

47. a.

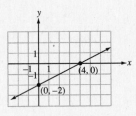

b. Two points on the line such as

$(-2, -3), (6, 1)$

48. a.

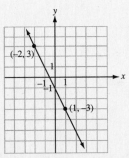

b. Yes

49. a. $y = 2x$

b.

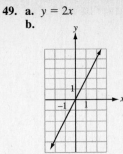

50. a. $y = x + 2$

b.

51. a. $x + y = 6$

b.

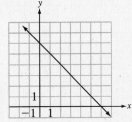

52. a. $y - x = 1$

b.

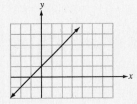

53. a. $2y - 3x = 6$

b.

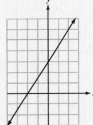

16-3 Graphing a Line Parallel to an Axis
(page 575)

1.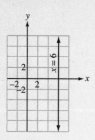

2.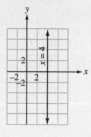

3.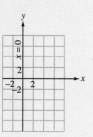

4.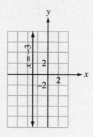

5.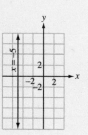

6.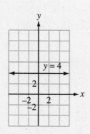

7.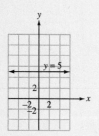

8.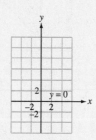

9.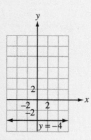

10.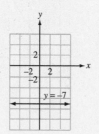

11.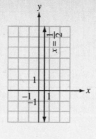

12.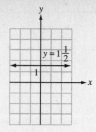

13.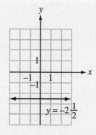

14.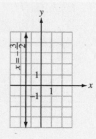

15.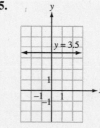

16. a. $y = 1$ **b.** $y = 5$ **c.** $y = -4$
    d. $y = -8$ **e.** $y = -2.5$

17. a. $x = 3$ **b.** $x = 10$ **c.** $x = 4\frac{1}{2}$
    d. $x = -6$ **e.** $x = -10$

18. a. (2)   **19.** (3)   **20.** (4)

21. a. $25.00   **b.** $y = 25$

16-4 The Slope of a Line *(pages 580–581)*

1. a. Positive   **b.** $\frac{3}{2}$

2. a. No Slope   **b.** No Slope

3. a. Zero   **b.** 0

4. a. Negative   **b.** -2

5. a. Positive   **b.** 2

6. a. Negative   **b.** -1

7. a.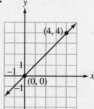

b. Slope $= 1$

8. a.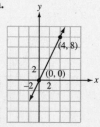

b. Slope $= 2$

9. a.

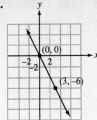

b. Slope = −2

10. a.

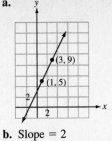

b. Slope = 2

11. a.

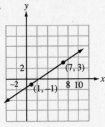

b. Slope = $\frac{2}{3}$

12. a.

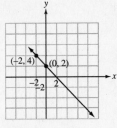

b. Slope = −1

13. a.

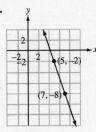

b. Slope = −3

14. a.

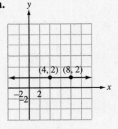

b. Slope = 0

15. a.

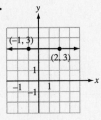

b. Slope = 0

16.

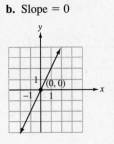

17.

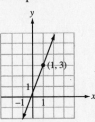

18.

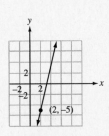

19.

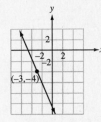

20.

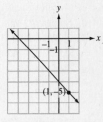

21.

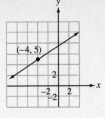

22.

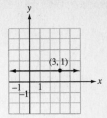

23.

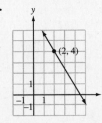

24.

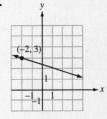

25.

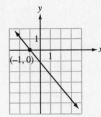

26.

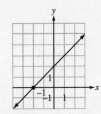

27.

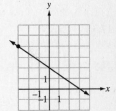

28. Slope of $\overline{AB}$ = 0; slope of $\overline{BC}$ = 1; slope of $\overline{AC}$ = −1

29. a.

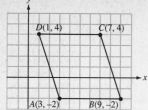

b. Parallelogram

c. Slope of $\overline{BC}$ = slope of $\overline{AD}$ = −3

d. Slopes $\overline{BC}$ and $\overline{AD}$ are equal.

e. Slopes are equal.

f. Slopes $\overline{AB}$ and $\overline{CD}$ are equal.

g. Slope of $\overline{AB}$ = slope of $\overline{CD}$ = 0

h. Yes

16-5 Slope–Intercept Form of a Linear Equation *(pages 583–584)*

1. $m = 3, b = 1$ **2.** $m = 1, b = -3$

3. $m = 2, b = 0$ **4.** $m = 1, b = 0$

5. $m = \dfrac{1}{2}, b = 5$ **6.** $m = -2, b = -3$

7. $m = -3, b = 0$ **8.** $m = 0, b = -2$

9. $m = -\dfrac{2}{3}, b = 4$ **10.** $m = 3, b = 7$

11. $m = -2, b = 5$ **12.** $m = 2, b = 3$

13. $m = \dfrac{5}{2}, b = -2$ **14.** $m = \dfrac{3}{2}, b = -\dfrac{9}{4}$

15. $m = \dfrac{4}{3}, b = 0$ **16.** $m = \dfrac{2}{5}, b = 2$

17. $y = 2x + 7$ **18.** $y = -x - 3$

19. $y = -5$ **20.** $y = -3x$

21. $y = \dfrac{2}{3}x + 1$ **22.** $y = \dfrac{1}{2}x$

23. $y = -\dfrac{1}{3}x + 2$ **24.** $y = -\dfrac{3}{2}x$

25. $y = 2x$; $y = 2x + 1$; $y = 2x - 5$
($y = 2x + b$, where b is any real number)

26. $y = x - 4$; $y = 2x - 4$; $y = -5x - 4$
($y = mx - 4$, where m is any real number)

27. Same slope; graphs will be parallel

28. Lines are parallel; will have different y-intercepts

29. Same y-intercept, 1

30. Graphs intersect y-axis at the same point.

31. Slopes are equal.   **32.** Lines are parallel.

33. Yes   **34.** No

35. Yes   **36.** Yes

37. (3)   **38.** (1)

16-6 Graphing Linear Functions Using Their Slopes *(pages 585–586)*

1.
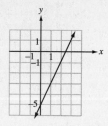

2.
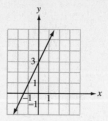

3.
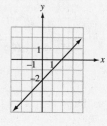

4.
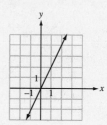

5.
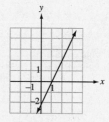

6.
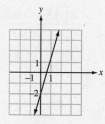

7.
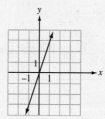

8.
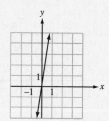

9.
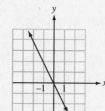

10.
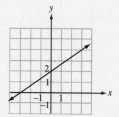

11.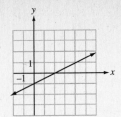

12.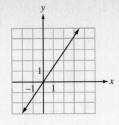

21.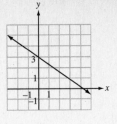

22.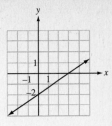

13.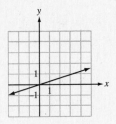

14.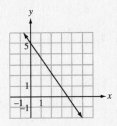

23.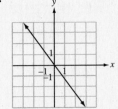

24.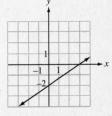

15.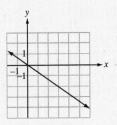

16.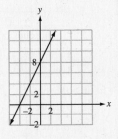

25. a.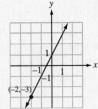

26. a.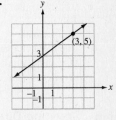

b. 1

c. $y = 2x + 1$

d. Yes

b. 3

c. $y = \frac{2}{3}x + 3$

d. Yes

27. a. Yes

b. $\frac{3}{2}$

c.

17.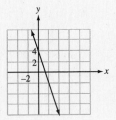

18.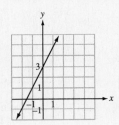

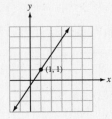

d. The y-intercept is a fractional value that is not easy to locate exactly on the graph.

19.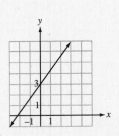

20.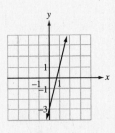

16-7 Writing an Equation of a Line
(pages 587–588)

1. $y = 2x + 2$

2. $y = 2x + 10$

3. $y = -3x - 7$

4. $y = \frac{1}{2}x$

5. $y = -\frac{3}{4}x$

6. $y = -\frac{5}{3}x - 5$

367

7. $y = 2x + 2$

8. $y = x - 2$

9. $y = \frac{4}{3}x + \frac{2}{3}$

10. $y = \frac{3}{2}x - 1$

11. $y = 3x + 1$

12. $y = -\frac{5}{3}x$

13. a. $y = 2x + 7$ **b.** $y = 3x - 2$

    c. $y = -\frac{2}{3}x$ or $2x + 3y = 0$

14. a. $y = 4x - 5$ **b.** $y = 3x + 7$

    c. $y = 4x - 3$ **d.** $y = -\frac{1}{2}x + 3$

15. a. $y = -\frac{1}{3}x + 6$ **b.** $y = x - 2$

    c. $y = 3x - 4$

16. a. (2, 7) (5, 13)

    b. $y = 2x + 3$
    c. Positive integers
    d. Odd integers greater than 3

17. a. (3, 123), (1, 65)

    b. $y = 29x + 36$
    c. $36
    d. $29 per hour
    e. The fixed charge for an estimate is the constant term in the equation and the hourly rate is the coefficient of x.

16-8 Graphing Direct Variation
(pages 590–591)

1. a. 4

    b. $y = 4x$

    c.

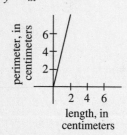

length, in centimeters

    d. 4

2. a. 45 words/min.

    b. $y = 45x$

    c.

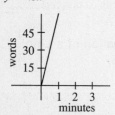

minutes

    d. 45

3. a. 16 characters/sec

    b. $y = 16x$

    c.

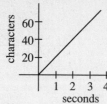

seconds

    d. 16

4. a. $\frac{4}{3}$

    b. $y = \frac{4}{3}x$

    c.

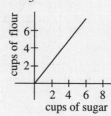

cups of sugar

    d. $\frac{4}{3}$

5. a. 10

    b. $y = 10x$

    c.

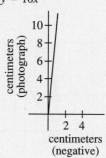

centimeters (negative)

    d. 10

6. a. $\frac{5}{3}$ slices/oz

    b. $y = \frac{5}{3}x$

    c.

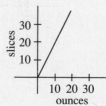

ounces

    d. $\frac{5}{3}$

7. a. $\frac{1}{5}$ lb/person

b. $y = \frac{1}{5}x$

c.

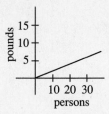

d. $\frac{1}{5}$

8. a. $\frac{3}{2}$ slices/oz

b. $y = \frac{3}{2}x$

c.

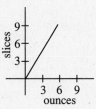

d. $\frac{3}{2}$

9. a. $\frac{1}{4}$ hit/time at bat

b. $y = \frac{1}{4}x$

c.

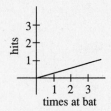

d. $\frac{1}{4}$

10. a. $\frac{20}{3}$ cal/cracker

b. $y = \frac{20}{3}x$

c.

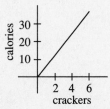

d. $\frac{20}{3}$

11. a. 30 mph

b. 44 ft/sec

16-9 Graphing First–Degree Inequalities in Two Variables *(page 595)*

1. $y > 2x$ **2.** $y < \frac{5}{2}x$ **3.** $y \geq x + 3$

4. $y \leq -2x$ **5.** $y \leq 3x - 4$ **6.** $y \leq \frac{3}{4}x + 3$

7.

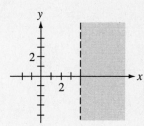

8.

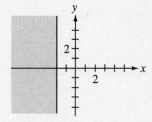

9.

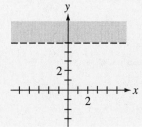

10.

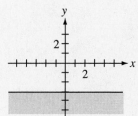

11.

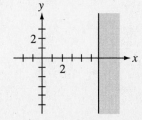

12.

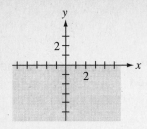

13.

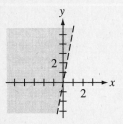

14.

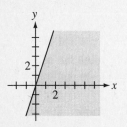

15.

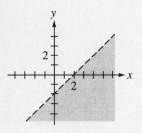

16.

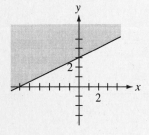

17.

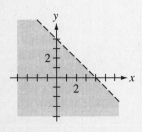

18.

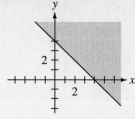

19.

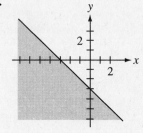

20.

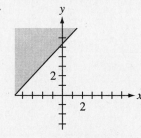

21.

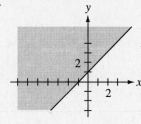

22.

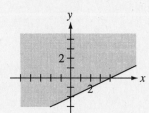

23.

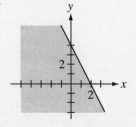

24.

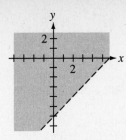

25.

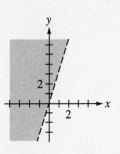

26.

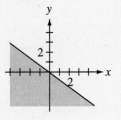

27.

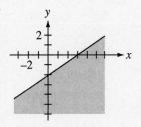

28.

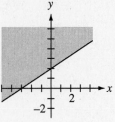

29.

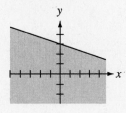

30.

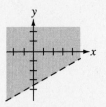

31. a. $y \geq 3 + x$
b.

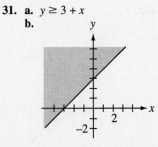

32. a. $x + y \leq 5$
b.

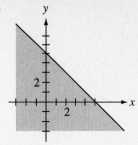

33. a. $y - 3x \geq 2$
b.

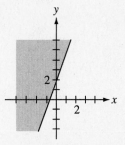

16-10 Graphs Involving Absolute Value
(page 598)

1.

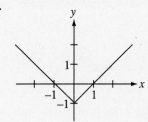

2.

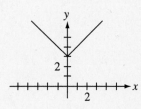

3.

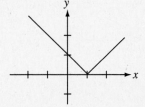

4.

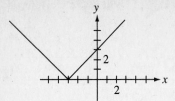

5.

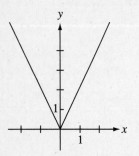

6.

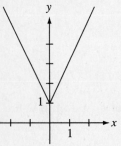

7.

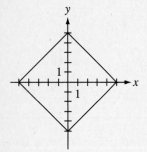

8.

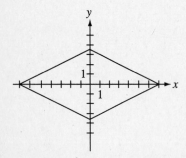

9.

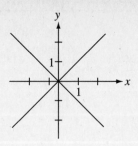

10. a.

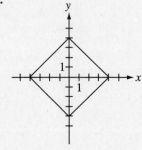

   b. $y = 0, x = 0, y = x, y = -x$

Review Exercises *(pages 599–600)*

1. -2

2. $y = \dfrac{3}{2}x - 6$

3. $y = -x + 7$

4. -2

5.

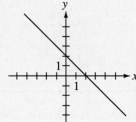

6.

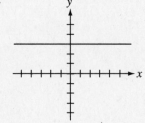

7.

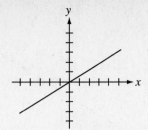

8.

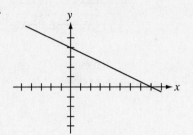

9.

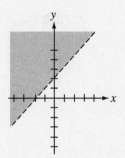

10.

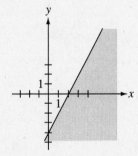

11. 2

12. −2

13. $x = 3$

14. $y = 2x$

15. 4

16. **a.** $y = 150 + 2x$
    b. $156

17. (2)

18. (1)

19. (2)

20. (4)

21. (2)

22. (4)

23. a, b.

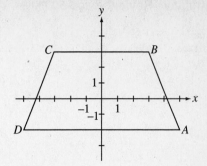

c. Isosceles trapezoid
d. $DA = 10$, $BC = 6$
e. 5
f. 40
g. $x = 0$ (the y-axis)

24.

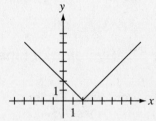

25.

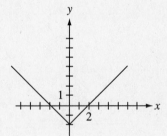

26.

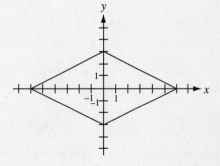

373

1. **a.** $x = 27$ **b.** $x = 3$
2. If today is Monday, then I do not play tennis.

Exploration

a, d, e.

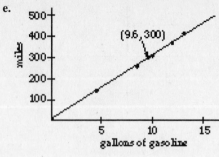

b. 9.6 gallons   **c.** 300 miles
f. $y = 31.25x$ **g.** 6.4 gallons

Chapter 17. Systems of Linear Open Sentences in Two Variables

17-1 Using a Graph to Solve a System of Linear Equations *(pages 605–606)*

1.

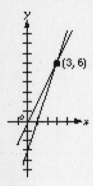

(3,6)

$[3,6]$

2.

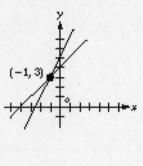

$(-1, 3)$

$(-1, 3)$

3.

(0, 3)

$(0, 3)$

4.

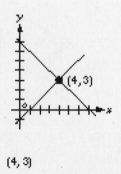

(4, 3)

$(4, 3)$

5.

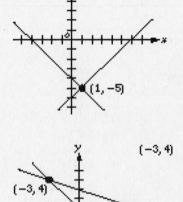

(2, 2)

(2, 2)

6.

(1, −5)

(1, −5)

7.

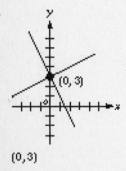

(−3, 4)

(−3, 4)

8. 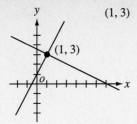 (1, 3)

(1, 3)

9. 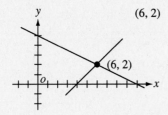 (6, 2)

(6, 2)

10. 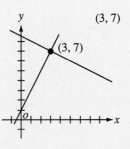 (3, 7)

(3, 7)

11. 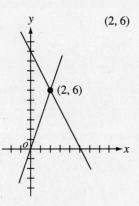 (2, 6)

(2, 6)

12. 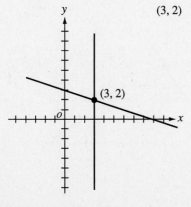 (3, 2)

(3, 2)

13. 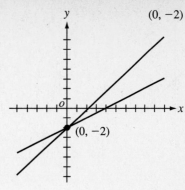 (0, −2)

(0, −2)

14. 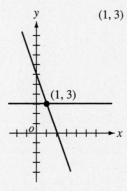 (1, 3)

(1, 3)

15. 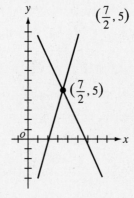 $\left(\dfrac{7}{2}, 5\right)$

$\left(\dfrac{7}{2}, 5\right)$

16. 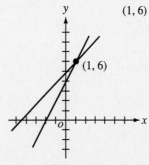 (1, 6)

(1, 6)

17. 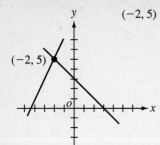 $(-2, 5)$

$(-2, 5)$

18. 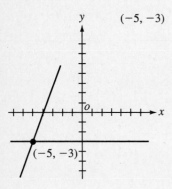 $(-5, -3)$

$(-5, -3)$

19. 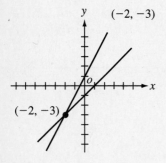 $(-2, -3)$

$(-2, -3)$

20. 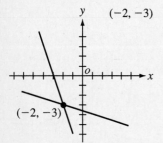 $(-2, -3)$

$(-2, -3)$

21. 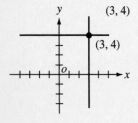 $(3, 4)$

$(3, 4)$

22. 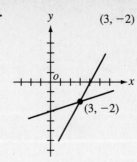 $(3, -2)$

$(3, -2)$

23. 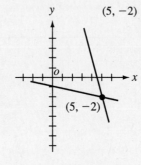 $(5, -2)$

$(5, -2)$

24. 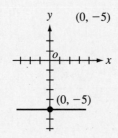 $(0, -5)$

$(0, -5)$

25. 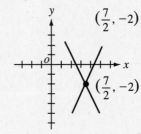 $\left(\dfrac{7}{2}, -2\right)$

$\left(\dfrac{7}{2}, -2\right)$

26. 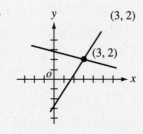 $(3, 2)$

$(3, 2)$

27.

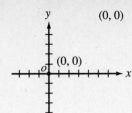

(0, 0)

(0, 0)

28.

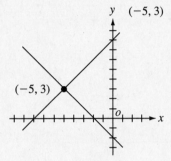

(−5, 3)

(−5, 3)

29.

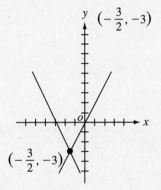

$\left(-\frac{3}{2}, -3\right)$

$\left(-\frac{3}{2}, -3\right)$

30.

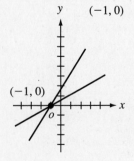

(−1, 0)

(−1, 0)

31. a.

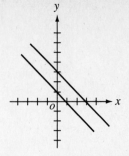

b. Inconsistent

32. a.

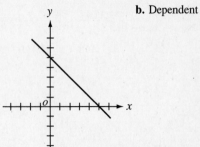

b. Dependent

33. a.

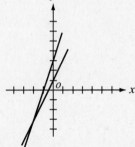

b. Consistent

34. a.

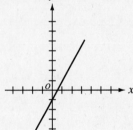

b. Dependent

35. a.

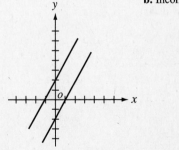

b. Inconsistent

36. a.

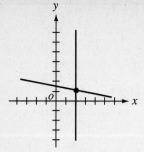

b. Consistent

37. a. No. **b.** System is inconsistent
38. a. No. **b.** System is dependent
39. a. $x + y = 8$ **b.** (5, 3)
$\quad\;\; x - y = 2$

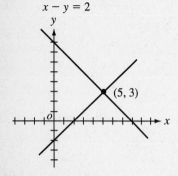

(5, 3)

40. a. $x + y = 3$ **b.** (−1, 4)
$\quad\;\; y = x + 5$

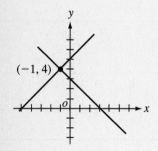

(−1, 4)

41. a. $2x + 2y = 12$ **b.** (2, 4)
$\quad\;\; y = 2x$

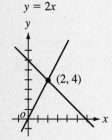

(2, 4)

42. a. $2x + 2y = 14$ **b.** (2, 4)
$\quad\;\; y = x + 3$

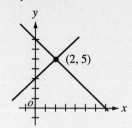

(2, 5)

43. a. $y = 50$
 b. $y = 30 + 0.20x$
 c.

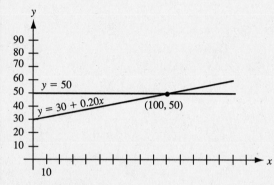

$y = 50$

$y = 30 + 0.20x$ (100, 50)

 d. U-Drive-It
 e. Safe Travel
 f. 100 mi

17-2 Using Addition to Solve a System of Linear Equations *(page 610)*

1. (2, 3)	**2.** (2, 1)	**3.** (8, 4)
4. (9, 4)	**5.** (−8, 2)	**6.** (5, 1)
7. (12, −1)	**8.** (5, 5)	**9.** (8, 4)
10. (6, 1)	**11.** $(\frac{1}{2}, 1)$	**12.** (2, 3)
13. $(-\frac{1}{2}, 3)$	**14.** (2, 3)	**15.** (1, 3)
16. (3, 2)	**17.** (4, −2)	**18.** (2, 5)
19. (5, 2)	**20.** (4, 5)	**21.** (1, 1)
22. (6, 2)	**23.** (−3, 2)	**24.** (5, 6)
25. (3, 6)	**26.** (6, 5)	**27.** (10, −6)
28. (−15, 12)	**29.** (2, 1)	**30.** (−3, 1)
31. (−7, 9)	**32.** $(0, -\frac{5}{2})$	**33.** (7, −3)
34. (2, 2)	**35.** (6, 5)	**36.** (6, 0)
37. (2, 12)	**38.** (7, 2)	**39.** (6, 4)
40. (−8, 3)	**41.** (24, 8)	**42.** (8, 12)
43. (9, 4)	**44.** (6, 4)	**45.** (90, 5)
46. (1, 3)	**47.** (200, 300)	**48.** (150, 250)
49. (500, 100)		

17-3 Using Substitution to Solve a System of Linear Equations (pages 612–613)

1. (7, 7)	**2.** (−2, −2)	**3.** (7, 14)
4. (8, 2)	**5.** (2, −1)	**6.** (−6, 2)
7. (4, 5)	**8.** (8, 10)	**9.** (4, 7)
10. (2, 5)	**11.** (−8, −3)	**12.** (6, 5)
13. (5, 2)	**14.** (4, 3)	**15.** (5, 4)
16. (2, −2)	**17.** (1, 7)	**18.** (6, 4)
19. (−4, 3)	**20.** (5, −1)	**21.** (9, 27)
22. (3, −3)	**23.** (5, 2)	**24.** (6, 4)
25. (2, 2)	**26.** (7, 5)	**27.** (3, −6)
28. $(4, \frac{1}{2})$	**29.** (6, 18)	**30.** (10, 9)
31. (−3, 4)	**32.** (60, 240)	**33.** (5, 1)
34. (4, 3)	**35.** (3, 9)	**36.** (12, −3)

17-4 Using Systems of Equations to Solve Verbal Problems (pages 616–617)

1. 30, 6   **2.** $35\frac{1}{2}, 38\frac{1}{2}$ **3.** 35, 69

4. $5\frac{1}{4}, 19\frac{3}{4}$ **5.** 33, 10   **6.** 30.4, 45.4

7. 17 cm, 8 cm   **8.** 14 ft by 5 ft   **9.** 150°, 30°
10. 65°, 115°   **11.** 60°, 30°   **12.** 32°, 58°
13. 40°, 70°, 70°
14. Pretzel, $0.75; soda, $0.50
15. Gardener, $60; helper, $30
16. Bat, $9.00; ball, $4.50
17. Veal, $6.25; pork, $2.50
18. Brown rice, $2.50; white rice, $2.90
19. 60 in advance, 40 at the door
20. 120
21. Four $20 bills, two $10 bills
22. Eight 30¢ stamps, six 20¢ stamps
23. 64 lb at $2, 16 lb at $3
24. $0.49 for squash, $0.69 for eggplant
25. Roger earned $25,500; Wilma earned $21,500.
26. 500, 400
27. $400 at 5%, $1,000 at 8%
28. $2,600 at 4%, $1,400 at 6%
29. $9,000 at 8%, $12,000 at 6%

17-5 Graphing the Solution Set of a System of Inequalities (page 620)

1.
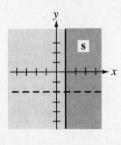

2.
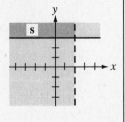

3.
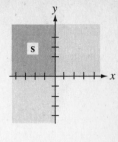

4.
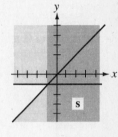

5.
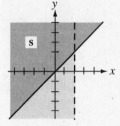

6.
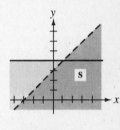

7.
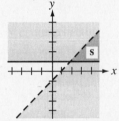

8.
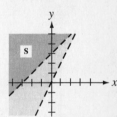

9.
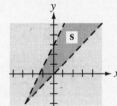

10.
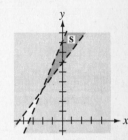

11.
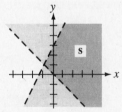

12.
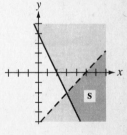

13.
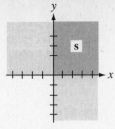

14.
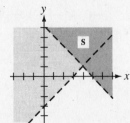

15.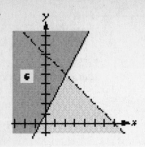

16.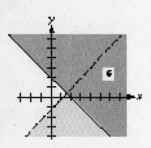

17.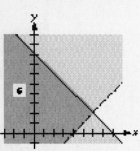

18.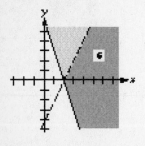

19.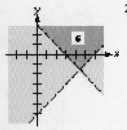

20.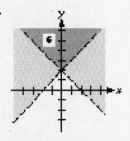

21.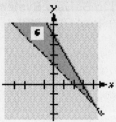

22.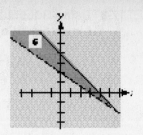

23.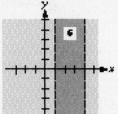

24.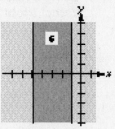

25.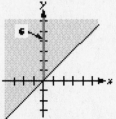

26.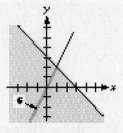

27.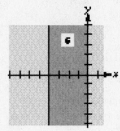

28.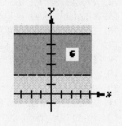

29.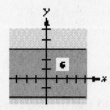

30.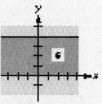

31.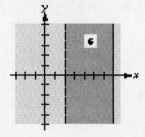

380

32.

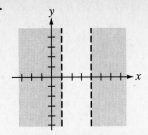

33.

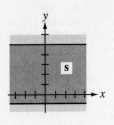

34.

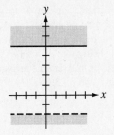

Review Exercises *(pages 621–622)*

1. $x = 4$

2.

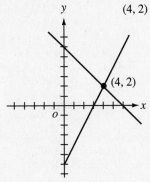

(4, 2)

3.

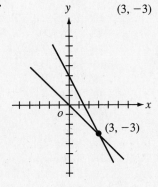

(3, −3)

4.

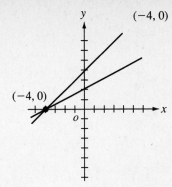

(−4, 0)

(−4, 0)

5. (7, −4) **6.** $(-1, \frac{1}{2})$ **7.** (4, −12)

8. (−3, 5) **9.** (10, −5) **10.** (0, 7)

11. (5, −5) **12.** (4, −1) **13.** (3, 9)

14. (8, 6) **15.** (400, 600) **16.** (2, 4)

17. 41 and 23

18. Notebook, $0.80; pencil, $0.20

19. 35 and 55

20. a. $(4\frac{1}{2}, 1\frac{1}{2})$ **b.**

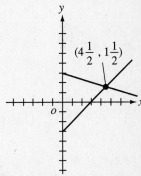

$(4\frac{1}{2}, 1\frac{1}{2})$

21.

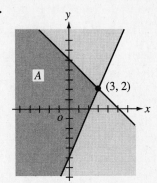

A

(3, 2)

381

22.

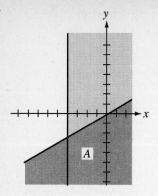

23.

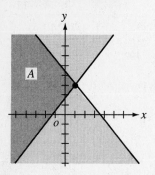

1.

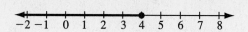

Exploration

Robby left first, at 8:00, and walked at a constant rate of 3 miles per hour for 1 mile. At 8:20 he stopped for 5 minutes. (He may have waited for a friend to join him.) At 8:25 he continued walking at the same rate until he reached the school at 8:30. Jason left at 8:15 and rode at a steady rate of 9 miles per hour. He passed Robby at about 8:22 and he arrived at school before Robby at about 8:23.

Chapter 18. Special Products and Factoring

18-1 Factors and Factoring
(pages 627–628)

1. Yes 2. No 3. Yes 4. No
5. Yes 6. No 7. Yes 8. No
9. No 10. No 11. $5 \cdot 7$ 12. $2 \cdot 3^2$
13. $2^4 \cdot 3^2$ 14. $7 \cdot 11$ 15. 2^7 16. $2^4 \cdot 5^2$
17. $2 \cdot 101$ 18. $3 \cdot 43$ 19. $2 \cdot 5 \cdot 59$
20. $2^2 \cdot 79$ 21. 1, 2, 13, 26
22. 1, 2, 5, 10, 25, 50
23. 1, 2, 3, 4, 6, 9, 12, 18, 36
24. 1, 2, 4, 8, 11, 22, 44, 88
25. 1, 2, 4, 5, 10, 20, 25, 50, 100
26. 1, 2, 11, 22, 121, 242
27. a. 72 b. 18 c. -8 d. 4 e. -3
28. a. $12xy$ b. $6y^2$ c. $3x^2y^2$ d. $-4y^3$ e. $2y^2$
29. 5 30. 4 31. 7 32. 6
33. 25 34. 36 35. 8 36. 1
37. 4 38. 6 39. $2r$ 40. $2x$
41. $5x$ 42. $7c^2d$ 43. $9xy^2z$ 44. $25m^3n$
45. $6ac^2$ 46. ab 47. xyz 48. 1

18-2 Common Monomial Factors
(page 629)

1. $2(a + b)$ 2. $5(c + d)$
3. $8(m + n)$ 4. $3(x - y)$
5. $7(l - n)$ 6. $6(R - r)$
7. $b(x + y)$ 8. $s(r - t)$
9. $x(c - d)$ 10. $4(x + 2y)$
11. $3(m - 2n)$ 12. $6(2t - r)$
13. $5(3c - 2d)$ 14. $6(2x - 3y)$
15. $9(2c - 3d)$ 16. $8(x + 2)$
17. $6(x - 3)$ 18. $4(2x - 3)$
19. $7(y - 1)$ 20. $4(2 - y)$
21. $6(1 - 3c)$ 22. $y(y - 3)$
23. $x(2x + 5)$ 24. $3x(x - 2)$
25. $x(32 + x)$ 26. $r(s^2 - 2)$
27. $a(x - 5b)$ 28. $3y^2(y^2 + 1)$
29. $5x(2 - 3x^2)$ 30. $2x(1 - 2x^2)$
31. $p(1 + rt)$ 32. $s(1 - r)$
33. $h(b + c)$ 34. $\pi(r^2 + R^2)$

35. $\pi r(r + \ell)$

36. $\pi r(r + 2h)$

37. $4(x^2 + y^2)$

38. $3(a^2 - 3)$

39. $5(x^2 + 1)$

40. $4y(3y - 1)$

41. $3ab(b - 2a)$

42. $5xy(2 - 3xy)$

43. $7r^2s(3rs - 2)$

44. $2(x^2 + 4x + 2)$

45. $3(x^2 - 2x - 10)$

46. $a(y - 4w - 12)$

47. $c(c^2 - c + 2)$

48. $2m(a + 2b + c)$

49. $3a(3b^2 - 2b - 1)$

50. $5xyz(3x^2y^2z^2 - 1)$

51. $4a^2b^2c^2(2a^2c + 3)$

52. $14m^2n^3(2m^2 - 5n)$

53. $2(\ell + w)$

54. $5(x + y)$

55. $6(3x + 1)$

56. $x(x + 2)$

57. $2x^2(2x + 3)$

18-3 The Square of a Monomial
(pages 630–631)

1. a^4

2. b^6

3. d^{10}

4. r^2s^2

5. m^4n^4

6. x^6y^4

7. $9x^4$

8. $25y^8$

9. $81a^2b^2$

10. $100x^4y^4$

11. $144c^2d^6$

12. $\frac{9}{16}a^2$

13. $\frac{25}{49}x^2y^2$

14. $\frac{49}{64}a^4b^4$

15. $\frac{x^2}{36}$

16. $\frac{16x^4}{25}$

17. $0.64x^2$

18. $0.25y^4$

19. $0.01x^2y^2$

20. $0.36a^4b^2$

21. a. $16x^2$ **b.** $100y^2$ **c.** $\frac{4}{9}x^2$

d. $2.25x^2$ **e.** $9x^4$ **f.** $16x^4y^4$

18-4 Multiplying the Sum and the Difference of Two Terms
(page 632)

1. $x^2 - 64$

2. $y^2 - 100$

3. $m^2 - 16$

4. $n^2 - 81$

5. $100 - a^2$

6. $144 - b^2$

7. $c^2 - d^2$

8. $r^2 - s^2$

9. $9x^2 - 1$

10. $25c^2 - 16$

11. $64x^2 - 9y^2$

12. $25r^2 - 49s^2$

13. $x^4 - 64$

14. $9 - 25y^4$

15. $a^2 - \frac{1}{4}$

16. $r^2 - 0.25$

17. $0.09 - m^2$

18. $a^2b^2 - 64$

19. $r^6 - 4s^8$

20. $a^4 - 625$

21. $x^4 - 81$

22. $a^4 - b^4$

23. $x^2 - 49$

24. $4x^2 - 9$

25. $c^2 - d^2$

26. $4a^2 - 9b^2$

18-5 Factoring the Difference of Two Squares
(pages 633–634)

1. $(y)^2 - (8)^2$

2. $(2r)^2 - (b)^2$

3. This binomial is not a difference.

4. 7 is not the square of an integer.

5. $(3n)^2 - (4m)^2$

6. $(c)^2 - (0.3d)^2$

7. $(p)^2 - (\frac{3}{5}q)^2$

8. $(4a^2)^2 - (5b^3)^2$

9. $(m)^2 - (3)^2$

10. $(a + 2)(a - 2)$

11. $(b + 5)(b - 5)$

12. $(c - 10)(c - 10)$

13. $(r + 4)(r - 4)$

14. $(s + 7)(s - 7)$

15. $(t + 9)(t - 9)$

16. $(3 + x)(3 - x)$

17. $(12 + c)(12 - c)$

18. $(11 + m)(11 - m)$

19. $(4a + b)(4a - b)$

20. $(5m + n)(5m - n)$

21. $(d + 2c)(d - 2c)$

22. $(r^2 + 3)(r^2 - 3)$

23. $(x^2 + 8)(x^2 - 8)$

24. $(5 + s^2)(5 - s^2)$

25. $(10x + 9y)(10x - 9y)$

26. $(8e + 3f)(8e - 3f)$

27. $(rs + 12)(rs - 12)$

28. $\left(w + \frac{1}{8}\right)\left(w - \frac{1}{8}\right)$

29. $\left(s + \frac{1}{10}\right)\left(s - \frac{1}{10}\right)$

30. $\left(\frac{1}{9} + t\right)\left(\frac{1}{9} - t\right)$

31. $\left(7x + \frac{1}{3}\right)\left(7x - \frac{1}{3}\right)$

32. $\left(\frac{2}{5} + \frac{7d}{9}\right)\left(\frac{2}{5} - \frac{7d}{9}\right)$

33. $\left(\frac{1}{3}r - \frac{8s}{11}\right)\left(\frac{1}{3}r - \frac{8s}{11}\right)$

34. $(x + 0.8)(x - 0.8)$

35. $(x + 1.2)(y - 1.2)$

36. $(0.2 + 7r)(0.2 - 7r)$

37. $(0.4m + 3)(0.4m - 3)$

38. $(9n + 0.1)(9n - 0.1)$

39. $(0.9x + y)(0.9x - y)$

40. $(8ab + cd)(8ab - cd)$

41. $(5rs + 3tu)(5rs - 3tu)$

42. $(9mn + 7xy)(9mn - 7xy)$

43. $(7m^2 + 8n^2)(7m^2 - 8n^2)$

44. $(5x^3 + 11y^5)(5x^3 - 11y^5)$

45. $(x^2y^4 - 12a^3b^5)(x^2y^4 + 12a^3b^5)$

46. $(x + 2)(x - 2)$

47. $(y + 3)(y - 3)$

48. $(t + 7)(t - 7)$

49. $(t + 8)(t - 8)$

50. $(2x + y)(2x - y)$

51. a. $(c^2 - d^2)$ **b.** $(c + d)(c - d)$

52. a. $4x^2 - y^2$ **b.** $(2x + y)(2x - y)$

53. a. $x^2 - y^2$ **b.** $(x + y)(x - y)$

54. a. $(5a + 2b)(5a - 2b)$ **55.** $(3x + 4y)(3x - 4y)$

18-6 Multiplying Binomials
(page 636)

1. $x^2 + 8x + 15$

2. $y^2 + 11y + 18$

3. $18 + 9d + d^2$

4. $x^2 - 15x + 50$

5. $y^2 - 10y + 9$

6. $24 - 11c + c^2$

7. $x^2 + 5x - 14$

8. $y^2 + 7y - 44$

9. $m^2 - 13m - 30$

10. $n^2 - 17n - 60$

11. $45 - 4t - t^2$

12. $2x^2 + 3x + 1$

13. $3x^2 + 17x + 10$
14. $3c^2 - 16c + 5$
15. $3m^2 - 16m - 12$
16. $y^2 + 16y + 64$
17. $a^2 - 8a + 16$
18. $y^2 + 10y + 25$
19. $1 - 2t + t^2$
20. $4x^2 + 4x + 1$
21. $9x^2 - 12x + 4$
22. $14x^2 - x - 3$
23. $6y^2 + 13y + 6$
24. $10k^2 - 31k + 15$
25. $4y^2 + 12y + 9$
26. $9x^2 + 24x + 16$
27. $4x^2 - 20x + 25$
28. $12t^2 + 13t - 14$
29. $25y^2 - 40y + 16$
30. $10t^2 + 17t + 3$
31. $4a^2 - 8a + 4$
32. $15x^2 + x - 28$
33. $10c^2 - 19cd + 6d^2$
34. $12a^2 - 5ab - 3b^2$
35. $25a^2 - 49b^2$
36. $25a^2 - 70ab + 49b^2$
37. $35a^2 - 74ab + 35b^2$
38. $35a^2 + 24ab - 35b^2$
39. **a.** $x^2 + 9x + 20$ **b.** $2x^2 + x - 3$
40. **a.** $x^2 + 12x + 36$ **b.** $x^2 - 4x + 4$
    c. $4x^2 + 4x + 1$ **d.** $9x^2 - 12x + 4$

18-7 Factoring Trinomials *(page 640)*

1. $(a + 2)(a + 1)$
2. $(c + 5)(c + 1)$
3. $(x + 7)(x + 1)$
4. $(r + 11)(r + 1)$
5. $(m + 4)(m + 1)$
6. $(y + 5)(y + 7)$
7. $(x + 8)(x + 3)$
8. $(a + 9)(a + 2)$
9. $(16 + c)(1 + c)$
10. $(x + 1)^2$
11. $(z + 5)^2$
12. $(a - 7)(a - 1)$
13. $(a - 5)(a - 1)$
14. $(x - 2)(x - 3)$
15. $(x - 10)(x - 1)$
16. $(y - 4)(y - 2)$
17. $(5 - y)(3 - y)$
18. $(x - 6)(x - 4)$
19. $(c - 10)(c - 4)$
20. $(x - 12)(x - 4)$
21. $(x - 7)^2$
22. $(x - 2)(x + 1)$
23. $(x - 7)(x + 1)$
24. $(y + 5)(y - 1)$
25. $(z - 13)(z + 1)$
26. $(c - 5)(c + 3)$
27. $(c + 7)(c - 5)$
28. $(x - 9)(x + 2)$
29. $(z + 12)(z - 3)$
30. $(x - 16)(x + 3)$
31. $(x - 8)^2$
32. $(2x + 1)(x + 2)$
33. $(2x + 3)(x + 2)$
34. $(3x + 4)(x + 2)$
35. $(4x + 1)^2$
36. $(2x + 3)(x - 1)$
37. $(3x + 5)(x - 1)$
38. $(2x - 3)(x + 2)$
39. $(2x - 5)(2x - 1)$
40. $(5a - 2)(2a - 1)$
41. $(9y + 2)(2y - 3)$
42. $(x + 2y)(x + y)$
43. $(r - 5s)(r + 2s)$
44. $(3a - b)(a - 2b)$
45. $(4x + 3y)(x - 2y)$
46. $(x + 6)(x + 3)$
47. $(x - 7)(x - 2)$
48. $(y - 8)(y + 3)$
49. $(x + 7)(x + 1)$
50. $(x + 4)(x + 5)$
51. $(3x + 5)(x + 3)$
52. $(x + 5)$
53. $(9x + 1)$
54. $(2x + 3)$

18-8 Factoring a Polynomial Completely
   (page 642)

1. $2(a + b)(a - b)$
2. $6(x + y)(x - y)$
3. $4(x + 1)(x - 1)$
4. $a(x + y)(x - y)$
5. $c(m + n)(m - n)$
6. $s(t + 1)(t - 1)$

7. $2(x + 3)(x - 3)$
8. $2(x + 4)(x - 4)$
9. $3(x + 3y)(x - 3y)$
10. $2(3m + 2)(3m - 2)$
11. $3(2a + 3b)(2a - 3b)$
12. $7(3c + 1)(3c - 1)$
13. $x(x + 2)(x - 2)$
14. $y(y + 5)(y - 5)$
15. $z(z + 1)(z - 1)$
16. $a(2a + b)(2a - b)$
17. $c(2c + 7)(2c - 7)$
18. $d(3b + 1)(3b - 1)$
19. $4(a + 3)(a - 3)$
20. $(x^2 + 1)(x + 1)(x - 1)$
21. $(y^2 + 9)(y + 3)(y - 3)$
22. $\pi(R + r)(R - r)$
23. $\pi(c + d)(c - d)$
24. $4(5x + 3y)(5x - 3y)$
25. $a(x + 2)(x + 1)$
26. $3(x + 1)^2$
27. $4(r - 4)(r + 3)$
28. $x(x + 5)(x + 2)$
29. $2(2x + 1)(x - 2)$
30. $y(a + 5)^2$
31. $d(d - 4)^2$
32. $2a(x - 3)(x + 2)$
33. $ab(x + 1)(x - 1)$
34. $z^2(z^2 + 1)(z + 1)(z - 1)$
35. $x^2(4 + y^2)(2 + y)(2 - y)$
36. $(x^2 + 2)(x + 1)(x - 1)$
37. $(a + 3)(a - 3)(a + 1)(a - 1)$
38. $(y + 3)(y - 3)(y + 2)(y - 2)$
39. $2(x^2 + 6x + 4)$
40. $5(x^2 + 1)^2$
41. $b(2a + 1)(a + 3)$
42. $4(2x - 1)^2$
43. $25(x + 2y)^2$
44. $2(3m + 2)^2$
45. $(4a + b)(3a - 2b)$
46. $10a(a + 1)^2$

Review Exercises *(pages 643–644)*

1. $2 \cdot 5 \cdot 5 \cdot 5 = 2 \cdot 5^3$
2. $4a$
3. $8a^2bc^2$
4. $9g^6$
5. $16x^8$
6. $0.04c^4y^2$
7. $x^2 + 4x - 45$
8. $y^2 - 14y + 48$
9. $a^2b^2 - 16$
10. $3d^2 - 5d - 2$
11. $4w^2 + 4w + 1$
12. $2x^2 + 11cx + 12c^2$
13. $3(2x + 9b)$
14. $y(3y + 10)$
15. $(m + 9)(m - 9)$
16. $(x + 4h)(x - 4h)$
17. $(x - 5)(x + 1)$
18. $(y - 2)(y - 7)$
19. $(8b - 3)(8b + 3)$
20. $(11 + k)(11 - k)$
21. $(x - 4)(x - 4)$
22. $(a + 3)(a - 10)$
23. $(x - 6)(x - 10)$
24. $16(y + 1)(y - 1)$
25. $(x + 8b)(x - 2b)$
26. $(2x + y)(x - 5y)$
27. $3x(x + 2)(x - 4)$
28. $k^2 - 225$
29. $16e^2z^2 - 4ez^3$
30. $6x^2 - 13x + 6$
31. $64m^2 + 16m + 1$
32. $3x + 5$
33. $(15a - 2)(4a + 3)$
34. **a.** 121 (The size of the group must be a multiple of 60, plus 1.)
    b. 11

Cumulative Review *(page 644)*

1. $1.90
2. **a.** $y = -2x + 5$

384

b.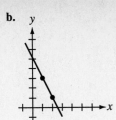

c. no
d. 2

3. a. $\dfrac{5}{30} = \dfrac{1}{6}$

b. $\dfrac{24}{30} = \dfrac{4}{5}$

c. $\dfrac{20}{870} = \dfrac{2}{87}$

d. $\dfrac{84}{870} = \dfrac{14}{145}$

4. Any one of the four polynomials can be a correct answer.

$x^2 - 9$ is a binomial. The others are trinomials.

$x^2 - 2x + 1$ is a perfect square trinomial, the square of a binomial. The others are not.

$x^2 - 2x - 1$ cannot be factored over the set of integers. The others have at least two binomial factors.

$x^3 + 5x^2 + 6x$ is a cubic, a polynomial of degree three and has three factors over the set of integers. The others are polynomials of degree two and have fewer than three factors.

Exploration

Let a equal the integer between the two consecutive even or two consecutive odd integers and let b equal 1. Then the smaller number is $(a - 1)$ and the larger number is $(a + 1)$. Their product is $a^2 - 1$. For example:
$24(26) = (25 - 1)(25 + 1) = 25^2 - 1^2 = 625 - 1 = 624$

Chapter 19. Algebraic Fractions, and Equations and Inequalities Involving Fractions

Introductory Page (page 645)

Andrea designed 30 eggs.

19-1   The Meaning of an Algebraic Fraction
(page 646)

1. 0 **2.** 0 **3.** 0 **4.** 5

5. 8 **6.** 2 **7.** -2 **8.** $\dfrac{1}{2}$

9. $-\dfrac{1}{2}$ **10.** $+2, -2$ **11.** $\dfrac{c}{5}$ **12.** $\dfrac{98}{p}$

13. $\dfrac{10x + 20}{y}$ **14.** $\dfrac{m}{60}$ **15.** $\dfrac{4x + 2y}{4}$

19-2   Reducing Fractions to Lowest Terms
(pages 649–650)

1. $\dfrac{1}{3}$ **2.** $\dfrac{3}{4}$ **3.** $\dfrac{2c}{3d}$ **4.** $\dfrac{9}{10}$

5. $\dfrac{a}{c}$ **6.** $\dfrac{a}{2b}$ **7.** $\dfrac{5}{9}$ **8.** $\dfrac{1}{2}$

9. $3x$ **10.** $\dfrac{1}{5x^2}$ **11.** $\dfrac{3}{4a}$ **12.** $\dfrac{y}{3x}$

13. $\dfrac{-3ab}{2c}$ **14.** $\dfrac{2x}{9}$ **15.** $-\dfrac{2}{3}$

16. $\dfrac{1}{9xy}$ **17.** $\dfrac{3x + 6}{4}$ or $\dfrac{3(x + 2)}{4}$

18. $\dfrac{4y - 6}{3}$ **19.** $\dfrac{x - 7}{x}$ **20.** $m + 5$

21. $\dfrac{a + b}{3x}$ **22.** $\dfrac{a - 2}{a}$ **23.** $\dfrac{4a - b}{a}$

24. $\dfrac{2x + 3y}{4}$ **25.** $\dfrac{6b + 10}{3b^2}$ **26.** $\dfrac{x}{x + 2}$

27. $\dfrac{d}{d + 2}$ **28.** $\dfrac{y}{y + x}$ **29.** $\dfrac{a}{3a - b}$

30. $\dfrac{2}{r - 3s}$ **31.** 4 **32.** $\dfrac{x - 3}{3}$

33. $\dfrac{x + 1}{5}$ **34.** -1 **35.** $\dfrac{-1}{b + 3}$

36. $\dfrac{2}{s + r}$ **37.** $-\dfrac{4 + a}{2}$ **38.** $-\dfrac{x + y}{3}$

39. $-\dfrac{2b}{b + 3}$ **40.** $\dfrac{r + 2}{3}$ **41.** $\dfrac{x + 3}{x - 4}$

42. $\dfrac{x - 1}{x + 2}$ **43.** $\dfrac{3}{y - 1}$ **44.** $\dfrac{x}{x - 1}$

45. $\dfrac{x + 5}{x + 3}$ **46.** $\dfrac{a + 2}{a + 3}$ **47.** $\dfrac{a}{a - 1}$

48. $\dfrac{2(x - 5)}{x + 3}$ **49.** $\dfrac{r + 1}{r + 3}$ **50.** $\dfrac{12 - x}{x - 3}$

51. $\dfrac{2x - 1}{x - 3}$ **52.** $\dfrac{x - 3y}{x + 5y}$

53. a. (*1*) 7　　(*2*) 10　　(*3*) 20　　(*4*) 2　　(*5*) −4

b. Each fraction, in reduced form, is equal to the value assigned to the variable x.

c. No. When $x = 5$, the denominator $x - 5 = 0$. The fraction is not defined when its denominator is 0.

d. x (for $x \neq 5$)　　　　**e.** 38,756

19-3 Multiplying Fractions (page 653)

1. $\dfrac{5}{9}$　　**2.** 20　　**3.** $10x$　　**4.** $5d$

5. $\dfrac{5x^2}{9}$　　**6.** $\dfrac{8}{mn}$　　**7.** $\dfrac{6}{5}$　　**8.** $\dfrac{y}{x}$

9. $\dfrac{4m}{3}$　　**10.** $\dfrac{2}{s}$　　**11.** $2m$　　**12.** $\dfrac{6a^2b}{c}$

13. $\dfrac{x + 2}{12}$　　**14.** $\dfrac{a^2(a + 3)}{90}$　　**15.** $\dfrac{y(x - y)}{5x}$

16. $\dfrac{b^2(3a - 1)}{3}$　　**17.** $(b - 1)^2$

18. $\dfrac{(x + 1)(x - 1)^2}{5x}$ or $\dfrac{(x^2 - 1)(x - 1)}{5x}$

19. $\dfrac{r}{5}$　　**20.** $\dfrac{2s}{3}$　　**21.** $\dfrac{4}{x}$　　**22.** $\dfrac{1}{3(x - 1)}$

23. $2(a + 3)$　　**24.** $\dfrac{7(x + 1)}{x + 2}$　　**25.** $\dfrac{a - b}{a + b}$

26. $-\dfrac{4b^2(a - 2)}{a + 2}$　　**27.** $\dfrac{5}{2}$　　**28.** $\dfrac{x + 5}{3y}$

29. $\dfrac{y - 3}{c}$　　**30.** $\dfrac{3(2a - 3)}{5(a - 3)}$　　**31.** $\dfrac{x + 5}{2x - 3}$

32. $\dfrac{10}{3(x - 2)}$　　**33.** 2　　**34.** $\dfrac{1}{x(x - 2)}$

35. $-\dfrac{1}{2}$　　**36.** $\dfrac{x}{x + 1}$　　**37.** −1

38. $-5(d - 5)$　　**39.** $-\dfrac{(a + 6)^2}{36 + a^2}$　　**40.** $\dfrac{2}{3}$

19-4 Dividing Fractions (page 655)

1. $\dfrac{1}{6}$　　**2.** $\dfrac{3}{5}$　　**3.** 16　　**4.** $\dfrac{1}{3}$

5. $\dfrac{2}{35}$　　**6.** $\dfrac{acd}{4b}$　　**7.** $\dfrac{y^4}{x^2}$　　**8.** $\dfrac{ab}{4c}$

9. $\dfrac{32x(x + 1)}{27}$　　**10.** $\dfrac{9(y + 3)}{10y}$　　**11.** $\dfrac{4b^2(a^2 - 1)}{a^2}$

12. $2(x + 1)$　　**13.** $2x(x - 4)$　　**14.** $\dfrac{2a - 3}{2}$

15. $\dfrac{b(b - 3)}{2(b - 2)}$　　**16.** $\dfrac{1}{4(a + b)}$　　**17.** $\dfrac{3}{4(y - 1)}$

18. $\dfrac{x - 2}{28x}$　　**19.** $\dfrac{3}{5}$　　**20.** $-\dfrac{1}{3}$

21. $2(3 - y)$　　**22.** $\dfrac{1}{2}$　　**23.** x

24. $-\dfrac{1}{2}$　　**25.** $-\dfrac{(a + b)}{(a - b)}$　　**26.** 0, 1, −1

27. 7　　**28.** 1

19-5 Adding or Subtracting Fractions That Have the Same Denominator (pages 656–657)

1. $\dfrac{5}{8}$　　**2.** $\dfrac{1}{5}$　　**3.** $\dfrac{5}{x}$　　**4.** $\dfrac{5}{2c}$

5. $\dfrac{5x}{4}$　　**6.** $\dfrac{8y}{5}$　　**7.** $\dfrac{2c - 3d}{5}$

8. $\dfrac{x - y + z}{2}$　　**9.** $\dfrac{x + y}{a}$　　**10.** $\dfrac{5r - 2s}{t}$

11. $\dfrac{15}{8x}$　　**12.** $\dfrac{1}{y}$　　**13.** $\dfrac{11a}{4x}$

14. $\dfrac{7b}{3y}$　　**15.** $\dfrac{7c}{3d}$　　**16.** $\dfrac{6}{5c}$

17. $\dfrac{5x + 7}{2}$　　**18.** $\dfrac{3x + 4}{4x}$　　**19.** $\dfrac{3x - 5}{3}$

20. $\dfrac{a - 3}{4a}$　　**21.** $\dfrac{8}{x + 2}$　　**22.** $\dfrac{1}{a - b}$

23. $\dfrac{r + x}{y - 2}$　　**24.** 1　　**25.** 2

26. $\dfrac{1}{y + 2}$　　**27.** $\dfrac{10x - 2}{3x + 2}$　　**28.** $\dfrac{4c + 2}{2c - 3}$

29. 1　　**30.** 1　　**31.** $\dfrac{2x + 1}{x + 3}$

32. $\dfrac{1}{x - 1}$　　**33.** $a + b$　　**34.** $x - y$

35. 2　　**36.** $\dfrac{2}{a + b}$　　**37.** $\dfrac{4}{r - 3}$

38. $\dfrac{2m - 1}{m + 2}$

	$a + b$	$a - b$	$a \cdot b$	$a \div b$
39.	$\dfrac{15}{y}$	$\dfrac{9}{y}$	$\dfrac{36}{y^2}$	4
40.	$\dfrac{x}{2}$	$\dfrac{x}{4}$	$\dfrac{3x^2}{64}$	3
41.	$\dfrac{r + p}{t}$	$\dfrac{r - p}{t}$	$\dfrac{rp}{t^2}$	$\dfrac{r}{p}$
42.	$\dfrac{6k}{x}$	$\dfrac{k}{x}$	$\dfrac{35k^2}{4x^2}$	$\dfrac{7}{5}$

19-6 Adding or Subtracting Fractions That Have Different Denominators
(pages 660–662)

1. 6 **2.** 30 **3.** $4x$

4. $24r$ **5.** xyz **6.** $60x^2y^2$

7. $15x(x + y)$ **8.** $12a(a + b)$ **9.** $12(y + z)$

10. $(x^2 - 9)$ **11.** $4x^2 + 1$ **12.** $\dfrac{19}{6}$

13. $\dfrac{17}{15}$ **14.** $\dfrac{61}{12}$ **15.** $\dfrac{33}{100}$

16. $\dfrac{11}{12}$ **17.** $\dfrac{5}{8}$ **18.** $\dfrac{1}{6}$

19. $\dfrac{29}{12}$ **20.** $\dfrac{5x}{6}$ **21.** $\dfrac{2d}{15}$

22. $\dfrac{x}{6}$ **23.** $-\dfrac{2y}{15}$ **24.** $\dfrac{9ab}{20}$

25. $\dfrac{31x}{20}$ **26.** $\dfrac{a}{12}$ **27.** $\dfrac{2a + b}{14}$

28. $\dfrac{15}{4x}$ **29.** $-\dfrac{1}{8x}$ **30.** $\dfrac{3a}{8b}$

31. $\dfrac{b + a}{ab}$ **32.** $\dfrac{2b - 5a^2}{a^2b}$ **33.** $\dfrac{z + x}{xyz}$

34. $\dfrac{5t + 9r}{rst}$ **35.** $\dfrac{2cx - 3ay}{6abc}$ **36.** $\dfrac{9c + 2a - 3b}{abc}$

37. $\dfrac{y^2 + 3xy - 5x^2}{x^2y^2}$ **38.** $\dfrac{3a - 5}{6}$

39. $\dfrac{-x + 44}{15}$ **40.** $\dfrac{7y - 6}{20}$ **41.** $\dfrac{a - 5b}{12}$

42. $\dfrac{4x + 9}{4x}$ **43.** $\dfrac{5d + 21}{4d}$ **44.** $\dfrac{b - 8}{10b}$

45. $\dfrac{19 - 8b}{20b}$ **46.** $\dfrac{12y^2 - 17y - 12}{12y^2}$

47. $\dfrac{3c^2 - 8c + 1}{2c^2}$ **48.** $\dfrac{9x}{5}$

49. $\dfrac{7(x - 1)}{6}$ **50.** $\dfrac{6(x - 2)}{7}$ **51.** $\dfrac{2x + 5}{12}$

52. $\dfrac{2(x - 5)}{15}$ **53.** $\dfrac{17}{3}$ **54.** $\dfrac{39}{4}$

55. $\dfrac{5x + 1}{x}$ **56.** $\dfrac{9s - 7}{s}$ **57.** $\dfrac{m^2 + 1}{m}$

58. $\dfrac{5d^2 - 7}{5d}$ **59.** $\dfrac{a + bc}{b}$ **60.** $\dfrac{3x + 8}{x + 1}$

61. $\dfrac{6x - 6y - 4}{x - y}$ **62.** $\dfrac{7b + 7c + 2a}{b + c}$

63. $\dfrac{t^2 + t + 1}{t + 1}$ **64.** $\dfrac{s^2 - s - 1}{s - 1}$

65. $\dfrac{3x + 5y}{x + y}$ **66.** $\dfrac{4y - 4}{y - 2}$ **67.** $\dfrac{9c - 22}{c - 3}$

68. $\dfrac{6x - 8y}{x - y}$ **69.** $\dfrac{a^2 + 2a + 2}{a + 1}$

70. $\dfrac{x^2 - 3x - 15}{x + 3}$ **71.** $\dfrac{2x^2 + 3x - 7}{x + 2}$

72. $\dfrac{17}{2(x - 3)}$ **73.** $\dfrac{33}{4(y + 1)}$ **74.** $\dfrac{17}{5(3a - 1)}$

75. $\dfrac{29}{6(x - 2)}$ **76.** $\dfrac{5x}{8(x - 1)}$ **77.** $\dfrac{-2}{2x - 3y}$

78. $\dfrac{a + 2b}{2(a - 2b)}$ **79.** $\dfrac{17x - 8}{6(x + 1)}$ **80.** $\dfrac{11x + 23}{12(2x - 1)}$

81. $\dfrac{2x}{(x + 5)(x - 5)}$ **82.** $\dfrac{3y - 60}{(y + 4)(y - 4)}$

83. $\dfrac{26 - 3a}{(a + 3)(2 - a)}$ **84.** $\dfrac{10x - 6}{x(x - 2)}$

85. $\dfrac{7c - 16}{c(c + 8)}$ **86.** $\dfrac{a^2 + ab + b^2}{b(a - b)}$

87. $\dfrac{3y + 14}{(y + 3)(y - 3)}$ **88.** $\dfrac{-5y + 26}{(y + 4)(y - 4)}$

89. $\dfrac{9 - 3a - 3b}{(a + b)(a - b)}$ **90.** $\dfrac{y - 4}{(y + 2)(y - 2)}$

91. $\dfrac{-x + 24}{3(x + 6)(x - 6)}$ **92.** $\dfrac{9b + 3a}{ab(a - b)}$

93. $\dfrac{2y^2 + 11y - 30}{3(y - 3)(y + 4)}$ **94.** $\dfrac{x^2 + 3x + 3}{(x + 2)^3}$

95. $\dfrac{9a^2 + 7a + 5}{(a - 1)(a + 3)(a + 2)}$

96. $\dfrac{2r + 19}{(r + 2)(r - 2)(r + 5)}$

97. $\dfrac{x^2 + xy - 2y^2 - 18x + 3y}{3(x + 4y)(x - y)}$

98. $\dfrac{-a^2 - 2a - 2}{(a - 5)(a + 3)(a - 2)}$

99. a. 2 **b.** 2

19-7 Solving Equations Containing Fractional Coefficients
(pages 665–667)

1. $x = 21$ **2.** $t = 108$ **3.** $x = 25$

4. $n = 49$ **5.** $x = 16$ **6.** $m = 29$

7. $y = 0.1$ **8.** $z = 0.04$ **9.** $t = 3.1$

10. $r = 40$ **11.** $t = 0.3$ **12.** $a = 24$

13. $r = -13$ **14.** $y = 6$ **15.** $x = \dfrac{3}{2}$ or 1.5

16. $m = 30$ **17.** $x = 4$ **18.** $y = 9$

19. $x = 1$ **20.** $x = 21$ **21.** $r = 12$

22. $t = \dfrac{15}{2}$ or 7.5 **23.** $r = 2$

24. $t = 9$ 25. $a = 24$ 26. $y = 1$
27. $y = 12$ 28. $t = 15$ 29. $m = 3$
30. $x = 2$ 31. $y = 330$ 32. $x = 10.4$
33. $x = 40$ 34. $c = 20$ 35. $y = 15$
36. $x = 20$ 37. $y = 1.3$ 38. $c = 150$
39. $m = 12$ 40. $x = 23$ 41. $x = 180$
42. $y = 1,000$ 43. $x = 395$ 44. $x = -20$
45. $x = 48$ 46. $x = 31$ 47. $x = 1,500$
48. $x = 600$ 49. $x = 700$ 50. $x = 40$
51. 30   52. 100   53. 30
54. 60   55. 13, 14   56. 19, 21
57. 12, 12, 18   58. 6, 18   59. 21, 35
60. 30, 60   61. 60, 90
62. First = 30 ft; second = 40 ft; third = 10 ft; fourth = 20 ft
63. Sam, 6; father, 36   64. Robert, 24; father, 48
65. 52   66. 20
67. $8   68. 27
69. 4 nickels, 12 dimes   70. 6 cans
71. 12 nickels, 17 dimes   72. 3 dimes, 10 quarters
73. 80 student tickets, 96 full-price tickets
74. No.   Let x = number of dimes.
Then $0.10x + 0.25(2x) = 4.50$
x = fraction
75. Yes; 15 coins of each type give a total of $6.
76. $1,500 at 7%, $1,900 at 8%
77. $1,750 at 10%, $250 at 11%

19-8   Solving Inequalities Containing Fractional Coefficients
(pages 669–670)

1–20 also require number-line graphs, where the domain = real numbers.
1. $x > 9$ 2. $y < 15$ 3. $c > 6$
4. $x \le 5$ 5. $y \ge 12$ 6. $y < -1$
7. $t \ge -40$ 8. $x \ge -6$ 9. $x > 4\frac{4}{9}$
10. $y \ge -1\frac{2}{3}$ 11. $x > 12$ 12. $y \le 6$
13. $d < 1$ 14. $c \ge 2\frac{1}{3}$ 15. $m \ge 3$
16. $x < 18$ 17. $x > 2$ 18. $y < 9$
19. $r \le 24$ 20. $t \ge 17$ 21. $a \ge 3$
22. 18   23. 38   24. 133
25. 113   26. 10, 25   27. 24, 20
28. 51 (Let x = number of calls. Then $15 + 0.10x > 20$.)
29. $11.96   30. 8   31. 4
32. Rhoda, 18; Alice, 27   33. Mary, 16; Bill, 20
34. $1,200
35. **a.** $120,000   **b.** $108,000   **c.** $105,000
36. 81 (Let x = original number. Then
$$\frac{2}{3}\left(\frac{2}{3}x + 3\right) + 6 < 45, \text{ and } x < 83.)$$

19-9   Solving Fractional Equations
(pages 672–673)

1. $x = 2$ 2. $y = 5$ 3. $x = \frac{1}{2}$ or 0.5
4. $b = -4$ 5. $x = 3$ 6. $x = 30$
7. $y = -7$ 8. $y = -8$ 9. $x = 2$
10. $y = 3$ 11. $c = \frac{1}{2}$ or 0.5   12. $x = \frac{1}{2}$ or 0.5
13. $x = 3$ 14. $y = 8$ 15. $c = 2$
16. $x = 6$ 17. $y = 3$ 18. $a = 4$
19. $b = 12$ 20. $x = 8$ 21. $x = 1$
22. $x = 2$ 23. $a = 2$ 24. $x = -5$
25. x cannot equal 0.
26. $4(a + 1) \ne 5(a + 1)$ since $a + 1$ cannot equal 0.
27. x cannot equal 0.
28. The equation obtained by multiplying by $x - 1$ is $x + 2x - 2 = 1$ whose solution is $x = 1$. But x cannot equal 1 in the given equation.
29. $x = 3$ 30. $x = 4$ 31. $x = 4$
32. $x = -\frac{1}{3}$ 33. $z = 1$ 34. $r = \frac{1}{5}$ or 0.2
35. $y = 3$ 36. $a = -10$ 37. $m = 2$
38. $a = 6$ 39. $x = -2$ 40. $y = \frac{1}{2}$
41. $a = \frac{2}{3}$ 42. $b = -13$ 43. $x = 5$
44. $x = \frac{3}{4}$ 45. $y = -\frac{1}{2}$ or -0.5
46. $x = \varnothing$ or { }   47. 4
48. $\frac{1}{3}$ 49. 3   50. 84
51. $\frac{1}{7}$ 52. $\frac{12}{20}$ 53. $\frac{15}{20}$

19-10   Equations and Formulas Involving Several Variables *(pages 674–675)*

1. $x = 5t$ 2. $x = cd$ 3. $x = 3ab$
4. $x = \frac{3b}{4}$ 5. $x = \frac{ab}{3}$ 6. $x = 9b$
7. $x = \frac{r}{t}$ 8. $x = \frac{t}{k}$ 9. $x = 44b$
10. $x = \frac{a + b}{c}$ 11. $x = \frac{dr}{m}$ 12. $x = 15a$
13. $n = \frac{360}{C}$ 14. $I = \frac{E}{R}$ 15. $t = \frac{s}{v}$
16. $m = \frac{Fgr}{v^2}$ 17. $R = \frac{L}{AV}$ 18. $C = \frac{5}{9}(F - 32)$
19. $a = \frac{2S}{t^2}$ 20. $t = \frac{A - p}{pr}$ 21. 30
22. 6   23. (1)

1. $\dfrac{x}{10}$　　2. 4　　3. $\dfrac{2}{3}$

4. $\dfrac{2}{d}$　　5. $x^2 - 12$　　6. $\dfrac{2y - 3}{2}$

7. $\dfrac{2x}{3}$　　8. $x - 1$　　9. $12c$

10. $\dfrac{5}{6b}$　　11. $\dfrac{2m}{3}$　　12. $\dfrac{10}{k}$

13. $\dfrac{7ax}{12}$　　14. $\dfrac{5z - 2x}{xyz}$　　15. $\dfrac{2x + 2}{x}$

16. $2b$　　17. 2　　18. 15

19. 11　　20. 12　　21. 7

22. 6　　23. no solution, or $\varnothing$

24. $r = \dfrac{S}{2\pi h}$　　25. $r = \dfrac{a}{n}$　　26. $r = \dfrac{C}{2\pi}$

27. $\dfrac{1}{2}$　　28. 2　　29. $\dfrac{13 - y}{20}$

30. $\dfrac{x + 5}{3(x - 5)}$　　31. $\dfrac{5c + 3}{24}$　　32. $\dfrac{3}{1 + 3a}$

33. $1,920　　34. 25　　35. 90

Cumulative Review *(page 677)*

1. $0.50 for coffee, $0.75 for a bagel

2. $3x(2x + 3)(2x - 3)$

Exploration

$$\dfrac{1}{2} = 0.5 \qquad \dfrac{1}{16} = 0.0625$$

$$\dfrac{1}{4} = 0.25 \qquad \dfrac{1}{20} = 0.05$$

$$\dfrac{1}{5} = 0.2 \qquad \dfrac{1}{25} = 0.04$$

$$\dfrac{1}{8} = 0.125 \qquad \dfrac{1}{50} = 0.02$$

$$\dfrac{1}{10} = 0.1 \qquad \dfrac{1}{100} = 0.01$$

Each of these rational numbers can be written as a terminating decimal. Only 2 and 5 are the prime factors of their denominators.

$$\dfrac{1}{3} = 0.3333... \qquad \dfrac{1}{15} = 0.06666...$$

$$\dfrac{1}{6} = 0.1666... \qquad \dfrac{1}{18} = 0.05555...$$

$$\dfrac{1}{9} = 0.1111... \qquad \dfrac{1}{22} = 0.0454545...$$

$$\dfrac{1}{11} = 0.090909... \qquad \dfrac{1}{24} = 0.041666...$$

$$\dfrac{1}{12} = 0.08333... \qquad \dfrac{1}{30} = 0.03333...$$

Each of these rational numbers can be written as an infinitely repeating decimal. Their denominators have at least one prime factor other than 2 or 5.

The ratio of two integers can be written as a terminating decimal if, when the fraction is in simplest form, the denominator has only 2 and/or 5 as prime factors. The ratio of two integers can be written as an infinitely repeating decimal if, when the fraction is in simplest form, the denominator has at least one prime factor other than 2 or 5.

Chapter 20. Operations with Radicals

20-1 Radicals and the Rational Numbers *(pages 683–684)*

1. Index 2, radicand 36　　2. Index 3, radicand 125

3. Index 4, radicand 81　　4. Index 5, radicand 32

5. Index n, radicand 1

6. 9　　7. 1　　8. 11　　9. 15

10. 30　　11. $\dfrac{1}{3}$　　12. $\dfrac{2}{5}$　　13. 0.7

14. 1.2　　15. 0.2　　16. 4　　17. 9

18. 11　　19. -8　　20. -12　　21. 0

22. ± 10　　23. ± 13　　24. 20　　25. -25

26. $\dfrac{1}{2}$　　27. $-\dfrac{3}{4}$　　28. $\pm \dfrac{5}{9}$　　29. $\dfrac{7}{10}$

30. $\pm \dfrac{12}{13}$　　31. 0.8　　32. -1.2　　33. ± 0.3

34. -0.1　　35. ± 0.02　　36. 1　　37. 3

38. 2　　39. -2　　40. 5　　41. 3.2

42. 6.8　　43. 1.3　　44. -15　　45. 8

46. -4　　47. 10　　48. 2　　49. 1.25

50. 0.6　　51. 2.9　　52. 0.5　　53. -5.7

54. -0.5　　55. 72　　56. 2.9　　57. 0.24

58. -0.8　　59. ± 2.4　　60. 37　　61. 8

62. $\dfrac{1}{2}$ **63.** 0.7   **64.** 3   **65.** $\dfrac{9}{5}$

66. 4   **67.** 36   **68.** 11   **69.** 39

70. 97   **71.** 13   **72.** 5   **73.** 24

74. -74

75. a. $\dfrac{1}{2} > \dfrac{1}{4}$ **b.** $\dfrac{3}{4} > \dfrac{9}{16}$ **c.** $1 = 1$

  d. $\dfrac{3}{2} < \dfrac{9}{4}$ **e.** $4 < 16$ **f.** $100 < 10{,}000$

76. a. $n > n^2$ **b.** $n = n^2$ **c.** $n < n^2$

77. a. $\dfrac{1}{3} > \dfrac{1}{9}$ **b.** $\dfrac{2}{5} > \dfrac{4}{25}$ **c.** $1 = 1$

  d. $\dfrac{7}{5} < \dfrac{49}{25}$ **e.** $2 < 4$ **f.** $3 < 9$

78. a. $\sqrt{m} > m$ **b.** $\sqrt{m} = m$ **c.** $\sqrt{m} < m$

79. $\{2, -2\}$ **80.** $\{10, -10\}$ **81.** $\left\{\dfrac{2}{9}, -\dfrac{2}{9}\right\}$

82. $\{0.7, -0.7\}$ **83.** $\{4, -4\}$ **84.** $\{6, -6\}$

85. $\{5, -5\}$ **86.** $\{3, -3\}$ **87.** $\{2\}$

88. $\{1\}$ **89.** $\{3, -3\}$ **90.** $\{2\}$

91. a. 6 ft   **b.** 24 ft

92. a. 14 yd   **b.** 56 yd

93. a. 11 cm   **b.** 44 cm

94. a. 15 m   **b.** 60 m

95. $4x$ $(x > 0)$

96. Some solutions are shown; others are also possible.

  $101 = 10^2 + 1^2$

  $102 = 10^2 + 1^2 + 1^2$ or $7^2 + 7^2 + 2^2$

  $103 = 9^2 + 3^2 + 3^2 + 2^2$ or $7^2 + 7^2 + 2^2 + 1^2$
     or $10^2 + 1^2 + 1^2 + 1^2$

  $104 = 10^2 + 2^2$

  $105 = 8^2 + 5^2 + 4^2$ or $10^2 + 2^2 + 1^2$

  $106 = 9^2 + 5^2$

  $107 = 9^2 + 5^2 + 1^2$ or $7^2 + 7^2 + 3^2$

  $108 = 10^2 + 2^2 + 2^2$ or $6^2 + 6^2 + 6^2$

  $109 = 10^2 + 3^2$

  $110 = 7^2 + 6^2 + 5^2$ or $10^2 + 3^2 + 1^2$

20-2 Radicals and the Irrational Numbers
(pages 688–689)

1. 2, 3   **2.** 3, 4   **3.** 6, 7

4. $-2, -1$ **5.** $-4, -3$ **6.** 7, 8

7. 8, 9   **8.** $-12, -11$ **9.** 11, 12

10. $-13, -12$ **11.** $-1, \sqrt{3}, 2$ **12.** $3, 4, \sqrt{17}$

13. $-4, -\sqrt{15}, -3$ **14.** $-\sqrt{7}, 0, \sqrt{7}$

15. $\sqrt{21}, 5, \sqrt{30}$ **16.** $-\sqrt{23}, -\sqrt{19}, -\sqrt{11}$

17. Rational   **18.** Irrational   **19.** Rational

20. Irrational   **21.** Irrational   **22.** Rational

23. Irrational   **24.** Rational   **25.** Rational

26. Irrational   **27.** Rational   **28.** Irrational

29. Rational   **30.** Rational   **31.** Irrational

In 32–46, the calculator display in part **a** will vary according to the number of digits (typically 8 or 10) displayed, and also according to whether the calculator truncates or rounds the rational approximation of the square root. An ending digit of 0 is usually not displayed.

32. a. 1.414213562 or 1.4142135 or 1.4142136
  b. 1.414

33. a. 1.732050808 or 1.7320508
  b. 1.732

34. a. 4.582575695 or 4.5825756 or 4.5825757
  b. 4.583

35. a. 6.244997998 or 6.2449979 or 6.244998
  b. 6.245

36. a. 8.94427191 or 8.9442719
  b. 8.944

37. a. 9.486832981 or 9.4868329 or 9.486833
  b. 9.487

38. a. 10.39230485 or 10.392304 or 10.392305
  b. 10.39

39. a. 4.847679857 or 4.8476798 or 4.8476799
  b. 4.848

40. a. 9.391485506 or 9.3914855
  b. 9.391

41. a. -10.73312629 or -10.733126
  b. -10.73

42. a. 5.344155686 or 5.3441556 or 5.3441557
  b. 5.344

43. a. 8.200609733 or 8.2006097
  b. 8.201

44. a. 66.2495283 or 66.249528
  b. 66.25

45. a. 11.12205017 or 11.12205
  b. 11.12

46. a. 11.59870682 or 11.598706 or 11.598707
  b. 11.60

47. 2.8 cm   **48.** 5.4 cm   **49.** 9.8 cm

50. 11.8 cm   **51.** 14.1 cm   **52.** 17.0 cm

53. 10   **54.** 13   **55.** 25

56. 39

57. a. 9.65   **b.** 9.646

58. a. 3.86   **b.** 2.864

59. a. 5.66   **b.** 5.657

60. a. 24.07   **b.** 24.071

61. a. 3.73   **b.** 3.732

62. a. 17.27   **b.** 17.268

63. a. 7.40   **b.** 7.402

64. a. 9.20   **b.** 9.200

65. 13.83   **66.** 8.76   **67.** 8.94

68. 38.72

69. Any rational number greater than 7.615773106 but less than 7.61642961, such as 7.616

70. a. $\sqrt{999{,}999} = 999.9995$ on most calculators
  b. Yes
  c. Irrational. The calculator rounded the value of $(999.995)^2$ to the whole number 999,999. If $\sqrt{999{,}999}$ were rational, the square root would be a whole number.

20-3 Finding the Principal Square Root of a Monomial *(page 690)*

1. $2a$ 2. $4d$ 3. $7z$ 4. $\frac{4}{5}r$
5. $0.9w$ 6. $3c$ 7. $6y^2$ 8. cd
9. x^2y 10. r^4s^3 11. $2xy$ 12. $6a^3b^2$
13. $12a^2b$ 14. $13x^2y$ 15. $0.6m$ 16. $0.7ab$
17. $17a^5$ 18. $22k^6$ 19. $8.4bx^5$ 20. $3.3y^8$
21. a. $7c$ $(c > 0)$ b. $28c$
22. a. $8x$ $(x > 0)$ b. $32x$
23. a. $10xy$ $(x, y > 0)$ b. $40xy$
24. a. $12ab$ $(a, b > 0)$ b. $48ab$

20-4 Simplifying a Square-Root Radical *(pages 692–693)*

1. $2\sqrt{2}$ 2. $2\sqrt{3}$ 3. $2\sqrt{5}$ 4. $2\sqrt{7}$
5. $2\sqrt{10}$ 6. $3\sqrt{3}$ 7. $3\sqrt{6}$ 8. $3\sqrt{7}$
9. $3\sqrt{10}$ 10. $7\sqrt{2}$ 11. $3\sqrt{11}$ 12. $6\sqrt{3}$
13. $9\sqrt{2}$ 14. $5\sqrt{7}$ 15. $10\sqrt{3}$ 16. $6\sqrt{2}$
17. $8\sqrt{3}$ 18. $4\sqrt{5}$ 19. $12\sqrt{10}$ 20. $6\sqrt{5}$
21. $30\sqrt{2}$ 22. $3\sqrt{2}$ 23. $\sqrt{3}$ 24. $3\sqrt{6}$
25. $2\sqrt{7}$ 26. $10\sqrt{6}$ 27. $8\sqrt{5}$ 28. $21\sqrt{5}$
29. $24\sqrt{x}$ 30. $x\sqrt{3x}$ 31. $7x^2\sqrt{x}$ 32. $6r\sqrt{s}$
33. $8x^3\sqrt{2}$ 34. $9y\sqrt{3x}$ 35. $12n^3\sqrt{5n}$
36. a. $\sqrt{12}$ is not in simplest form because $\sqrt{12} = \sqrt{4 \cdot 3} = 2\sqrt{3}$.
    b. $8\sqrt{3}$
    c. (*1*) 13.8564 (*2*) 13.8564 (*3*) 13.8564
37. (3) 38. (3) 39. (3) 40. (4)
41. a. 17.32050808 or 17.320508
    b. $10\sqrt{3}$ c. Same as **a** d. Equal
42. a. 13.41640787 or 13.416407 or 13.416408
    b. $6\sqrt{5}$ c. Same as **a** d. Equal
43. a. 33.9411255 or 33.941125 or 33.941126
    b. $24\sqrt{2}$ c. Same as **a** d. Equal
44. a. 5.291502622 or 5.2915026
    b. $2\sqrt{7}$ c. Same as **a** d. Equal
45. a. No; $\sqrt{25} \neq \sqrt{9} + \sqrt{16}$, or $5 \neq 3 + 4$
    b. No
46. a. No; $\sqrt{16} \neq \sqrt{25} - \sqrt{9}$, or $4 \neq 5 - 3$
    b. No

20-5 Addition and Subtraction of Radicals *(pages 695–696)*

1. $15\sqrt{2}$ 2. $9\sqrt{5}$ 3. $15\sqrt{3}$
4. $12\sqrt{6}$ 5. $6\sqrt{2}$ 6. 0
7. $4\sqrt{3}$ 8. $-2\sqrt{7}$ 9. $4\sqrt{5} + 3\sqrt{2}$
10. $12\sqrt{x}$ $(x \geq 0)$ 11. $8\sqrt{y}$ $(y \geq 0)$
12. $6\sqrt{2}$ 13. $8\sqrt{3}$ 14. $3\sqrt{5}$
15. $\sqrt{2}$ 16. $-\sqrt{3}$ 17. 0

18. $19\sqrt{3}$ 19. $5\sqrt{2}$ 20. $\sqrt{2} + \sqrt{3}$
21. 0 22. $23\sqrt{2}$ 23. $-4\sqrt{2}$
24. $3\sqrt{7a}$ $(a \geq 0)$ 25. $14\sqrt{x}$ $(x \geq 0)$
26. $5\sqrt{b}$ $(b \geq 0)$ 27. $\sqrt{3x}$ $(x \geq 0)$
28. $3a\sqrt{3}$ $(a \geq 0)$
29. a. $10\sqrt{2}$ b. $8\sqrt{3}$ c. $24\sqrt{3}$
30. a. $\sqrt{2}$ b. $3\sqrt{3}$ c. 0
31. (1) 32. (4) 33. (4)
34. a. $12\sqrt{5}$ b. 26.833
35. a. $10\sqrt{3}$ b. 17.321

20-6 Multiplication of Square-Root Radicals *(page 698)*

1. 3 2. 7 3. a $(a \geq 0)$
4. $2x$ $(x \geq 0)$ 5. 6 6. 72
7. $2\sqrt{7}$ 8. $10\sqrt{3}$ 9. $9\sqrt{2}$
10. $70\sqrt{6}$ 11. $36\sqrt{2}$ 12. $10\sqrt{10}$
13. $-12a$ 14. $3y$ 15. 2
16. y 17. t 18. 54
19. $10x$ 20. $9a$ 21. $3x\sqrt{5}$
22. $3a\sqrt{b}$ 23. $5x$ 24. $4t$
25. a. 120 b. Rational
26. a. 48 b. Rational
27. a. $108\sqrt{2}$ b. Irrational
28. a. $20\sqrt{2}$ b. Irrational
29. a. $\frac{20}{9}$ b. Rational
30. a. 1 b. Rational
31. 2 32. 12 33. 72 34. 75
35. a. $2\sqrt{6}$
    b. Multiply length by width.

Enter: 2 $\boxed{\times}$ 3 $\boxed{\sqrt{x}}$ $\boxed{\times}$ 2 $\boxed{\sqrt{x}}$ $\boxed{=}$

Display: $\boxed{4.898979486}$

Evaluate the product $2\sqrt{6}$ from part **a**:

Enter: 2 $\boxed{\times}$ 6 $\boxed{\sqrt{x}}$ $\boxed{=}$

Display: $\boxed{4.898979486}$

The products in the two displays are equal.
36. a. 12
    b. Multiply length by width:

Enter: 2 $\boxed{\times}$ 12 $\boxed{\sqrt{x}}$ $\boxed{\times}$ 3 $\boxed{\sqrt{x}}$ $\boxed{=}$

Display: $\boxed{12.}$

This product equals the product from part **a**:
$$2\sqrt{36} = 2 \cdot 6 = 12.$$
37. Student answers will vary. Examples are shown here:
    a. $\sqrt{2} \cdot \sqrt{3} = \sqrt{6}$; $\sqrt{5} \cdot \sqrt{7} = \sqrt{35}$
    b. $\sqrt{2} \cdot \sqrt{8} = 4$; $\sqrt{5} \cdot \sqrt{5} = 5$

20-7 Division of Square-Root Radicals
(page 700)

1. 6
2. 5
3. $\sqrt{7}$
4. $\sqrt{7}$
5. 16
6. $2\sqrt{3}$
7. $5\sqrt{2}$
8. $42\sqrt{2}$
9. 3
10. $\dfrac{7}{3}$
11. $\dfrac{1}{4}$
12. 3
13. 8
14. 25
15. $10\sqrt{3}$
16. $\dfrac{3}{2}\sqrt{2}$
17. Irrational
18. Rational
19. Irrational
20. Irrational
21. Rational
22. Irrational
23. $\dfrac{6}{7}$
24. $\dfrac{1}{2}\sqrt{3}$ or $\dfrac{\sqrt{3}}{2}$
25. $\sqrt{5}$
26. $\dfrac{2}{7}\sqrt{2}$ or $\dfrac{2\sqrt{2}}{7}$
27. $4\sqrt{2}$
28. 1
29. **a.** 2
   b. Divide area A by base b to find height h:

   Enter:
   $7 \;\boxed{\times}\; 12 \;\boxed{\sqrt{x}}\; \boxed{\div}\; \boxed{(}\; 7 \;\boxed{\times}\; 3 \;\boxed{\sqrt{x}}\; \boxed{)}\; \boxed{=}$

   Display: $\boxed{ 2.}$

30. **a.** $2\sqrt{5}$
   b. Divide area A by base b to find height h:

   Enter: $640 \;\boxed{\sqrt{x}}\; \boxed{\div}\; 32 \;\boxed{\sqrt{x}}\; \boxed{=}$

   Display: $\boxed{4.472135955}$

   Evaluate 25 from part **a:**

   Enter: $2 \;\boxed{\times}\; 5 \;\boxed{\sqrt{x}}\; \boxed{=}$

   Display: $\boxed{4.472135955}$

31. **a.** $4\sqrt{3}$
   b. Divide area A by base b to find height h:

   Enter:
   $8 \;\boxed{\times}\; 45 \;\boxed{\sqrt{x}}\; \boxed{\div}\; \boxed{(}\; 2 \;\boxed{\times}\; 15 \;\boxed{\sqrt{x}}\; \boxed{)}\; \boxed{=}$

   Display: $\boxed{6.92820323}$

   Evaluate $4\sqrt{3}$ from part **a:**

   Enter: $4 \;\boxed{\times}\; 3 \;\boxed{\sqrt{x}}\; \boxed{=}$

   Display: $\boxed{6.92820323}$

32. **a.** $\dfrac{7}{2}$ or 3.5
   b. Divide area A by base b to find height h:

   Enter: $2 \;\boxed{\times}\; 98 \;\boxed{\sqrt{x}}\; \boxed{\div}\; 32 \;\boxed{\sqrt{x}}\; \boxed{=}$

   Display: $\boxed{ 3.5 }$

33. **a.** $\dfrac{2}{5}$
   b. $\dfrac{3}{5}$
   c. $\dfrac{1}{5}$
   d. 0
   e. $\dfrac{2}{5}$
   f. 1

Review Exercises *(pages 702–703)*

1. 35
2. $2\sqrt{2}$, 3, $\sqrt{18}$
3. $\dfrac{3}{5}$
4. -7
5. -3
6. ± 1.1
7. $y = \pm 9$
8. $m = \pm 0.3$
9. $x = \pm 10$
10. $k = \pm 12$
11. **a.** 17.76
   b. Rational, because $(17.76)^2 = 315.4176$, or because 315.4176 is a perfect square
12. $20x$
13. $2y^2$
14. $c^5 d$
15. $0.1m^8$
16. $6\sqrt{5}$
17. $9\sqrt{2}$
18. $\sqrt{7}$
19. $4\sqrt{3b}$
20. $\sqrt{2}$
21. 0
22. $6\sqrt{2}$
23. $-\sqrt{3}$
24. 32
25. 45
26. $14\sqrt{10}$
27. 7
28. $8\sqrt{3}$
29. 1
30. (3)
31. (2)
32. **a.** 13.92838828 or 13.928388
   b. 13.93
33. **a.** 2.5198421
   b. 2.520
34. **a.** -0.836660027 or -0.83666
   b. -0.8367
35. **a.** 5.292 m **b.** 21.166 m
   c. The length of a side given in part **a** is a rounded value, and 4 times this rounded value is not the perimeter.

Cumulative Review *(page 703)*

1. $2x^2 - 11x - 21$
2. $21.7x^5$

Exploration

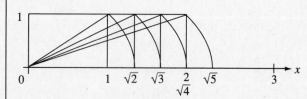

(4) After locating $\sqrt{n-1}$ on the number line, repeat step (2), drawing a rectangle whose dimensions are
$\sqrt{n-1}$ by 1 to locate $\sqrt{n}$ on the number line.
$$(\sqrt{n-1})^2 + 1^2 = (\sqrt{n})^2$$

Chapter 21. Quadratic Equations

21-1 The Standard Form of a Quadratic Equation (page 705)

1. $x^2 + 9x - 10 = 0$; $a = 1$, $b = 9$, $c = -10$
2. $2x^2 + 4x = 0$; $a = 2$, $b = 4$, $c = 0$
3. $x^2 - 3x + 8 = 0$; $a = 1$, $b = -3$, $c = 8$
4. $x^2 - 4x - 3 = 0$; $a = 1$, $b = -4$, $c = -3$
5. $3x^2 - 27x = 0$; $a = 3$, $b = -27$, $c = 0$
6. $x^2 - 3x - 10 = 0$; $a = 1$, $b = -3$, $c = -10$
7. $x^2 - 5x - 20 = 0$; $a = 1$, $b = -5$, $c = -20$
8. $\dfrac{x^2}{2} - \dfrac{x}{4} + 3 = 0$; $a = \dfrac{1}{2}$, $b = =\dfrac{1}{4}$, $c = 3$
9. $x^2 + \dfrac{x}{2} - 6 = 0$; $a = 1$, $b = \dfrac{1}{2}$, $c = -6$
10. When simplified, the equation becomes $13x + 2 = 0$, a linear or first-degree equation.

21-2 Solving a Quadratic Equation by Factoring (pages 709–710)

1. $x = 2$ or $x = 1$
2. $z = 4$ or $z = 1$
3. $x = 4$ or $x = 4$
4. $r = 7$ or $r = 5$
5. $c = -5$ or $c = -1$
6. $m = -9$ or $m = -1$
7. $x = -1$ or $x = -1$
8. $y = -8$ or $y = -3$
9. $x = 5$ or $x = -1$
10. $x = 6$ or $x = -1$
11. $x = -3$ or $x = 2$
12. $x = -5$ or $x = 3$
13. $r = 9$ or $r = -8$
14. $x = 4$ or $x = -3$
15. $x = 7$ or $x = -7$
16. $z = 2$ or $z = -2$
17. $m = 8$ or $m = -8$
18. $x = 2$ or $x = -2$
19. $d = 2$ or $d = 0$
20. $s = 1$ or $s = 0$
21. $x = -3$ or $x = 0$
22. $z = -8$ or $z = 0$
23. $x = 2$ or $x = \dfrac{1}{2}$
24. $x = 3$ or $x = \dfrac{1}{3}$
25. $x = 2$ or $x = \dfrac{2}{3}$
26. $x = -2$ or $x = -\dfrac{1}{5}$
27. $x = 3$ or $x = -2$
28. $y = 7$ or $y = -4$
29. $c = 5$ or $c = 3$
30. $m = -\dfrac{3}{2}$ or $m = -2$
31. $r = 2$ or $r = -2$
32. $x = 11$ or $x = -11$
33. $y = 6$ or $y = 0$
34. $s = -4$ or $s = 0$
35. $y = 10$ or $y = -2$
36. $x = -\dfrac{5}{2}$ or $x = 3$
37. $x = 5$ or $x = 4$
38. $x = 6$ or $x = -5$
39. $x = -9$ or $x = 6$
40. $x = -\dfrac{1}{2}$ or $x = -2$
41. $x = -3$ or $x = -1$
42. $x = -\dfrac{2}{3}$ or $x = 3$
43. $x = 7$ or $x = -5$
44. $y = 4$ or $y = -1$
45. $x = 5$ or $x = -8$
46. $x = 4$ or $x = -6$
47. $y = 3$ or $y = -6$
48. $x = 6$ or $x = -6$

49. $t = 1$ sec or $t = 2$ sec   50. 4 sec

21-3 Solving Incomplete Quadratic Equations (pages 712–713)

1. $x = \pm 2$
2. $a = \pm 6$
3. $x = \pm 10$
4. $y = \pm 3$
5. $k = \pm 7$
6. $x = \pm 4$
7. $r = \pm 9$
8. $x = \pm 8$
9. $x = \pm 5$
10. $x = \pm 12$
11. $x = \pm 7$
12. $y = \pm 1.5$
13. $y = \pm 6$
14. $x = \pm 36$
15. $x = \pm 7.5$
16. $x = \pm\sqrt{10}$
17. $x = \pm 2\sqrt{5}$
18. $x = \pm\sqrt{2}$
19. $x = \pm 2\sqrt{2}$
20. $x = \pm 5\sqrt{3}$
21. $x = \pm 3\sqrt{2}$
22. $x = \pm 3\sqrt{7}$
23. $x = \pm\sqrt{61}$
24. $x = \pm 3\sqrt{3}$
25. $x = 4.899$
26. $x = 6.325$
27. $x = 5.745$
28. $x = \pm b$
29. $x = \pm 5a$
30. $x = \pm\dfrac{r}{3}$
31. $x = \pm\dfrac{a}{2}$
32. $x = \pm\sqrt{c^2 - a^2}$ $(|c| \geq |a|)$
33. $x = \pm\sqrt{c^2 - b^2}$ $(|c| \geq |b|)$
34. $s = \pm\sqrt{A}$ $(A \geq 0)$
35. $r = \pm\sqrt{\dfrac{A}{\pi}}$ $(A \geq 0)$
36. $r = \pm\sqrt{\dfrac{S}{4\pi}}$ or $\pm\dfrac{1}{2}\sqrt{\dfrac{S}{\pi}}$ $(S \geq 0)$
37. $r = \pm\sqrt{\dfrac{V}{\pi h}}$ $(V \geq 0, h > 0)$
38. $t = \pm\sqrt{\dfrac{2s}{g}}$ $\left(\dfrac{s}{g} \geq 0\right)$
39. $v = \pm\sqrt{\dfrac{Fgr}{m}}$ $\left(\dfrac{Fgr}{m} \geq 0\right)$
40. 24 ft
41. 6 m by 18 m
42. $2\sqrt{10}$ in.
43. 12 cm
44. 10

21-4 Solving a Quadratic Equation by Using the Quadratic Formula (pages 716–717)

1. $x = 1$ or $x = 6$
2. $x = 1$ or $x = -5$
3. $x = -1$ or $x = -2$
4. $x = \dfrac{1}{2}$ or $x = -1$
5. $x = \dfrac{1}{3}$ or $x = -2$
6. $x = -\dfrac{2}{3}$ or $x = -1$
7. $x = -3$
8. $x = \dfrac{1}{2}$
9. $x = -5$
10. $x = -4$ or $x = 3$
11. $x = -6$ or $x = 4$
12. $x = -1$ or $x = 2$

13. $x = 2$ or $x = 4$ **14.** $x = \dfrac{5}{2}$ or $x = -2$

15. $x = \pm 3$ **16.** $x = \pm 2$

17. $x = 0$ or $x = 3$ **18.** $x = 0$ or $x = 5$

19. $x = 1 \pm \sqrt{3}$ **20.** $x = 5 \pm \sqrt{21}$

21. $x = -1 \pm \sqrt{5}$ **22.** $x = 2 \pm \sqrt{6}$

23. $x = \dfrac{4 \pm \sqrt{2}}{2}$ **24.** $x = \dfrac{1 \pm \sqrt{5}}{4}$

25. $x = \dfrac{2 \pm \sqrt{3}}{3}$ **26.** $x = \pm 2\sqrt{5}$

27. $x = \pm \sqrt{\dfrac{5}{2}} = \pm \dfrac{\sqrt{10}}{2}$

21-5 The Theorem of Pythagoras
(pages 721–723)

1. $c = 5$ **2.** $c = 17$ **3.** $b = 8$

4. $b = 5$ **5.** $a = 8$ **6.** $a = 15$

7. $c = 2$ **8.** $c = 8$ **9.** $b = 5$

10. a. $c = \sqrt{13}$ **b.** $c = 3.61$

11. a. $c = 3\sqrt{2}$ **b.** $c = 4.24$

12. a. $b = 4\sqrt{3}$ **b.** $b = 6.93$

13. a. $c = 5\sqrt{2}$ **b.** $c = 7.07$

14. a. $a = 2\sqrt{3}$ **b.** $a = 3.46$

15. a. $b = 4\sqrt{2}$ **b.** $b = 5.66$

16. $x = 4\sqrt{2}$ **17.** $x = 3\sqrt{3}$ **18.** $x = 4\sqrt{3}$

19. $x = 2\sqrt{2}$ **20.** 36 ft   **21.** 15.8 ft

22. 26 km   **23.** 40 yd   **24.** 25 in.

25. 41 cm   **26.** 53 ft   **27.** 61 m

28. a. 56 cm   **b.** 1,848 cm^2

29. 31.2   **30.** 17 in.   **31.** 2.8 m

32. 5.7 m   **33.** 7.1 m   **34.** 8.5 m

35. 9.9 m   **36.** 127.3 ft

37. a. 24 cm   **b.** 240 cm^2

38. a. 40 in.   **b.** 420 sq in.

39. $2\sqrt{3}$ cm   **40.** $3\sqrt{3}$ cm   **41.** $4\sqrt{3}$ cm

42. $5\sqrt{3}$ cm   **43.** $\dfrac{5\sqrt{3}}{2}$ cm or $\dfrac{5}{2}\sqrt{3}$ cm

44. $\dfrac{15}{2}\sqrt{3}$ or $\dfrac{15\sqrt{3}}{2}$

45. Yes   **46.** No   **47.** Yes

48. No

49. a.

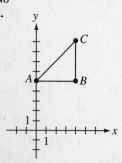

b. $AB = 4, BC = 4, AC = 4\sqrt{2}$

c. 8

50. a.

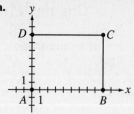

b. $AB = 9, BC = 7, CD = 9, AD = 7$

c. $\sqrt{130}$

d. 11.4

51.
$$d^2 = s^2 + s^2$$
$$= 2s^2$$
$$d = \sqrt{2} \cdot \sqrt{s^2}$$
$$= s\sqrt{2}$$

21-6 Using Quadratic Equations to Solve Problems *(pages 725–726)*

1. 4 or -7 **2.** 12 or -3 **3.** 1 m by 6 m

4. Base = 16 cm, altitude = 5 cm

5. 40 and 60   **6.** 35 ft by 49 ft

7. 6 m   **8.** 17, 12 or -12, -17

9. 7, 8 or -8, -7 **10.** 11, 13, or -13, -11

11. 6, 7   **12.** 3, 4, 5 or -6, -5, -4

13. 2 m

14. Base = 12 cm, altitude = 7 cm

15. 3 cm, 4 cm   **16.** 5 in., 12 in., 13 in.

17. 14, 48   **18.** 13 m

19. 4, 6   **20.** 5, 6 or -6, -5

21. 8 in. by 2 in.   **22.** 7 cm by 20 cm

23. a. Length = $10\sqrt{2}$ ft, width = $15\sqrt{2}$ ft

    b. Length = 14.14 ft, width = 21.21 ft

24. a. Base = $8\sqrt{3}$ m, altitude = $10\sqrt{3}$ m

    b. Base = 13.86 m, altitude = 17.32 m

25. a. $x(x + 4) = 4$

    b. Width = $(-2 + 2\sqrt{2})$ in., length = $(2 + 2\sqrt{2})$ in.

    c. Width = 0.83 in., length = 4.83 in.

21-7 The Graph of a Quadratic Function
(pages 728–729)

1.

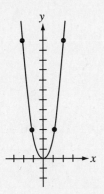

2.

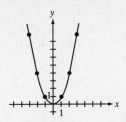

3.

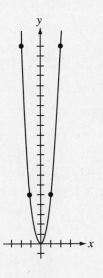

4.

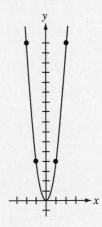

5.

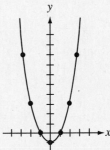

6.

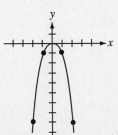

7.

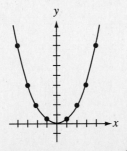

8.

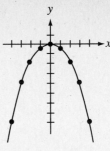

9.

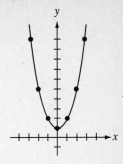

10.

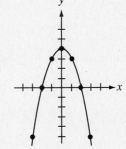

11.

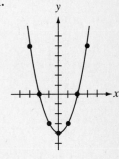

12.

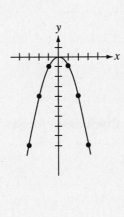

13.

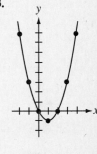

14.

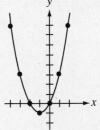

15.

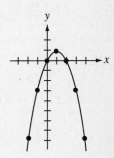

16.

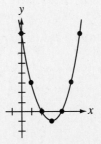

17.

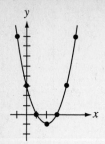

18.

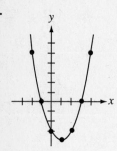

19.

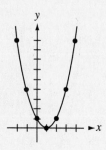

20.

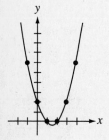

21. a.

x	y
0	3
1	51
2	67
3	51
4	3

b.

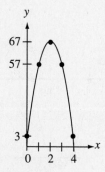

c. 3 ft

d. (*1*) 67 ft
(*2*) 2 sec

Review Exercises *(pages 730–731)*

1. $x = 9$ or $x = 2$ **2.** $y = 6$ or $y = -6$

3. $x = 5$ or $x = -3$ **4.** $k = 0$ or $k = -2\frac{1}{2}$

5. $w = 2$ or $w = -9$ **6.** $t = 4$ or $t = -3$

7. $m = 2$ **8.** $x = \pm 3\sqrt{2}$

9. $c = 13$ **10.** $a = 9$

---

11. $c = 6$ **12.** $\sqrt{40}$ or $2\sqrt{10}$
13. 30 m
14. a. 8   **b.** 4   **c.** 11   **d.** 6   **e.** 38
15. 6   **16.** 5 and 14
17. 6, 7
18.

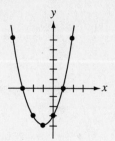

19. 17 ft by 8 ft
20. a.

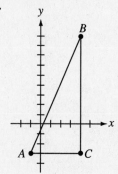

b. Right triangle
c. $AC = 5$, $BC = 12$
d. $AB = 13$
21. a. 1 ± 3
b. 2.73, -0.73

Cumulative Review *(page 731)*

1. a. 6 $b = 2, c = 3; b = 3, c = -4; b = 2, c = -4;$
$b = 3, c = 2; b = -4, c = 3; b = -4, c = 2$
b. 3 $b = -3, c = -4; b = -4, c = 3; b = 3, c = 2$
c. $\frac{3}{6} = \frac{1}{2}$

2. a. 2 hr, 1 hr, $\frac{1}{2}$ hr, $\frac{1}{4}$ hr
b. $\frac{15}{16}$ hr or 0.9375 hr

3. 153.2
4. True
5. $\frac{x + 2}{3}$
6. 14 and 15 or -15 and -14

Exploration

$2^2 = 4 = 2^2$

$3^2 = 9 = 3^2$

$4^2 = 16 = 2^4$

$5^2 = 25 = 5^2$

$6^2 = 36 = 2^2 \cdot 3^2$

$7^2 = 49 = 7^2$

$8^2 = 64 = 2^6$

$9^2 = 81 = 3^4$

$10^2 = 100 = 2^2 \cdot 5^2$

$11^2 = 121 = 11^2$

$12^2 = 144 = 2^4 \cdot 3^2$

$13^2 = 169 = 13^2$

$14^2 = 196 = 2^2 \cdot 7^2$

$15^2 = 225 = 3^2 \cdot 5^2$

$16^2 = 256 = 2^8$

$17^2 = 289 = 17^2$

$18^2 = 324 = 2^2 \cdot 3^4$

$19^2 = 361 = 19^2$

$20^2 = 400 = 2^4 \cdot 5^2$

In the prime factorization of the squares, the exponents of the prime factors are always even.

If $n = a^3 \cdot b^2 \cdot c^4$, n is not a perfect square because the exponent of a is odd. Therefore $\sqrt{n}$ is irrational.